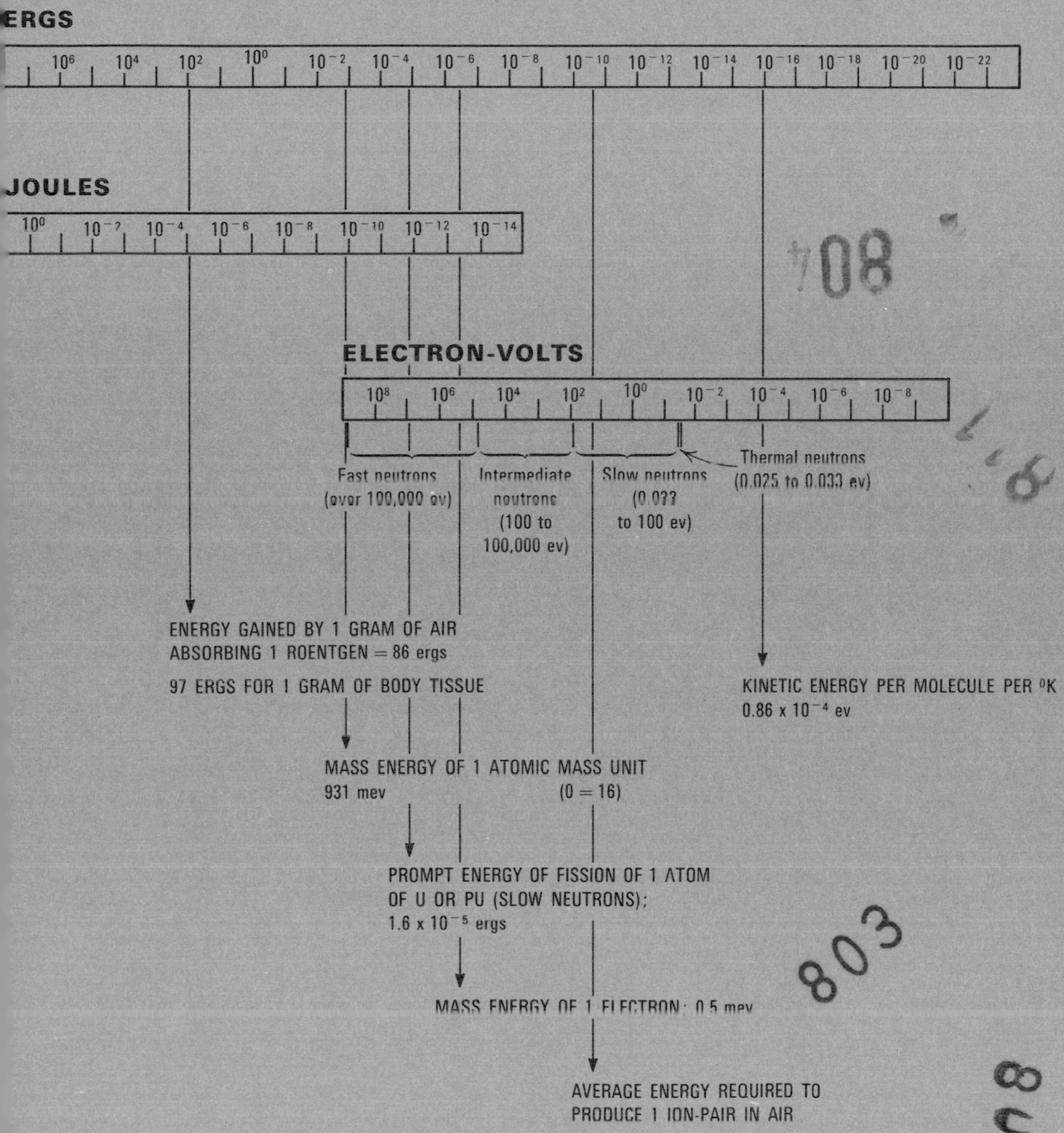

THE ENERGY LEVEL OF THINGS

From J. R. Williams, *Missiles and Rockets*, October 3, 1960

THERMODYNAMICS

SECOND EDITION

THERMODYNAMICS

WILLIAM C. REYNOLDS Department of Mechanical Engineering
Stanford University

$$X = X_L + (X_H - X_L)\frac{Y - Y_L}{Y_H - Y_L}$$

McGRAW-HILL BOOK COMPANY New York / San Francisco / St. Louis / Toronto / London / Sydney

THERMODYNAMICS

Printed in the United States of America.

Library of Congress catalog card number: 68-20722

89-MAMM-7987

52039

PREFACE

This text was developed for a fundamental first course in thermodynamics for engineers. For a number of reasons it departs from the classical, purely macroscopic approaches to the subject. Today's junior engineering students have remarkable insight into the microscopic world. They know about molecules, energy levels, and ionization and have acquired the rudimentary quantum concepts from their basic physics courses; it seems advantageous to capitalize as much as possible on this understanding in teaching thermodynamics. As little as twenty years ago the prime area of application of thermodynamics by engineers was in thermal power systems, but the modern engineer continually encounters new situations in which he must generate the basic theory himself, sometimes from macroscopic considerations and sometimes by application of microscopic theories. Many engineering programs now include courses in quantum mechanics, in which the basic ideas of thermodynamics are derived from statistical considerations (though usually only for special cases). As a result, the student is faced with a dual set of concepts and definitions for energy, entropy, temperature, etc., and correlating these two sets of ideas is not always easy. Our objective, therefore, is to develop the subject matter in a way that retains the generality and simplicity of purely macroscopic thermodynamics, draws upon the student's insight into microscopic matters, and provides a common conceptual foundation for thermodynamics and quantum-statistical mechanics.

To this end, microscopic arguments are used to provide an intuitive basis for macroscopic postulates; the laws of thermodynamics are *not* derived from microscopic postulates. This approach preserves the generality of macroscopic thermodynamics and at the same time places the roots for energy, entropy, and temperature firmly in the microscopic world. The additional concepts necessary for quantum-statistical mechanics are then introduced in later chapters and used in some simple analyses. Our intention is to clearly establish the tie between the macroscopic and microscopic viewpoints at an early stage and provide the student with a full appreciation of the importance of both views.

Throughout the text the value of a systematic methodology in analyses is emphasized. Nearly equal weight is placed on the thermodynamics of substances and the analysis of thermodynamic systems, with a broad range of both being considered. We have found that getting into the analysis of simpler thermodynamic systems as soon as possible provides good motivation for further developments in theory. For this reason energy-balance applications are taken up before the introduction of second-law concepts. This arrangement also provides a period for digestion of state and first-law concepts and helps spread the introduction of new ideas more evenly over the course.

The objectives and general approach remain unchanged in this second edition, but there has been an important change as to detail. The first edition employed the Boltzmann approach to entropy, which views the entropy as a measure of disorder, and defines entropy in terms of the number of ways by which a particular microscopic state can be realized. In this edition we use the more general Gibbs definition in terms of the probabilities of the system quantum-states, $S = -k\Sigma p_i \ln p_i$. The Gibbs definition is found very simply by seeking an *extensive* measure of the microscopic *randomness,* or of our *uncertainty* about the exact quantum state. Ideas relating to the information which macroscopic properties reveal about the microscopic state have therefore been incorporated on an equal basis with the randomness-disorder notions in the conceptual development of entropy. These relations have been explained without any digressions into information or probability theory. The randomness-uncertainty ideas have been threaded through the text; the uncertainty ideas are particularly useful in discussing the macroscopic availability of microscopically disorganized energy.

The use of the Gibbs entropy permits a simpler treatment of statistical thermodynamics, and consequently this material has been extended in the second edition to include some additional examples. Microcanonical, canonical, and grand canonical systems are now treated in an introductory way, using a new approach which completely eliminates any need for undetermined multipliers. The discussions of negative absolute temperature have been strengthened by consideration of spin systems of importance in masers.

Examples have been added throughout the text where experience with the first edition indicated they might be helpful, and a few of the new terms which were introduced in the first edition have been eliminated in the interests of simplicity. The treatment of second-law consequences has been completely rewritten to take advantage of the uncertainty concept of entropy. Additional problems have been provided, with particular emphasis in the later chapters on open-ended engineering design problems.

Many of the improvements in this edition result from the helpful comments received from users of the first edition. Professor H. C. Perkins, who collaborated with me on the applications-oriented version of this approach, made numerous contributions to the first seven chapters. Dr. Philip Schmidt made many helpful criticisms and suggestions during the development of the current approach to entropy, and has been particularly successful in helping us bring these ideas into our companion laboratory-demonstration sessions.

Professor Joseph Keenan provided the initial spark which led me to recast the conceptual development of entropy, thereby opening the door to many other simplifications and improvements over the first edition.

This book could not have been written without the continued encouragement, support and suggestions of my colleagues and students. I am particularly indebted to Professor S. J. Kline, who has provided many valuable suggestions, and to Professor A. L. London, from whom I obtained a real appreciation for the methodology of thermodynamic analysis.

Finally, I should like to thank the many undergraduates who made suggestions during trial teaching with this material; their complaints and compliments were equally appreciated.

The development of this approach was assisted by a Ford Foundation grant to Stanford University.

William C. Reynolds

CONTENTS

THERMODYNAMICS

CHAPTER ONE

SOME INTRODUCTORY CONSIDERATIONS

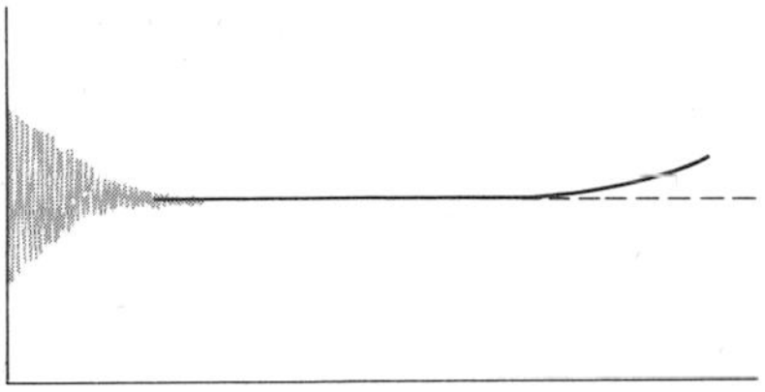

1·1 THE NATURE OF THERMODYNAMICS

Thermodynamics deals with matter and interactions between matter; since every technological system involves matter, thermodynamic analysis is very important in engineering. Examples of thermodynamic analysis are given throughout this text. In particular, the examples of Chaps. Five and Nine show applications to engineering systems, and those of Chaps. Eight and Ten indicate the role of thermodynamics in the study of substances. The student may wish to scan these examples now to get some idea about the direction and scope of the subject.

Thermodynamics centers about the notions of *energy;* the idea that energy is always conserved is both the fundamental starting point and the basis for quantitative analysis. A second concept in thermodynamics is *entropy;* entropy provides a means for determining if a process is possible. Processes which produce entropy are possible, those which destroy entropy are impossible. These ideas of energy and entropy provide the framework of thermodynamics, and a clear understanding of them is therefore crucial. For this reason we shall place heavy emphasis on the development of real understanding of these and related concepts. This development requires exposure to the ideas, a chance to use them operationally, and time for satisfactory digestion. Consequently we shall introduce new concepts gradually and with some repetition, and shall make use of the ideas in practical analysis shortly after their first introduction. The successful student will be one who works hardest on understanding concepts. The engineering calculations that we shall do are intended as vehicles for gaining understanding of the concepts and for developing the ability to carry out such a calculation independently.

What do we need to know about matter in order to carry out an engineering analysis of a system of interest? Matter is composed of particles; any visible piece of matter contains a tremendous number of molecules, atoms, electrons, etc., each of which can have energy in a variety of ways. A *microscopic* description of such a piece would require the enumeration of the state of each particle, an obviously impractical task. In thermodynamics we seek to reduce the bits of information required to adequately describe states of matter from something of the order of 10^{23} to "few." This is accomplished by some sort of *statistical averaging;* we are willing to forego knowledge of microscopic detail in favor of simplicity. Thermodynamics is therefore a *macroscopic* science, which allows us to relate the averaged (macroscopic) properties of matter. Fortunately, the microscopic aspects are not essential in many important technical problems, and we can obtain excellent engineering solutions using the simpler macroscopic ideas.

The ultimate nature of matter is microscopic, of course, and our understanding of macroscopic theories can be considerably enhanced by drawing on microscopic concepts. For instance, it may be hard to visualize an object sitting motionless on a table as having any energy; but the thought of electrons whirling about vibrating nuclei provides a vivid physical picture of that energy and makes it much easier to visualize various means for changing the energy of the object. In this text we shall take optimum advantage of microscopic ideas, using them to provide physical interpretations of macroscopic properties and intuitive bases for macroscopic postulates.

Thermodynamic theory allows us to relate various properties of matter, so that by measuring some of them we can calculate others. Although microscopic ideas are indeed helpful to understanding, thermodynamics does not require the postulation of any particular microscopic models of matter. Other physical theories have been developed which do require specific microscopic models, and from these emerge predictions for the *values* of properties of the substance represented by the model. In statistical mechanics some sort of statistical model of the substance is postulated, and in kinetic theory a dynamic model is employed. These theories, although more specific in their output, are less general than those of thermodynamics. In fact, results from thermodynamics are usually used in association with the microscopic theories. Historically thermodynamics, statistical mechanics, and kinetic theory have developed separately, usually from somewhat different foundations. Our use of microscopic concepts allows us to lay a more common foundation for these three subjects, such that their relation and interdependence can more easily be appreciated. We shall go into some simple microscopic analyses following development of the key thermodynamic ideas.

The knowledge of the behavior of matter obtained from thermodynamics is extremely important in engineering analysis. When carried out in a systematic fashion, such analyses are not very difficult; but we cannot emphasize enough the importance of a systematic methodology, without which easy problems become hard. In parallel with more theoretical thermodynamic developments we shall use the methodology in illustrative engineering examples. Understanding of the basic thermodynamic concepts and principles and the ability to apply them in engineering are the primary objectives of our study.

In this chapter we shall attempt to establish a point of view through discussion of ideas already familiar to the student. The fundamental approach and philosophy adopted in this review of the basic concepts, models, and laws of related branches of physics will be carried over to the new thermodynamic ideas in subsequent chapters.

1·2 CONCEPTS, MODELS, AND LAWS

Concepts form the basis for any science. These are ideas, usually somewhat vague (especially when first encountered), which often defy really adequate definition. The meaning of a new concept can seldom be grasped from reading a one-paragraph discussion. There must be time to become accustomed to the concept, to integrate it with prior knowledge, and to associate it with personal experience. Inability to work with the details of a new subject can often be traced to inadequate understanding of its basic concepts.

The physical world is very complicated, and to include every minute detail in a theoretical analysis would be impracticable. Science has made big steps forward by the use of *models*, which, although always representing some simplifications over reality, reduce the mathematics to a tractable level. The range of validity and utility of the resulting theory is consequently restricted by the idealizations made in formulating the model. Newtonian mechanics is quite adequate for analysis of the great majority of everyday mechanical processes, and inclusion of relativistic effects in such mechanical analysis is an unnecessary complication. However, in many instances such effects are important, and it is the responsibility of the user of any theory to know both its bases and its limitations.

Concepts and models are not enough in themselves for a physical theory. These notions must be expressed in appropriate mathematical terms through basic equations, or *laws*. We choose to look upon a physical law as a contrivance of man that allows him to explain and predict phenomena of nature. Such predictions will be only as accurate and encompassing as the models on which the laws are based, and as new information is gathered and new understanding is developed, man may find it convenient, or perhaps necessary, to alter the basic laws. For example, mechanics is a direct outgrowth of Kepler's astronomical studies and his laws relating to the motion of planets about the sun. Newton generalized these observations and formed new, more basic laws, from which Kepler's rules could be deduced as special consequences. Later Newton's mechanics became merely a special case of Einstein's relativistic mechanics. In general, laws are replaced not because they are incorrect, but because their range of validity is restricted. Such was the case in the early development of thermodynamics, where at one time heat was thought of as something contained within matter. A useful but extremely limited caloric theory of heat, built upon this concept, was discarded more than a century ago; unfortunately, carryover of this misconception inhibits understanding of contemporary thermodynamics.

In many fields of science the concepts are very close to everyday experience, and the difficulties are primarily mathematical in nature. In most of thermodynamics the converse is true; the mathematics is not complicated but the concepts are sometimes difficult to grasp at the beginning, and most of the errors in thermodynamic analysis arise because of lack of clarity in either concepts or methodology. For this reason we shall spend a good deal of time on these matters; they should not be taken lightly, even though it may not be evident why so much attention is paid to apparently small details. To begin the discussion, let us review some concepts that are already familiar, examining them in the manner we shall subsequently employ in thermodynamics.

1·3 A FRESH LOOK AT SOME FAMILIAR CONCEPTS

One of the most important and central concepts in physics is *force*. It took man millenniums to evolve the force concept as a tool for explaining the varied interactions between objects in his environment. He observed that any one of a number of things can cause a given object to assume a certain position or undergo a certain gyration. The perception that in discussing the behavior of the object a particular cause can be replaced by a hypothetical "force" heralded the beginning of mechanics. Today we use this concept almost unconsciously whenever we replace the action of one body upon another by an appropriate force (see Fig. 1·1).

Forces are conceived as those pushes and pulls that tend to make objects move, and an essential part of the concept is that forces are somehow in balance when the object under study is motionless (or when its motion is uniform). It is essential to appreciate that the notion of a balance of forces in the absence of acceleration is an integral part of the force concept; whether or not forces "really exist" is a philosophical question which we need not debate. The fact is that the force concept allows us accurately to predict events in the real world, and this alone justifies its invention.

Forces are conceived as having both magnitude and direction and are treated mathematically as vectors. The vector sum of all forces acting on a body that is not accelerating must be zero.

We imagine that any two bodies in contact will exert forces upon one another. When we analyze the motion of one body, we mentally remove the

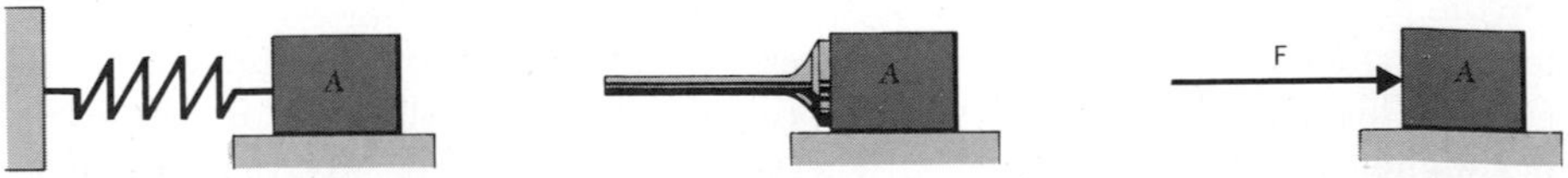

FIG. 1·1 *The effect of either the spring or the shaft on body A can be replaced by* F

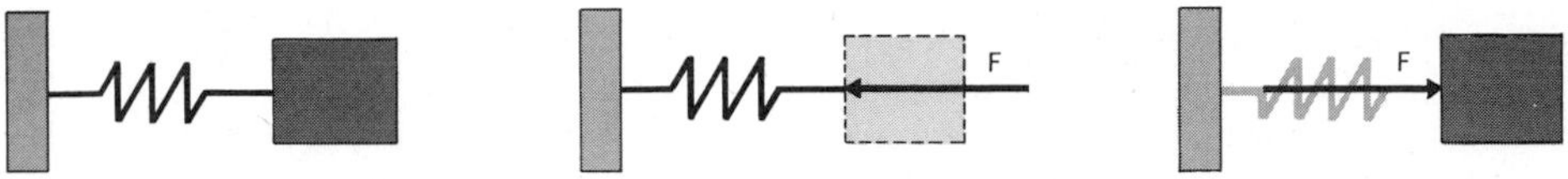

FIG. 1·2 *The notion that "action equals reaction" is an integral part of the force concept*

other and replace its influence on the first by a force (Fig. 1·2). If we wish instead to study the motion of the second body, the first body would be replaced by a force of exactly the same magnitude but acting in the opposite direction. This "action-reaction" principle was formulated by Newton as his third law, but it is really an integral part of the concept of force.

No conceptual quantity becomes operationally useful until some way for its measurement has been established. One possible way of setting up a scale for force is to select some standard spring and say that the force it exerts is some selected constant times its deflection. This scheme has the distinct disadvantage of making the force scale dependent on the choice of material in the spring, among other factors. Suppose someone else set up a similar scale, based on a different kind of spring; the two scales could be adjusted to agree at one point but could not be expected to agree elsewhere. To each one the other would be nonlinear. It is always more desirable to devise scales of measure that are completely independent of the nature of any substance. In principle it is possible to do this for force, taking advantage of the notion that the resultant force on a stationary body is zero. Imagine selecting any reproducible force, such as that produced by a selected spring compressed some selected amount, and designating this as a unit force. Let this force act on a body in sole opposition to two identical forces selected so as to keep the spring at its standard deflection when the body is motionless (the two identical forces could be obtained from any two identical springs, for example). The two identical forces must each be half the unit force, and either can be used to measure such a force (see Fig. 1·3). This process can be continued, and we can collect a set of springs, each measuring some rational fraction or multiple of the unit force. We can therefore, in principle, measure any unknown force to any desired degree of accuracy. The force scale is unique in that it is independent of the nature of any substance. It will be the same regardless of the material of which the springs are made.

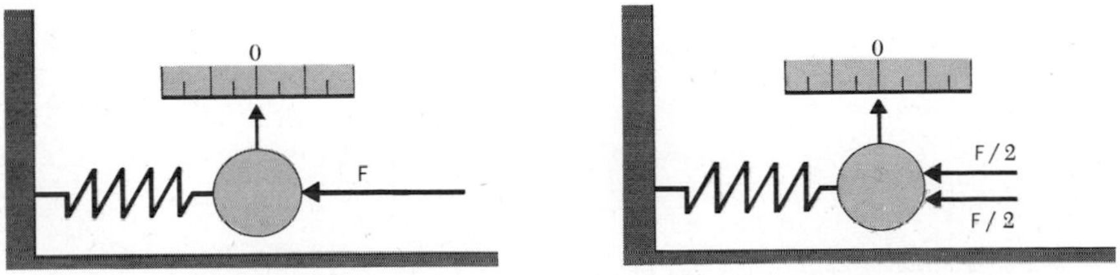

FIG. 1·3 *A unique force scale can be established using symmetry and the concepts of force*

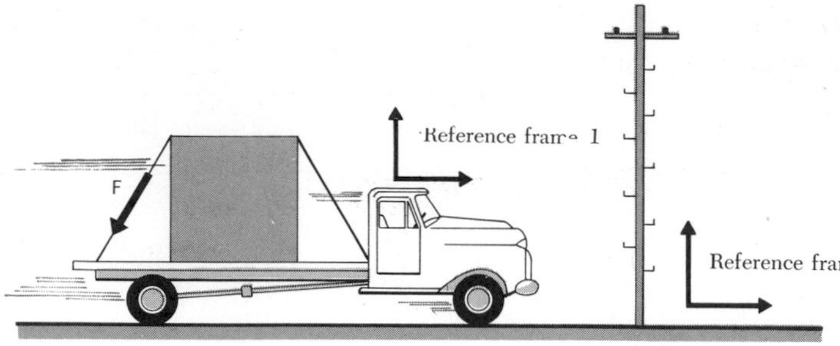

FIG. 1·4 *The force is the same in both reference frames*

An important part of the concept of force is that the magnitude of a force is unchanged by a change in the *reference frame*. Forces are therefore absolute, while the motions they produce are relative (see Fig. 1·4).

The force concept allows us to explain the lack of translational accelerations but is in itself insufficient when rotational accelerations are involved. For example, consider the bar of Fig. 1·5, acted upon by three horizontal coplanar forces. The vector sum of these forces is indeed zero, yet we know from experience that the bar would undergo clockwise rotational acceleration. The additional concept of the *moment* of a force provides the explanation, and that moment is the product of the force times its distance from some reference point. But why should the first power of the distance, and not its square, or its cube, or its logarithm, be involved? We used symmetry arguments in setting up a unique force scale, and they can be used again to deduce an appropriate definition for the moment of a force. The thought processes involved are shown in Fig. 1·6. The symmetry of the coplanar force set of Fig. 1·6*a* requires that it be a *zero set*, meaning that the forces would produce neither translational nor rotational accelerations if they acted on the bar. Figure 1·6*b* also shows a zero set, and the sum of these two zero sets (Fig. 1·6*c*) forms a third *non-symmetric zero set*. In Fig. 1·6*d* the ratio of the forces at A and C is the inverse of the ratio of their distance from point O. This argument can be continued, and one can construct an infinite number of zero sets with one force at O, another at C, and the third force at some point A along the bar. In every case the ratio of the force at A to that at C is found to be exactly the inverse of the

FIG. 1·5 *The bar would pivot about* 0

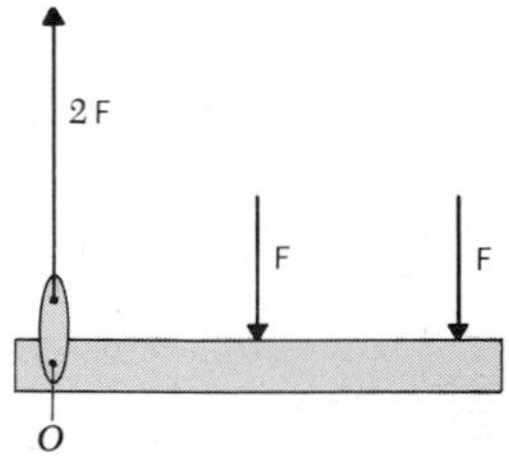

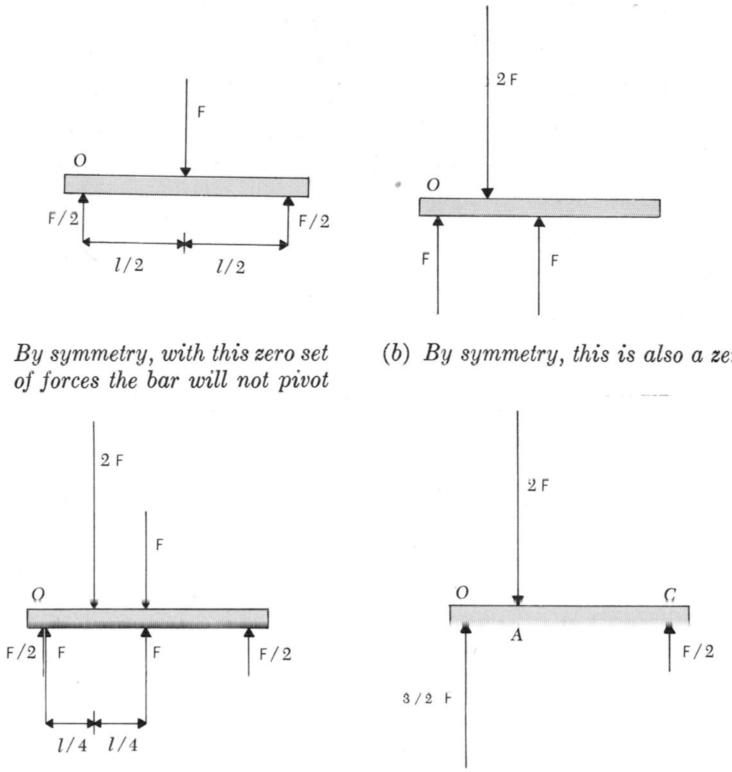

(a) *By symmetry, with this zero set of forces the bar will not pivot*

(b) *By symmetry, this is also a zero set*

(c) *Therefore this is also a zero set*

(d) *So this must be a zero set*

FIG. 1·6 *Deducing the law of the lever by symmetry*

ratio of their distances from the potential pivot point O,

$$\frac{F_A}{F_C} = \frac{L_C}{L_A} \tag{1·1}$$

which is well known as the *law of the lever* (see Fig. 1·7). An equivalent statement is that the *moments* of the forces F_A and F_C are equal but opposite, where we define the moment of a force F about a point O by

$$M_{F/O} = Fr$$

where the distance r has the meaning indicated in Fig. 1·8.

The approach to the concept of force presented above is typical of the approach we shall take to other thermodynamics concepts. In particular, recall the development of the unique force scale, which is independent of any arbitrary choice of spring material. It should be possible to define scales for all fundamental properties of matter that are independent of this type of arbitrariness. In a moment we shall see how this can be done for the concepts of mass and

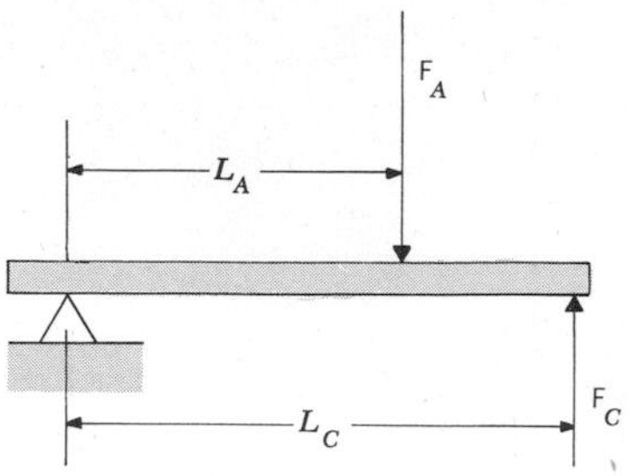

FIG. 1·7 *The law of the lever;* $F_A/F_C = L_C/L_A$

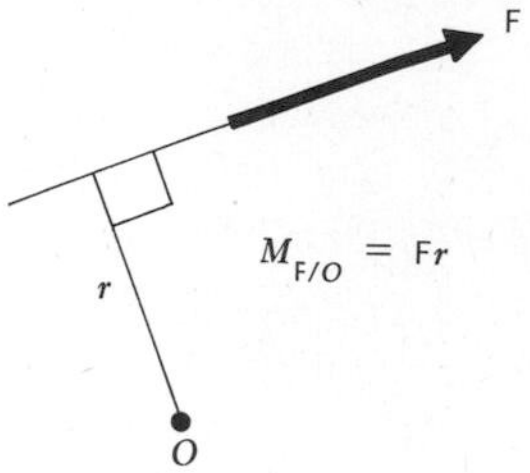

FIG. 1·8 *The moment of a force*

charge. Temperature is a fundamental property in thermodynamics, and it should be possible to establish a temperature scale that does not depend on arbitrary thermometer materials or markings. One of the important contributions of thermodynamics is a real conceptual basis for temperature, including a temperature scale that is independent of such arbitrary choices. We shall introduce this concept of temperature and the associated means for its measurement in Chap. Seven.

Quantitative prediction of the acceleration of bodies requires the introduction of another familiar concept, *mass.* A body acted on by an unbalanced force does not suddenly increase its speed, but rather accelerates gradually at a rate which is dependent on the magnitude of the force. The *inertial mass*

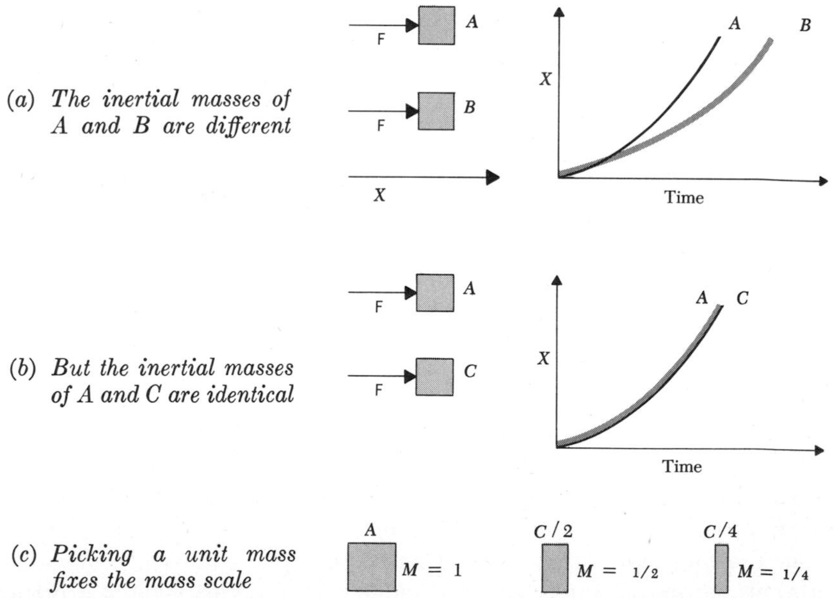

FIG. 1·9 *Devising a unique scale for inertial mass using symmetry arguments*

of an object is conceived as a property characteristic of its resistance to velocity change. Any two objects that undergo identical translational accelerations when acted upon by the same force have identical inertial masses (Fig. 1·9).

An idea inherent in the Newtonian concept of inertial mass is that the mass of two objects taken together is the sum of their individual inertial masses; cutting a homogeneous body into two identical parts produces two identical masses, each with half the original mass. The notion of *conservation of mass* is therefore an integral part of the concept of mass. In principle, a unique scale for inertial mass may be constructed using the same sort of arguments used to construct a force scale. The reasoning involved is indicated in Fig. 1·9.

Any object that is dropped will accelerate as it falls, even though the object is not in physical contact with any other body. To explain this behavior man had to conceive *gravitational forces,* which one body, such as the earth, can exert on another, even though they are far apart. This leads to the concept of *gravitational mass,* conceived as that property of matter representative of its distant interactions with other bodies. If the forces exerted by the earth (or any other mass) on any two objects are identical, they must have identical gravitational masses. A unique scale for gravitational mass can be devised using a simple laboratory balance, as shown in Fig. 1·10.

Suppose we use the same object for a unit mass in constructing both the inertial- and gravitational-mass scales. While the inertial and gravitational masses of this object will be identical, there is no reason to expect the scales to be identical. Yet very careful experiments have shown that the two scales are equivalent to within at least one part in 10^{10}, and consequently we consider them as fully identical.†

The terms "mass" and "weight" are frequently confused. By *weight* we mean the gravitational force exerted by the earth on an object near the earth's

† R. H. Dicke, The Eötvös Experiment, *Scientific American,* December, 1961.

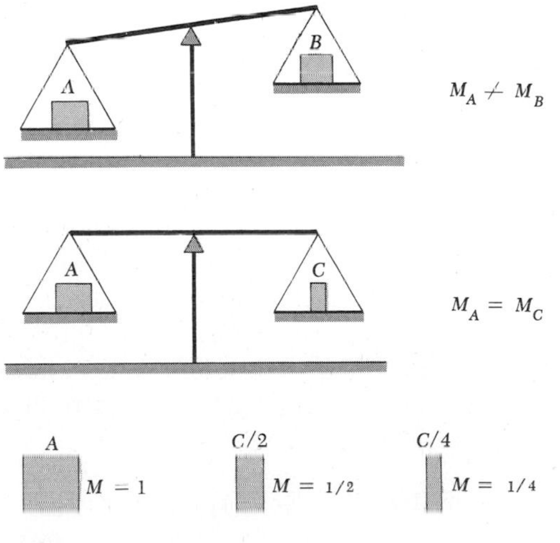

FIG. 1·10 *Symmetry can also be used to establish a unique scale of gravitational mass*

surface. The weight of a body depends on its location, while its mass is conceived as being independent of position. Two exceptions are forced upon us by historical circumstances. The term "atomic weight" has come to be used to denote the ratio of the mass of an atom to $\frac{1}{16}$ the mass of an oxygen atom. The atomic weight is therefore a number without dimensions. "Molecular weight" is used for the sum of the atomic weights of all atoms in a molecule and is also dimensionless.

The *molal mass* is important in chemistry and thermodynamics. A *mole* is defined as an amount of a given substance numerically equal to its molecular weight. For example, a gram mole of helium (molecular weight = 4.003) would have a mass of 4.003 g. The mass of any sample of a given substance is then simply the number of moles present times the molal mass, which is the mass of a single mole of the substance. The molal mass of helium is 4.003 g/gmole.

Consider now a group of N molecules of a substance whose molecular weight and molal mass are m and $\hat{M}$, respectively. If the mass of individual molecules is m, the total mass of the N molecules is

$$M = N\mathsf{m} = Nm\frac{\mathsf{m}_0}{16}$$

where m_0 is the mass of an oxygen atom. However, it is also true that

$$\blacktriangleright \qquad M = \mathfrak{N}\hat{M}$$

where $\mathfrak{N}$ denotes the number of moles present. It therefore follows that

$$\frac{\mathfrak{N}}{N}\frac{\hat{M}}{m} = \frac{\mathsf{m}_0}{16}$$

Since $\hat{M}$ and m are numerically equal, it follows that *the number of molecules in a mole is the same for every substance,*

$$\blacktriangleright \qquad \frac{N}{\mathfrak{N}} = \mathrm{N}_0 = \text{constant} \tag{1·2}$$

The constant N_0 is called *Avogadro's number;* its value is 6.025×10^{23}/gmole.

A convenient concept in mechanics is the *particle*, an idealized body in which all the mass is imagined to be concentrated at a single point. A particle has no shape and can undergo only translational motions. Experimentally it is found that the product of the acceleration and the mass of an object treated as a particle is proportional to the force acting on it. If we were to set up *arbitrary* scales of mass, force, length, and time, there would be no reason to expect the constant of proportionality to be unity. The equation describing the motion would then be

$$\mathsf{F} = k_N M a \tag{1·3}$$

which is merely *Newton's second law* in a somewhat more general form. There may be some virtue in adjusting the scales of force and mass to make the constant k_N come out to be unity, and we shall discuss this later in the chapter.

The classical model of gravitational attraction is that the attractive force exerted mutually by two particles follows the law

$$\mathbf{F} = k_G \frac{M_1 M_2}{R^2} \tag{1·4}$$

Here M_1 and M_2 are the two masses, R is the distance between them, and k_G is a *universal gravitational constant.* The mechanism by which these forces are exerted is not well understood; perhaps when the concept of gravitation is more fully developed it will be possible to deduce that the inverse square of the distance is appropriate in a more fundamental manner.

The fundamental concept of electromagnetics is that of *charge.* Its invention arose out of the need for an explanation of forces which can exist between physically separated objects, forces which could not be accounted for in terms of gravitation. Charge is conceived as a property of electric particles and can give rise to either attractive or repulsive forces. The concept of charge is intimately tied to the idea that charge is a conserved quantity. Two objects that have been rubbed together will attract one another; we explain this by saying that one object has been positively charged and the other negatively charged (in order to conserve charge). We observe that bodies having charges of equal sign repel one another and that objects with opposite charge attract, and we adopt these conventions as part of the charge concept.

With the concept that electrostatic forces are somehow associated with charge, it becomes possible to tell when two objects have the same charge. This occurs when they each exert the same force on a third charged body. When a charged object is touched to an identical uncharged object, the objects assume identical charges. Symmetry considerations, together with the concept of charge as a conserved quantity, indicate that each object then has half the original charge. The notion that charge is conserved allows us to establish a unique scale of charge which is independent of the nature of any substance (see Fig. 1·11).

Experimentally it is found that the repulsive force between two stationary point charges is proportional to the product of their charges and inversely

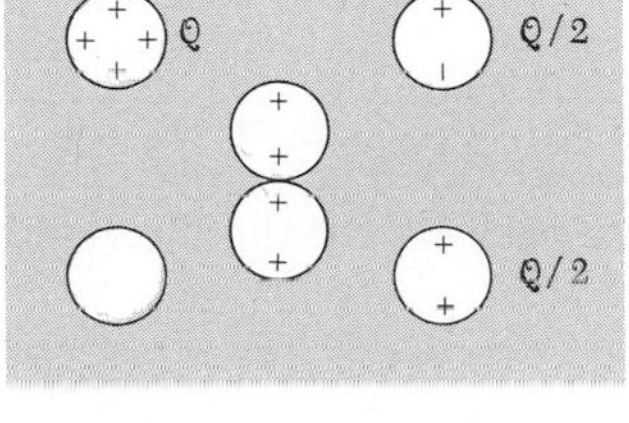

FIG. 1·11 *Establishing a unique charge scale with symmetry arguments*

proportional to the square of the distance between them,

$$F = k_C \frac{Q_1 Q_2}{R^2} \tag{1·5}$$

This is *Coulomb's law;* the constant k_C depends upon the arbitrary choices of unit forces and charges. It is possible to construct dimensional systems in which k_C comes out to be unity, and we shall discuss this later in the chapter.

Moving charges exert additional forces upon one another. If the charges are not moving too rapidly, the additional forces are given by the *Biot-Savart law.*† The constant of proportionality in this expression similarly depends upon the particular choices of force and charge scales.

1·4 MECHANICAL CONCEPTS OF ENERGY

Consider the equation of motion of a single particle,

$$\mathbf{F} = k_N M \frac{d\mathbf{V}}{dt} \tag{1·6}$$

Multiplying by dt and integrating from t_1 to t_2,

$$\int_{t_1}^{t_2} \mathbf{F}\,dt = k_N M(\mathbf{V}_2 - \mathbf{V}_1) \tag{1·7}$$

It is customary to call the integral the *impulse* and to call the quantity $M\mathbf{V}$ the *momentum.* The basic equation of mechanics therefore tells us that the impulse provided is proportional to the increase in momentum of the particle.

Recognizing that by definition $\mathbf{V} = d\mathbf{X}/dt$, we can multiply Eq. (1·6) by $d\mathbf{X}$ (vector dot product) and integrate between any two points in space, obtaining‡

$$\int_{\mathbf{X}_1}^{\mathbf{X}_2} \mathbf{F} \cdot d\mathbf{X} = k_N \frac{M}{2} (V_2^2 - V_1^2) \tag{1·8}$$

It is customary to call the integral the *work* done on the particle and to refer to the quantity $k_N M V^2/2$ as the *kinetic energy* of the particle. The basic mechanical law then tells us that the work done by the force on the particle is equal to the increase in its kinetic energy. Note that the expression for kinetic energy is developed by manipulations from a fundamental equation.

In discussing the motion of a particle it is often convenient to conceive a *force field.* For example, the gravitational force on a mass is sometimes expressed in terms of a gravitational field $\mathbf{G}$ as

$$\mathbf{F} = M\mathbf{G}$$

In Eq. (1·8) the energy transferred as work to a particle by the gravitational

† See Appendix A, Table A·2.
‡ Here V^2 means $\mathbf{V} \cdot \mathbf{V}$.

force would then be

$$\int_{X_1}^{X_2} M\mathbf{G} \cdot d\mathbf{X} = k_N \frac{M}{2} (\mathsf{V}_2^2 - \mathsf{V}_1^2)$$

One can show that the gravitational field may alternatively be expressed in terms of a scalar potential ϕ such that†

$$\mathbf{G} = -\operatorname{grad} \phi$$

Force fields having a potential are said to be *conservative*. The integral of Eq. (1·8) may therefore be evaluated and the result expressed as

$$k_N \frac{M}{2} \mathsf{V}_1^2 + M\phi_1 = k_N \frac{M}{2} \mathsf{V}_2^2 + M\phi_2$$

The term $M\phi$ is called the *potential energy* of the particle. We see that the laws of mechanics require that the energy of such a particle, that is, the sum of the kinetic and potential energies, be *conserved*.‡ Derivation of an expression for the potential energy of a body near the earth's surface is left as an exercise (Prob. 1·20).

The concept of energy as a conserved quantity has been central in science since the late seventeenth century. At first the idea was applied only to a freely falling body; as additional systems were considered, new kinds of energy had to be introduced in order that the conservation aspect be retained. Considerations of charge led to coulomb energy and eventually to the concept of energy in an electromagnetic field. With the modifications of mechanics introduced by relativity theory, came rest-mass energy. Physicists have conceived new particles solely in order to retain the conservation of energy at the nuclear and subnuclear levels. Man has become fond of the conservation-of-energy concept and, being unwilling to discard it, has been forced to visualize new kinds of energy. One wonders if simpler explanations of nature might be obtained by forgetting about the concepts of force and energy and starting over with new concepts. While this may some day happen, the engineer of today must use present-day concepts, models, and laws to devise his systems, and the notions of force, mass, work, and in particular, the conservation of energy, are quite adequate for his purposes.

1·5 CONTINUUM CONCEPTS

The concept of the particle is useful on both the smallest and largest scales, and it is indeed amazing that the motion of planets and electrons can be described in such similar terms. When considering systems of many, many particles, the concept of a *continuum* is often useful. In the continuum view matter is seen as being distributed through space and not, as in the particle

† In one-dimensional terms, $\mathsf{G} = -d\phi/dx$.
‡ When only gravitational forces act on the particle.

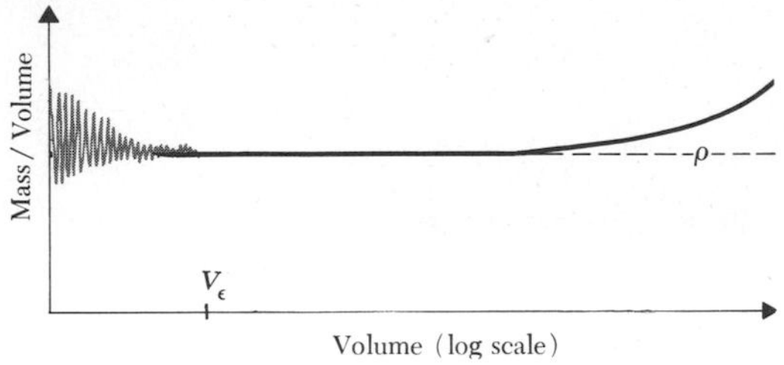

FIG. 1·12 *Density at a point*

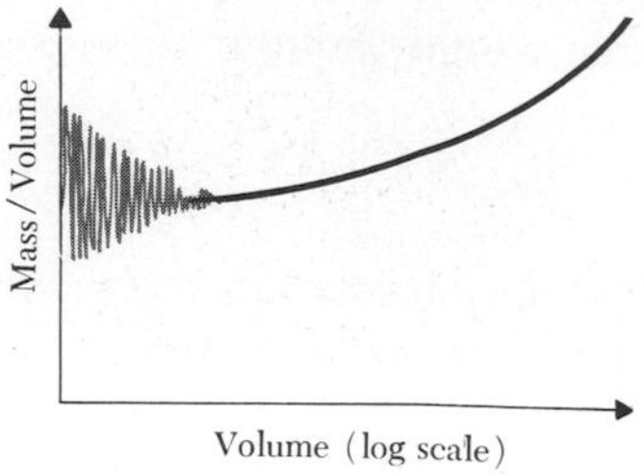

FIG. 1·13 *Density cannot be defined if the spatial variations are too great*

view, localized. Matter exists in "big chunks," having mass, energy, and momentum, as do particles, but also possessing some additional continuum characteristics, such as volume, density, and temperature.

From the continuum standpoint we can speak of properties at a point. For example, consider taking smaller and smaller sized volumes about a point and measuring the ratio mass/volume. This ratio will approach a limit, defined as the *density at the point* (Fig. 1·12),

$$\rho = \lim_{V \to V_\epsilon} \frac{M}{V}$$

If the volume is made too small (smaller than V_ϵ), the ratio will fluctuate in time as the molecular population of the volume changes. The continuum idealization is therefore not useful for volumes which are too small. If the spatial variations in mass/volume are too great, a limit may not exist, and the continuum method would be invalid. Such a case is shown in Fig. 1·13.

Other continuum concepts include *mass-flow rate, electric current*, and *mass flux*. Consider an imaginary plane within a fluid; molecules will continually cross this plane in both directions, but if more cross one way than go the other there will be a net mass flow. Denoting δM_r and δM_l as the amounts of mass which cross to the right and left during the time interval δt, the mass-flow rate to the right is defined as

$$\dot{M} = \lim_{\delta t \to \delta t_\epsilon} \frac{\delta M_r - \delta M_l}{\delta t}$$

where δt_ϵ denotes some very small time interval (see Fig. 1·14). δt_ϵ must be

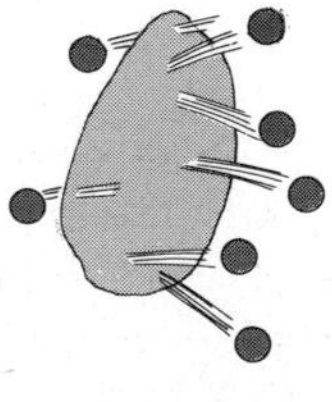

FIG. 1·14 *A net passage of molecules to the right gives rise to an equivalent mass flow*

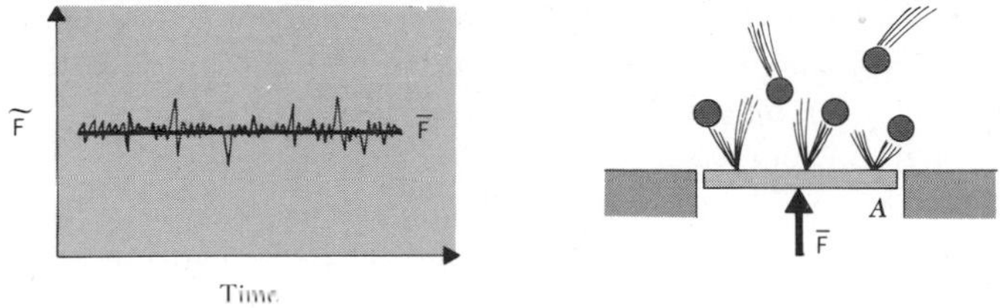

FIG. 1·15 *Pressure;* $P = \bar{F}/A$

sufficiently long that many particles cross the plane in this period; consequently the mass-flow rate loses its usefulness in processes which occur at extremely rapid rates. The terms "mass flux" and "current flux" refer to limiting rates of flow *per unit of area*. Formal definitions of these quantities are left as exercises.

The *pressure* exerted by a fluid on the walls of a container is also a continuum concept (see Fig. 1·15). At the microscopic level we can explain pressure as resulting from impacts of particles on the wall. These impacts result in a force which is macroscopically measurable, and in the continuum view we think of this force as being uniformly distributed over the wall. The pressure is then the limiting *force per unit of area*, which we can evaluate at any point on the wall.

In continuum analyses the manipulations of calculus are employed; for example, the mass of a body can be expressed in terms of the integrated density distribution as

$$M = \int_{\text{vol}} \rho \, dV$$

Thermodynamics is essentially a continuum science, and hence these continuum concepts will be very important throughout our study.

1·6 THE CONCEPTUAL BASIS OF DIMENSIONAL SYSTEMS

There probably never was a student who at one time or another was not confused by the many different systems of units used in various fields of engineering. Such confusion disappears once the *concepts* behind dimensions and unit systems are properly understood. We shall work in various unit systems throughout this text, and it is well that we spend some time clarifying these concepts now.

We have emphasized that it is possible to construct scales of measure for the conceptual quantities and that it is most desirable that these scales be independent of the nature of the materials employed in setting the standards. There is a great deal of choice as to the scales which we arbitrarily select. For example, we normally work in dimensional systems in which arbitrary scales of length and time have been established, and in which velocity has the dimensions of length divided by time. We could alternatively set up a system in which scales for velocity and time were arbitrarily chosen, and then length would have the dimensions of velocity multiplied by time. We could select arbitrary standards for length, velocity, and time; however, in such a system velocity would be proportional, but not necessarily equal, to the rate of change of length with time. The essential idea to grasp is that the quantities for which arbitrary scales of measure are set up can be picked in many ways, and it just happens that the early scientists picked certain sets.

We use the word "dimension" to mean a name given to any measurable quantity. Length, time, mass, area, and velocity are *dimensions*. The *primary quantities* of a particular dimensional system are those for which we decide to set up arbitrary scales of measure. *Secondary quantities* are those whose dimensions are expressed in terms of the dimensions of primary quantities. In the dimensional systems we customarily employ, length and time are primary quantities and velocity and area are secondary quantities.

The primary scales of measure are expressed in terms of *units*. For example, foot, inch, and meter are all different *units* with the common *dimension* of length. Each of the primary scales is based on a carefully chosen standard. In olden times the standards of measure were things like the king's foot, but today we are in the midst of a switch to more available, more highly reproducible standards. The international standard of length used to be the distance between two marks on a platinum-iridium bar, but in 1960 an atomic standard based on the wavelength of the orange-red line in the spectrum of krypton 86 was adopted by international agreement. The meter is now defined as 1,650,763.73 times this wavelength. The present standard of time is the second. Until 1960 it was defined as 1/86,400 of a mean solar day; then the definition was changed to 1/31,556,925.9747 of the tropical year 1900.† Hopefully a more accessible, precisely reproducible atomic standard will be adopted in the not-too-distant future.‡

Length and time are primary quantities in all dimensional systems in common use. In some systems *mass* is also taken as a primary quantity. A standard 1-kg mass of platinum-iridium is kept at the International Bureau of Weights and Measures in France. In other dimensional systems *force* is chosen as a primary quantity; the standard of force can be taken as the weight of the platinum-iridium mass at some prescribed point on earth. Nature has provided an excellent standard of charge in the electron, and we can think of using this as a basis for a charge scale.

The dimensions of secondary quantities are fixed by the equations which relate them to the primary quantities. For example, in the mks system length (meter), mass (kilogram), and time (second) are taken as the primary quantities. Force is a secondary quantity in this dimensional system; the dimensions and

† *National Bureau of Standards Technical News Bulletin*, vol. 44, no. 12, December, 1960.

‡ At the 1964 International Conference on Weights and Measures a definition of a cesium radiation frequency was adopted as a temporary atomic standard.

magnitudes of forces result from the arbitrary selection of unity for the value of the constant k_N in Newton's second law, which then becomes (for a particle)

$$\mathsf{F} = Ma$$

The secondary quantity acceleration has the dimensions of length/time², so force has the dimensions of mass × length/time² and the units of kg-m/sec² in the mks system.

Another common system is the absolute engineering flt system, in which force, length, and time are the primary quantities. Here the dimensions and units of mass result from arbitrarily setting $k_N = 1$. Newton's law then is again $\mathsf{F} = Ma$, but mass has the dimensions of force/(length/time²) and the units of lbf-sec²/ft in this system.

It is important to realize that the constants in physical laws do not just happen to be equal to 1; they are often picked to have this or some other value. Confusion about electrical-unit systems is often a result of failure to understand this point.

A third dimensional system used a great deal in engineering is the fmlt engineering system, in which both force *and* mass plus length and time are chosen as the primary quantities. The scales for force and mass are chosen such that the weight of an object at sea level on earth is numerically equal to its mass. Force and mass are assigned the units of lbf (pound force) and lbm (pound mass), respectively. Newton's law is not $\mathsf{F} = Ma$ in this unit system; instead the constant k_N is considered as having the experimentally determined value of

$$k_N = \frac{1}{32.1739} \text{ lbf-sec}^2\text{/ft-lbm}$$

It is customary to denote the reciprocal of k_N by g_c; in the fmlt engineering system,

$$\blacktriangleright \quad g_c = 32.1739 \text{ ft-lbm/lbf-sec}^2$$

This is a *universal constant* which emerges in Newton's law as a result of the arbitrary choices for standards of measure. In this text we shall henceforth write Newton's second law for a particle as

$$\blacktriangleright \quad \mathsf{F} = \frac{1}{g_c} Ma \tag{1·9}$$

The constant g_c has the value unity and is dimensionless in the mks, cgs, and absolute engineering systems. The term g_c should not be confused with the local acceleration of gravity g_0. While g_c and g_0 are *numerically* equal in the fmlt engineering system, their dimensions are different. A tabulation of four dimensional systems used in mechanics and physics is presented in Table A·1 of Appendix A.

Electrical-unit systems show even more variance. The absolute electrostatic cgs system is simply an extension of the cgs system in which the dimensions and units of charge are fixed by selecting the constant in Coulomb's law to be 1. In the absolute electromagnetic cgs system the constant in the Biot-Savart law is picked to be 1, and the constant in Coulomb's law then emerges as an experimentally determined value. Most contemporary work is done in the rationalized practical mksc system, in which charge is a primary quantity, and the constants in both Coulomb's and the Biot-Savart laws have odd experimentally determined values. Table A·2 shows these three dimensional systems.

Sometimes the units of secondary quantities, expressed in terms of the primary units, become sufficiently complicated that we find it convenient to give names, or *aliases*, to particular combinations. Some important examples are evident in Tables A·1 and A·2. One can appreciate the desirability of denoting the combination coul^2-sec^2-kg^{-1}-m^{-2} by the simple alias "farad," but the desirability of also calling a centimeter an "abhenry" might be argued.

To illustrate the ideas of dimensional systems, let us set up a system in which only length and time are chosen as primary quantities. Both force and mass will be secondary quantities, and we shall determine their dimensions and units by arbitrarily selecting the constant in Newton's law to be 2 and the constant in the gravitational law to be unity. In our new system these laws would be

$$\mathsf{F} = 2Ma$$

$$\mathsf{F} = \frac{M_1 M_2}{R^2}$$

Considering two identical mutually gravitating masses and the accelerations they undergo, we equate the above two equations and solve for M, finding

$$M = 2aR^2 \tag{1·10}$$

Mass will therefore have the dimensions of length^3/time^2 in this new system. If we adopt the meter and the second as primary standards, mass would have the units m^3/sec^2. We might choose the alias "chunk" for this combination of primary units. The dimensions of force would then be length^4/time^4, and we could give the alias "push" to 1 m^4/sec^4.

Conversion factors from the mks system to our new system would not be found in standard tables, but we can work out our own conversion factors for this system. Consider two bodies, each having a mass of 1 kg in the mks system, freely gravitating toward one another. Suppose they are 1 m apart. The acceleration which they undergo can be computed first from the mks equations

$$\mathsf{F} = Ma$$

$$\mathsf{F} = \frac{k_G M^2}{R^2}$$

Then

$$a = \frac{k_G M}{R^2} = \frac{6.67 \times 10^{-11}\ \text{m}^3/\text{kg-sec}^2 \times 1\ \text{kg}}{1\ \text{m}^2}$$

$$= 6.67 \times 10^{-11}\ \text{m/sec}^2$$

The mass in the new unit system may now be computed from Eq. (1·10) as

$$M = 2(6.67 \times 10^{-11}\ \text{m/sec}^2)\ 1\ \text{m}^2 = 13.34 \times 10^{-11}\ \text{m}^3/\text{sec}^2$$

We therefore have the conversion equivalence

$$1\ \text{kg} = 13.34 \times 10^{-11}\ \text{m}^3/\text{sec}^2 = 13.34 \times 10^{-11}\ \text{chunks}$$

The conversion between newtons and pushes could be obtained in the same way. Appendix A is devoted to further consideration of unit systems.

SELECTED READING

Resnick, R., and D. Halliday, *Physics, Part 1*, chap. 1, chap. 5, John Wiley & Sons, Inc., New York, 1966.

Kestin, J., *A Course in Thermodynamics*, chap. 1, Blaisdell Publishing Co., Inc., Waltham, Mass., 1966.

Zemansky, M. W., and H. C. Van Ness, *Basic Engineering Thermodynamics*, secs. 1.1–1.4, McGraw-Hill Book Company, New York, 1966.

QUESTIONS

1·1 What are your concepts of length and time?

1·2 What is the value of g_c on the moon?

1·3 Why is it not true that $g_g/g_c = 1$ in the engineering system, even though the numerical values of g_g and g_c may be the same?

1·4 What is the difference between work and power?

1·5 No one has ever seen an electron. Why do we say that they exist?

1·6 Consider $\mathsf{F}\, dX$, $d\,(\mathsf{F}X)$, and $X\, d\mathsf{F}$. Which is work, and why? Which can be integrated without knowing how F varies with X?

1·7 Invent an analogy of the microscopic and macroscopic viewpoints that would be useful in explaining these concepts to a layman.

1·8 How might you explain the concepts of energy, force, and charge to a high school freshman?

1·9 How do concepts differ from definitions?

1·10 Estimate the length of time and amount of paper required to write down the coordinates of every molecule in a mole of gas.

1·11 At what age did you first hear about energy? At what age did you first understand the concept? Have you ever heard about entropy?

1·12 Is it wrong, or merely inconvenient, to conceive of the earth as the center of the solar system?

1·13 What is your mass in lbm? What is your height in statfarads?

1·14 Push very hard on a stone wall. How much work did you do on the wall? Why did you get tired?

1·15 In Newtonian mechanics which of the following are absolute, which are relative, and why? (*a*) Force, (*b*) mass, (*c*) length, (*d*) time, (*e*) momentum, (*f*) energy, (*g*) work, and (*h*) velocity.

1·16 Why is it important to make a distinction between lbm and lbf? Can they be canceled in an equation?

1·17 What is a gmole? A lbmole?

1·18 What is a continuum? Under what circumstances might the continuum idealizations be invalid?

PROBLEMS

1·1 Discuss the differences between concepts and definitions. What are the basic concepts of geometry? What are some geometrical definitions?

1·2 In the Middle Ages it was thought that length up was somehow not the same as length horizontally ("after all, things fall down but never fall sideways!"). Discuss how the concepts of these two lengths have changed since that time. Can you draw any parallelisms with the present dual concepts of mass?

1·3 Discuss the possible means for devising fundamental measures of length and time.

1·4 Derive an expression for the electric field strength **E** in the vicinity of a point charge Q using Coulomb's law.

1·5 Derive an expression for the gravitational field strength **G** in the vicinity of a point mass M using the universal gravitation law.

1·6 Consider an observer in a frame which is accelerating linearly at acceleration a_0. What should he write for Newton's law in his coordinate frame? What would be his energy accounting for the work done by a force on a particle?

1·7 A body having a mass of 1 kg falls from rest from a height of 30 ft. Express its kinetic energy in Btu, ft-lbf, and ev.

1·8 Using the inverse-square gravitational law, calculate the work required to lift a 1000-kg satellite from the earth's surface to an altitude of 100 miles and inject it into orbit at 17,500 mph. How long would a 300-hp engine have to be run to produce this much energy? How many automotive batteries would be required if the orbiting could be done electrically (600 watt-hr is the total available energy from a typical automotive wet cell)? Why is this not the procedure normally used?

1·9 Estimate your kinetic energy while running 10 mph. State the result in ergs, Btu, and ev. Did you do any work on the ground in achieving this speed?

1·10 A 100-megaton hydrogen bomb releases 10^{25} ergs of energy. Compare this to the kinetic energy of an iron asteroid 10 km in diameter approaching the earth at 50,000 m/sec.

1·11 Determine the value of g_c in the engineering unit system from things which you know in the mks system and the conversions from kg to lbm, m to ft, and newtons to lbf.

1·12 Set up a dimension system in which length and time are the only primary quantities. Pick the constants in Newton's law, Coulomb's law, and the universal gravitational law to be unity. Use the meter and the second as the primary standards and determine the equivalence of a 1-kg mass and a 1-coul charge in the new unit system.

1·13 Set up a dimension system in which the mass of the earth is taken as 1 chunk, the diameter of the earth is 1 clearthru, and the period of the earth around the sun is 1 oncearound. Fix the units of force by selecting the gravitational constant to be unity. Obtain a table of conversion factors in the form

1 m = (   ) clearthrus
1 kg = (   ) chunks
1 sec = (   ) oncearounds
1 lbf = (   ) $\text{chunk}^2/\text{clearthru}^2$

Write Newton's second law in this unit system, and determine the value for g_c. Selecting k_C to be unity in Coulomb's law, express the units of charge, and give the conversion factor from coul to charge in the new unit system.

1·14 Set up a dimension system in which time is the only primary quantity. Pick the constants in Newton's second law, Coulomb's law, and the gravitational law to be unity, and in addition, pick the speed of light to be unity (dimensionless). Length will then have the dimensions of time. Use the sec as the unit of time, and determine the equivalents of 1 kg, 1 m, and 1 coul.

1·15 Set up a dimension system in which force and charge are the primary quantities. Pick the constants in Coulomb's law, Newton's law, and the universal gravitational law to be ½, and state the dimensions of length, time, and mass in terms of the primary dimensions. Determine the equivalents of 1 m, 1 kg, and 1 sec in the new unit system, taking the newton and the coulomb as the fundamental units of force and charge.

1·16 Set up a dimension system in which the primary quantities are mass, length, time, and charge. Pick the constant in Coulomb's law to be unity. Find the dimensions of force and of the constant in Newton's law in this system (in terms of M, L, T, and Q). Choosing the kg, m, sec, and coul as the basic units for the primary quantities, calculate the value of the constant in Newton's law for the new dimensional system, and determine the equivalence of 1 newton in the new system. Is this the same as 1 newton in the mksc system?

1·17 Set up a dimension system in which the only primary quantities are length and time. Pick the constants in Newton's law, the gravitational law, and Coulomb's law to be π. State the dimensions of force, mass, and charge (in terms of length and time) in this new system. Taking the unit time as the leap year (1 leap year = 366 days) and the unit of length as the earthrad (1 earthrad = 4000 miles), find the equivalents of 1 kgm, 1 lbf, 1 cal, 1 Btu, 1 coul, and 1 amp in the new system.

1·18 Discuss the point of the previous six problems.

1·19 Discuss the implications of Prob. 1·14; do you think there might be any unknown basic laws relating mass, force, length, time, and charge?

1·20 Show that the potential energy of a body of mass M in a uniform gravitational field, where the free-fall acceleration is g_g, is equal to Mg_g/g_c.

CHAPTER TWO

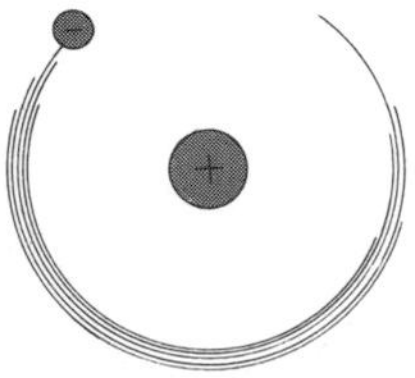

ENERGY AND THE FIRST LAW

2·1 INTRODUCTION

We are about to lay the foundations for a broad physical theory. While thermodynamics can be developed from purely macroscopic postulates and definitions, without any reference at all to the microscopic, we shall follow a somewhat different approach. Microscopic concepts will be used to develop understanding about the nature of matter and to provide an intuitive basis for the fundamental macroscopic postulates.

Any physical theory is couched in terms of abstract mathematical symbols which in some way are presumed to be associated with physical measurables. Simplicity and economy are two important features of any really successful theory; nothing could be simpler than $\mathsf{F} = Ma$, and yet look at the tremendous number of important problems the analyst can solve with this one basic idea. Thermodynamics also seeks simplicity; rather than insisting on knowing what each and every particle in a mole of gas is doing at every instant, we content ourselves with knowledge of certain averages, and in so doing reduce the number of bits of information required to sufficiently describe the gas from something of the order of 10^{23} to "few." Just how many this "few" is depends on what system we are analyzing; we shall give some rules for determining this number later on.

The simplest type of basic "law" is one which states that some physical quantity is conserved. The central concept in thermodynamics is energy, and thermodynamic theory is constructed in such a way that energy is conserved. The conservation of energy is the key equation of the theory, playing much the same role in thermodynamic analysis as does Newton's second law in mechanics. In mechanics one deals with only a few kinds of energy; in electromagnetics and chemistry other kinds of energy appear. Thermodynamics provides the common tie among these various forms of energy and will provide deeper insight into a variety of subjects already studied. This chapter deals with the concept of energy and its conservation in macroscopic systems.

2·2 SYSTEMS

In any scientific or engineering analysis it is very important to identify clearly whatever it is that is under consideration. We shall use the term *system* in a very broad sense to identify the subject of discussion or analysis. The system is something defined by the analyst for his particular problem at hand. A system might be a particular collection of matter, such as the gas in a bottle. Or it might be a region in space, such as the bottle and whatever happens to be in it at the moment. Sometimes we include fields in our definition of the system; for example, the gas in the bottle and the electric field in the bottle might be defined as the system. At other times fields are defined to be "outside" of the system; thus, the gas may be the system, but the fields that occupy the same space are considered "external" to the system. Another situation in which two systems share the same space occurs in analysis of ionized gases; the ions are often treated as one system, and the electrons as another. Interacting systems are often of quite different types; for example, in the study of liquid droplets the liquid interior to the surface is sometimes treated as one system, and the surface molecules as another. A system might be very simple, such as a piece of matter, or very complex, such as a nuclear power generation plant. Matter may flow through a system, such as a jet engine, or the system may be completely devoid of matter, such as the system of radiation in an enclosed volume. The system is whatever we wish to discuss, and we must be very careful each time to describe precisely just what it is that we are talking about. Hence we shall place considerable emphasis on the definition of systems in this text.

When motions are involved, the definition of the system must include a *reference frame* in which the motions will be measured. An *inertial frame* is one in which any free particle moves at constant velocity. The laws of mechanics as normally written apply only in inertial frames, and hence one must be careful in choosing the reference frame if these laws are to be invoked in the analysis.

It is often helpful to indicate the system under consideration by enclosing it with dotted lines in a sketch. Of course, one cannot tell from the sketch whether the system is the *matter* inside the lines or the *space* inside the lines (which may contain different material at different times). In order to differentiate, the term *control mass* is used to indicate a system consisting of specified matter, and the term *control volume* is used to indicate a system specified by space. In working with the properties of materials one usually uses control masses; however, much engineering analysis involves some sort of flow process, and then control volumes are used instead. Often the sketch is not enough to convey the system definition to the reader, in which case a few words of definition are desirable. The student should learn to give adequate system definitions, for much confusion can result when an analyst and his reader are talking about different systems ("Do you mean the space or the matter in it?"). Many examples of system definition can be found in this and later chapters, particularly in Chaps. Five and Nine; inspection of these systems at this time will also give the student some idea of where we are going in our study of thermodynamics.

Having carefully defined the system, everything else is automatically its *environment*. The interactions between a system and its environment are the main interest in thermodynamics. It is frequently convenient to make the conceptual idealization that the system is *isolated* from any interaction with its environment; we say conceptual because isolation requires walls around the system that are impermeable to matter, rigid, nonconducting to electric charge, and so on. All conserved quantities are "trapped" within an isolated system. For example, since no mass can escape, the mass of an isolated system is constant. So is its charge. The notion that a similar restriction applies to energy is central in thermodynamics.

In the rest of this chapter we shall confine our attention to systems consisting of specified matter, that is, to control masses. Energy, but *not* matter, can cross the boundary of such a system; the various mechanisms for this energy transfer are the main topic of this chapter.

2·3 ENERGY

What is energy? In Chap. One we reviewed the mechanics of a particle, and found that integration of the equations of motion leads to a term $M\mathsf{V}^2/2g_c$, which is called the kinetic energy of the particle. This term is a function of the velocity and mass of the particle, and can be computed without knowledge of how this velocity was attained. In this sense it is something that belongs to the particle, that is, it is a *property* of the particle.† If the particle collides with another particle, the second particle can be put into motion, that is, its kinetic energy will be increased, and the laws of mechanics tell us that the kinetic energy of the first particle will decrease. It is clear that this particular type of energy, kinetic energy, is somehow associated with the motions of the particle; it is "what makes the particle go." In thermodynamics we want to generalize the concept of energy; all matter, all systems have energy, and energy plays a dominant role in the explanation of interactions between systems.

We can view each piece of matter as being composed of many fundamental particles, each whizzing about in accordance with the laws of mechanics. We know from physics that each particle can have energy in several forms, and it will be helpful to review these forms now. We shall call them "microscopic energy modes" (Fig. 2·1).

Molecules possess energy by virtue of their translation through space. This

† The concept of property will be developed more fully in the next chapters.

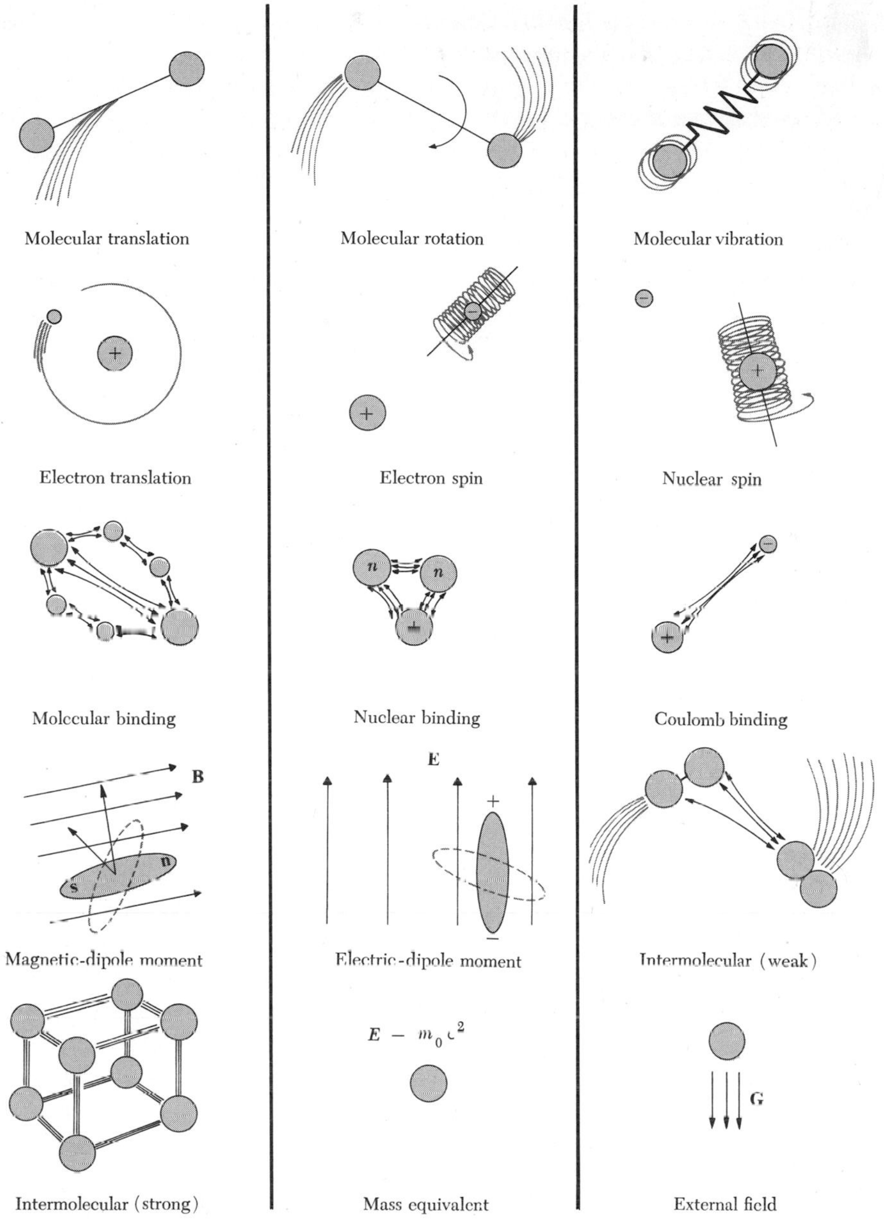
Molecular translation
Molecular rotation
Molecular vibration
Electron translation
Electron spin
Nuclear spin
n
n
Molecular binding
Nuclear binding
Coulomb binding
B
s
n
E
+
−
Magnetic-dipole moment
Electric-dipole moment
Intermolecular (weak)
E = m_0c^2
G
Intermolecular (strong)
Mass equivalent
External field

FIG. 2·1 *Microscopic energy modes*

kinetic energy is termed *translational energy*. For polyatomic molecules *rotational kinetic energy* is also important. If the atoms of the molecule are vibrating back and forth about their common center of mass we say that the molecule also has *vibrational energy*. The energy of gas molecules at low temperatures is largely associated with the translational and rotational modes, while at higher temperatures the vibrational modes begin to contribute significantly to the total energy.

Electrons whirling about their nucleus have kinetic energy, the amount of which depends on their orbit. Usually the electrons tend to be in the inner low-energy orbits; atoms with electrons in more distant orbits are said to be in *excited states* and have more energy than normal atoms of that species. It is also necessary to think of electrons as spinning and thereby possessing some *spin energy*. Many of the other fundamental particles also seem to have spin energy.

Molecules are held together by molecular binding forces, including coulomb and gravitational forces. All these forces seem to be conservative, and thus we think of potential energy in association with these intermolecular forces. Forces between the electrons and the nucleus are responsible for keeping the electrons in orbit, and there is potential energy associated with these forces. The nucleus is held together by forces much stronger than molecular binding forces, and consequently the nuclear binding energy is considerably larger than the binding energy of a molecule.

The orbiting electrons constitute tiny electric currents, producing little magnetic dipoles. In the presence of an external magnetic field these dipoles can be twisted, and there is energy associated with these dipole moments. An electrically neutral atom does not have all its charges in the same place, and consequently constitutes an electric-dipole moment, which can have energy in the presence of an external electric field. These dipole-moment energies are important in dielectrics and paramagnetic substances.

Ionized molecules and free electrons have forces exerted on them by external electric and magnetic fields, and consequently can have associated energies. All particles with mass possess potential energy in gravitational fields.

Collections of particles have additional energy associated with the forces between molecules. In liquids and solids these energies are especially important, but in low-density gases the amount of energy due to intermolecular potentials is quite small. Evaporation is a process requiring enough energy to free molecules from these strong bonds.

In relativistic mechanics it becomes necessary to include the energy equivalence of matter; we think of a particle having rest mass M_0 as possessing rest-mass energy M_0c^2. This energy constitutes a large percentage of the energy of a molecule, but in nonnuclear reactions the change in rest mass is so small that changes in rest-mass energy are negligible compared to changes in the other forms of energy.

These various microscopic energy modes are not very much in evidence when we look at a piece of metal on a table, or at gas in a bottle. If we pick up the metal and hurl it away it clearly acquires kinetic energy. It is easy to measure the velocity of the metal piece, and thereby to determine the kinetic energy of the object as a whole. This is called the "bulk" kinetic energy of the piece. It is not really the kinetic energy of all the molecules, because in addition to the easily observed bulk motion the molecules are executing very small-scale motions that also contribute to their kinetic energy. There are other "bulk" energy modes that are easy to measure macroscopically. For example, the metal piece would have a potential energy in a gravitational field, and this energy could be computed from simple macroscopic data. It is usually convenient to separate the "bulk" or macroscopically measurable mechanical energy from the energy of the "hidden microscopic modes." We do this by saying that the total system energy, E, is the sum of the bulk kinetic and potential energies KE and PE, and the *internal energy*, customarily denoted by U. This split of the total energy is expressible as

$$E = KE + PE + U \tag{2·1}$$

The internal energy U therefore represents all the energy associated with the microscopic modes, that is, the energy not accounted for in the bulk mechanical energy terms. Since U cannot be measured directly, it must somehow be determined by inference. Evaluation of the internal energy U as a function of the "state" or "condition" of the system is one of the central problems in thermodynamics.

An aspect of the energy concept to which we have already alluded is that the energy of two systems taken together is the sum of their individual energies. Hence, the energy of the whole is the sum of the energy of the parts. This idea is very useful when we want to evaluate the energy of a complex system, for we can evaluate the energy of individual pieces and then add to get the total system energy. In the language of thermodynamics, this additive feature is indicated by saying that energy is *extensive*.

Let us make a remark at this point which indicates the flavor of things to come. Most matter exists in forms with the energy tied up as internal energy. The internal energy is "randomly oriented," that is, "disorganized" (this is what "hides" it from a macroscopic view), and hence is not readily useful. One job of the engineer is to devise means for converting disordered molecular motions into organized motions capable of being used macroscopically. A brief inspection now of the systems described in Chap. Nine will give a preview of some of the ways in which this "unraveling" of internal energy can be accomplished.

2·4 CONSERVATION OF ENERGY

A fundamental aspect of the energy concept is that energy is conserved, that is, the energy of an isolated system is constant. Equations stating this

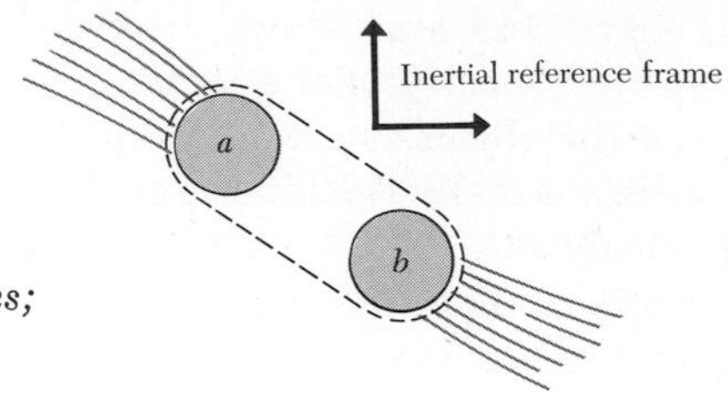

FIG. 2·2 *The system includes both bodies; it is an isolated system*

"law" provide the basis for quantitative analysis of the changes that take place between interacting systems.

For example, suppose that two moving bodies hit head on, and then come to rest. One of the laws of matter, the momentum principle, says that, since the bodies come to rest, the momenta of the two bodies must have been exactly equal in magnitude and opposite in sign at the moment of collision. What happens to their energy? Two frequently heard *incorrect* statements are

1 The energy was lost.
2 The energy was dissipated into heat.

The first statement is correct only if applied to the organized mechanical energy of motion. As a result of the impact, the bulk kinetic energy of the bodies is "converted" into internal energy. The energy is no longer macroscopically evident as kinetic energy, but the increase in internal energy is clearly evidenced by increase in the temperature of each body. No energy was lost, the energy was just rearranged. The second statement could be made correct by replacing "heat" by "internal energy." As we shall shortly see, heat and internal energy are two quite different things; the energy associated with microscopic motions and forces is internal energy, not heat. The use of the term "dissipation" in the second statement suggests that energy in the form of bulk kinetic energy is somehow more desirable than internal energy. This is indeed true, for the perfect organization of bulk motion makes it fully useful (say to raise a weight), but the random, disorganized microscopic motions reflected by the internal energy make energy in this form less "available" for use in a practical macroscopic device.

The conservation of energy can be expressed algebraically for the two colliding bodies a and b; the *system* we consider consists of the two bodies together (Fig. 2·2), and we consider them over the *time period* from an instant before collision, denoted by 1, to just after collision, when both are at rest. The initial energy of the system is

$$E_1 = E_{a1} + E_{b1} = \frac{1}{2g_c} M_a \mathsf{V}_{a1}^2 + \frac{1}{2g_c} M_b \mathsf{V}_{b1}^2 + U_{a1} + U_{b1} \tag{2·2a}$$

The final energy of the system is

$$E_2 = U_{a2} + U_{b2} \tag{2·2b}$$

Since the two bodies form an isolated system, the energy of the system must not change, and hence

$$\underset{\text{initial energy}}{E_1} = \underset{\text{final energy}}{E_2} \tag{2·3}$$

Substituting Eqs. (2·2) into Eq. (2·3), we can solve for the total increase in internal energy U of the system,

$$U_2 - U_1 = (U_{a2} - U_{a1}) + (U_{b2} - U_{b1}) = \frac{1}{2g_c}(M_a V_{a1}^2 + M_b V_{b1}^2) \tag{2·4}$$

Knowing the masses and velocities, we could calculate $U_2 - U_1$. However, we do not have enough information to determine the increase in internal energy of each body individually.

The example above illustrates two important things. First, the notion of conservation of energy, as applied to an *isolated system*, says that the energy of the isolated system is constant. Second, the "energy balance" provides a means for determining the *change* in internal energy of a body from *macroscopic* data (in this case the mass and velocities of the bodies). Thus, the very idea that energy is conserved provides a means for inferring changes in the internal energy.

Where does the principle of conservation of energy come from? Can it be proved? These are frequent questions, the answers for which lie in the understanding of the *concept* of energy. We want to be able to predict nature, and so we conceive of energy. In a very real sense, energy is an invention of *man*, not of nature. Rather than being "that which makes things go," perhaps we should view it as something that we use to predict and explain how things go. Whenever conservation of energy is apparently violated, the physicist "discovers" a new form of energy. That is, he *defines* a new form of energy in order to keep the principle of energy conservation unviolated. The thing that makes energy "real" is that it is very useful. It is not very often that man has had to "invent" new energy forms, and hence he can proceed with his scientific and engineering analysis with considerable confidence that his "energy balances" contain the relevant energy terms. Asking for proof of the conservation-of-energy principle is like asking for proof that addition is communitive; the fact that $A + B = B + A$ is an inherent part of the concept of addition. What *is* a relevant question is, "What can I do with addition?" In thermodynamics, the relevant counterpart is "What can I do with the conservation-of-energy principle?" and the answer to this is that practically all scientific and engineering analysis involves energy considerations.

An additional idea is required to make the energy concept quantitative; we must have some *scale* of energy. This is obtained from the notion that the increase in energy of a particle is equal to the *work done* by the force acting on the particle. The work done on the particle is defined as

$$W = \int_1^2 \mathbf{F} \cdot d\mathbf{X} \tag{2·5}$$

where 1 and 2 represent two consecutive times. **F** is the force on the particle, taken positive in the direction of positive **X**, where **X** is the particle position. We then put

$$E_2 - E_1 = W = \int_1^2 \mathbf{F} \cdot d\mathbf{X} \tag{2·6}$$

which allows us to compute the change in energy if we know **F**(**X**) (this is exactly the procedure reviewed in Sec. 1·4). The connection between the energy change of a particle and *work* is fundamental in both the Newtonian and relativistic mechanics. Work, then, provides the *fundamental measure* of energy.

To summarize, there are four ideas inherent in the concept of energy:

1 Every system has energy (E).
2 Energy is extensive ($E_{a+b} = E_a + E_b$).
3 The energy of an isolated system is constant.
4 Work provides the fundamental measure of energy.

2·5 ENERGY TRANSFER AS WORK

We come now to considering the mechanisms by which the energy of a nonisolated system can be altered. Since the system and its environment form an isolated system, if the energy of the system increases the energy of the environment must decrease a corresponding amount in order to maintain conservation of energy. We can therefore view the interaction as a process of energy transfer, and *work* is one of the mechanisms for such energy transfer.

Following the definition used in mechanics, the amount of energy transfer *to* a system as work (the "work done *on* the system") associated with some infinitesimal change in the position of matter inside is

$$\blacktriangleright \qquad đW = \mathbf{F} \cdot d\mathbf{X} = \mathsf{F}\, dX \tag{2·7a}$$

Here F is a force exerted by the environment on matter within the system, and dX is the infinitesimal motion of that matter in the direction of F which occurs during the period of observation. $\mathbf{F} \cdot d\mathbf{X}$ is the equivalent vector definition. Both F and X must be macroscopic measurables; they represent the net visible effect of billions of molecules, and not forces or motions of individual molecules.

We emphasize that dX must be motion observed with respect to a chosen coordinate frame. If the frame is attached to the matter, then there is no energy transfer as work in that particular analysis. Also, the force must be exerted by the environment on the matter within the system; forces exerted between matter in different parts of the system may cause internal rearrangements of energy, but lead to no energy transfer across the system boundary. One must therefore focus on the boundary of the system in order to identify and evaluate energy transfer as work.

If the motion extends from point 1 to point 2 in space, then the total amount of energy transfer as work is obtained by summing over all infinitesimal displacements, that is, by integrating Eq. (2·7a). If we represent the total amount of energy transfer as work by W_{12}, then we have

$$W_{12} \equiv \int_1^2 đW = \int_1^2 \mathbf{F} \cdot d\mathbf{X} \tag{2·7b}$$

There are important physical differences between the quantities standing behind the symbols $đ$ and d. The term dX may be immediately integrated, and the change in X thereby found,

$$\int_{X_1}^{X_2} dX = X_2 - X_1$$

The quantity X is something which exists at each point in space, and the symbols X_1 and X_2 have definite meaning. In contrast, the integral of $đW$ cannot be computed unless we know how the force F varies with X. The value of the integral of $đW$ between any two points X_1 and X_2 therefore depends on how the force varies with position, that is, on the particular process involved. The work at a given point has absolutely no meaning. Whereas the integral of dX represents the difference in the values of X at two points, the integral of $đW$ depends upon the particular manner in which the system is taken from one configuration to another. The ratio dX/dt would mean the derivative of X with respect to t, or the rate of change of X. In contrast, the ratio $\dot{W} \equiv đW/dt$ would be the *amount* of work done per unit of time, or the *rate of energy transfer as work.* We have adopted this special symbology to emphasize the conceptual physical differences between things that are associated with the conditions of a system and those that are associated with the processes which the system undergoes.

2·6 EVALUATION OF ENERGY TRANSFER AS WORK

In order to carry out a successful system energy analysis one must be able to evaluate the magnitudes of energy transfers as work, that is, the work done on or by the system. Having defined the system, the next step in this evaluation is to define the direction of positive energy transfer. We shall *always* indicate our choice for positive energy transfers by showing the energy transfers on the system sketch. For example, consider the system of Fig. 2·3*a*. The system is defined by the dotted lines, and is the little cart. The reference coordinate system is attached to the ground, and the force F is exerted as a push on the back of the cart by a metal rod. Note that we have elected to consider the work done by F positive if it leads to an energy transfer *into* the system. (If the work was subsequently calculated to be −35 ft-lbf we would then know that the energy transfer actually took place in the direction opposite to our initial assumption.)

Let us analyze the system of Fig. 2·3*a*. The amount of energy transfer as

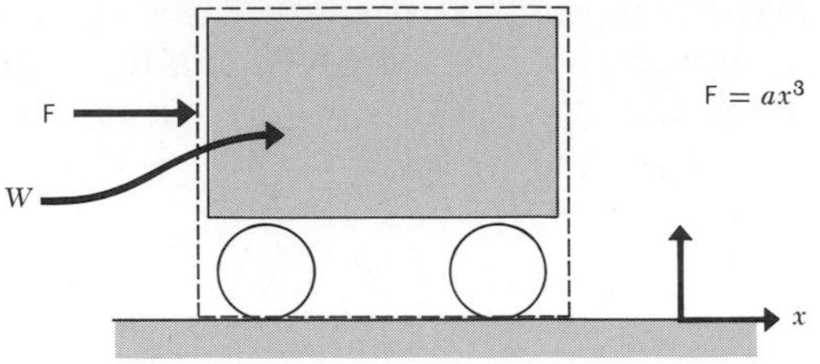

(*a*) *Note that here work is positive as an energy input*

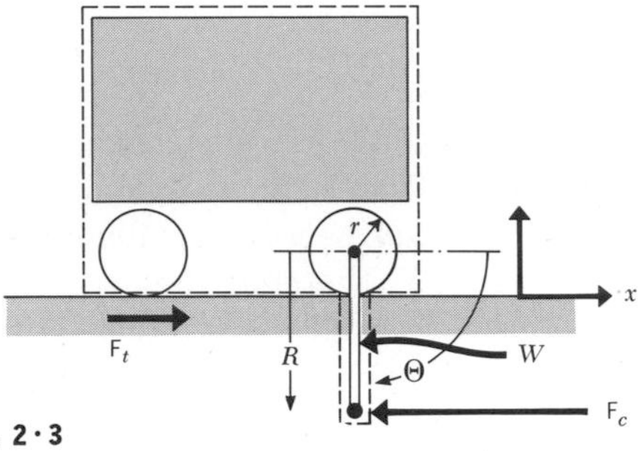

(*b*) *The reference frame is fixed on the ground*

FIG. 2·3

work to the cart due to its motion under the influence of F is, from the basic definition,

$$W_{12} = \int_1^2 \mathsf{F}\,dx = \int_1^2 ax^3\,dx = \frac{a}{4}(x_2^4 - x_1^4) \tag{2·8}$$

If there were no other energy transfers involved, this work would show up as an increase in the energy stored within the system. We might neglect any changes in the internal energy or in the rotational energy of the wheels, in which case the only significant energy change would be in the bulk translational kinetic energy of the cart as a whole. An energy balance on the cart could then be used to calculate the final cart velocity.

A somewhat more subtle example is provided by the system of Fig. 2·3*b*. Now we have added a crank to one of the wheels, and we exert a force F_c to the left on the crank handle causing the cart to move to the right. There is also a traction force F_t on the wheels; under ideal rolling conditions, the motion of the material in the wheel at the contact point is vertically up and down, and hence this matter has *no* component of motion in the direction of F_t. Consequently there is no energy transfer as work associated with the force F_t. There is some work associated with F_c, however, and a common mistake is to say that this work is $\int F_c\,dx$, where x is the position of the cart. Recalling the basic definition of work, the proper displacement is that of the matter on which the force acts, which in this case is the handle and not the cart body. If R is the length of the handle, then $R\,d\theta$ is the horizontal displacement of the handle relative to the wheel axis associated with an infinitesimal rotation $d\theta$ (when the crank shaft is in the position shown). Is the work associated with F_c equal to $F_cR\,d\theta$? *No*, not for the system as defined, for the displacement $R\,d\theta$ is relative to a reference frame on the cart, while we chose a frame on the ground! The displacement relative to the ground frame is $r\,d\theta - R\,d\theta$, where r is the wheel radius. But this is a displacement to the *right*, while the force F_c acts to the *left*. Hence, the amount of energy transfer as work to the system as defined, relative to the indicated reference frame, is

$$đW = -F_c(r - R)\,d\theta = F_c(R - r)\,d\theta \tag{2·9a}$$

This example illustrates the need for very careful consideration of just what the system is *before* one begins to evaluate work.

Suppose in the example of Fig. 2·3*b* we instead choose a reference frame attached to the cart. In this frame the displacement of the handle in the direction of F_c *is* $R\,d\theta$, and hence the amount of energy transfer as work in this frame is

$$đW' = F_cR\,d\theta \tag{2·9b}$$

The product F_cR is defined as the *torque* T on the wheel shaft, and hence $đW'$ could be written as†

$$đW' = T\,d\theta \tag{2·9c}$$

Equation (2·9*c*) is a special case of the general expression for the work done on a system by a torque. If $\mathbf{T}$ is the torque vector, and $d\boldsymbol{\theta}$ is the vector angular displacement of the matter within the system on which the torque acts, then the amount of energy transfer as work *to* the system relative to a frame attached to the torque axis, is

$$\blacktriangleright \quad đW = \mathbf{T} \cdot d\boldsymbol{\theta} \tag{2·10}$$

Since mechanical systems frequently involve rotating shafts, the expression is rather important.

The forces of Fig. 2·3 are examples of *surface forces*. They are exerted on the matter at the surface of the system and the appropriate displacement is the displacement of the matter at the surface. Another type of force is a *body force*, which acts on the material in the system interior. For such forces the appropriate displacement must be that of the matter on which the body force acts. This may or may not be the same as the displacement of a system boundary. For example, consider the system of Fig. 2·4*a*. The system does not include the electric field. The system boundaries are held stationary, but the charged plate within the system moves when the electric field strength is increased. If the charge on the plate is $\mathcal{Q}$, and the electric field strength is $\mathbf{E}$, the force

† Note that the cart would not have any kinetic energy in this reference frame (see Prob. 1·6).

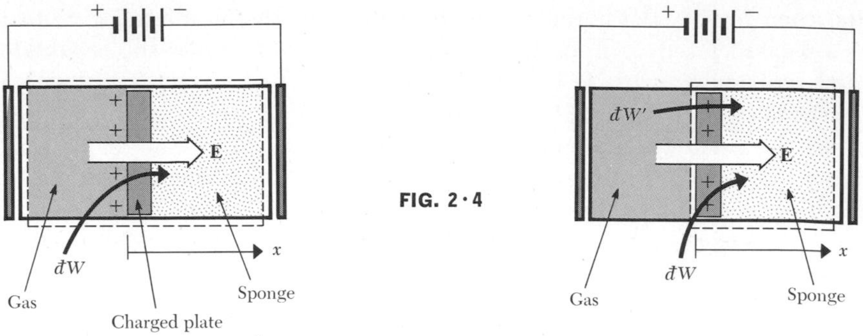

FIG. 2·4

(a) *The system includes the material but not the electric field*

(b) *Note that the work terms depend on the system definition*

on the plate is $\mathbf{F} = \mathcal{Q}\mathbf{E}$ to the right. The amount of energy transfer as work to the system associated with motion of the plate an infinitesimal amount $d\mathbf{x}$ to the right is then

$$đW = \mathcal{Q}(\mathbf{E} \cdot d\mathbf{x}) \tag{2·11a}$$

Integrating between two positions x_1 and x_2, the total energy transfer as work for the process 1-2 is

$$W_{12} = \int_1^2 \mathcal{Q}\mathbf{E} \cdot d\mathbf{x} \tag{2·11b}$$

To complete the integration we would have to know $\mathbf{E}(\mathbf{x})$ during the process. The energy transferred into the system as work would result in an increase in the system energy, and an energy balance would be the central tool for analysis of this system.

In the example of Fig. 2·4*a* the system was defined to include the plate, the sponge, and the gas, but to exclude the electric field. The energy transfer as work between the plate and the gas was internal to the system, and hence would not appear as an energy transfer term in the energy balance. However, if the system is instead defined as in Fig. 2·4*b* the energy transfer as work from the gas to the plate must be considered. The energy transfer as work from the environment (that is, the electric field, which is external to the system) is again given by Eqs. (2·11). If the pressure exerted by the gas on the plate is P, and the plate area is A, the force on the plate is PA, and the amount of energy transfer as work at the left-hand boundary of the system is

$$đW' = PA\,dx \tag{2·12a}$$

Integrating, the total amount of energy transfer as work from the gas to the plate is

$$W'_{12} = \int_1^2 PA\,dx \tag{2·12b}$$

We would have to know how the gas pressure varied with x in order to complete the integration. This example illustrates that the work terms included in an energy analysis depend very much on the choice of the system. A clear system definition is therefore essential to a clear analysis.

Let us think about the microscopic aspects of the work terms discussed above. As the molecules in the metal rod that pushes the cart of Fig. 2·3 move to the right, strong repulsive forces are developed between them and the molecules at the surface of the cart. As a result, the cart molecules are made to move, and the work expression Eq. (2·8) represents the net effect of these billions of individual molecular interactions. The charged particles in the plate of Fig. 2·4*a* are each acted on by the electric field, and as they move, each receives energy from the electric field. The total energy transfer as work to all the charged particles is what Eq. (2·11) represents. The molecules in the gas in Fig. 2·4 are flying about, and occasionally collide with the plate. When they do they exert forces on the molecules in the plate, and if they move the plate there is a transfer of energy from the gas molecules to the plate molecules. This is the energy transfer as work which we evaluated in Eqs. (2·12).

Correct evaluation of the energy transfer as work is a necessary part in any thermodynamic analysis. The steps in this evaluation are summarized below.

1 Define the system and reference frame.
2 Define the forces acting on the system and the motions of the material on which these forces act.
3 Define the sign of positive energy transfer for each different "work mode" by an arrow on the system sketch.
4 Apply the basic definition of work [Eq. (2·7)] consistently with the above definitions over the time period under examination.
5 Bring in the additional information needed to complete the integrations.

One must be particularly consistent in evaluating work done by a conservative force field in order to avoid "double accounting" in the subsequent energy balance. The potential-energy change is by definition the work done by the conservative force, and hence both the potential energy and the work done by the conservative force must never appear in the same energy analysis. Two alternative approaches are demonstrated in Fig. 2·5. In Fig. 2·5*a* we account for the work done by the rope force F_{II} and the body force w, but do not include a potential-energy term in the system energy. In Fig. 2·5*b* we instead use the potential energy, and include only the work done by the rope force. The net energy input as work, $đW$, is equal to the increase in energy, dE, in either case.†

† Another approach is to assign the potential energy to the "field." If the field is part of the system, Fig. 2·5*b* is appropriate. If the system is defined to exclude the field, Fig. 2·5*a* is proper.

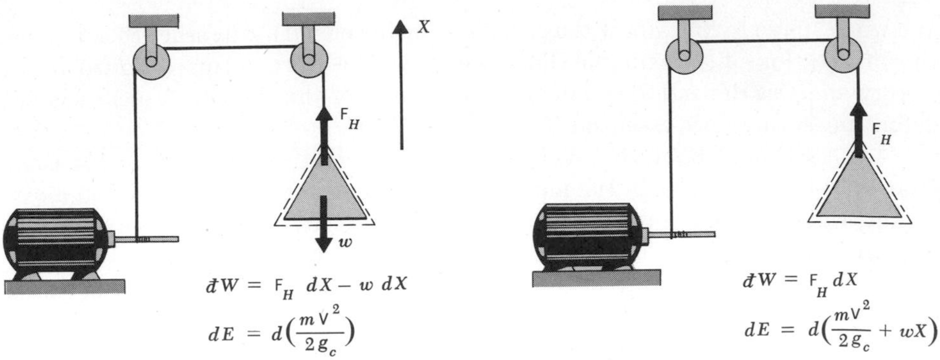

(*a*) *Without potential-energy concept (the system excludes the gravitational field)*

(*b*) *With potential-energy concept (the system includes the gravitational field)*

FIG. 2·5 *One must be consistent when making an energy analysis where a conservative force is involved. Note* $đW = dE$ *in either case*

2·7 SOME PARTICULAR WORK MODES

There are a number of work modes that occur frequently in thermodynamic analysis, and they deserve special mention here.

Expansion or compression of a fluid. A great many thermodynamic systems involve fluids (that is, a liquid or a gas), and hence the work associated with expansion or compression of a fluid is very important. The piston-cylinder system of Fig. 2·6*a* provides an easy way to visualize and compute the amount of energy transfer as work associated with a change in the fluid volume. Denoting the fluid pressure by P, and the piston area by A, the force on the piston is PA, and the amount of energy transfer as work *from* the fluid *to* the piston (see the sign convention of the sketch!) is, for an elemental expansion dx,

$$đW = PA\,dx$$

But since $A\,dx = dV$ is the increase in fluid volume, the amount of energy transfer as work from the fluid may be written as

$$\blacktriangleright \quad đW = P\,dV \qquad (2\cdot 13a)$$

By considering a fluid volume of *arbitrary* shape it may easily be shown that

FIG. 2·6

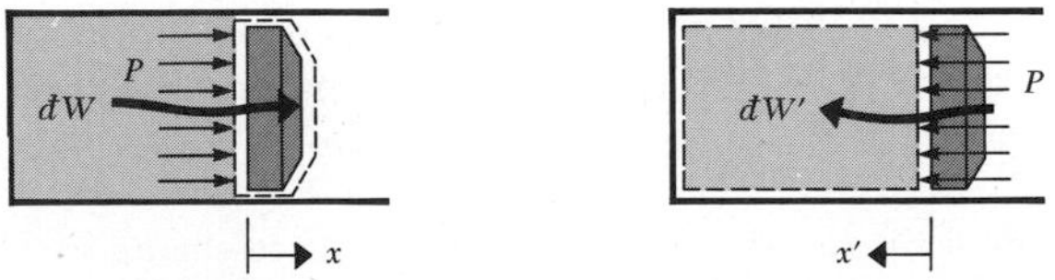

(*a*) *The fluid is expanding* (*b*) *The fluid is being compressed* this same expression applies for the energy transfer as work *from* the fluid *to* its environment, and hence Eq. (2·13*a*) has considerable utility in thermodynamic analysis.

Suppose we consider the compression of a fluid. Now it is easier to consider the work positive if energy is transferred *to* the fluid (Fig. 2·6*b*). The force which the piston exerts on the fluid at the system boundaries is PA and displacement of the fluid at the piston surface is dx'. Hence, the amount of energy transfer as work *from* the piston *to* the fluid is

$$đW' = PA\, dx'$$

We can again relate this work to the change in fluid volume. Denoting the *increase* in fluid volume by dV (in the conventions of calculus dx always represents an increase in x), we write $dV = -A\, dx'$ (dx' is positive, so dV will be negative). Hence,

$$đW' = -P\, dV \tag{2·13b}$$

is the amount of work done *by* the piston *on* the fluid. Comparing the energy-transfer sign conventions of Figs. 2·6*a* and 2·6*b*, we see that $đW' = -đW$. Hence Eqs. (2·13*a*) and (2·13*b*) are consistent. This will always be the case; for a particular choice of the direction of positive energy transfer as work, the expression for the work will be independent of whether the energy is actually added or removed (dx will be positive in one case and negative in the other).

Extension of a solid. We consider extension of a solid rod as shown in Fig. 2·7. Denoting the normal stress in the x direction by σ_x, the "pulling" force exerted by the holder on the solid is $\sigma_x A$. The amount of energy transfer as work *from* the holder *to* the solid when the solid is stretched is†

$$đW = \sigma_x A\, dx$$

Now, the *strain* ϵ_x in the x direction is defined as the deformation per unit length, so

$$d\epsilon_x = \frac{dx}{L} = \frac{A\, dx}{V}$$

† Note if we replace σ_x by $-P$ (P is a "push," σ_x is a "pull"), and take proper account of the differing directions of positive energy transfer in this and the fluid expansion case, equivalent results are obtained.

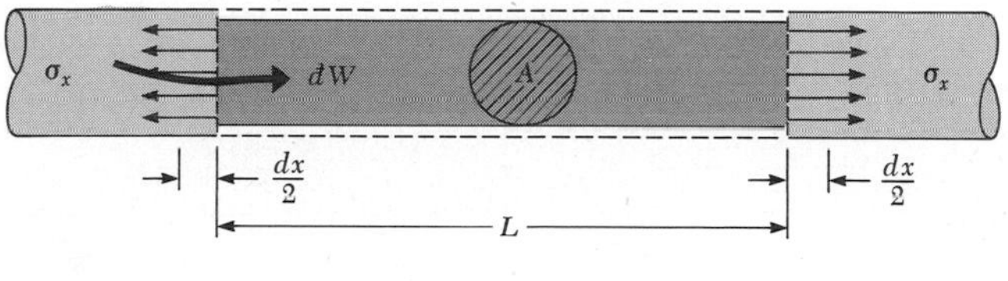

FIG. 2·7 *Stretching a thin rod requires work.*

and hence the amount of energy transfer as work *to* the solid can be written as†

$$\blacktriangleright \quad đW = V\sigma_x \, d\epsilon_x \tag{2·14}$$

In the microscopic view we see individual molecules of the holder pulling on molecules of the solid, thereby straining the crystal bonds in the solid structure. The net macroscopic effect of these microscopic interactions is represented by Eq. (2·14).

Stretching of a liquid surface. Consider a liquid sheet suspended between two plates, as shown in Fig. 2·8. The molecules near the liquid surface are

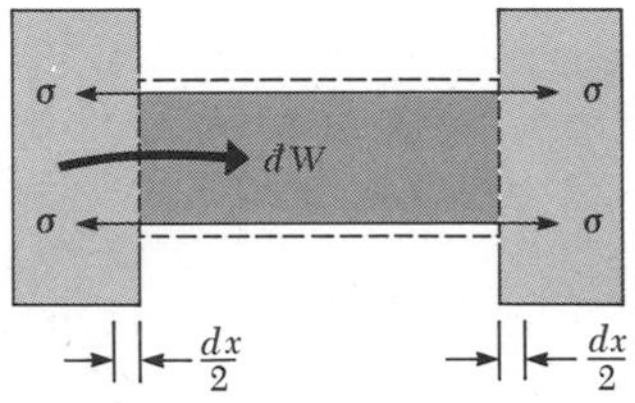

FIG. 2·8 *The liquid extends a large distance b into the paper*

attracted more strongly by internal liquid molecules than by the very distant gas molecules, and this gives rise to a macroscopically measurable force in the liquid-gas surface. The *interfacial tension*, σ, is defined as the force *per unit of length* acting normal to a line in the surface. The total interfacial tension force exerted on each plate is therefore $2\sigma b$, where b is the depth of the liquid sheet normal to the plane of the paper. The energy transfer as work *from* the plates *to* the liquid when the plate separation is increased an amount dx is

$$đW = 4\sigma b \frac{dx}{2} = 2\sigma b \, dx$$

Now, the change in surface area is simply $dA = 2b\,dx$, and hence the energy transfer as work *to* the liquid can be written as

$$\blacktriangleright \quad đW = \sigma \, dA \tag{2·15}$$

In the microscopic view, work is required to pull individual molecules into the new surface, and Eq. (2·15) represents the macroscopic evaluation of this microscopic effect.

Work due to magnetization and polarization. Microscopic electric dipoles within dielectrics resist turning, and work is therefore done on such substances

† Here we considered only one-dimensional deformation. It may be shown that the amount of energy transfer as work per unit volume *to* a solid undergoing arbitrary three-dimensional deformation is

$$đW = \sum_{i=1}^{3} \sum_{j=1}^{3} \sigma_{ij} \, d\epsilon_{ij}$$

where σ_{ij} and ϵ_{ij} are the stress and deformation tensors.

when they are polarized. For a system through which the electric and polarization fields are uniform, it may be shown that the energy transfer as work to the dielectric material† from the electric field when the polarization is infinitesimally increased is

$$\blacktriangleright \quad đW = \mathbf{E} \cdot d(V\mathbf{P}) \tag{2·16}$$

Here **E** represents the strength of the electric field within the dielectric, **P** the polarization field (electric-dipole moment per unit of volume), and V the system volume.

Similarly, work can be done on magnetic materials when the magnetization is changed, for the microscopic magnetic-dipole moments resist turning. For a system through which the magnetic and magnetization fields are uniform, it may be shown that the energy transfer as work to the material† from the magnetic field when the magnetization is increased an infinitesimal amount is

$$\blacktriangleright \quad đW = \mu_0 \mathbf{H} \cdot d(V\mathbf{M}) \tag{2·17}$$

Here **H** is the strength of the applied magnetic field, **M** is the magnetization vector (magnetic-dipole moment per unit of volume), and μ_0 is a constant (the "permeability" of free-space). Unlike work due to compression or extension, polarization and magnetization do not result in macroscopic motions. However, they do result in alignment of the particles, and this ordered alignment is macroscopically detectable as an increase in the total dipole moment.

TABLE 2·1 SOME PARTICULAR WORK MODES

Mode	*đW, energy transfer to substance as work*	*Restrictions*
Fluid compression	$-P\,dV$	P uniform over volume
Solid extension	$V\sigma_x\,d\epsilon_x$	One-dimensional strain only
Liquid surface extension	$\sigma\,dA$	σ uniform over area
Polarization	$\mathbf{E} \cdot d(V\mathbf{P})$	**P** and **E** uniform through volume
Magnetization	$\mu_0\mathbf{H} \cdot d(V\mathbf{M})$	**H** and **M** uniform through volume

The expressions for work in the particular cases discussed here are all of the form

$$đW = \mathsf{F}\,dX$$

For example, for liquid extension $\mathsf{F} = \sigma$ and $X = A$. They may be scalars (P and V), vectors (**E** and **P**), or tensors (σ_{ij} and ϵ_{ij}). F and dX do not necessarily

† The electric and magnetic fields are excluded from the systems. These expressions are for the rationalized mksc unit system. See, for example, David Halliday and Robert Resnick, *Physics*, combined ed., secs. 27-26 and 33-34, John Wiley & Sons, Inc., New York, 1962.

have the dimensions of force and displacement, but they are frequently called the "generalized force" and "generalized displacement," respectively. These F's and X's are very important in the general thermodynamic theory of materials. The amounts of energy transfer as work for these several modes are summarized in Table 2·1.

2·8 WORK FOR PARTICULAR PROCESSES

The amount of energy transfer as work for a given process can be computed if the variation of F with X during the process is known. For example, consider a system consisting of mass M of a certain gas, which we compress from some state 1 to another state 2. The work done *on* the gas is determined by integrating Eq. (2·13*b*), and is

$$W_{12} = -\int_1^2 MP\,dv$$

where v is the volume per unit of mass, that is, the *specific volume,*

$$v \equiv V/M$$

We must know how P varies with v during the process in order to complete the integration; Fig. 2·9 demonstrates two different cases.

For example, suppose we idealize that the pressure exerted by the gas is related to the specific volume and temperature by†

$$Pv = RT$$

where R is a constant for the gas. The energy transfer as work to the gas is then

$$W_{12} = -M\int_{v_1}^{v_2} \frac{RT}{v}\,dv$$

† This is valid for an "ideal," or "perfect," gas. The concept of temperature will be developed in the next chapter.

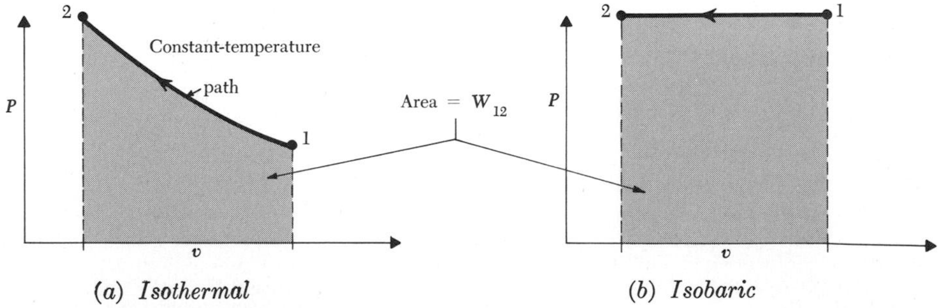

FIG. 2·9 *Doing work on a gas*

We would have to know how the temperature varies with the specific volume during this process in order to perform the integration. In particular, for an *isothermal* (constant-temperature) *process*

$$W_{12} = -MRT \ln \frac{v_2}{v_1}$$

Another case of interest is the *isobaric* (constant-pressure) *process*, where the energy transfer as work to a unit of mass of the gas is

$$W_{12} = \int_1^2 -P\,dv = P(v_1 - v_2)$$

As a second example, consider the amount of energy transfer as work to a paramagnetic Curie salt,† for which the magnetic field strength and magnetization are related to the temperature by

$$\mathsf{M} = \frac{C\mathsf{H}}{T}$$

Here C is the "Curie constant" of the salt. From Eq. (2·17),

$$W_{12} = \int_{\mathsf{M}_1}^{\mathsf{M}_2} \frac{\mu_0 VT}{C} \mathsf{M}\,d\mathsf{M}$$

The manner in which the temperature varies during this process would be an important factor in determining the amount of work done for a given increase in magnetization (see Fig. 2·10). In particular, for an *isothermal* magnetization process

$$W_{12} = \frac{\mu_0 VT}{2C} (\mathsf{M}_2^2 - \mathsf{M}_1^2)$$

† We assume constant volume.

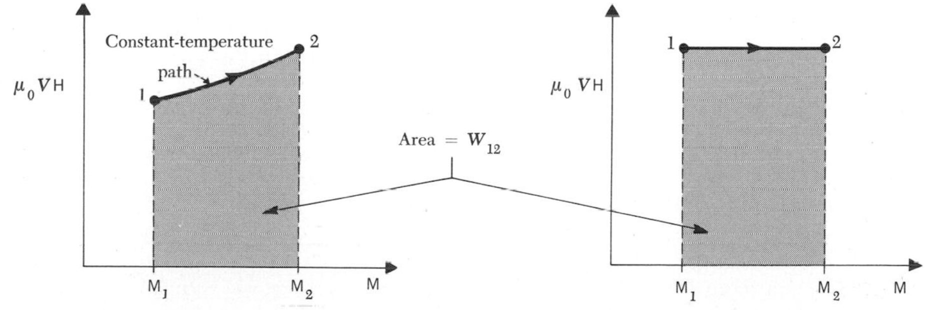

(*a*) *Isothermal* (*b*) *Constant external field*

FIG. 2·10 *Doing work on a magnetic substance*

Alternatively, if the substance were magnetized in a constant external field (H constant), the amount of energy transfer to the material as work would be

$$W_{12} = \mu_0 V \mathsf{H}(\mathsf{M}_2 - \mathsf{M}_1)$$

In these examples simple algebraic expressions could be found. In many cases of interest it will be necessary to integrate numerically or graphically to obtain the amount of energy transfer as work for a given process.

2·9 ENERGY TRANSFER AS HEAT

We have discussed several means by which macroscopic work can be done on a system, causing its energy to change. However, it is possible to transfer energy to a system in ways which are not observable as macroscopic work. Consider the system shown in Fig. 2·11. We might picture the atoms in the walls surrounding the system as little vibrating masses. Some will be heading toward the boundary when some are heading away, and as a result, there might be no observable motion. However, the interaction of these atoms with the molecules in the system can result in changes of the energy of individual particles and hence a change in the internal energy of the system. The macroscopically observable work is zero, so we must find some other way to account for the energy change. This second mechanism of energy transfer depicted in Fig. 2·11 is called *energy transfer as heat*. *Heat* is energy transfer as work on the microscopic scale which fails to be accounted for by macroscopic evaluations of work. In the microscopic view there is no such thing as heat; heat is required in the macroscopic view as a means for accounting for microscopically disorganized energy transfer which, through its disorganization, is "hidden" from direct macroscopic view. Heat is a central *concept* in thermodynamics.

Heat, like work, is energy in the process of being transferred. Heat and work are not "stored" within matter; they are "done on" or "done by" matter. Energy is what is stored, and work and heat are two ways of transferring energy across the boundaries of a system. Once energy has gotten into the system it is impossible to tell whether the energy was transferred in as heat or as work. The term "heat of a substance"† is thus as meaningless as "work of a substance."

The symbol Q is usually employed to represent an amount of energy transfer

† The literature contains some remnants of the caloric theory of heat, in which heat was pictured as a conserved substance. In present thermodynamic theory heat is not conserved and is not a property of matter. Still, some handbooks tabulate "heats of the liquid," "sensible heats," and "latent heats." These terms will be related to modern terminology in subsequent chapters.

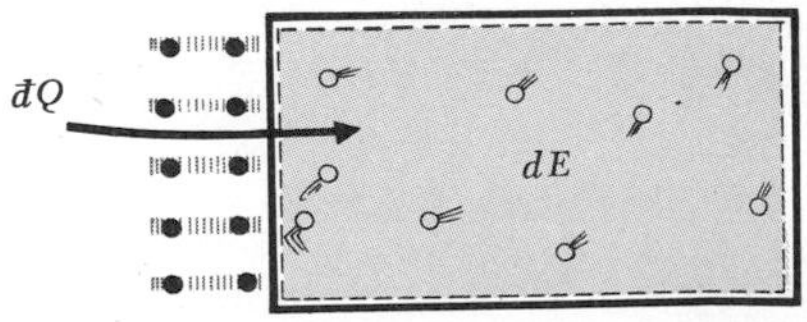

FIG. 2·11 *Energy transfer not observable as macroscopic work is called energy transfer as heat.*

as heat; $đQ$ therefore represents an infinitesimal amount of energy transfer as heat. As with work, we shall always indicate the direction of positive energy transfer as heat by an arrow on the system sketch. The value of Q depends on the details of the process, and not on the end conditions of the system. For example, consider the system in Fig. 2·12. The fluid temperature can be changed by transferring energy in as work through the stirrer, or as heat via the flame. In the first case $Q = 0$, and in the second case $Q > 0$. The initial and final system states, and the change in the system internal energy, could be the same in both cases.†

† It is very important to distinguish clearly between the concepts of internal energy and heat, and an account of the experiences of Professor J. Yule will assist in this regard. Professor J. Yule was experimenting with the apparatus of Fig. 2·12, which involved a fluid in a container with a mechanical stirrer. On one Friday afternoon in December, 1843, Professor Yule left the device in his laboratory under the care of his assistant, Dr. B. T. Ewe, who was known for his clever practical jokes. At that time the fluid temperature was 25°C. Upon return to the laboratory the following Monday, Professor Yule found that the fluid temperature was 40°C, indicating a greater internal energy. His student, Cal Orick, immediately presumed that Ewe had heated the device with the bunsen flame during the chilly weekend. "It *must* be so," said Orick, "for see, the temperature has clearly risen!" But Yule, being a properly cautious scientist, was not so sure. He had previously discovered that it was possible to increase the fluid temperature (and the internal energy) by driving the stirrer, a process that clearly fits in the category of *work*. Even after much argument Yule could not convince Orick that they just could not tell whether the clever Ewe had added the extra energy to the fluid as work using the stirrer or as heat using the bunsen flame. Ewe finally confessed to a very neat trick: he had first taken energy *out* of the fluid as heat by placing the device on a block of ice, and then had raised the temperature using the stirrer. Hence, in the actual process carried out by Ewe, there had been a *removal* of energy as heat and an *addition* of energy as work! The *net* effect of this *cooling-work* process had been an *increase* in the *internal energy* (and temperature) of the fluid! After this experience Cal Orick went mad, Professor J. Yule became a fellow of the Royal Society, and Dr. B. T. Ewe became a laboratory instructor at an obscure western university.

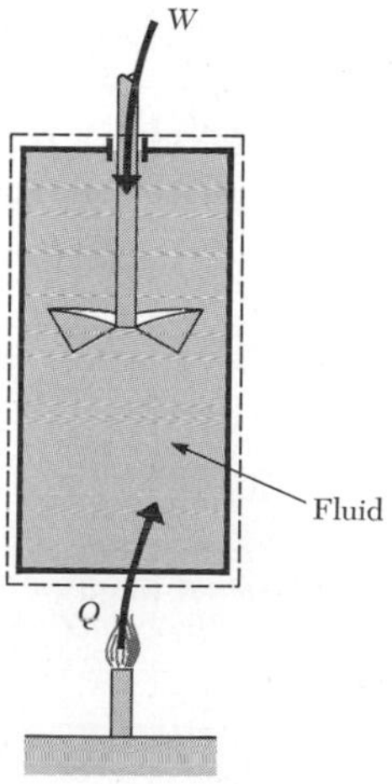

FIG. 2·12 *The addition of energy either as heat or as work will increase the fluid temperature*

In the next chapter we shall carefully treat a concept closely related to energy transfer as heat, namely *temperature*. We mention it now in the hope of preventing any confusion between the concepts of heat, temperature, and internal energy. If two bodies are brought into contact, and any energy transfer as heat takes place between them, we say that the energy passed from the body at the higher temperature to the one at the lower temperature. The words "hot" and "cold" describe the relative temperatures of the two bodies, respectively. Temperature can be viewed as a driving potential for energy transfer as heat.

If we wish to isolate a system we must prevent all flows of energy to or from the system. A rigid wall will prevent any $P\,dV$ work; a wall impermeable to electric fields will prevent any polarization work. In order to prevent any energy transfer as heat we conceive of an *adiabatic wall*, which cannot transmit any energy as heat. The adiabatic wall is a useful fiction (like the rigid wall). The hollow space in a vacuum flask forms adequate approximation to an adiabatic wall for many laboratory experiments. The term "adiabatic process" is used to denote any process in which no energy transfer as heat occurs across the boundaries of the system under study. The concepts of an adiabatic wall and an adiabatic process are very important in thermodynamics.

2·10 THE FIRST LAW FOR A CONTROL MASS

We are now able to express the conservation of energy notion analytically for an important special kind of system, a control mass. A *control mass* is a system of specified matter; its mass is therefore fixed. As our previous discussion indicates, we can change the energy of a control mass by transfer of energy either as heat or as work, and *these are the only ways*. The control mass and its environment together form an isolated system; their total energy must remain constant. If the energy of one increases, the energy of the other must decrease by precisely the same amount. Work and heat are the sole mechanisms by which such energy transfers take place.

The total energy input to the control mass must account precisely for the increase in the control mass energy; the algebraic statement of this accounting is called the *energy balance*. In terms of the system and symbols of Fig. 2·13,

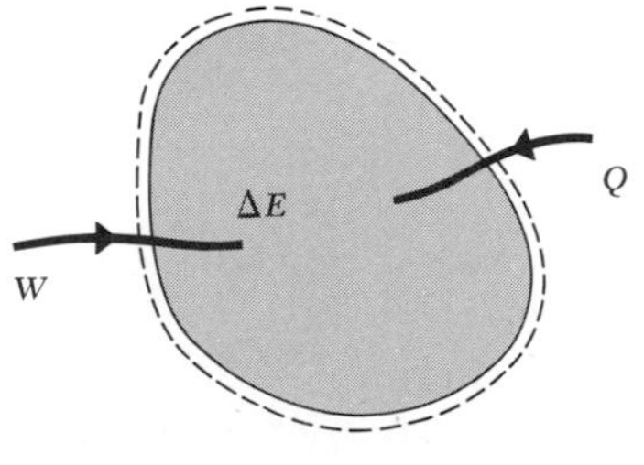

FIG. 2·13 *Show the boundaries and all energy flows on the control-mass diagram. Note the definitions of the directions of positive energy transfer*

the energy balance is

$$\blacktriangleright \quad \underset{\substack{\text{energy}\\ \text{input}}}{W + Q} = \underset{\substack{\text{increase in}\\ \text{energy storage}}}{\Delta E} \tag{2·18a}$$

Here W and Q represent the amounts of energy transfer *to* the control mass as work and heat, respectively, and ΔE is the *increase* in the energy of the control mass,

$$\blacktriangleright \quad \Delta E \equiv E_{\text{final}} - E_{\text{initial}}$$

(The symbol Δ will *always* be used to mean "final-minus-initial," that is, "the increase in . . . .") Alternatively, we could analyze the control mass over an infinitesimal part of the process, in which case the energy balance would be

$$\blacktriangleright \quad \underset{\substack{\text{energy}\\ \text{input}}}{đW + đQ} = \underset{\substack{\text{increase in}\\ \text{energy storage}}}{dE} \tag{2·18b}$$

Here $đW$ and $đQ$ represent infinitesimal amounts of energy transfer to the control mass, and dE represents the infinitesimal increase in the control-mass energy. (The symbol d always means "an infinitesimal increase in . . ."; the symbol $đ$ means "an infinitesimal amount of . . . .")

The first basic principle of thermodynamics is that matter has energy, and energy is conserved; we call this idea the *first law of thermodynamics*. Equations (2·18) are particular forms of the first law of thermodynamics and apply only to a collection of given particles; later we shall extend the mathematical representations of the first law to a wider class of systems. The analysis of a thermodynamic system invariably begins with energy-balance considerations, which are called *first-law analyses;* some simple examples of such analyses follow.

2·11 EXAMPLES OF CONTROL-MASS ENERGY BALANCES

The primary aim of this chapter is the development of the concepts of energy, internal energy, work, and heat. We need more tools before we can begin to do much productive thermodynamic analysis, but some examples at this stage should assist in clarifying the basic ideas. The examples that follow are intended to point up some important ideas from the preceding discussions and to indicate a general approach to analysis of thermodynamic systems. A more complete energy-balance methodology will be given in Chap. Five.

Gas compression. Two lbm of a gas is squeezed in a device from a volume of 14 ft^3 to a volume of 9 ft^3. During this time the pressure remains constant at 2000 lbf/ft^2, and it is known from other considerations that the internal energy decreases by 6000 ft-lbf. How much energy was transferred as heat to or from the gas for this process?

We first define the control mass to include only the gas. It is clear from the problem statement that energy will be put into the system as work, and so we

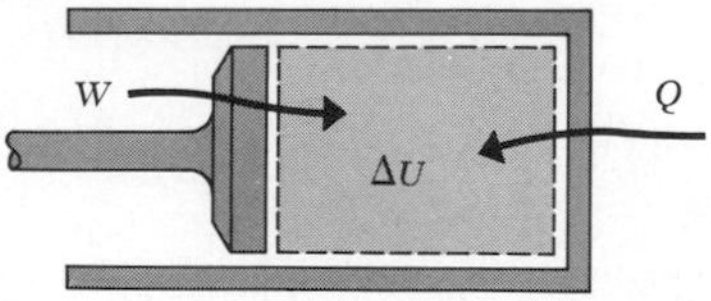

FIG. 2·14 *The control mass and energy flows*

choose the sign of positive work as indicated in Fig. 2·14. It may not be immediately clear which way the energy transfer as heat takes place; let's define Q to be positive as an energy input, and we indicate this on Fig. 2·14. We also assume that the only system energy is its internal energy U. In terms of the system and symbols of Fig. 2·14, the energy balance is then

$$\underbrace{W + Q}_{\text{energy input}} = \underbrace{\Delta U}_{\text{increase in energy storage}} \tag{2·19}$$

where $\Delta U = U_2 - U_1$ and the subscripts 1 and 2 denote the initial and final states. We know the internal energy change, and can compute Q from the energy balance if we can evaluate W. We have already derived an expression for the work done *on* a gas during compression, namely

$$W = -\int_1^2 P\,dV$$

Since the pressure P is constant, we integrate and have

$$W = P(V_1 - V_2) = 2000\text{ lbf/ft}^2 \times (14 - 9)\text{ ft}^3 = 10{,}000\text{ ft-lbf}$$

Solving Eq. (2·19) for Q,

$$Q = \Delta U - W = -6000 - 10{,}000 = -16{,}000\text{ ft-lbf}$$

The minus number means that we guessed the actual direction of energy transfer as heat incorrectly. The answer is that 16,000 ft-lbf of energy was transferred as heat *from* the gas.

If we had correctly guessed the actual direction of energy transfer as heat, and pointed the Q arrow the other way on Fig. 2·14, the energy balance would read

$$\underbrace{W}_{\text{energy input}} = \underbrace{Q}_{\text{energy output}} + \underbrace{\Delta U}_{\text{increase in energy storage}}$$

and the calculation would lead to

$$Q = W - \Delta U = 16{,}000\text{ ft-lbf}$$

Note that the correct problem solution can be obtained with either analysis; the main requirement is self-consistency.

A pneumatic catapult. A light airplane catapult uses high-pressure steam to launch aircraft with the system shown schematically in Fig. 2·15. Initially

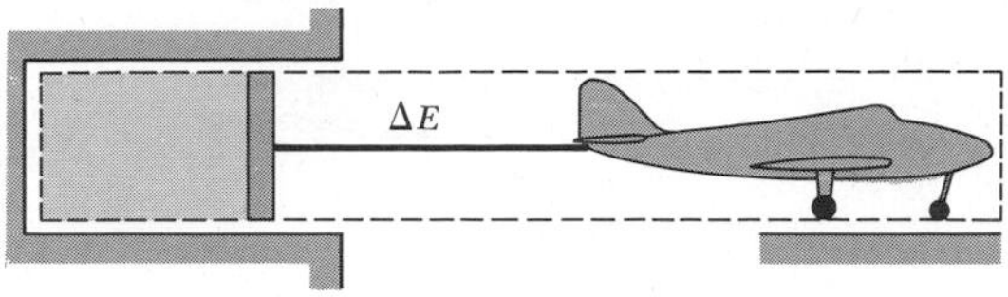

FIG. 2·15 *The control mass includes the steam and all moving mechanical parts. We neglect interaction with the air*

the cylinder volume is 10 ft³, and finally it is 35 ft³. The launch velocity is 200 ft/sec, and the combined mass of the piston, linkage, and aircraft is 6000 lbm. The process occurs very rapidly, so there is not much time for energy transfer as heat between the steam and the cylinder walls and hence $Q = 0$ is a good idealization. We wish to determine the change in internal energy of the steam for this process.

We take the control mass shown in Fig. 2·15. It includes the steam, the launch gear, and the aircraft, and we consider it over the launch period. To simplify the analysis we shall neglect the interaction with the air during the launch, and we shall neglect friction. These idealizations permit us to treat the control mass as an isolated system. There is no transfer of either energy or matter across its boundaries. The energy balance is therefore simply

$$\underset{\text{increase in energy storage}}{\Delta E} = 0 \tag{2·20}$$

Now, the energy consists of the internal energy U_s of the steam, the internal energy of the mechanical parts, and bulk kinetic energy KE. We assume that the internal energy of the metal does not change during the process, and that the bulk kinetic energy of the steam is negligible. Then, denoting the initial and final conditions by subscripts 1 and 2, respectively, the energy change ΔE is

$$\Delta E = \Delta U_s + \Delta KE_m$$

The increase in the kinetic energy of the mechanical parts

$$\Delta KE_m = \Delta\left(\frac{1}{2}\frac{M}{g_c}\mathsf{V}^2\right) = \frac{1}{2}\frac{M}{g_c}(\mathsf{V}_2^2 - \mathsf{V}_1^2)$$

$$= \frac{6000 \text{ lbm}}{2 \times 32.2 \text{ ft-lbm/lbf-sec}^2}[(200)^2 - 0] \text{ ft}^2/\text{sec}^2$$

$$= 3.74 \times 10^6 \text{ ft-lbf}$$

The energy balance, Eq. (2·20), then says

$$\Delta U_s = -\Delta KE_m = -3.74 \times 10^6 \text{ ft-lbf}$$

Hence, the internal energy of the steam *decreases* by 3.74×10^6 ft-lbf during

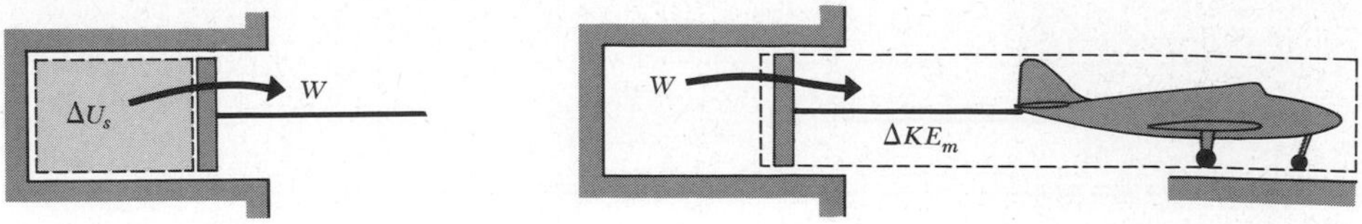

(*a*) *The control mass is just the gas*

(*b*) *The control mass is just the moving mechanical parts*

FIG. 2·16

the launch. The catapult extracts some of the disorganized molecular kinetic energy and transforms it into organized kinetic energy of the aircraft.

Suppose we wished to calculate the work done by the steam on the piston. We could analyze either of the control masses of Fig. 2·16. If we take the steam as the system, the energy balance is

$$\underset{\substack{\text{energy}\\\text{input}}}{0} = \underset{\substack{\text{energy}\\\text{output}}}{W} + \underset{\substack{\text{increase in}\\\text{energy storage}}}{\Delta U_s}$$

or

$$W = 3.74 \times 10^6 \text{ ft-lbf}$$

If instead we take the launch gear and aircraft as the system, the energy balance is

$$\underset{\substack{\text{energy}\\\text{input}}}{W} = \underset{\substack{\text{increase in}\\\text{energy storage}}}{\Delta KE_m} = 3.74 \times 10^6 \text{ ft-lbf}$$

Neglect of interaction with the air in the analysis above may introduce significant error if the steam pressure is not well above atmospheric pressure. The next approximation should include work done by the system in pushing air out of the way as the control mass expands. Calculation of this work would require more detailed knowledge of the geometry of the cylinder system. We see that the analyst must sometimes consider more than one system to complete his calculation. There are often several ways to do the analysis, and all correct ways will give the same answer. It might be noted that the work could not be computed as $\int P\,dV$ because we don't know enough about the steam pressure during the expansion.

The energetics of a dielectric medium. Consider a dielectric in which the dipole moment per unit volume **P** is related to the applied electric field **E** by

$$\mathbf{P} = \epsilon_0(\kappa - 1)\mathbf{E} \tag{2·21}$$

where κ is the "dielectric constant." Derive an expression for the work done by the electric field when the electric field is changed from $\mathbf{E}_1$ to $\mathbf{E}_2$.

The control mass consists of the dielectric, but does not include the external

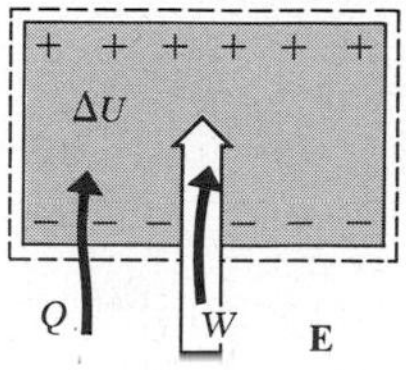

FIG. 2·17 *The system includes the dielectric but not the electric field*

electric field which occupies the same space. The amount of energy transfer as work from the electric field to the dielectric material is [Eq. (2·16)]

$$W = \int_1^2 \mathbf{E}V \cdot d\mathbf{P} \tag{2·22}$$

where V is the system volume. Using Eq. (2·21),

$$W = \epsilon_0 V(\kappa - 1) \int_1^2 \mathbf{E} \cdot d\mathbf{E} = \tfrac{1}{2}\epsilon_0 V(\kappa - 1)(\mathsf{E}_2^2 - \mathsf{E}_1^2) \tag{2·23}$$

Now, the energy balance on the control mass is (Fig. 2·17)

$$\underset{\text{energy input}}{Q + W} = \underset{\text{increase in energy storage}}{\Delta U} \tag{2·24}$$

where U is the internal energy of the dielectric. Combining Eqs. (2·23) and (2·24),

$$\Delta U = Q + \tfrac{1}{2}\epsilon_0 V(\kappa - 1)(\mathsf{E}_2^2 - \mathsf{E}_1^2) \tag{2·25}$$

In particular, for the special case of $Q = 0$, which is called an *adiabatic process*, the increase in the energy of the dielectric is equal to the work done by the electric field, which may be represented as the change in the quantity $\tfrac{1}{2}\epsilon_0 V(\kappa - 1)\mathbf{E}^2$. It is sometimes stated in books on electrostatics that this quantity is the energy of the dielectric. We see that this is the case only if it is assumed that the dielectric always undergoes adiabatic polarization. This is normally an excellent assumption in electronic circuits where the frequencies of polarization are so rapid that there is no time for any significant amount of energy transfer as heat to take place.

A complex power system. A nuclear power station consists of the hardware shown in Fig. 2·18. In the primary circulation loop, liquid NaK (sodium-potassium eutectic) is circulated by a pump through the reactor, which provides the energy source, and then through a boiler in which water flowing in the secondary loop becomes steam. This steam is fed to a turbine, which drives the electrical power generation equipment. In order to close the secondary loop, the steam is condensed and then pumped up to a high pressure. This complicated system is the sort that we shall be able to analyze in detail before very long; a simple analysis of certain aspects is possible now with only the tools at hand.

Suppose the desired turbine shaft power output is 100 Mw, and it is expected

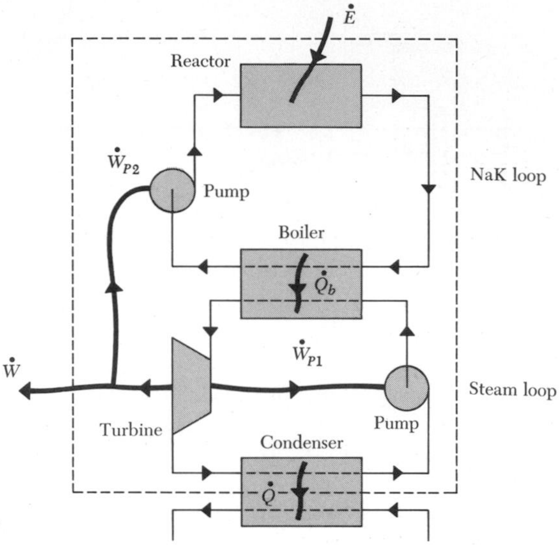

FIG. 2·18 *A nuclear power generation system*

that a system having an energy-conversion efficiency of 33 percent can be built. The energy-conversion efficiency η is the ratio of the power output $\dot{W}$ to the reactor power input $\dot{E}$. A simple energy balance will permit us to determine the required reactor power and the rate at which energy is discarded to the atmosphere via the condenser.

From the definition of the efficiency,

$$\eta = \dot{W}/\dot{E}$$

so

$$\dot{E} = \frac{\dot{W}}{\eta} = \frac{100 \text{ Mw}}{0.33} = 300 \text{ Mw}$$

Now, consider an energy balance on the control mass shown. It includes all the complicated hardware, but does not include the fissionable material. The rate of energy transfer to the control mass from the fission system is $\dot{E}$. The rate of energy transfer from the control mass as heat is $\dot{Q}$, and the rate of energy transfer from the control mass as work is $\dot{W}$. We assume that the system is operating steadily, and consequently as time passes there is no change in the energy stored inside the control mass. The energy balance, made over any time period t, therefore gives

$$\underbrace{\dot{E}t}_{\text{energy input}} = \underbrace{\dot{W}t + \dot{Q}t}_{\text{energy output}}$$

Hence,

$$\dot{Q} = \dot{E} - \dot{W} = 300 - 100 = 200 \text{ Mw}$$

This large energy-rejection rate may seem outlandish; we discard more energy than we use. Yet the efficiency of 33 percent is typical of modern power stations. We shall see why these efficiencies are so low later in our study.

2·12 ENERGY EQUIVALENTS

Magnitudes of energy can be assigned in many ways. Fundamentally the dimensions of energy are force times distance. For example, in the engineering system of units ft-lbf is the basic energy unit. Note that kg-m is not an energy unit, since the kilogram is a unit of mass rather than force. The unit of energy in the rationalized mksc system is the kg-m²/sec², or joule (see Table A·1).

Two important remnants of the caloric theory of heat are the Btu (British thermal unit) and the calorie. At one time these were defined in terms of the amount of energy transfer as heat required to raise a unit of mass of water 1 F° and 1 C°, respectively. Today they are related by definition to the mechanical units as shown below:

1 Btu $\equiv$ 778.16 ft-lbf	Approximately the amount of energy transfer as heat required to increase the temperature of 1 lbm of water 1 F° at "room" conditions.
1 kcal $\equiv$ 4186.05 kg-m^2/sec^2 = 1000 cal	Approximately the amount of energy transfer as heat required to increase the temperature of 1 kg of water 1 C° at "room" conditions.

An important energy unit in physics is the *electron volt.* This is the amount of energy required to move an electron against a 1-volt potential, and is defined as

$$1 \text{ ev} \equiv 1.602 \times 10^{-19} \text{ joule}$$

In high-energy physics the kev, mev, bev, and gev, respectively 10^3, 10^6, 10^9, 10^{12} ev, are often employed.

The engineer frequently talks in terms of *power,* the rate of energy transfer or expenditure. The watt is an alias for 1 joule/sec (see Table A·1). The horsepower had historic roots not unlike those of the Btu, but today by definition

$$1 \text{ hp} \equiv 550 \text{ ft-lbf/sec}$$

A compilation of some important conversion factors, including energy and power, is contained in Appendix A.

2·13 SUMMARY OF SOME IMPORTANT TERMS

A number of concepts and definitions have been introduced in this chapter; the key ideas are summarized below.

System Whatever we define as the thing being studied.

Control mass A system defined to be a specific piece of matter.

Environment Everything except the system.

Isolated system A system which does not interact with its environment.

Internal energy Energy of matter associated with the randomly oriented motions of the molecules and the forces between them (the energy of the "hidden microscopic modes").

Work Energy transfer by the action of a macroscopically measurable force on matter within the system ("organized" microscopic work).

Heat Energy transfer which is not recognized macroscopically as work ("disorganized" microscopic work).

Temperature A characteristic of matter which serves as a driving potential for energy transfer as heat. Energy is transferred as heat from the body at the greater temperature to the one at the lower temperature.

Hot, cold Adjectives describing bodies of high and low temperature.

Adiabatic wall One which prevents energy transfer as heat.

SELECTED READING

Lee, J. F., and F. W. Sears, *Thermodynamics*, secs. 3-1 through 3-10, Addison-Wesley Publishing Co., Inc., Reading, Mass., 1963.

Reif, F., *Fundamentals of Statistical and Thermal Physics*, secs. 2.6–2.11, McGraw-Hill Book Company, New York, 1965.

Resnick, R., and D. Halliday, *Physics, Part 1*, chap. 21, secs. 22-1, 22-6, 22-7, John Wiley & Sons, Inc., New York, 1966.

Van Wylen, G. J., and R. E. Sonntag, *Fundamentals of Classical Thermodynamics*, chap. 4, John Wiley & Sons, Inc., New York, 1965.

Zemansky, M. W., and G. C. Van Ness, *Basic Engineering Thermodynamics*, secs. 3.1–4.8, McGraw-Hill Book Company, New York, 1966.

QUESTIONS

2·1 What concepts were introduced in this chapter? What basic postulates? What definitions?

2·2 A control volume is any defined region in space; under what conditions will a control volume be a control mass? An isolated system?

2·3 How might you explain the concepts of energy, heat, work, and internal energy to a six-year-old?

2·4 "The oven is at 300 degrees of heat." What is wrong with this statement?

2·5 "The heat within a gas is evidenced by the random motion of its molecules." What is wrong with this statement?

2·6 Can energy be transferred to one molecule as work? As heat?

2·7 When two molecules of a gas collide, is there any friction?

2·8 Stir a pail of water. What happens to the energy that you transfer to the water as work?

2·9 If you say that a rock has potential energy in the earth's gravitational field, what must you say about the work done by the weight force when the rock is dropped?

2·10 Explain the difference between heat and internal energy.

2·11 Can you conceive of matter in a zero energy state?

2·12 Under what circumstances is work equal to $F(X_2 - X_1)$?

2·13 A house is receiving energy as heat from resistance heating elements, but the temperature of the house is not changing. What do you think is happening to the energy transferred as heat?

2·14 It is possible to increase the temperature of a substance, such as a gas, without any energy being transferred as heat. Think of an example, define the system, and identify the energy transfers across the boundaries.

PROBLEMS

2·1 Consider the rectangular free-surface water piston-cylinder system shown. The width of the chamber is b (normal to paper), and the atmospheric pressure is P_0. (*a*) From basic considerations, show that the force exerted by the water on the piston is $F = (P_0 + \gamma h/2)hb$, where γ is the weight density (weight per unit of volume) of water. (*b*) Calculate the work done by the water on the piston and the work done by the atmosphere on the water when the chamber length is increased slowly from X_1 to X_2. Express in terms of P_0, b, h_1, h_2, X_1, X_2 and γ.

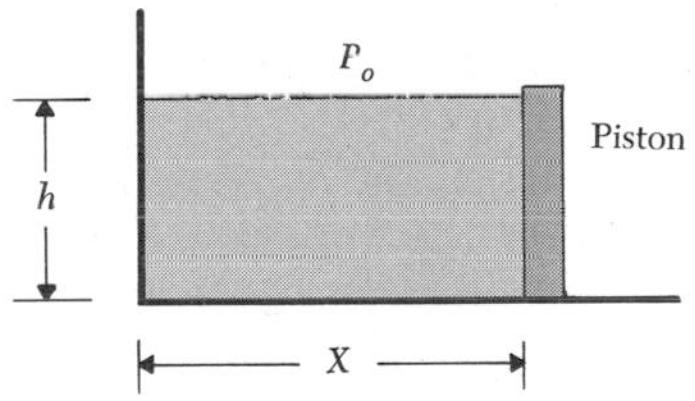

2·2 A hollow steel sphere of mass M and volume V is hung from a cable in a fluid having weight density (weight per unit of volume) γ. Compute the work that an external agent must do on the cable in order to lift the sphere a distance h through the fluid. The motion is very slow, and frictional forces may be neglected. Is there any work done on the fluid in this process? What happens to the energy transferred as work?

2·3 Consider the pulley-belt system shown. The tension force in the top belt is T, and the tension in the lower part may be neglected. The pulleys rotate at angular velocity ω. Which is the driving pulley? The power being transmitted is $T\,D\omega/2$. Define a system, show the forces acting on it and the direction through which they move, and derive this result from the definition of work.

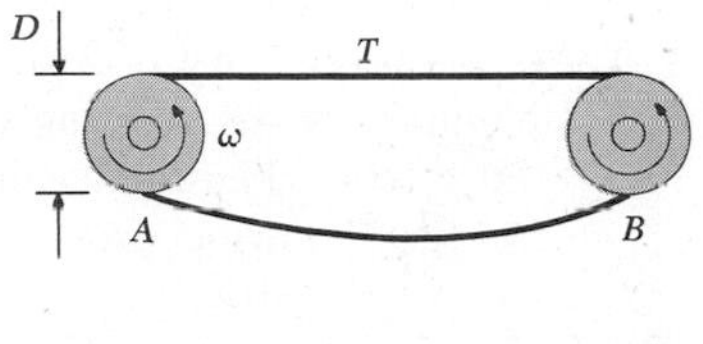

2·4 Repeat the development of Eq. (2 · 13) for a spherical system where the boundaries move radially.

2·5 Assuming that the atmosphere is locally isothermal, the density variation with pressure is given by

$$\rho = \rho_0 \frac{P}{P_0}$$

where ρ is the density, P the pressure, and the subscript zero denotes the earth's surface. Show that the pressure variation through the isothermal atmosphere is

$$\frac{P}{P_0} = \exp\left(-\frac{\rho_0 g_g z}{g_c P_0}\right)$$

where z is the height above the surface, and g_g is the (constant) acceleration of gravity.

2·6 Using the atmospheric pressure distribution of Prob. 2·5, derive an expression for the work done by the skin of a balloon on the atmosphere in rising slowly to a height h above the surface. Assume that the initial balloon volume is V_0 and that the volume varies inversely with pressure during the ascent. Neglect local variations in pressure around the balloon.

2·7 Using the atmospheric pressure distribution of Prob. 2·5, derive an expression for the work done by the skin of a balloon in rising slowly to a height h above the surface. Assume that the initial balloon volume is V_0, and that the volume varies linearly with height, attaining a value V_1 at h.

2·8 Work Prob. 2·7 assuming that the volume varies exponentially with height.

2·9 Using the atmospheric pressure distribution of Prob. 2·5, derive an expression for the work done by the skin of a balloon on the atmosphere in rising slowly from the earth's surface to a height h. Assume that the balloon is spherical and does not change size. (Some approximations relating to the small size of the balloon may be useful in carrying out necessary integrations.)

2·10 A man on a moving truck lifts a 100-lbm weight 2 ft vertically. If the truck is moving horizontally, how much work did the man do on the weight relative to a man on the opposite side of the earth? How much relative to a pixie on the weight? How much relative to the truck driver? In which reference frame did the man get the most tired?

2·11 A man in an elevator moving upward at a velocity of 10 ft/sec lifts a 50-lbf weight 3 ft off the elevator floor. This all takes 30 sec. How much work did the man do on the weight relative to the elevator operator? How much relative to an observer on the ground floor? How much relative to an observer in an elevator going down at the same speed? Explain why the work is different and what happens to the energy transferred to the weight as work in the three cases. In which reference frame does the man get the most tired?

2·12 A 3-lbm quantity of a substance is made to undergo a process within a piston-cylinder system, starting from an initial volume of 2 ft^3 and an initial pressure of 100 lbf/in.^{2} The final volume is 4 ft^3. Compute the work done by the substance for the following processes: (*a*) pressure remains constant, (*b*) pressure times volume remains constant, (*c*) pressure is directly proportional to volume, and (*d*) pressure is proportional to the square of the volume.

2·13 Liquid water at 32°F weighs 62.42 lbf/ft³, and ice at the same temperature weighs 57.2 lbf/ft³. Consider a system which is initially an ice cube 1 in. on a side. How much work does this system do on the atmosphere when it melts?

2·14 Six lbm of a substance is compressed in a piston-cylinder system from an initial volume of 4 ft³ to a final volume of 2 ft³. The initial pressure is 100 lbf/in.² Compute the amount of energy transfer as work (ft-lbf and Btu) to the substance if (*a*) the pressure is constant during compression, and (*b*) the pressure varies inversely with volume. If the process of case (*b*) is adiabatic, what is the change in internal energy of the substance?

2·15 Consider the cylinder of liquid suspended between two cones as shown in the sketch. Show that the amount of work done on the cones when the cone separation is increased an infinitesimal amount can be written as

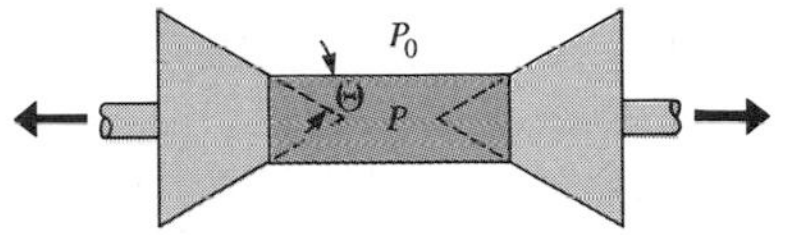

$$đW = \sigma(dA - \cos\theta \, dA_w)$$

where σ is the interfacial tension between the liquid and the gas, A is the liquid-gas interfacial area, A_w is the "wetted area," and θ is the contact angle. *Hint:* What is the liquid pressure?

2·16 Most dielectrics are such that the polarization is related to the electric field by $\mathbf{P} = (\kappa - 1)\epsilon_0\mathbf{E}$, where κ is the dielectric constant, and ϵ_0 is a physical constant (Table A·2). The dielectric constant is typically a function of temperature. (*a*) Derive an expression for the work done on a dielectric when it is polarized at constant temperature. (*b*) The dielectric constant of acetone as a function of temperature is given in the table. Compute the work done (joules) on 1 cm³ of acetone when the electric field **E** is increased from zero to 10^4 volt/m while the temperature varies from 0 to 50°C, if the temperature varies linearly with **E** during this process. *Hint:* Don't be afraid of graphical integration.

T, °C	κ
−80	31.0
20	21.4
50	18.7

2·17 Five lbm of a material is heated at constant volume from a state where its internal energy is 40 Btu/lbm to a state where its internal energy is 60 Btu/lbm. Compute the amount of energy transfer as heat for this process (Btu).

2·18 A substance expands from $V_1 = 1$ ft³ to $V_2 = 6$ ft³ in a constant pressure process at 100 lbf/in.² The initial and final internal energies are $U_1 = 40$ Btu and $U_2 = 20$ Btu, respectively. Find the direction and magnitude of the energy transfer as heat for this process (Btu).

2·19 A sample of gas (not ideal) is made to undergo an expansion process during which its pressure and volume are related as shown in the table below. The energy of the gas at the start and finish of the process are measured and found to be 5 Btu and 3.2 Btu, respectively. Determine the amounts of energy transferred as heat and work during this process. Express in Btu's.

V, ft^3	P, lbf/in.^{2}
1	40
2	27
3	21
4	18

2·20 A 200-lbm chunk of lead falls from a height of 30 ft and smashes into a rigid concrete floor. Calculate the increase in the internal energy ΔU (Btu's), assuming that no energy is transferred as heat from the lead.

2·21 An ideal gas ($Pv = RT$) is heated at constant volume until its temperature is doubled and then cooled at constant pressure until it is returned to its initial temperature. Derive an expression for the work done on the gas. It is a peculiarity of an ideal gas that its internal energy is a function only of temperature. What is the net energy transfer as heat for the process described?

2·22 A paramagnetic salt obeying Curie's law ($\mathbf{M} = C\mathbf{H}/T$) is made to undergo a process at constant $\mathbf{M}$ in which the applied field $\mathbf{H}$ is doubled (and the temperature doubled), followed by a magnetization process during which the applied field is held constant. This process returns the salt to its initial temperature. Derive an expression for the energy transfer as work for this process in terms of the initial values of $\mathbf{H}$ and $\mathbf{M}$. It may be shown that the internal energy U of such a salt is a function only of temperature. What is the net energy transfer as heat for the process described?

2·23 A paramagnetic salt obeying Curie's law ($\mathbf{M} = C\mathbf{H}/T$) is made to undergo a process at constant temperature T during which its magnetization $\mathbf{M}$ is doubled. This is followed by a heating process in which its temperature is doubled while the applied magnetic field $\mathbf{H}$ is held fixed. It may be shown that the internal energy of such a "Curie substance" depends only on temperature. Derive expressions for the total amounts of energy transfer as heat and work to the substance for the two-step process; express the results in terms of the initial values of T, $\mathbf{H}$, and $\mathbf{M}$, and the initial and final values of the internal energy U.

2·24 Assuming that the internal energy of iron is $0.1T$ Btu per lbm, where T is the iron temperature, estimate the maximum increase in temperature of the iron asteroid of Prob. 1·10 when it crashes to earth.

CHAPTER THREE

PROPERTIES AND STATE

3·1 CONCEPTS OF PROPERTY AND STATE

Any engineering system is made up of various amounts and kinds of matter. Description of such a system and prediction of its performance characteristics requires knowledge of the properties of the various materials and the ability to predict changes in their states. Thus, understanding of the concepts of state and property are essential to any engineer; these are the goals of this chapter.

A *property* is any characteristic or attribute which can in principle be quantitatively evaluated. Volume, mass, energy, temperature, pressure, magnetization, polarization, and color are all properties of matter. Both single particles and systems of many particles which we treat as continua have the properties mass and energy, but only a continuum has the properties volume, pressure, and temperature.

Properties are things that matter "has." *Work and heat are not properties*, for they are things that are "done" on a system in order to produce changes in the properties. Energy transfer as work or heat will be evidenced by changes in properties, but the amounts of energy transfer depend on the manner in which a given change takes place. For example, consider the problem of compressing a gas from one condition where the pressure is P_1 and the volume is V_1 to some other state P_2, V_2. This can be accomplished in an infinite variety of ways, two of which are shown in Fig. 3·1. The amount of work done on the gas in these two cases is obviously different, yet the changes in properties are identical. The integral $\int đW = \int P\,dV$ between two states depends on the path of integration $P(V)$; in contrast, the integral of any property, such as $\int dV$ or $\int dP$, depends only on the initial and final properties.

The *state* of something is its condition, as described by a list of the values of its properties. For example, the position coordinates and velocity components can completely describe the state of a single particle. On the other hand, in some instances it is sufficient merely to know the mass and energy of the particle, and its state is therefore satisfactorily described by fewer properties. The complete description of a system of many particles, such as 1 cm^3 of a gas,

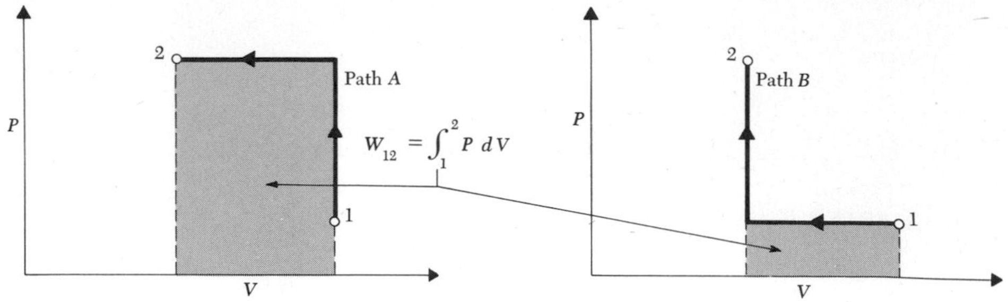

FIG. 3·1 *Note that the amount of energy transfer as work depends on the process path, and hence the work done is not a property of the end states.*

would require specification of the position coordinates and velocity components for each particle within the boundaries. The list of these properties would be very long—indeed, so long that it probably could never be written down, certainly not before some of the properties had changed. More economical descriptions of state are certainly desirable; we must find some way to reduce the number of relevant properties from something of the order of 10^{23} to "few." We might settle for knowing merely the volume of the system and the energy of each particle; still, this list would also be very long. A less complete way to describe the system would be to give merely its energy and volume, but these may fluctuate rapidly in time as the particles within the system interact with the particles outside the boundary (see Fig. 3·2). We might hope that the *average* properties would be sufficiently informative to allow adequate solution to our engineering problems; indeed, we normally work with properties representing the average of some feature of all the particles comprising the system. These averages are called *macroscopic properties.*

We can further reduce the list of relevant properties by noting that not all macroscopic properties are relevant in a particular analysis. For example, the color of a jet airplane is certainly not relevant in an analysis of its lift-drag characteristics. On the other hand, the color may be relevant in an analysis of its sales potential. It is helpful to group properties into classes that are relevant in different kinds of analysis. We do this by thinking about different subclasses of state. For example, the lift-drag characteristics of the airplane would be a property of its geometry, that is, of its *geometric state.* Its speed and altitude would be properties of its *kinetic state,* and the temperature and humidity in the cabin would be properties of its *thermodynamic state.* The color would be a

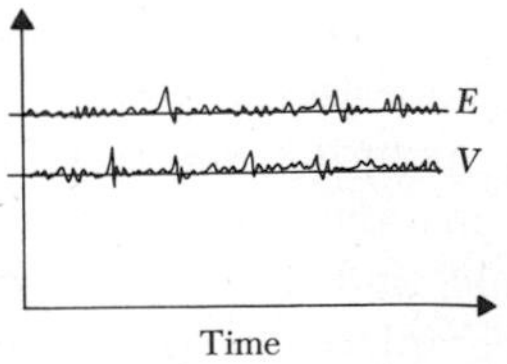

FIG. 3·2 *The average properties are used in thermodynamics*

TABLE 3·1 SOME DIFFERENT SUBCLASSES OF STATE

State	*Properties*
Geometric	Length, width, breadth, moment of inertia, volume, etc.
Kinematic	Position, speed, acceleration, etc.
Hydrodynamic	Pressure, shearing stress, strain rate, etc.
Electromagnetic	Electric field strength, magnetic-dipole moment, charge, etc.
Chemical	Chemical composition, free charge, energy, entropy, etc.
Esthetic	Smell, color, eye-catchingness, etc.
Thermodynamic	Energy, temperature, volume, pressure, stress, magnetic-dipole moment, entropy, etc.
Quantum-mechanical	Momentum and energy of each particle, total volume, etc.

property of its *esthetic state*. Some different subclasses of state are listed in Table 3·1.

In thermodynamics the central theme is energy and energy transfer. The properties of interest are therefore those that are involved with energy in some way. These we call *thermodynamic properties*. For example, the amount of energy transfer as work *to* a fluid when it is compressed is $đW = -P\,dV$, where P is the pressure and V is the volume. The *pressure* is therefore clearly a thermodynamic property. This equation holds regardless of how the volume changes, that is, irrespective of the *shape* of the fluid. The shape is therefore irrelevant in the thermodynamic analysis of fluids; the length, width, and depth of a fluid piece are properties of its *geometric* state, but are *irrelevant* to its thermodynamic state. But the *volume* is relevant to the energy transfer as work and hence volume is a thermodynamic property. We shall enlarge on the concepts of the thermodynamic state and thermodynamic properties in the next section.

In order to complete a thermodynamic analysis it may be necessary to consider other kinds of state. For example, a consideration of the geometric state might allow one to calculate the volume needed in the thermodynamic analysis. Consideration of the kinematic state of an accelerating gas stream may be necessary in order to calculate the gas temperature. A thermodynamic analysis therefore often involves a companion geometrical, dynamical, electrodynamic, or chemical analysis.

3·2 EQUILIBRIUM AND THE THERMODYNAMIC STATE

The state of a system is determined by the molecules within the system boundaries. These molecules undergo continual changes in their individual

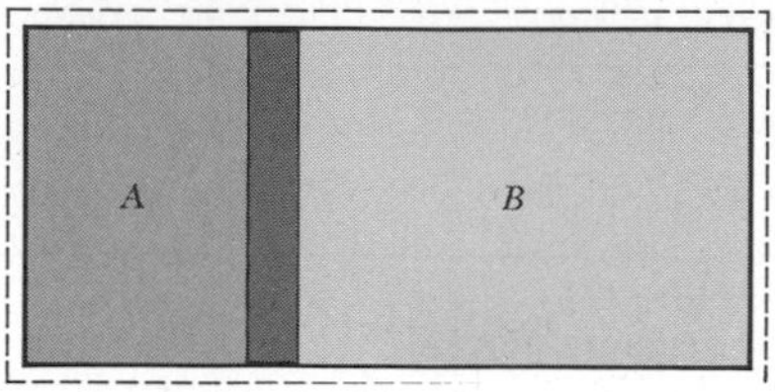

FIG. 3·3 *The pressures of A and B must be equal for mechanical equilibrium*

states as they interact with one another. If we isolate a system and allow its molecules to freely interact with one another, the state of the system will undergo visible macroscopic change. But after some time the changes that can be detected with macroscopic instruments will cease; the microscopic activity continues, but somehow the macroscopic state has "reached equilibrium." The macroscopic measurables have definite constant values. Just what equilibrium is, and how it can be identified, we shall now discuss.

Consider the system of Fig. 3·3. The cylinder contains a floating piston, with different amounts of two different gases A and B on opposite sides. Suppose the piston is locked in a certain position, and the pressures of the two gases are unequal. If we unlock the piston the unbalance of pressure will accelerate the piston in one direction. We would say that the two gas systems A and B were not in *mechanical equilibrium* with one another. If, on the other hand, the two pressures were identical, then the piston would not move upon release; A and B would be in mechanical equilibrium with one another. We see that *pressure* is a property that two systems have in common when they are in *mechanical equilibrium*. This, in fact, is the *thermodynamic concept of pressure*.

Suppose now we lock the piston, and allow the two gases to interact across the piston. Any energy transfer that takes place must be as heat, for locking the piston prevents energy transfer as work. When energy transfer as heat is possible, but none occurs, we say that the systems A and B are in *thermal equilibrium*, and that they have the same *temperature*. Temperature is the property that two systems have in common when they are in thermal equilibrium; this is the *thermodynamic concept of temperature*.

There are other kinds of equilibrium, three of which deserve brief comment. Two systems are said to be in *electrostatic equilibrium* if there is no tendency for a net charge flow between them when they are brought into contact. The electrostatic potential is a property that two systems have in common when they are in electrostatic equilibrium. Two phases of a substance (for example, solid and liquid) are said to be in *phase equilibrium* if there is no tendency for phase transformation (for example, melting) when they are brought into contact. A mixture of gases is said to be in *chemical equilibrium* if there is no tendency for a net reaction to take place when they are allowed to interact.

The term *thermodynamic equilibrium* is used to indicate a condition of equilibrium with respect to *all* possible macroscopic changes in a system where the molecules are free to interact with one another in any way. There is no macroscopic energy, matter, or charge flow within a system in thermodynamic equilibrium, though the molecules are free to produce such flows. In order to test a piece of matter to see if it is in thermodynamic equilibrium, we imagine isolating the matter and watching for macroscopically observable changes. If none occur, the matter was in thermodynamic equilibrium at the moment of isolation. We emphasize that the molecules must be free to move about in order to rearrange the energy, mass, or charge when we make this test.

When we treat a complex system not in equilibrium, the usual procedure is to mentally dissect the system into small pieces which we can treat *individually* as being in thermodynamic equilibrium. For example, in studying the gas flow in a rocket nozzle we might treat each small piece of fluid as being in thermodynamic equilibrium, and then consider the changes in its state as it interacts with the other fluid pieces. The electrons and ions in a plasma are often treated as separate systems, each in thermodynamic equilibrium, but not in equilibrium with each other. The analysis of the interaction between these two systems allows one to predict the approach to equilibrium for the entire plasma. By dissecting the systems in this manner their states can be evaluated by giving the equilibrium properties of each part. The equilibrium properties are therefore of paramount importance in thermodynamic theory and thermodynamic analysis.

Those macroscopic properties that can in principle be measured as functions of the thermodynamic equilibrium state and that are in some way relevant to energy are called *thermodynamic properties*. Any conglomerate feature of all the molecules, such as their total energy, is a thermodynamic property. Any property defined in terms of other thermodynamic properties must be a thermodynamic property. The *thermodynamic state* is the condition of the matter as described by all the thermodynamic properties. The thermodynamic properties are all fixed when the thermodynamic state is fixed. But they are not all independently variable, and hence the thermodynamic state can be "fixed" by giving values for just a few thermodynamic properties. We shall shortly develop a rule for telling how many properties must be known to fix the thermodynamic state. In later chapters we shall use thermodynamic theory to discover equations relating various thermodynamic properties.

3·3 TEMPERATURE

One of the important properties is temperature. What is temperature? A primitive view is that temperature is the reading on a mercury-in-glass thermometer. But who put the markings there, and what do they really mean? What was so special about the mercury-glass combination? These are deeply probing questions, questions which seek some more fundamental idea of the *concept* of temperature.

The housewife thinks of temperature as how hot she must set the oven to cook the roast. The computer engineer thinks of temperature as how cool he must keep the transistors to make them work reliably. The plasma physicist views temperature as a measure of the kinetic energy of the molecules or electrons. And the astronomer views temperature as a measure of the radiant energy emission from stars. These rather diverging concepts of temperature have one thing in common: they all relate to energy or energy transfer, and hence clearly mark temperature as a *thermodynamic* property.

Another common element in these remarks about temperature is that they each suggest that matter is somehow more energetic at a high temperature than at a low temperature. When two systems not in thermal equilibrium are brought into contact, energy transfer as heat will take place between them from the "hotter" one to the "cooler." We say that the hotter system has a greater temperature; the temperature then provides a means for telling in which direction the energy transfer as heat occurs when the systems come into contact. In the absence of other energy flows, there will be no energy transfer as heat between two systems at the same temperature.

Now, if two systems are in thermal equilibrium, then they must have the same temperature. If each is in equilibrium with a third, then all three have the same temperature, and hence any two or all three are in thermal equilibrium. This notion is sometimes called the *zeroth law of thermodynamics*. It is actually an implicit part of the concept of temperature.

It is important to make a clear distinction in one's mind between the concepts of heat, temperature, and internal energy, and hence we now review these again. Internal energy is the energy possessed by molecules that is "hidden" from direct macroscopic view by the disorganized character of the microscopic state. That energy may or may not have been put into the matter through transfer of energy as heat. Heat is energy transfer that is not accounted for in macroscopic evaluation of energy transfer as work; heat is microscopic work that is hidden from direct macroscopic view by the disorganized nature of the energy transfer process. Temperature is a property of matter; if the temperature of one body is greater than the temperature of a second, then any energy transfer as heat will take place from the first body to the second. The internal energy of a substance will depend in part, but not exclusively, on the temperature. Hence the temperature is *not* in general a complete measure of the internal energy. As we shall see, temperature can only be defined when a body is in equilibrium; the body has energy regardless of whether it is in equilibrium or not. A body doesn't "have" any heat; it may have received some energy as heat, but now that energy appears as internal energy, and one cannot tell from the body's state whether that energy entered the body as heat or as work. Internal energy and temperatures are *properties* of matter; heat is not a property. Temperature and internal energy are also inherently different kinds of properties. The temperature of a small piece of a large body is the same as the temperature of the body as a whole; the energy of the small piece is but a small fraction of the energy of the entire body.

To make the temperature concept operational, we need some sort of temperature *scale*. The uniformly spaced markings on a mercury-in-glass thermometer provide one such scale over a limited range. If instead a uniformly marked alcohol-in-glass thermometer is used, the two temperature scales can be made to agree at two points, but not in between. It seems odd that if temperature is such a fundamental concept its scales should be subject to the whims of a thermometer maker. It would be much more desirable if some scale of temperature could be established which is independent of the choice of thermometers. This can indeed be done; means can be devised for measuring the *ratio* of two temperatures without reference to any thermometric material. A conceptually unique scale for temperature can thereby be established in a manner similar to the way we outlined in Chap. One for establishing unique scales for force, mass, and charge. Being able to measure ratios, one is free to select the value for *one* point on the temperature scale, and the measured ratios then give all other temperatures.

In order to develop the thermodynamic definition and scales for temperature we need to understand both the first and second laws of thermodynamics, and we are not yet ready to make these developments. Consequently we shall for the moment work with an empirical temperature scale, that based on the gas thermometer. This scale appears to be identical with the thermodynamic temperature scale, and so we can consider the perfect-gas thermometer as a device for measuring thermodynamic temperature. In Chap. Seven we shall develop the thermodynamic definition of temperature and show the equivalence with the empirical perfect-gas temperature scale.

The empirical gas temperature is based on the observation that the temperature of a gas confined at constant volume is a monotone-increasing function of the gas pressure. The scale is established by arbitrarily selecting a value for the temperature of a mixture of water, water vapor, and ice in thermal equilibrium. Such a mixture can exist at only one temperature (called the *triple point*) and the temperature of this mixture provides an excellent easily reproducible standard.

The thermometer consists of a glass bulb into which various amounts of gas can be placed. The pressure may be measured in several ways, but the volume change so introduced must be zero. Suppose we wish to determine a particular temperature, say, the boiling point of water at 1 atm pressure. A given amount of gas is placed in the bulb, which is then immersed in the triple-point mixture. The thermometer is allowed to reach thermal equilibrium with the mixture, and the gas pressure is then measured. We denote this pressure by P_s. The thermometer is then inserted into the boiling water and the procedure is repeated; the new pressure we call P_m. The ratio P_m/P_s might be taken to be the ratio of the two temperatures T_m/T_s; however, if this is done one obtains different temperature scales depending on the amount of gas in the thermometer. The procedure followed in precision thermometry is to repeat the above measurements with less and less gas in the bulb and to plot the ratio P_m/P_s versus P_s, extrapolating to zero pressure, as shown in Fig. 3·4. The surprising result is that many gases seem to yield the same limiting ratio,

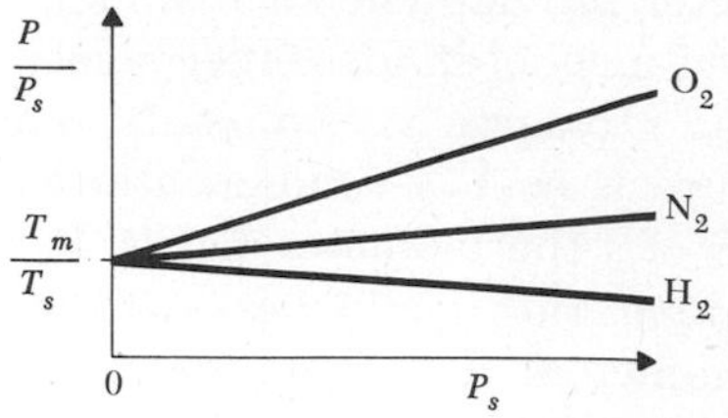

FIG. 3·4 *Readings from a constant-volume gas thermometer*

which is therefore, in a limited way, independent of the nature of the substance chosen. The temperature scale is then set by putting

$$\frac{T_m}{T_s} = \lim_{P_s \to 0} \frac{P_m}{P_s}$$

By an international agreement made in 1954, the temperature at the H_2O triple point is set at 273.16°K (*degrees Kelvin*). The number may seem quite arbitrary, but with this particular choice the newer *one-point scale* corresponds closely with earlier temperature scales defined on the basis of assumed linear behavior between two arbitrarily selected points. It is important to emphasize that the scales of force, mass, length, time, charge, and temperature are all one-point scales, which are set by selecting values and units for only *one* easily reproducible situation.

It is convenient to distinguish between *levels* of temperature and temperature *intervals*. Sometimes actual temperatures are specified in terms of degrees Kelvin, or °K, and temperature intervals or differences are given in terms of Kelvin degrees, or K°.

The thermodynamic temperature scale, to which the Kelvin scale is equivalent, is called an *absolute temperature scale;* its zero would always occur at the same condition, regardless of what value we happened to choose for the triple-point temperature. A second absolute temperature scale in use is the Rankine scale, defined by setting

$$1\ \text{K}^\circ = \tfrac{9}{5}\ \text{R}^\circ$$

This makes the H_2O triple-point temperature correspond to 491.69°R.

Associated with the Kelvin and Rankine scales are the Celsius (formerly centigrade) and Fahrenheit *relative temperature scales*. The Celsius scale is such that 1 C° = 1 K°, but it has its zero point shifted to 273.15°K; this makes 0°K correspond to −273.15°C. Similarly, 1 F° = 1 R°, but 0°F corresponds to 459.67°R. These four temperature scales are compared in Fig. 3·5.

It should be pointed out that the empirical gas scale can be used only at temperatures above the boiling point of the gas and below the melting point of the container. Outside this range other empirical temperatures must be used. The thermodynamic definition of temperature given in Chap. Seven is a continuous definition of temperature valid over all ranges and therefore provides an essential link between the several empirical measures of temperature.

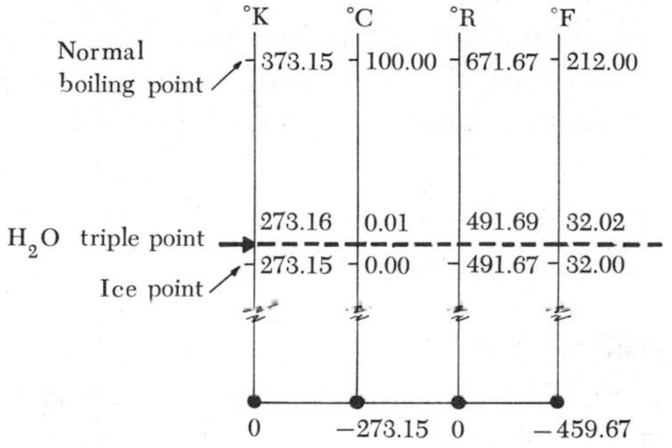

FIG. 3·5 *The °R and °K scales are "absolute" temperature scales*

3·4 INTENSIVE AND EXTENSIVE STATE

It is convenient to distinguish between two types of properties. Suppose we have two pieces of the same substance in equilibrium with one another. If we bring them together, and consider them as one system, the energy and volume of the new system will be the *sum* of the energies and volumes of the two parts. But the temperature and pressure of the new system will be the same as the temperature and pressure of each part. Those properties that depend on the *size* or *extent* of the system are called *extensive* properties; volume, mass, energy, surface area, and electric-dipole moment are all extensive properties. Extensive properties have values regardless of whether the system is in equilibrium state or not. In contrast, those properties that are independent of the size of the system are called *intensive* properties; temperature, pressure, and electric field intensity are intensive properties. As a rule these properties only have meaning for systems in equilibrium states.

It is customary to define some additional intensive properties associated with the extensive properties. For example, the volume per unit mass is called the *specific volume*,

$$v \equiv \frac{V}{M}$$

and the internal energy per unit mass is called the *specific internal energy*,

$$u \equiv \frac{U}{M}$$

Thus, the specific volume and specific internal energy of a system made up of two identical pieces are the same as those of each piece.

The intensive properties are useful because they can be tabulated or graphed without reference to the amount of material under study. The charts and tables in Appendix B are examples.

A great deal is known about a system when the intensive properties are specified. In fact, its thermodynamic state is completely known apart from a single measure of size (say the mass). The state of the system as specified by the intensive thermodynamic properties is called the *intensive thermodynamic state*. The addition of a size measure (mass) completes the description of the *extensive thermodynamic state*.

3·5 INDEPENDENT VARIATIONS OF THE THERMODYNAMIC STATE

The thermodynamic properties of a substance are not independently variable, for various relationships exist between the intensive thermodynamic properties. For example, the pressure, temperature, and specific volume of a gas are frequently idealized to be related by

$$Pv = RT$$

where R is a constant for the gas. Only two of P, v, and T can be independently varied. In this section we shall develop a rule for determining the number of independently variable thermodynamic properties for any substance.

Thermodynamics deals with energy, and the thermodynamic properties are those which in some way are related to energy. The number of ways in which we can independently vary the energy of a given substance tells us the number of independent thermodynamic properties.

Let's first consider the various ways in which we can transfer energy as work to the substance under study. If the substance is compressible we can increase its energy through $-P\,dV$ work. If it is magnetic we can increase its energy through magnetization work $\mu_0\mathbf{H} \cdot d(\mathbf{M}V)$. For a particular substance we consider all the relevant work modes shown in Table 2·1; there will be at least one independently variable property for each mode (volume, magnetic moment, and so on). In addition, we can hold these properties fixed and vary the energy through transfer of energy as heat (which varies the temperature). This gives us one more free variable. The count is in fact complete; for each of the independent ways of varying the energy of a given substance there is one independently variable thermodynamic property. We shall formalize this idea following some additional arguments in its behalf.

Let us first consider the nature of the work modes. As we noted in Chap. Two, each is of the form $\mathsf{F}\,dX$, where F is some sort of "generalized force" and dX is a "generalized displacement." If F is independent of the direction and rate of change of the process, then the amount of energy transfer to the system when X is increased by dX will be exactly the same as the amount of energy transfer from the system when X is decreased by this same amount. This means that *the work mode is reversible;* the amount of energy added in a forward process can be removed by the reverse process. It is clear that any work mode for which F is a *property* of the thermodynamic state of the substance will be reversible in this sense. Each of the work modes listed in Table 2·1 is of this category. If, on the other hand, F depends on the direction or rate of the process, and not just on the thermodynamic state, the process can exhibit hysteresis, and hence is irreversible. Viscous work on a fluid falls into this category; in contrast, $-P\,dV$ work for the same fluid can be reversible. The concept of reversible work developed here will suffice for the moment. In Chap. Seven we shall give a somewhat deeper meaning to reversible processes.

Let us now consider a piece of fluid, and see how we might change its thermodynamic state. We take a certain mass of a given fluid, so the composition of the system is fixed. Now, we can clearly change the state by compressing the fluid, thereby changing both the volume and energy. We can simultaneously cool the fluid in order to keep its energy fixed; this gives us a change of state at fixed energy, where the volume is the adjustable variable. We can also hold the volume fixed and adjust the energy independently through energy transfer as heat. So, the volume and energy are clearly two independently variable properties. Can we hold the volume and energy fixed, and vary other thermodynamic properties? We might think of trying to vary the pressure, but this is impossible if we keep the volume and energy fixed. Squeezing the fluid would indeed raise the pressure, but would change the volume; heating would also raise the pressure, but would change the energy. Suppose we stir the fluid; this will increase the pressure, but it will also increase the energy. In fact, the same change of state could alternatively be produced through energy transfer as heat. We might try other irreversible work modes, but we always see that the effects of the irreversible work modes can be accomplished by a combination of reversible work and energy transfer as heat. We are inescapably led to the conclusion that there is but one freely variable property for each *reversible* work mode; this free variable is the generalized displacement X. But we can also hold all the X's fixed and vary the energy through energy transfer as heat. Thus, if there are n relevant reversible work modes for a given substance, there are only $n + 1$ independently variable thermodynamic properties.

We can view the set of properties $(X_1, X_2, \ldots, X_n, E)$ to be the independently variable set. However, we can give up control over one of these and thereby obtain the freedom to vary some other property. For example, we can vary the pressure and volume of a fluid system independently if we do not simultaneously insist on control over the energy simply by heating the substance at the desired volume until the desired pressure is achieved.

3·6 THE STATE POSTULATE

We formalize the ideas discussed above in the *state postulate:*

The number of independently variable thermodynamic properties for a specified system is equal to the number of relevant reversible work modes plus one.

There are several ideas implicit in the words used. "Specified system" implies a specified amount of some specified matter; "thermodynamic properties" implies that we refer to those characteristics relevant to energy and to *thermodynamic equilibrium states.* The reference "relevant reversible work modes" means that we count only important work modes for the system in question and do not count irreversible work modes. The "plus one" is for the independent control of energy through heating or irreversible work.

Note that the rule gives the number of independent properties but does *not* say that *any* $n + 1$ properties are independent. The n X's and the energy always constitute an independent set, however.

The postulate as stated above deals with any amount of a specified substance. It is often convenient to work with a unit mass of the substance, and a form of the state postulate relating to intensive thermodynamic properties is therefore useful. Imagine that the system consists of a unit mass of the substance. The state postulate then can be interpreted as a rule for the number of independent thermodynamic properties of a unit mass, that is, for the number of independent *intensive* thermodynamic properties of the substance:

> *The number of independent intensive thermodynamic properties of a specified substance is equal to the number of reversible work modes plus one.*

Again we interpret the implications of the wording; "specified substance" implies the percentages of each kind of molecule; "thermodynamic properties" implies those properties of the substance relevant to energy and to *thermodynamic equilibrium states.* Again only the relevant reversible work modes are to be counted. The rule gives the number of independent intensive thermodynamic properties, but does *not* imply that *any* set of $n + 1$ intensive properties will always be independently variable. For example, the internal energy and temperature of an "ideal gas" are not independently variable, as we shall see.

To illustrate the use of the state postulate, consider a substance for which the only important reversible work mode is compression or expansion ($P\,dv$ work). The rule says that there will be two independently variable intensive thermodynamic properties for such a substance; specification of the values for any two independent intensive thermodynamic properties will fix the values of all other intensive thermodynamic properties. For example, specification of the specific volume v and the specific internal energy u fixes the intensive thermodynamic state completely; temperature, pressure, and all other intensive thermodynamic properties for that substance are unique functions of u and v,

$$T = T(u, v) \qquad P = P(u, v)$$

Figures B·1 in Appendix B give examples of these relationships for water in graphical form. If we set $u = 1400$ Btu/lbm and $v = 0.3$ ft^3/lbm, then we read from this graph that P is 3000 psia and T is 1200°F. Figures B·1 to B·11 are all examples of substances of this type; the student should familiarize himself with these "graphical equations of state" that we shall be using continually in engineering analysis.

As a second example, suppose we consider a substance for which the relevant reversible work modes are volume change ($P\,dv$ work) and electrostatic polarization [$\mathbf{E} \cdot d(v\mathbf{P})$ work]. Such a substance would have three independent intensive thermodynamic properties; the specific volume v, dipole moment per unit volume $\mathbf{P}$, and specific internal energy u are an independent set. The values for all other intensive thermodynamic properties are dependent on the values of these three properties. Thus,

$$P = P(u, v, \mathbf{P}) \qquad T = T(u, v, \mathbf{P}) \qquad \mathbf{E} = \mathbf{E}(u, v, \mathbf{P})$$

The relationships between the properties are called *equations of state.* Examples of such "equations" in graphical and tabular form constitute Appendix B. For certain idealized substances the equations of state are algebraic (such as $Pv = RT$). Today a modern engineering center will have the equation of state information stored within the memory of a digital computer as tables or fitted equations for use when needed in engineering analysis. The next chapter is devoted to discussion of the equations of state for a very special but extremely important class of substances.

SELECTED READING

Keenan, J., *A Course in Thermodynamics,* chap. 2, Blaisdell Publishing Co., Inc., Waltham, Mass., 1966.

Lee, J. F., and F. W. Sears, *Thermodynamics,* secs. 1-1 through 1-2, Addison-Wesley Publishing Co., Inc., Reading, Mass., 1963.

Van Wylen, G. J., and R. E. Sonntag, *Fundamentals of Classical Thermodynamics,* secs. 2.1–3.1, John Wiley & Sons, Inc., New York, 1965.

Zemansky, M. W., and H. C. Van Ness, *Basic Engineering Thermodynamics,* secs. 1.5–2.2, McGraw-Hill Book Company, New York, 1966.

QUESTIONS

3·1 What concepts were introduced in this chapter? What basic postulates? What definitions?

3·2 Give an example of a property which is relevant to the thermodynamic state, and one which is irrelevant.

3·3 Why is heat not a property?

3·4 In handbooks we sometimes find something called the "heat of the liquid" tabulated as a function of temperature and pressure. Is it possible to tabulate heat as a function of state?

3·5 Give an example of a system which is not in equilibrium and an example of one which is in a thermodynamic state.

3·6 "Heat and energy bear the same relation to matter as rain and water bear to a reservoir." Explain this analogy.

3·7 How would you explain the concepts of property and state to your grandmother?

3·8 Why is the differential quantity $đW$ not the differential of a property?

3·9 Can changes of state occur within a system without energy transfer across the boundaries?

3·10 Can the thermodynamic state of a substance be changed without any energy transfer?

3·11 What is a reversible work mode?

3·12 Can you visualize a substance for which shear work would be reversible?

3·13 Devise means for independently varying the pressure and volume of a gas; can the pressure and volume be treated as independent properties?

3·14 What is the difference between intensive and extensive properties?

3·15 Invent a test which will allow you to discover whether a property is intensive or extensive.

PROBLEMS

3·1 The simplest equations of state are obtained when only one work mode is considered important, that is, where there are only two independent intensive properties. Give a set of independent intensive thermodynamic properties for each of the following "simple substances":
(*a*) "Simple compressible substance," $P\,dV$ work only
(*b*) "Simple magnetic substance," magnetization only
(*c*) "Simple dielectric substance," polarization only
(*d*) "Simple surface," surface extension only
(*e*) "Simple elastic substance," one-dimensional pure strain only

3·2 For most substances the internal energy can be varied by varying the temperature and density, but for some special substances the internal energy is a function only of temperature. When work is done in an isothermal process on a substance whose internal energy is dependent only on the temperature, how much energy is transferred as heat, and in what direction?

3·3 Consider the "generalized forces and displacements" for a liquid-vapor-solid capillary system, as derived in Prob. 2·15. Assuming the liquid is incompressible, list a set of independent extensive properties for the system. What must you add if the liquid is compressible? Is the contact angle an intensive or extensive property?

√ 3·4 A system initially consists of 3 lbm of a substance having specific internal energy u of 20 Btu/lbm and 6 lbm of the same substance having an internal energy of 30 Btu/lbm. 150 Btu of energy is transferred as heat to this system, and it is allowed to come to equilibrium. What will be the specific internal energy of the substance in the final equilibrium state?

3·5 Consider a simple substance for which the temperature may be expressed functionally in terms of energy and volume or, alternatively, in terms of energy and pressure: $T = T(u, v)$ or $T = T(u, P)$. Differentiate these two expressions using the chain rule of calculus; use a subscript on the partial derivatives to indicate which variables are kept constant [for example, $(\partial T/\partial u)_P$ for the partial derivative of T with respect to u, with the pressure held constant].

√ 3·6 In a study of the properties of a liquid a 2-lbm sample was heated at constant volume from 400 to 450°F. This required an energy input as heat of 11.2 watt-hr. Calculate the difference in specific internal energy (Btu/lbm) between the initial and final states.

3·7 In a study of the properties of a gas a 3-lbm sample was heated at constant volume from 1100 to 1140°F. This required an energy input as heat of 35.0 Btu. Calculate the difference in specific internal energy between the initial and final states.

3·8 In a study of the properties of a liquid, a 2-lbm sample of liquid was heated at a constant pressure of 1 atm from 200 to 250°F. The density of the liquid is 38 lbm/ft³ and 36 lbm/ft³ at the initial and final states, respectively. An energy input as heat of 42 Btu was required. Determine the difference in the specific internal energies between the initial and final states.

3·9 In order to determine the properties of a dense gas at high pressures, 10 lbm of the gas was heated at 4000 psia from 700 to 740°F. The gas volumes were 0.287 ft³ and 0.328 ft³ in the initial and final states, respectively, and the required energy transfer as heat to the gas was 537 Btu. Determine the difference in the specific internal energy between the initial and final states.

3·10 In order to determine the properties of a gas, 0.1 lbm was heated in a 2-ft³ container. The amounts of energy input as heat required to achieve temperatures above the initial temperature $T_1 = 500°R$ value were as follows:

T_2, °R	Q_{12}, Btu
600	1.71
700	3.44
800	5.18
900	0.94
1000	8.72
1100	10.54
1200	12.39

Calculate the internal energy of the gas and plot as a function of T for this v.

3·11 The pressure may be thought of as a function of the temperature and specific volume for the perfect gas ($Pv = RT$). Prepare a three-dimensional sketch of this equation of state; project lines of constant temperature onto a P-v plane and sketch the resulting two-dimensional "map." How many "coordinates" are necessary for a "fix" on the state?

3·12 Make a table of all the intensive and extensive properties of matter that you know. List some means of measurement for as many as you can.

3·13 A substance for which the only reversible work mode is $-P\,dV$ is made to undergo first an adiabatic expansion process, then a constant-pressure compression process, and finally a constant-volume pressurization process which returns the substance to its initial state. What is the total change in internal energy for this "cycle"? Is there a net transfer of energy to or from the substance as work for this cycle? Is there any net energy transfer as heat? If so, is it to or from the substance?

3·14 In some presentations of thermodynamics a basic starting point is the hypothesis that for any control mass

$$\oint đW = \oint đQ$$

The integrals are to be taken around a cycle which returns the control mass to its initial state. If $đW$ is interpreted as positive if work is done by the control mass, what must be the interpretation of $đQ$ in the above equation? Derive this equation invoking the first law and the state postulate.

CHAPTER FOUR

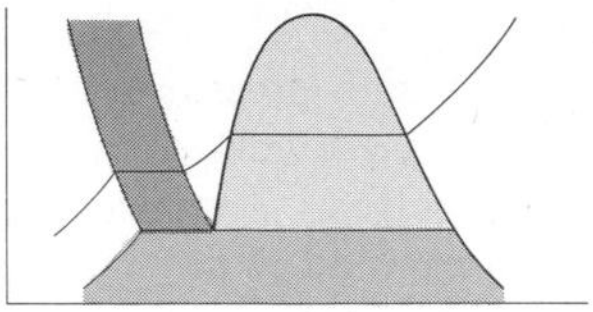

STATES OF SIMPLE SUBSTANCES

4·1 THE SIMPLE SUBSTANCE

The simplest descriptions of matter are obtained for substances idealized as having only one relevant reversible work mode. We call such a substance a *simple substance.* The state postulate tells us that the number of independently variable intensive thermodynamic properties of such a simple substance is only *two.*

The term *simple compressible substance* is applied to any substance for which the only important reversible work mode is volume change ($P\,dv$ work). The theory of simple compressible substances is quite well developed, and considerable data have been accumulated relating the thermodynamic properties of many such substances. No substance is truly simple, but we find that satisfactory engineering analyses can usually be made by treating the substances involved as simple compressible substances.

The simplest descriptions of magnetic substances are obtained when magnetization is considered to be the only significant reversible work mode. Since most magnetic materials are solids, the work of volume change is usually small, and the idealization that a material is a *simple magnetic substance* is often quite valid. Similarly, we can speak of the *simple dielectric substance* as one for which the only important reversible work mode is electric polarization.

Pairs of independent intensive thermodynamic properties for these three simple substances are as follows:

Simple compressible substance, $P\,dv$ work only: (u, v) or (u, P)
Simple magnetic substance, magnetization only: $(u, \mathbf{M})$ or $(u, \mathbf{H})$
Simple dielectric substance, polarization only: $(u, \mathbf{P})$ or $(u, \mathbf{E})$

Thermodynamics concentrates most heavily on the simple compressible substance, which is often called merely a "simple substance."† We shall examine this and other types of simple substances in this chapter.

† In some texts the term "simple system" is used instead.

4·2 EQUATIONS OF STATE

From the state postulate we know that the temperature and pressure of a simple compressible substance can be expressed functionally as

$$T = T(u, v)$$
$$P = P(u, v)$$

These relations imply that we could completely fix the intensive thermodynamic state of a simple compressible substance by specification of any two independently variable intensive thermodynamic properties. As we shall see in a moment, temperature and pressure are not always independently variable. However, temperature and specific volume are always independent properties for a simple compressible substance, and we can alternatively think of the pressure and specific internal energy as being functions of these properties,

$$P = P(T, v)$$
$$u = u(T, v)$$

In certain special cases these equations can be expressed in explicit algebraic form, but in general it is easier to represent them graphically or by tables.† The equations, in algebraic, graphical, or tabular form, which relate the intensive thermodynamic properties of any substance are termed the *equations of state* of the substance.

A simple compressible substance can exist in different forms. In the gaseous form the molecules are far apart and move about freely, continually finding that they have new neighbors. Very little of the energy is associated with intermolecular forces. In the liquid form the molecules are much more densely packed but are still free to move about. A considerable amount of energy must be added to a liquid to break the strong force bonds which keep the liquid dense (compared to a gas). In solid forms the molecules are restrained to definite positions in the crystal lattice, and consequently always have the same neighbors. Melting of a solid is accomplished by adding enough energy to free individual molecules from one another. There may be different structures in the crystal lattice, and hence different forms of the solid.

Some equilibrium states involve the presence of more than one form. For example, solid and liquid forms of water coexist in thermodynamic equilibrium at approximately 0°C. At a certain pressure and temperature near 0°C three forms of water can coexist in thermodynamic equilibrium. Such coexisting forms are called *phases*, and the group of phases is called a *multiphase mixture.*

The properties of each phase of a mixture can be treated separately, and the properties of the mixture then determined by appropriate combination. For example, the energy of the mixture is the sum of the energies of all phases.

† Property tabulations are now available for many substances in forms suitable for use in a digital computer.

However, the temperature and pressure of the mixture are the same as the common temperature and pressure of each phase. In graphical representations it is equally convenient to treat the mixture properties directly; the fractions by mass of each phase then become relevant intensive thermodynamic properties.

In engineering we continually use equation-of-state information provided in textbooks, Bureau of Standards brochures, the International Critical Tables, and various engineering, physics, and chemistry handbooks. There are three primary means by which these charts, tables, and equations are developed. First, laboratory measurements provide the main source of numerical values. Second, equations relating various properties can be developed by application of thermodynamic theory (Chap. Eight); these play a very important role in checking laboratory data, in interpolation, extrapolation, and even in evaluation of other thermodynamic properties (such as the entropy). A third way that equations of state are obtained is through application of quantum-statistical thermodynamics (Chap. Twelve). By postulation of an appropriate microscopic model of the substance, application of certain quantum-mechanical fundamentals allows one to predict the equations of state. These must of course be checked against laboratory data, and must be consistent with the equations obtained from thermodynamic theory. The quantum-statistical thermodynamic method is perhaps the most fundamental but is also the most sophisticated. In fact, only the simplest of molecules can be treated by routine applications of this theory. Hence the large body of equation-of-state information presently available is based primarily on laboratory data and thermodynamic theory, and these are the tools we shall emphasize in the main portion of this text.

Laboratory measurement of temperature, pressure, and specific volume are relatively straightforward. Measurement of the specific internal energy requires that the substance be put through some process where the amounts of energy transfer can be measured accurately. The energy transfer as work can be calculated from its basic definition, for example, $đW = -P\,dV$. The energy transfer as heat can be supplied from a device that takes in energy as measurable work and rejects all this energy to the substance as heat. Such a device might consist of an electric generator with a resistive load. Knowing these energy transfers, the change in internal energy for the test specimen can be determined. Execution of a large number of such experiments allows one to map out the specific internal energy as a function of the thermodynamic state (say as a function of the specific volume and temperature), *relative* to the energy at some arbitrarily chosen *datum state*. The value of the energy at the datum state is normally chosen as zero. Since energy-balance analyses always involve energy changes, and not absolute values of energy, the use of an arbitrary datum suffices as long as the substance is not involved in any chemical reactions with other substances. When reactions are involved, one must be careful to tie the energies of the various substances together properly in order to have a proper energy accounting for the chemical reaction. We shall discuss how this is done in Chap. Eleven.

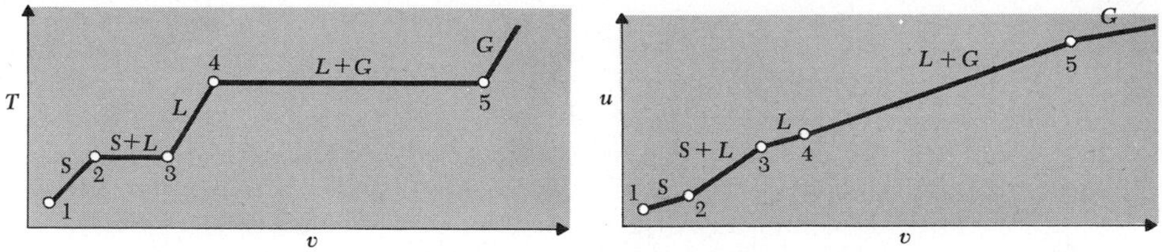

FIG. 4·1 *History of a constant-pressure heating experiment*

4·3 THE GENERAL NATURE OF A SIMPLE COMPRESSIBLE SUBSTANCE

Let us now imagine performing an experiment on a sample of some simple compressible substance. Suppose we carry out a heating process in a piston-cylinder system in a manner that keeps the pressure constant. At each step in the process we add a small amount of energy as heat, allow the substance to expand (thereby doing work) to keep the pressure constant, and then after waiting for equilibrium to be established we record the values for temperature, pressure, and volume. The energy balance then allows us to calculate the incremental change in internal energy between the first and second thermodynamic states. By this experiment we can map out the thermodynamic properties at states having this certain pressure, and these could become part of a basic tabulation of the type given in Appendix B.

A typical outcome of such an experiment is shown in Fig. 4·1. If we start with a solid at state 1, adding energy would raise the temperature to state 2, where the solid would begin to melt. For a given pressure there is one certain temperature at which solid and liquid phases exist in thermodynamic equilibrium. Further energy addition at this pressure results only in more melting,

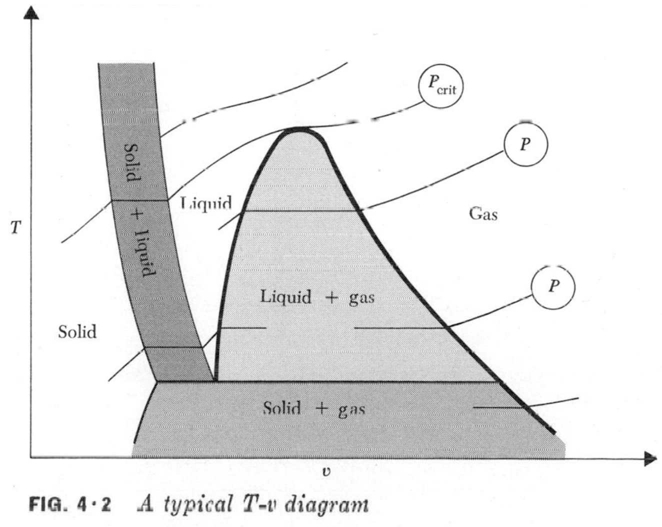

FIG. 4·2 *A typical T-v diagram*

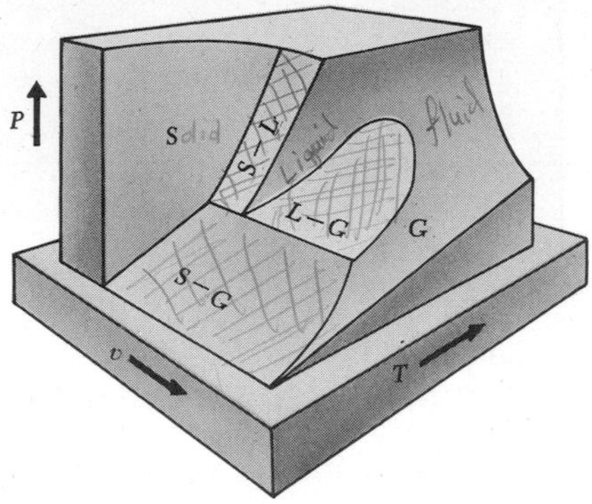

all hashed area's are excluded regions There are no solutions for these states

FIG. 4·3 *P-v-T surface for a substance which expands upon melting*

FIG. 4·4 *A typical T-P diagram*

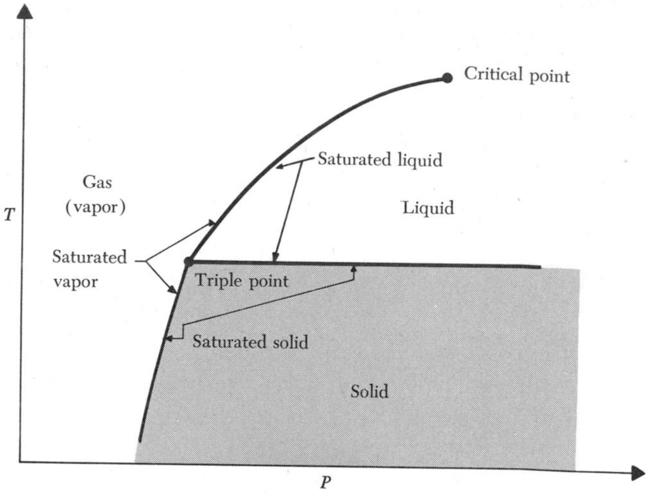

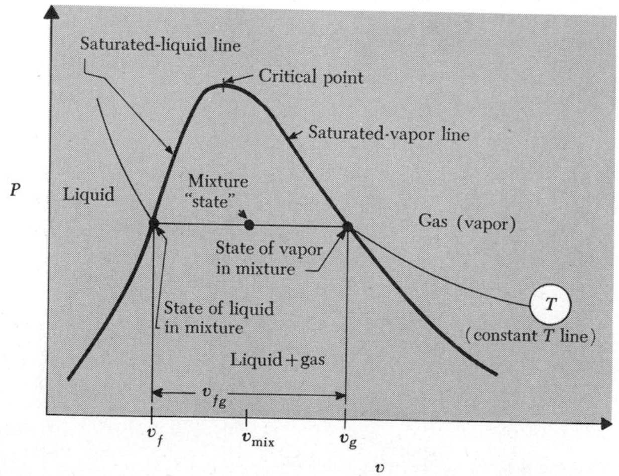

FIG. 4·5 *The vapor dome on a P-v plane*

with the intensive thermodynamic states of the solid and liquid remaining constant. This melting would continue until only liquid remains (mixture state 3); for most substances this would be a state of larger mixture, specific volume. A further increase in energy would result in increasing the temperature, until at state 4 the liquid would begin to evaporate. From state 4 to state 5 liquid and gas phases would exist together at a constant temperature and pressure, and the volume might undergo a tremendous increase. At state 5 the liquid would finally be completely evaporated, and further additions of energy would cause the temperature of the gas (vapor) to increase. Eventually, at very high temperatures, the molecules would become ionized and we would call the ion-electron mixture a *plasma*. In plasma states the electric and magnetic work modes might be important, and idealization that the substance is a simple substance might no longer be realistic.

Repeating the experiment with different starting states, a whole series of "constant-pressure lines" could be traced out (Fig. 4·2). At pressures below a certain "critical pressure" we would always encounter a region of coexisting liquid and gas phases; but at greater pressures there would cease to be a well-defined "boiling point," and the transition from the liquid form to the gas form would be continuous rather than abrupt.

Figure 4·2 constitutes part of the graphical equation of state for a simple compressible substance. We see clearly that the pressure is a unique function of the temperature and volume. Moreover, the temperature of a multiphase mixture is fixed solely by the pressure. In other words, *in the mixed-phase regions temperature and pressure cannot be specified independently.*

Graphing the functional relation $P = P(T, v)$ would require a three-dimensional map, and the projections of Fig. 4·2 are more convenient for quantitative work. However, it is instructive to examine a qualitative three-dimensional P-v-T surface, and one is shown in Fig. 4·3. The equation of state $P = P(T, v)$ is represented by a surface standing in the P-v-T space. Figure 4·2 represents a view of this surface from above, and the lines of constant pressure are obtained by taking horizontal sections through the surface.

States at which a phase change begins or ends are called *saturation states.* The highest pressure and temperature at which distinct liquid and gas phases can coexist define the *critical point.* The dome-shaped region in Figs. 4·2 and 4·5 bounded by the saturated-liquid line and the saturated-vapor line is referred to as the *vapor dome.* In thermodynamic systems the engineer is primarily concerned with liquid, vapor (gas),† and the liquid-vapor mixed-phase region. The area to the right of the vapor dome is commonly called the *superheated-vapor region.* To the left of the saturated-liquid line the substance is said to be in a *subcooled-liquid state.* States at pressures greater than the critical pressure are commonly called *supercritical states.* Note that the three-phase line appears as a point when the surface is viewed in a T-P plane (Fig. 4·4). This point is called the *triple point.*

† We shall use the terms "vapor" and "gas" interchangeably.

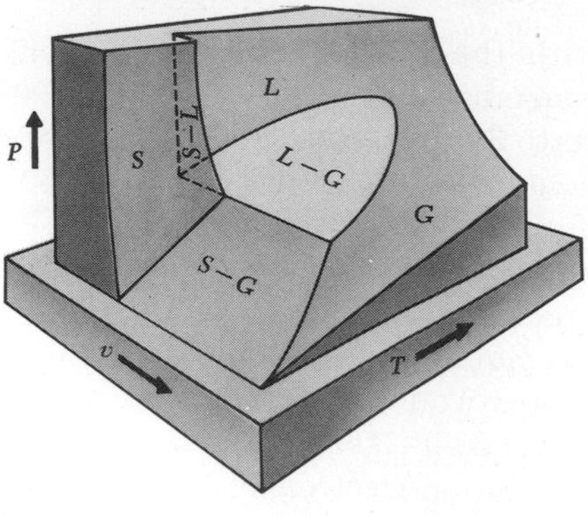

FIG. 4·6 *P-v-T surface for a substance which contracts upon melting*

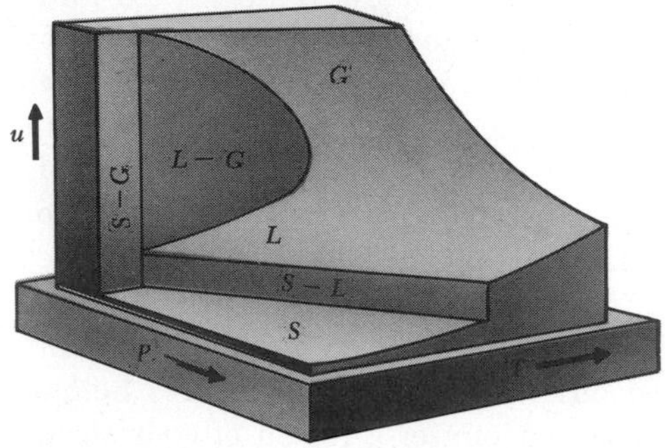

FIG. 4·7 *A typical u-T-P surface*

It is common practice to denote states on the saturated-liquid line by the subscript f and states on the saturated-vapor line by the subscript g. The difference between the saturated-vapor and saturated-liquid properties is frequently denoted by the subscript fg. For example,

$$v_{fg} \equiv v_g - v_f$$
$$u_{fg} \equiv u_g - u_f$$

Figures 4·1 to 4·3 represent the behavior of a substance that expands upon melting, and most substances are of this nature. However, one of the most important substances, water,† contracts upon melting. A three-dimensional *P-v-T* relationship for such a substance is shown in Fig. 4·6. A typical *u-T-P* surface would appear as shown in Fig. 4·7. Simple compressible substances differ markedly in their thermodynamic characteristics, as is illustrated by the variations in the critical-point properties shown in Table B·8, Appendix B.

4·4 USING THE TABULAR AND GRAPHICAL EQUATIONS OF STATE

Measurements of P, v, T, u, and other thermodynamic properties have been obtained for many substances, and graphical or tabular equations of state are now available for use in engineering analysis. Tables B·1, B·3, B·4, and B·5 are typical examples of *saturation tables.* Such tables give the properties of the individual liquid and gas (vapor) phases of a liquid-gas mixture. Tables of the properties of gaseous forms (for example, Table B·2) are called *superheat tables.* Note that the saturation tables have a *single* entry point; knowledge of the temperature, or alternatively the pressure, suffices to fix the state of each

† We use the term "water" to mean H_2O in any of its forms.

phase of the mixture. The mixture state is fixed when a second property of the mixture, say its specific volume, is fixed. In contrast, the superheat tables have *two* entry points; knowledge of both T and P fixes the intensive state of the vapor completely.

Graphical representations of the equation of state are particularly convenient, because most of the pertinent information can be put on a single page. Such a representation for H_2O is shown in Fig. B·1. Here the internal energy u and volume v are used as the independent coordinates, and the thermodynamic state is completely specified by fixing the values of these two properties. Note that the state can be fixed by specifying values for any two independent properties. For example, water at a pressure of 100 psia and density of 0.2 lbm/ft^3 (corresponding to $v = 5.0$ ft^3/lbm) will be in the gaseous phase at a temperature of 405°F and will have a specific internal energy of 1139 Btu/lbm. The u-v plot of Fig. B·1 is included here primarily for purposes of illustration. Thermodynamic data are usually presented on other "planes," using as coordinates properties that we have yet to define, but we can make use of the charts even before we know the meaning of all the properties. For example, using Fig. B·5, we find the volume of saturated O_2 vapor at 100°K as slightly under 3000 ml/gmole, and the saturation pressure as about 2.5 atm. On Fig. B·6, we read the specific volume of CO_2 vapor at 0°F and 100 psia as about 1.2 ft^3/lbm.

The properties of a liquid-vapor mixture can be read directly from the graphical equations. Alternatively, the mixture properties can be computed from the properties of the individual phases as tabulated in the saturation tables if we know the relative amounts of the two phases present in the mixture. It is convenient to introduce an additional property, the *quality*, defined as the fraction of the total mass which is saturated *vapor*. The symbol x is commonly used for this mixture property; $1 - x$ is then the fraction of the mass that is saturated liquid. Then, if M is the total mass, the volume and internal energy are

$$V = (1 - x)Mv_f + xMv_g$$
$$U = (1 - x)Mu_f + xMu_g$$

The specific volume and specific internal energy of a simple compressible substance in the mixed-phase region are then

$$▶ \quad v = (1 - x)v_f + xv_g \tag{4·1}$$
$$▶ \quad u = (1 - x)u_f + xu_g \tag{4·2}$$

The pressure and temperature of the mixture are, of course, the same as the pressure and temperature of the saturated liquid and vapor. For example, consider 2.5 lbm of H_2O at 100 psia in a two-phase state, with a quality of 0.6. The liquid and vapor masses are

$$M_f = (1 - 0.6) \times 2.5 = 1 \text{ lbm}$$
$$M_g = 0.6 \times 2.5 = 1.5 \text{ lbm}$$

We find values for v_f, v_g, u_f, and u_g in Table B·1b. The volume occupied by the mixture is then

$$V = Mv = 2.5 \times [(1 - 0.6) \times 0.0177 + 0.6 \times 4.43] = 6.66 \text{ ft}^3$$

The internal energy of the mixture is

$$U = Mu = 2.5 \times [(1 - 0.6) \times 298 + 0.6 \times 1105] = 1950 \text{ Btu}$$

The temperature of the mixture is 327.8°F, or 787.5°R.

4·5 METASTABLE STATES IN PHASE TRANSITIONS

It is important to realize that the phase transitions discussed above are not always observed at precisely the points indicated in the tables. Suppose we expand the volume available to a liquid-vapor mixture. The pressure within the liquid might actually be significantly reduced below the saturation pressure before any vapor is formed, for vapor can only be formed at a "nucleus," such as a small vapor bubble. Rough walls normally contain many such nuclei, but with a smooth glass container one can virtually eliminate all nuclei, and hence prevent the formation of new vapor within the liquid. Water in a clean beaker can be heated several degrees above 212°F without noticeable boiling. The insertion of a roughened glass rod, which provides nucleation sites, gives rise to immediate vapor formation from these sites. The state of the "superheated liquid" in this demonstration is not given in any of the tables of thermodynamic properties, for the superheated liquid is not in an equilibrium state. A small disturbance (the insertion of the rod) initiates a dramatic change in state (vaporization). A similar effect is observed when water is cooled in a clean beaker at 1 atm. With care, the water can be cooled well below 32°F without solidification. A tap on the beaker then triggers a sudden crystallization throughout the liquid. The "supercooled liquid" is likewise not in an equilibrium state. A related phenomenon occurs during condensation; the vapor requires some small liquid droplets to act as nuclei for the condensation process. This has considerable importance in steam turbine nozzles, where the vapor is usually expanded to somewhat below the saturation pressure before condensation actually occurs.

Analysis of these *metastable equilibrium states* is beyond our present scope. Most engineering problems can be adequately treated by assuming that the phase transitions occur exactly at the saturation conditions, and this is the approach that we shall take.

4·6 AN ENGINEERING EXAMPLE

The tabular and graphical equations of state are used in conjunction with the energy balance in analysis of engineering systems. The energy balance provides quantitative information relating the change in internal energy to the energy transfers for the process, and the equations of state relate the energy to other thermodynamic properties whose values may be of interest in the particular system. For example, suppose we wish to compute the amount of energy which must be transferred as heat to 5 lbm of H_2O initially at 200°F and 2 psia pressure in order to increase the temperature to 1200°F if the heating occurs at constant volume.

We begin the solution by defining a control mass consisting of thc 5 lbm of water. As shown in Fig. 4·8*a*, energy inflow as heat will be considered positive, and there is no work involved. The only energy possessed by the system is its internal energy U, so the energy balance, made over the time for the state change to take place, is

$$\underset{\text{energy input}}{Q} = \underset{\text{increase in energy storage}}{\Delta U}$$

Here

$$\Delta U = M(u_2 - u_1)$$

where u_1 and u_2 represent the internal energy in the initial and final states.

At this point it becomes necessary to make the idealization that the substance is in a state of thermodynamic equilibrium at the start of the process and in another such state at the end of the process. The equation of state for water, treated as a simple compressible substance, can then be employed (see Appendix B). For the initial state, from Fig. B·1 we find

$$P_1 = 2 \text{ psia} \qquad u_1 = 1080 \text{ Btu/lbm}$$
$$T_1 = 200°\text{F} \qquad v_1 = 198 \text{ ft}^3/\text{lbm}$$

The final state is fixed with the aid of a *process representation*, Fig. 4·8*b*. Such a diagram shows the reader how the problem is solved as well as helping the analyst in his solution. Then, reading from Fig. B·1, we find that the final

FIG. 4·8

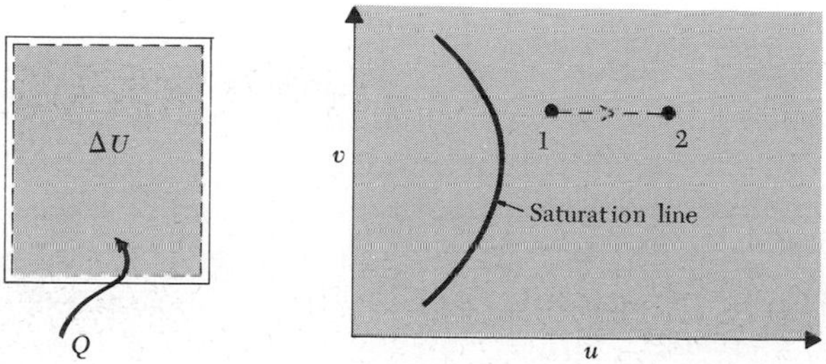

(*a*) *The control mass* (*b*) *The process representation*

state is

$$v_2 = 198 \text{ ft}^3/\text{lbm} \qquad P_2 = 5 \text{ psia}$$
$$T_2 = 1200°\text{F} \qquad u_2 = 1440 \text{ Btu/lbm}$$

Substituting into the energy balance, we find

$$Q = 5 \text{ lbm} \times (1440 - 1080) \text{ Btu/lbm} = 1800 \text{ Btu}$$

In Chap. Five we shall see many other examples illustrating the use of equations of state in engineering analysis.

4·7 SOME OTHER THERMODYNAMIC PROPERTIES

Quite frequently other thermodynamic properties will be defined in terms of P, v, T, and u, and we shall now discuss some of these. In single-phase regions, where pressure and temperature are independent, we can think of the volume as being a function of pressure and temperature,

$$v = v(T, P)$$

The difference in specific volume between any two states separated by infinitesimal differences dT and dP can be obtained by expanding the function $v(T, P)$ in a Taylor's series about the point (T, P),

$$v(T + dT, P + dP) = v(T, P) + \left(\frac{\partial v}{\partial T}\right)_P dT + \left(\frac{\partial v}{\partial P}\right)_T dP + \cdots$$

The partial derivatives are to be evaluated at the point (T, P), and the subscripts on the partial derivatives indicate which other variable is held constant during the differentiation. The *difference* between the specific volumes of the two states is then (to first order)

$$dv = v(T + dT, P + dP) - v(T, P)$$

or,†

$$dv = \left(\frac{\partial v}{\partial T}\right)_P dT + \left(\frac{\partial v}{\partial P}\right)_T dP \qquad (4\cdot3)$$

The derivative $(\partial v/\partial T)_P$ represents the slope of a line of constant pressure on a v-T plane. A similar interpretation can be given to the second derivative (Fig. 4·9). These derivatives are themselves intensive thermodynamic properties, since they have definite values at any fixed thermodynamic state. The first represents the sensitivity of the specific volume to changes in temperature at constant pressure, and the second is a measure of the change in specific volume associated with a change in pressure at constant temperature. Two

† Alternatively, this result can be obtained directly from the chain rule of the calculus of a function of two variables.

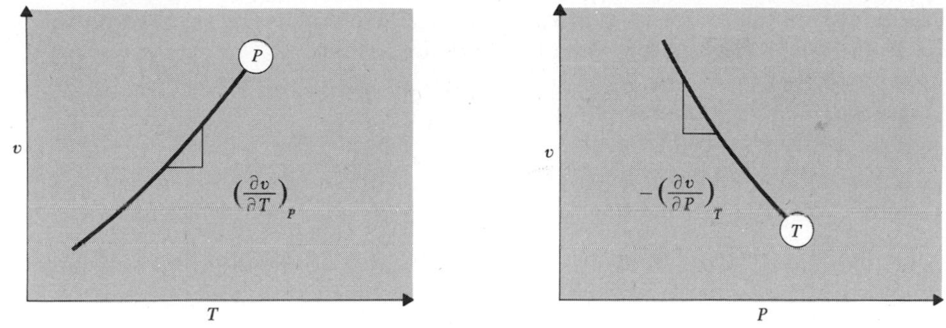

FIG. 4·9 *The slopes are intensive thermodynamic properties*

thermodynamic properties related to these derivatives are the *isobaric* (constant-pressure) *compressibility*,

$$\blacktriangleright \quad \beta \equiv \frac{1}{v}\left(\frac{\partial v}{\partial T}\right)_P \tag{4·4}$$

and the *isothermal* (constant-temperature) *compressibility*,

$$\blacktriangleright \quad \kappa \equiv -\frac{1}{v}\left(\frac{\partial v}{\partial P}\right)_T \tag{4·5}$$

These compressibility factors are frequently tabulated functions of state. The "coefficient of linear expansion" used in elementary strength-of-materials texts is $\frac{1}{3}\beta$. "Young's modulus of elasticity" is proportional to κ.

In terms of β and κ, Eq. (Eq. 4·3) becomes

$$dv = \beta v\, dT - \kappa v\, dP \tag{4·6}$$

This represents a differential equation relating specific volume to temperature and pressure on the equation-of-state surface. Its usefulness arises from the fact that β and κ are sometimes slowly varying functions of T and P. Equation (4·6) can be written as

$$\int_{v_0}^{v} \frac{dv}{v} = \int_{T_0}^{T} \beta\, dT - \int_{P_0}^{P} \kappa\, dP$$

If β and κ are constants, we can integrate from some state (T_0, P_0), where the specific volume is v_0, to any other state (T, P), obtaining

$$\ln \frac{v}{v_0} = \beta(T - T_0) - \kappa(P - P_0)$$

This is often an adequate approximation over limited pressure and temperature ranges.

It should be apparent that the calculus of functions of two variables is of considerable utility in the thermodynamics of simple substances. In particular, consider three functions x, y, and z, any two of which may be selected as the independent pair. Then, from calculus, it follows that†

$$\blacktriangleright \quad \left(\frac{\partial x}{\partial y}\right)_z = \frac{1}{(\partial y/\partial x)_z} \tag{4·7}$$

$$\blacktriangleright \quad \left(\frac{\partial x}{\partial y}\right)_z \left(\frac{\partial y}{\partial z}\right)_x \left(\frac{\partial z}{\partial x}\right)_y = -1 \tag{4·8}$$

To use these mathematical properties of functions, we for example note that, in regions of P-v-T space where P and T are independent, $v = v(P, T)$, so

$$\left(\frac{\partial P}{\partial T}\right)_v \left(\frac{\partial T}{\partial v}\right)_P \left(\frac{\partial v}{\partial P}\right)_T = -1$$

or

$$\left(\frac{\partial P}{\partial T}\right)_v = -\frac{(\partial v/\partial T)_P}{(\partial v/\partial P)_T} = \frac{\beta}{\kappa} \tag{4·9}$$

Hence, knowledge of the isobaric compressibility β and the isothermal compressibility κ would allow us to determine from Eq. (4·9) how the pressure changes with temperature for a constant-volume heating process. We shall make considerable use of the calculus of functions of several variables, and the student is urged to review this material now if necessary.

There are several properties related to the internal energy that are important. Suppose we view the specific internal energy u as being fixed by specification of T and v,

$$u = u(T, v)$$

The difference in energy between any two states separated by infinitesimal temperature and specific-volume differences dT and dv is then

$$du = \left(\frac{\partial u}{\partial T}\right)_v dT + \left(\frac{\partial u}{\partial v}\right)_T dv \tag{4·10}$$

† Consider $x = x(y, z)$ and $y = y(x, z)$. Then, from the chain rule,

$$dx = \left(\frac{\partial x}{\partial y}\right)_z dy + \left(\frac{\partial x}{\partial z}\right)_y dz$$

$$dy = \left(\frac{\partial y}{\partial x}\right)_z dx + \left(\frac{\partial y}{\partial z}\right)_x dz$$

Eliminating dy from these two equations,

$$\left[1 - \left(\frac{\partial x}{\partial y}\right)_z \left(\frac{\partial y}{\partial x}\right)_z\right] dx = \left[\left(\frac{\partial x}{\partial y}\right)_z \left(\frac{\partial y}{\partial z}\right)_x + \left(\frac{\partial x}{\partial z}\right)_y\right] dz$$

But the changes dx and dz are independent. Letting $dz = 0$, Eq. (4·7) follows. Letting $dx = 0$ and using Eq. (4·7), Eq. (4·8) is obtained.

The derivative $(\partial u/\partial T)_v$ represents the slope of a line of constant v on a u-T thermodynamic plane. The derivative is also a function of state, that is, a thermodynamic property, and is called the *specific heat at constant volume,*†

$$▶ \quad c_v \equiv \left(\frac{\partial u}{\partial T}\right)_v \tag{4·11}$$

Another thermodynamic property which we shall find to be of particular importance is the *enthalpy* h defined by‡

$$▶ \quad h \equiv u + Pv \tag{4·12}$$

We leave as an exercise the proof that the enthalpy of a liquid-vapor mixture is

$$▶ \quad h = (1 - x)h_f + xh_g \tag{4·13}$$

The enthalpy of a simple substance is obviously only a function of the thermodynamic state. For states where T and P are independent (single-phase states), we may put

$$h = h(T, P)$$

Then, taking the differential,

$$dh = \left(\frac{\partial h}{\partial T}\right)_P dT + \left(\frac{\partial h}{\partial P}\right)_T dP \tag{4·14}$$

The derivative $(\partial h/\partial T)_P$ is called the *specific heat at constant pressure,*§

$$▶ \quad c_P \equiv \left(\frac{\partial h}{\partial T}\right)_P \tag{4·15}$$

† The name given to c_v is somewhat unfortunate in that only for very special conditions is the derivative $(\partial u/\partial T)_v$ related to energy transfer as heat. If a process is carried out slowly at constant volume no work will be done, and any energy increase will be due solely to energy transfer as heat. For such a process c_v does represent the energy increase per unit of temperature rise (per unit of mass), and consequently historically was called the "specific heat at constant volume." We feel that c_v should be thought of in terms of its definition as a certain partial derivative, and not as being related to energy transfer as heat in the special constant-volume process.

‡ The product of pressure and specific volume has the units of energy per unit of mass, as does u. However, it is customary to give u values in Btu/lbm and measure pressure and volume in mechanical units (lbf and ft). One must be careful to make the two parts of the enthalpy dimensionally equivalent in any numerical computations. Enthalpy is sometimes called the "heat content," another term with more historical than physical significance.

§ c_P is sometimes called the "heat capacity at constant pressure." As with c_v, it is best to think of c_P as a partial derivative. Only in very special processes (constant pressure) is c_P related to energy transfer as heat, yet it is a useful thermodynamic function in many other situations. In engineering units the dimensions of c_P and c_v are usually written as Btu/lbm-°R. However, it would be better to write them as Btu/lbm-R°.

The derivatives c_P and c_v constitute two of the most important thermodynamic derivative functions, and values have been experimentally determined as functions of the thermodynamic state for a tremendous number of simple compressible substances.

4·8 THE PERFECT GAS

Under appropriate conditions, the equations of state for the vapor of any substance can be approximated by the algebraic equations of state for an "ideal" or "perfect" gas. The defining equation for the perfect gas is

$$\blacktriangleright \quad Pv = RT \tag{4·16}$$

Here R is a constant for a particular gas, and is related to the *universal gas constant* $\mathcal{R}$ and the molal mass $\hat{M}$ by

$$\blacktriangleright \quad R = \frac{\mathcal{R}}{\hat{M}} \tag{4·17}$$

where†

$$\mathcal{R} = 1545 \text{ ft-lbf/lbmole-°R}$$

Note that T is the *absolute* temperature, °K or °R.

The value of R can be determined by plotting Pv/T as a function of state. In any region where this value is constant the perfect-gas approximation is adequate. Figure 8·10 shows the value of the *compressibility factor* $Z \equiv Pv/RT$ as a function of the ratio of the temperature and pressure to their values at the critical point; where the ratio Z is near unity the perfect-gas approximation is valid. Note that the perfect-gas model is best at pressures low compared to the critical pressure or at temperatures high compared to the critical temperature. We shall discuss the perfect-gas model in more detail in Chap. Eight, and here state only a few of its important features, which will be useful in the next chapter. Of particular importance are the algebraic equations of state, which are very useful in obtaining closed-form analytical solutions in engineering analysis.

One of the important features of a perfect gas is that its internal energy depends only upon its temperature. In Chap. Eight we will show that this must be the case for any gas obeying Eq. (4·16). This feature is also shown nicely in Figs. B·1 and B·4, where the isotherms are seen to coincide with lines of constant u in the vapor range at pressures well below the critical pressure. This type of inspection of the graphical equations of state for different substances provides an easy way to determine if the perfect-gas approximation will be valid in the range of interest. Since the Pv product for a perfect gas also depends only upon temperature, the enthalpy $h = u + Pv$ is also a function only of

† See also Table A·4.

temperature. Figures B·2, B·7, and B·8 likewise show that the isotherms correspond with lines of constant h for gases at low pressures. The region of perfect-gas behavior can be found by this type of examination. For example, in Fig. B·6 we see that the h and T lines for CO_2 do *not* coincide, indicating that it would not be reasonable to treat CO_2 as a perfect gas in the region covered. However, at higher temperatures CO_2 can be idealized as a perfect gas, provided that the pressure is not too great.

Since u depends only on T for a perfect gas, it follows from Eqs. (4·10) and (4·11) that

$$du = c_v(T)\, dT \tag{4·18}$$

Note that c_v depends only upon T for a perfect gas. Since h depends only on T for a perfect gas, it likewise follows from Eqs. (4·14) and (4·15) that

$$dh = c_P(T)\, dT \tag{4·19}$$

We also have

$$dh = du + d(Pv) = c_v\, dT + R\, dT$$

and hence, *for a perfect gas,*

$$c_P = c_v + R \tag{4·20}$$

We emphasize that in general u and h depend on the density as well as temperature; the perfect gas is a very special gas.

Figure B·17 shows the values of c_P, c_v, and $k = c_P/c_v$ for several gases. Note the specific heats do not depend very much on pressure; the $P = 0$ limit represents perfect gas behavior. Note that the low-pressure specific heats are slowly varying functions of temperature, increasing slightly with increasing temperature. At low temperatures the main contribution to the energy of a gas is provided by molecular translation. At higher temperatures there is more and more energy associated with molecular vibration and rotation, and this causes the slight increase in specific heats. We shall discuss the evaluation of c_P and c_v from the microscopic point of view in Chaps. Eight and Twelve (see Fig. 12.10).

Since the specific heats are nearly constant over fairly wide ranges in temperature, it is often useful to treat them as constants, which allows us to integrate Eqs. (4·18) and (4·19) in closed form. Replacing c_v and c_P by their averages over the range of temperature in question, we integrate and find

$$u_1 - u_0 = c_v \cdot (T_1 - T_0) \tag{4·21}$$
$$h_1 - h_0 = c_P \cdot (T_1 - T_0) \tag{4·22}$$

These equations are very useful in calculating internal energy or enthalpy differences. It must be remembered that they hold only for a *perfect gas with constant specific heats;* it is the responsibility of the analyst to establish that this approximation is sufficiently good for the problem at hand. Appreciable errors can result if the gas involved departs significantly from this idealized behavior.

Table B·6 gives the values of R and nominal values for c_v, c_P, and k for several gases. If one needs to consider the variation of the specific heats with temperature, then the integrations must be performed numerically, using the measured functions $c_v(T)$ and $c_P(T)$. This has been done for several gases. Table B·9 gives the values for $h(T)$ and $u(T)$ for air, treated as a perfect gas with variable specific heats. An arbitrary temperature datum point was used for the lower limit of the u integration. Table B·13 gives additional data for the enthalpy *per mole* for several gases. The arbitrary datum for this tabulation is different than that for the other graphs and tables in Appendix B, and hence one should use either this data or other data, *but not both,* in any particular analysis. The other entries in these tables will be explained later in the text.

To illustrate the use of the perfect-gas equation of state in an engineering problem, suppose we consider the process of slow compression of air in a piston-cylinder system. Since the process is slow, there is adequate time for equalization of the gas and cylinder-wall temperatures through energy transfer as heat. We therefore assume that the process is one of constant temperature, and wish to calculate the amount of energy transfer as heat from the gas to the cylinder walls. The system diagram and process representation are shown in Fig. 4·10.

With some experience in thermodynamic analysis, the student will learn that this type of problem can be handled with reasonable accuracy by treating the air as a perfect gas with constant specific heats. The critical temperature for air is about 132°K, and the critical pressure is about 37 atmospheres. Thus, for room temperatures (300°K) and above the ratio $T^* = T/T_{\text{crit}}$ exceeds 2.2, and for pressures up to 10 atm the ratio $P^* = P/P_{\text{crit}}$ is less than 0.27. Figure 8·10 then indicates that the compressibility factor $Z \equiv Pv/RT$ is very close to unity in this range, and the perfect-gas model is therefore quite adequate for many purposes. Figure B·8 shows that the enthalpy and temperature lines nearly coincide over this range, which again suggests that the perfect-gas model might be adequate. Figure B·17 indicates that the specific heat of air will not vary much

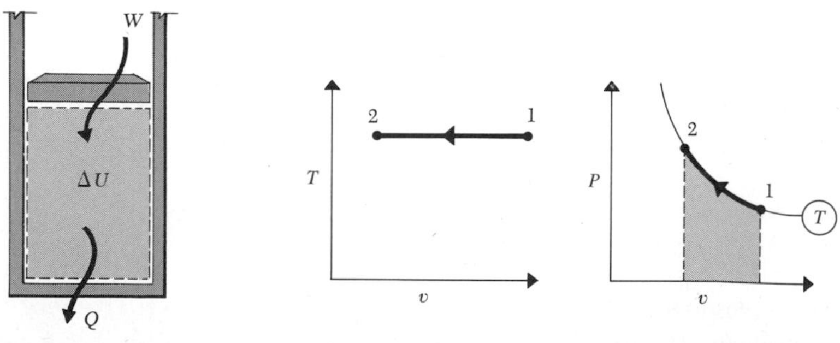

FIG. 4·10

(*a*) *The control mass* (*b*) *The process representation*

over a wide range of temperatures, so let's carry out the analysis treating air as a perfect gas with constant specific heats.

An energy balance on the control mass gives

$$\underset{\text{energy input}}{W} = \underset{\text{energy output}}{Q} + \underset{\text{increase in energy storage}}{\Delta U}$$

where W and Q are the energy transfer as work and heat as defined in Fig. 4·10*a*. Since the initial and final temperatures are identical, the initial and final internal energies of the gas (treated as a perfect gas) are identical, and hence $\Delta U = 0$ (*we again remark that this is a feature peculiar to the perfect gas*). We can use the energy balance to calculate Q if W can be evaluated. Assuming that the P-v-T relationship during the process is the same as those for equilibrium states (this will be a good approximation if the process is slow such that at any instant the gas is nearly in thermodynamic equilibrium), the work done on the gas for the isothermal process is

$$W = \int_1^2 - P\,dV = -M\int_1^2 P\,dv = -MRT\int_1^2 \frac{1}{v}\,dv$$

$$- MRT \ln\frac{v_1}{v_2} = MRT \ln\frac{V_1}{V_2}$$

So, if we have 4 lbm of air for which $R = 0.0686$ Btu/lbm-°R (Table B·6), T is 20°F (480°R), and $V_1/V_2 = 2$,

$$W = 4 \times 0.0686 \times 480 \times \ln(2) = 91 \text{ Btu}$$

Then, from the energy balance, since $\Delta u = 0$,

$$Q = 0 + W = 91 \text{ Btu}$$

This example forms a good point for the student to focus sharply on the differences between internal energy, heat, and temperature.

As a second example, let's solve the problem of Sec. 4·6 using the perfect-gas approximation. The energy balance is the same (Fig. 4·8), namely

$$Q = M(u_2 - u_1)$$

This time we treat the H_2O vapor as a perfect gas, with (Table B·6) $c_v = 0.336$ Btu/lbm-°R. Then, using Eq. (4·21),

$$u_2 - u_1 = c_v(T_2 - T_1) = 0.336 \times (1660 - 660) = 336 \text{ Btu/lbm}$$

and

$$Q = 5 \times 336 = 1680 \text{ Btu}$$

Note that this result is in error by approximately 7 percent in comparison to the exact value previously determined as 1800 Btu. Now, the final pressure is calculated from Eq. (4·16), which gives

$$\frac{P_2}{P_1} = \frac{T_2}{T_1}$$

Hence,

$$P_2 = {}^{1660}\!/_{660} \times 2 = 5.03 \text{ psia}$$

If we did not have access to the exact property tabulations for water vapor, we might estimate the specific volume using Eq. (4·16). For H_2O, $R = 85.58$ ft-lbf/lbm-°R (Table B·6). Then, at state 1,

$$v_1 = \frac{RT_1}{P_1} = 85.58 \times \frac{(200 + 460)}{2 \times 144} = 196 \text{ ft}^3/\text{lbm}$$

which is within about 1 percent of the tabulated value.

We can check the applicability of the perfect-gas approximation by computing the value of $Z \equiv Pv/RT$ at states 1 and 2. Using the state data collected in Sec. 4·6,

$$Z_1 = \frac{P_1v_1}{RT_1} = \frac{2 \times 144 \times 198}{85.58 \times (200 + 460)} = 1.01$$

$$Z_2 = \frac{P_2v_2}{RT_2} = \frac{5 \times 144 \times 198}{85.58 \times (1200 + 460)} = 1.003$$

Note that both values are very close to unity. Since both states have the same density, the state of higher temperature (2) should more closely resemble the perfect gas, and this is indeed the case. The main error in the simplified analysis is not the assumption that $Pv = RT$, but the idealization that c_v is constant over the wide range of temperatures involved.

4·9 THE SIMPLE MAGNETIC SUBSTANCE

While magnetic solids are indeed compressible, the work associated with magnetization usually is much more important than the work of compression, and it is often reasonable to idealize that such a substance is a *simple magnetic substance*. The temperature and magnetization (magnetic-dipole moment) may be taken as an independent set of intensive thermodynamic properties, and the internal energy may be expressed as

$$u = u(T, \mathbf{M})$$

A *specific heat at constant magnetization* can be defined as

$$c_{\mathbf{M}} \equiv \left(\frac{\partial u}{\partial T}\right)_{\mathbf{M}} \tag{4·23}$$

Using the manipulations of calculus, we can develop the analog of Eq. (4·9),

$$\left(\frac{\partial \mathbf{H}}{\partial T}\right)_{\mathbf{M}} = -\frac{(\partial \mathbf{M}/\partial T)_{\mathbf{H}}}{(\partial \mathbf{M}/\partial \mathbf{H})_T} \tag{4·24}$$

A graphical equation of state for one common paramagnetic salt is shown in Fig. B·12.

SELECTED READING

Jones, J. B., and G. A. Hawkins, *Engineering Thermodynamics*, chaps. 3 and 5, John Wiley & Sons, Inc., New York, 1960.

Keenan, J. H., and F. G. Keys, *Thermodynamic Properties of Steam*, introduction, John Wiley & Sons, Inc., New York, 1936.

Lee, J. F., and F. W. Sears, *Thermodynamics*, chap. 2, Addison-Wesley Publishing Co., Inc., Reading, Mass., 1963.

Van Wylen, G. J., and R. E. Sonntag, *Fundamentals of Classical Thermodynamics*, chap. 3, secs. 5.11 and 5.13, John Wiley & Sons, Inc., New York, 1965.

Zemansky, M. W., and H. C. Van Ness, *Basic Engineering Thermodynamics*, chap. 5, secs. 11.1–11.10, McGraw-Hill Book Company, New York, 1966.

QUESTIONS

4·1 What is state? What is a property? How many independent intensive thermodynamic properties does a simple substance have?

4·2 What is a phase? What is the vapor dome? What is a superheated vapor? What is a supercritical state? What is a saturated liquid?

4·3 What happens when a saturated liquid is heated at constant pressure? What happens when it is cooled at constant pressure?

4·4 What happens when a saturated liquid is heated at constant volume?

4·5 What do you think happens when a saturated vapor is compressed adiabatically? What happens when it is expanded adiabatically?

4·6 What are the definitions of h, c_v, and c_P?

4·7 Lead blocks sink in liquid lead; does lead expand or contract upon melting?

4·8 Why do the liquid and vapor in a mixture of the same substance have the same temperature and pressure? Would two gases in a mixture each exert the same pressure?

4·9 What is your estimate of the pressure of the freon-12 (liquid and vapor) in the pipes of a refrigerator that has been idle for several days (see Fig. B·7)?

4·10 If ice is thrown into a hot pressure cooker and the mixture is allowed to cool on the stove, will it end up at the triple point?

4·11 Give a molecular explanation of evaporation and one of sublimation.

4·12 What thermodynamic-property data can you find in your chemistry or engineering handbook?

4·13 Why are saturation states simpler to tabulate than superheated-vapor or subcooled-liquid states?

4·14 Why do we arbitrarily select the energy of a substance to be zero at some point? How must this point be described (pressure, temperature, or both)?

4·15 Why is it not true that $\rho = (1 - x)\rho_f + x\rho_g$, where ρ is the mass density ($\rho = 1/v$)?

4·16 How can we tell if a gas behaves like a perfect gas?

PROBLEMS

4·1 What are the enthalpy and internal energy of a mixture of mercury of 0.40 quality at 1000°F? What are the volume fractions of the liquid and vapor in the mixture (see Table B·3)?

√ 4·2 Calculate the values of ρ, u, and h for a liquid-vapor H_2O mixture of 0.2 quality at 1 atm (Table B·1*b*).

4·3 Calculate the values of v, u, and h for a liquid-vapor H_2O mixture of 0.2 quality at 600°F (Table B·1*a*).

4·4 Calculate the value of h_{fg} for nitrogen at 1 atm using the data of Fig. B·4.

4·5 Calculate the value of u_{fg} for CO_2 at 100 psia using the data of Fig. B·6.

4·6 Look up the enthalpy of saturated methyl-chloride vapor at 100°F in the *Handbook of Chemistry and Physics.*

4·7 Liquid oxygen in a rocket-propellant tank is at a pressure somewhere near 1 atm. From Fig. B·5 estimate the temperature of the lox-vapor mixture.

4·8 Compare the volume changes undergone by 1 lbm of water upon evaporation at 1 atm pressure, at 500°F, and at the critical point.

4·9 In order to illustrate the nature of the critical point, one can place CO_2 in a quartz vial, and seal the device. Assuming that $v_{crit} = 0.04$ ft³/lbm, and that the device is filled at "room temperature" (60°F), and using Fig. B·6, find: (*a*) the pressure in the vial at room temperature; (*b*) the proper percent liquid mass to assure passage through the critical point upon heating; (*c*) the percent liquid *volume* associated with part (*b*). (Calculate v_f from x, v_{mix}, and v_g.)

4·10 Using the data of Appendix B, estimate β, κ, h, c_v, and c_P for H_2O at 1000°F and 100 psia.

4·11 Using the data of Table B·7, estimate the density of copper, in lbm/in.³, at 100°F and 5 atm pressure.

4·12 Taking the internal energy of copper to be zero at 50°K and 1 atm pressure, prepare a curve showing the internal energy as a function of temperature at 1 atm, using the data of Table B·7. Give u in Btu/lbm and T in °F.

√ 4·13 Calculate the approximate value of c_v for the liquid studied in Prob. 3·6.

4·14 Calculate the approximate value of c_v for the gas studied in Prob. 3·7.

4·15 Calculate the value of c_P for the liquid material in Prob. 3·8.

√ 4·16 Calculate the approximate value of c_P for the gas studied in Prob. 3·9.

4·17 Calculate the value of c_v for the gas studied in Prob. 3·10 and plot as a function of temperature at that specific volume.

4·18 Using Fig. B·12 as a guide, sketch a three-dimensional **M-H-***T* surface for a paramagnetic salt.

4·19 Sketch u-T and v-T diagrams for H_2O, showing lines of constant pressure. Include the liquid, vapor, and mixed-phase regions.

4·20 Verify that Eq. (4·9) holds for a perfect gas by differentiation and substitution

4·21 Estimate the temperature to which water at the bottom of a 500-ft-deep lake would have to be heated before it would begin to boil.

4·22 Plot the ratio Pv/T versus T for H_2O along a line of 1 atm pressure and show the conditions under which the perfect-gas approximation is reasonable. Taking $\hat{M}$ to be 18.016 lbm/lbmole, evaluate the universal-gas constant and compare with the accepted value.

4·23 A Curie substance is any magnetic substance obeying the simple equation of state $\mathbf{M} = C\mathbf{H}/T$, where C is the Curie constant. Plot $\mathbf{M}$ versus $\mathbf{H}$ for iron-ammonium alum (Fig. B·12) along a line of $T = 1°K$, find the region in which Curie's law is obeyed, and determine the value of the Curie constant.

4·24 What are the values of the specific heat at constant volume and the specific heat at constant pressure of H_2O of 0.30 quality at 100 psia?

4·25 Determine the value of $c_\mathbf{M}$ for iron-ammonium alum (Fig. B·12) at 1°K in a weak external field. Express the result in Btu/lbm-°R and compare with the corresponding specific heat of saturated H_2O vapor at 1 atm pressure.

4·26 What are the values of $(\partial v/\partial T)_P$, $(\partial P/\partial v)_T$, $(\partial v/\partial P)_T$, and $(\partial T/\partial P)_v$ for a perfect gas?

4·27 For a Curie substance $\mathbf{M}$, $\mathbf{H}$, and T are related by $\mathbf{M} = C\mathbf{H}/T$, where C is a constant. Evaluate $(\partial \mathbf{H}/\partial T)_\mathbf{M}$, $(\partial \mathbf{M}/\partial \mathbf{H})_T$, $(\partial T/\partial \mathbf{H})_\mathbf{M}$, and $(\partial T/\partial \mathbf{M})_\mathbf{H}$. Express the meaning of each term in words.

4·28 Consider a dielectric substance for which $\mathbf{P} = (\kappa - 1)\epsilon_0\mathbf{E}$, where κ is the dielectric "constant" and ϵ_0 is a physical constant (Table A·2). κ normally depends upon temperature. Assuming $\kappa = \kappa_0[1 + a(T - T_0)]$, evaluate $(\partial \mathbf{P}/\partial T)_\mathbf{E}$, $(\partial \mathbf{P}/\partial \mathbf{E})_T$, $(\partial \mathbf{E}/\partial T)_\mathbf{P}$, and $(\partial \mathbf{E}/\partial \mathbf{P})_T$. Express the meaning of each in words.

4·29 Compute the density of gaseous H_2O at each of the following states using the perfect-gas model, and compare with the actual values given in Table B·2.
1 psia, 200°F   1 atm, 800°F   3000 psia, 700°F

4·30 Compute the density of gaseous CO_2 at each of the following states using the perfect-gas model, and compare with the actual values given in Fig. B·6.
10 psia, 20°F   150 psia, 60°F   1500 psia, 140°F

CHAPTER FIVE

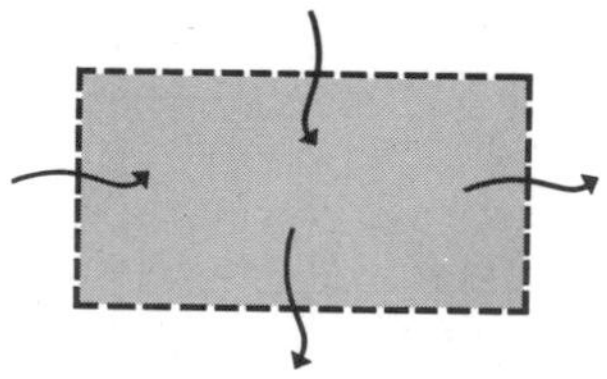

ENERGY ANALYSIS OF THERMODYNAMIC SYSTEMS

5·1 GENERAL METHODOLOGY

The conservation-of-energy statement and equations of state permit solution of a number of interesting and important technical problems. Additional concepts and tools are needed for complete thermodynamic analysis, but we shall begin to apply the ideas of the first law and state at this point in order to indicate the manner in which thermodynamics is used in engineering.

First-law analysis is essentially an accounting procedure, in which we take account of energy transfers to and from a system and of changes of energy inside the system. There are two main types of accounting procedures. In *control-mass analysis* we write the conservation-of-energy equation for a specified piece of matter, while in *control-volume analysis* we work instead with specified regions in space.† The latter being somewhat more difficult, we shall begin by illustrating energy analysis for a control mass.

An accounting procedure must be carried out over a set accounting period, and an essential step in control-mass analysis is specification of the *time base.* This might be a given period of time, or the time required for something to happen, or we might specify that our accounting be done on an *instantaneous-rate* basis. Some specification is necessary.

The accounting will be carried out with symbols used to represent energy transfers to and from the control mass, and some sort of sign convention must always be set up for the energy flows. The important thing in first-law analysis is to recognize all the energy transfers and changes that take place and to relate these in a proper mathematical manner. The sign convention chosen for W and

† The terms "system," or "closed system," and "open system" are used by many texts instead of "control mass" and "control volume."

Q is not particularly important, provided that both the person doing the analysis and the one reading it understand what it is. We shall adopt the policy of selecting whatever convention seems appropriate for the analysis at hand and indicate the directions of *positive* energy flows by arrows on the system sketch. This scheme has the additional advantage that the energy flows to be considered are all identified, and where and how the energy crosses the boundary is quite clear. There should always be a one-to-one correspondence between the energy flows shown on the system sketch and those that appear in the energy balance.

In working with energy changes we shall follow the conventions of calculus, in which dx and Δx always represent *increases* in the value of x. ΔE will always represent an *increase* in the energy stored within the control mass.

Having made the energy balance, the next step is to bring in enough other information to permit reduction of the problem to one equation in one unknown. This information might be in the form of equations of state, information about the nature of the process, or other information obtained by applying the principle of conservation of mass, Newton's law, or other fundamental principles to the system.

In any analysis various approximations, or *idealizations*, must be made to reduce the problem to a manageable size. These idealizations must be clearly understood by both the analyst and the reader of his analysis, and hence we prefer to list these specifically at the start of the analysis. Sometimes idealizations are implicitly indicated on the system sketch; for example, the absence of an energy transfer term Q would imply that we idealize that energy transfer as heat is negligible during the time period over which the energy balance will be made. Such idealizations should be specifically listed to assure their communication to the reader.

We cannot emphasize enough the importance of a good system sketch, complete with all the relevant energy-transfer terms. A good sketch can be of great value to the analyst in getting his thinking straight about the process, in helping him be consistent throughout the analysis, and also in helping him see what steps must be taken to complete the analysis.

An equally important working diagram is the *process representation*. This is one or more diagrams showing what happens to matter within the system on suitable thermodynamic planes. In most analyses one must find some way to fix the states of the matter at the start or finish of the process, and the process representation is of great value in helping the analyst feel his way through a complex problem. Hence, one should always try to draw the process representation *before* carrying out the analysis in order to orient his thinking properly and efficiently.

In summary, the general methodology for energy-balance analysis is as follows:

1 Define the system carefully and completely, indicating its boundaries on a sketch (control mass or control volume?).

2 List the relevant idealizations.
3 Indicate the flows of energy to be considered in the energy balance, and set up their sign convention on the system sketch.
4 Indicate the time basis for the energy balance.
5 Sketch the process representation.
6 Write the energy balance in terms of the symbols shown on the system sketch; there should be a one-to-one correspondence between the terms in the equation and those on the sketch.
7 Bring in equations of state or other information as necessary to allow solution of the problem.

We shall now illustrate this methodology for the control mass by example. The analyses which follow were selected to illustrate different aspects of first-law analysis from the control-mass viewpoint. Different kinds of idealizations are introduced in the various developments, the use of graphical and tabular equations of state are demonstrated, and some important definitions and general consequences are given. Every one of the examples should be studied carefully, even though they may appear to be extremely simple and straightforward (as indeed they are, if a systematic methodology is followed).

5·2 EXAMPLES OF CONTROL-MASS ENERGY ANALYSIS

Evaporation at constant pressure. Three lbm of H_2O, in a piston-cylinder system, is initially in the saturated-liquid state at 100 psia. Energy is added slowly to the water as heat, and the piston moves in such a way that the pressure remains constant. How much work is done by the water, and how much energy must be transferred as heat in order to bring the water to the saturated-vapor state? See Fig. 5·1.

We could select the water or the water plus the piston as the control mass. Since we are interested in energy transfers to the water, and the piston is merely a means for maintaining the constant pressure, we take only the water as our

FIG. 5·1

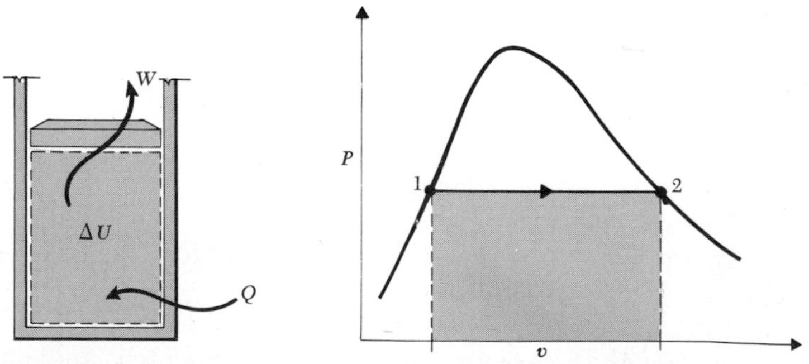

(a) The control mass (b) The process representation

control mass. The change of state is depicted by the process representation, which is nicely shown on a P-v plane.

In order to solve the problem we idealize that the changes in the gravitational potential energy of the water are negligible in comparison with the changes in the internal energy. We idealize further that the presence of the gravitational field does not significantly alter the behavior of the water molecules, so that the relationships between the thermodynamic properties are the same as if the water were truly a simple compressible substance. In short, we idealize that the water behaves like a simple compressible substance and is in equilibrium states at the start and end of the process.

Employing these idealizations, the energy balance, made over the period for the process to occur, is

$$\underset{\substack{\text{energy}\\\text{input}}}{Q} = \underset{\substack{\text{energy}\\\text{output}}}{W} + \underset{\substack{\text{increase in}\\\text{energy storage}}}{\Delta U}$$

where

$$\Delta U = M(u_2 - u_1)$$

Fixing the initial and final states from Table B·1, at the initial state (saturated liquid at 100 psia)

$$P_1 = 100 \text{ psia} \qquad T_1 = 327.81°\text{F}$$
$$u_1 = 298.08 \text{ Btu/lbm} \qquad v_1 = 0.01774 \text{ ft}^3\text{/lbm}$$

and at the final state (saturated vapor at 100 psia)

$$P_2 = 100 \text{ psia} \qquad T_2 = 327.81°\text{F}$$
$$u_2 = 1105.2 \text{ Btu/lbm} \qquad v_2 = 4.432 \text{ ft}^3\text{/lbm}$$

Note that the volume occupied by the water increases tremendously.

We could now compute the net energy added to the water, but as yet we cannot tell how much is added as heat and how much is taken away as work. The fact that the pressure remains constant during the process allows us to compute the work very simply. The work done by the water is

$$W = \int_1^2 dW = \int_1^2 P\,dV = M \int_1^2 P\,dv$$

Since the pressure is constant,

$$W = MP(v_2 - v_1)$$

The work done is therefore

$$W = 3 \text{ lbm} \times 100 \text{ lbf/in.}^2 \times 144 \text{ in.}^2\text{/ft}^2 \times (4.432 - 0.017) \text{ ft}^3\text{/lbm}$$
$$= 191{,}000 \text{ ft-lbf} \times \frac{1 \text{ Btu}}{778 \text{ ft-lbf}} = 245 \text{ Btu}$$

We can finally calculate the energy added as heat:

$$Q = 245\ \text{Btu} + 3\ \text{lbm} \times (1105.2 - 298.08)\ \text{Btu/lbm} = 2665\ \text{Btu}$$

The energy transfer as heat could have been calculated directly if we had noticed that it is expressible as

$$Q = M[P(v_2 - v_1) + (u_2 - u_1)] = M(h_2 - h_1)$$

Note that the energy transfer as heat (per unit of mass) to a simple compressible substance during a constant pressure process is equal to the increase in its enthalpy.

Values for h_1 and h_2 could have been obtained from Table B·1.

The energy transfer as heat required to evaporate a unit of mass of a simple compressible substance at *constant pressure* is therefore simply $h_g - h_f = h_{fg}$ and is sometimes called the *enthalpy of evaporation*† of that substance. Note that it depends on pressure and vanishes at the critical point.

A dry-ice cooler. One lbm of dry ice (CO_2) at 1 atm pressure is placed on top of a piece of meat in a cooler. The dry ice sublimes at constant pressure as a result of energy transfer as heat from the warmer meat. What is the temperature of the CO_2, and how much energy is transferred as heat from the meat? See Fig. 5·2.

For the control mass we pick the CO_2, including the solid and vapor. The boundary of this control mass moves as the solid sublimes, and so there will be energy transfer as work, in this case from the expanding CO_2 to the environment. We assume no energy transfer as heat from the CO_2 to the surrounding air and neglect mixing of the CO_2 with the air. The energy balance is then

$$\underset{\substack{\text{energy}\\ \text{input}}}{Q} = \underset{\substack{\text{energy}\\ \text{output}}}{W} + \underset{\substack{\text{increase in}\\ \text{energy storage}}}{\Delta U}$$

† The term "latent heat of vaporization" is also used.

FIG. 5·2

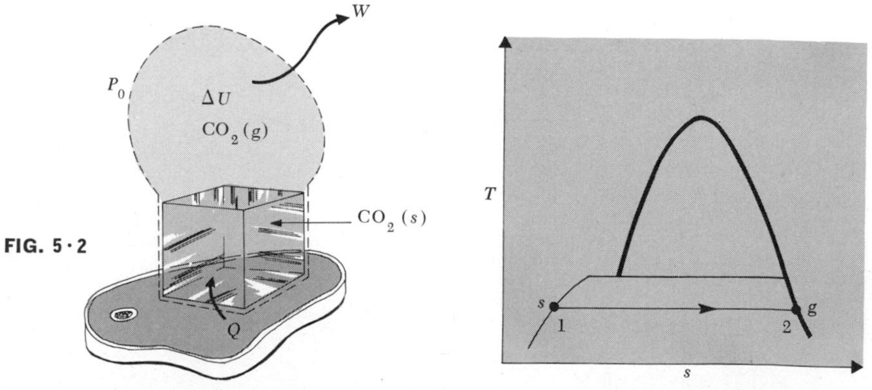

(*a*) *The control mass* (*b*) *The process representation*

where

$$\Delta U = M(u_2 - u_1)$$

As in the previous example, the work done by the expanding CO_2 is related to the pressure (constant by assumption) and the volume change,

$$W = MP(v_2 - v_1)$$

Solving for the energy transfer as heat to the CO_2 and expressing it in terms of the change in the enthalpy property,

$$\begin{aligned} Q &= M[(u_2 - u_1) + P(v_2 - v_1)] \\ &= M[(u_2 + P_2v_2) - (u_1 + P_1v_1)] = M(h_2 - h_1) \end{aligned}$$

The equation of state for CO_2 is given on a *temperature-entropy plane* in Fig. B·6. The entropy is an important thermodynamic property which we shall discuss in the next chapters. For the time being we can use the equation of state as given in Fig. B·6 without worrying about this property. The initial state is saturated solid at 1 atm, and from Fig. B·6 we read the enthalpy of this state as 31 Btu/lbm. The final state, 2, is saturated vapor at 1 atm, for which we read the enthalpy as 276 Btu/lbm. The positions of these states on the temperature-entropy diagram are indicated on the process representation in Fig. 5·2*b*.

From Fig. B·6 we also read the saturation temperature corresponding to 15 psia as −108°F. The energy transferred as heat from the meat to the CO_2 is then

$$Q = 1 \text{ lbm} \times (276 - 31) \text{ Btu/lbm} = 245 \text{ Btu}$$

The difference h_{sg} is called the *enthalpy of sublimation*† and represents the energy which must be added as heat to completely sublime a unit of mass of a substance at constant pressure.

Thermal magnetization. One cm³ of the paramagnetic substance iron-ammonium alum is magnetized in a constant external field H of 5000 gauss by cooling. The initial temperature is 1°K and the final temperature is 0.5°K; how much energy must be transferred as heat from the alum? See Fig. 5·3.

† Sublimation is the transformation of a solid directly into a gas at constant pressure. The term "latent heat of sublimation" is sometimes used for $h_{sg} = h_g - h_s$.

FIG. 5·3

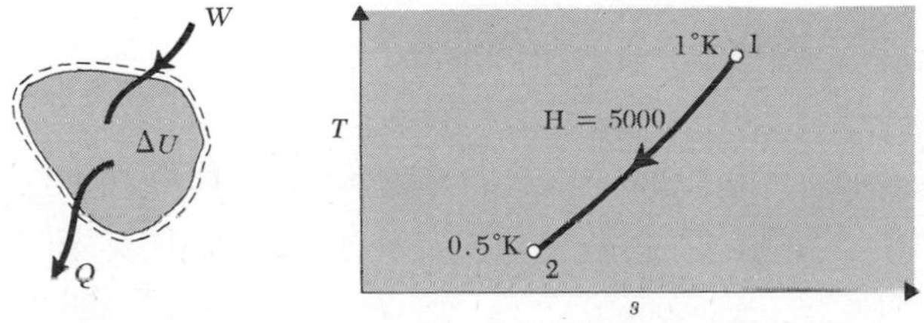

(*a*) *The control mass* (*b*) *The process representation*

This problem is complicated by the fact that the thermodynamic-property data (Fig. B·12) are given in absolute magnetostatic units, while the expressions for work of magnetization given in Chap. Two are in the rationalized mksc system. The required unit conversions will be good practice.

The energy terms considered to be important are shown on the control-mass diagram; the energy balance, made over the time for the process to occur, is

$$\underset{\text{energy input}}{W} = \underset{\text{energy output}}{Q} + \underset{\text{increase in energy storage}}{\Delta U}$$

where

$$\Delta U = M(u_2 - u_1)$$

From the graphical equation of state we obtain the initial and final internal energies (assuming that the initial and final states are states of thermodynamic equilibrium),

$$u_1 = 1.56 \times 10^4 \text{ ergs/g} \qquad u_2 = 1.39 \times 10^4 \text{ ergs/g}$$

Idealizing the alum as a simple magnetic substance, the work done on the alum by the external field is [see Eq. (2·17)]

$$W = \int_1^2 đW = \int_1^2 V\mu_0 \mathsf{H}\, d\mathsf{M}$$

The work calculation is made particularly simple by the fact that the applied field is held constant. For constant H the work becomes

$$W = \mu_0 V \mathsf{H}(\mathsf{M}_2 - \mathsf{M}_1)$$

From Fig. B·12 we read the initial and final magnetizations as

$$\mathsf{M}_1 = 62 \text{ gauss} \qquad \mathsf{M}_2 = 84 \text{ gauss}$$

We choose to convert everything to the rationalized mksc unit system. From Appendix A we find the dimensional equivalents

$$1 \text{ gauss of } \mathsf{H} = 79.6 \text{ coul/sec-m of } \mathsf{H}$$
$$1 \text{ gauss of } \mathsf{M} = 1000 \text{ coul/sec-m of } \mathsf{M}$$

Then, in the rationalized mksc system we have

$$\mathsf{H} = 40 \times 10^4 \text{ coul/sec-m}$$
$$\mathsf{M}_1 = 62 \times 10^3 \text{ coul/sec-m}$$
$$\mathsf{M}_2 = 84 \times 10^3 \text{ coul/sec-m}$$
$$\mu_0 = 1.256 \times 10^{-6} \text{ kg-m/coul}^2$$

The energy transfer as work to the alum is therefore

$$W = (0.01 \text{ m})^3 \times 1.256 \times 10^{-6} \text{ kg-m/coul}^2 \times 40 \times 10^4 \text{ coul/sec-m} \times (84 - 62) \times 10^3 \text{ coul/sec-m}$$
$$= 0.0109 \text{ kg-m}^2/\text{sec}^2 = 0.0109 \text{ joule}$$

The density of the alum is (Fig. B · 12) 1.71 g/cm³. The internal-energy increase is therefore

$$M(u_2 - u_1) = 1.71 \text{ g} \times (1.39 \times 10^4 - 1.56 \times 10^4)(\text{g-cm}^2/\text{sec})/\text{g}$$
$$= -0.3 \times 10^4 \text{ erg} = -0.0003 \text{ joule}$$

So the energy which must be transferred from the alum as heat is

$$Q = 0.0109 - (-0.0003) \text{ joule} = 0.0112 \text{ joule}$$

This energy is transferred to some environment at a temperature *lower* than 0.5°K.

Thermal mixing at constant pressure. Two lbm of saturated-liquid mercury at 1 psia is mixed with 4 lbm of 1400°F mercury vapor at 1 psia. The mixing vessel is such that the pressure remains constant during this process, and no energy transfer as heat occurs between the vessel and the mercury. Determine the equilibrium state reached by this mixture.

In the previous examples the control mass was in a state of equilibrium at the start of the process, so the calculation of the initial energy was quite straightforward. In this example we shall see how to make the corresponding evaluation for a system that is not in equilibrium.

Since the amount of liquid might change during the process, we cannot take only the liquid or only the vapor as the control mass. Instead we take the entire 6 lbm of mercury. By assumption, no energy transfer as heat occurs, but we do expect the volume to change, resulting in an energy transfer as work. The only energy stored within the control mass is the internal energy of the mercury; the energy balance, made over the time for the process to take place, is therefore (Fig. 5.4)

$$\underset{\text{energy input}}{W} = \underset{\text{increase in energy storage}}{\Delta U}$$

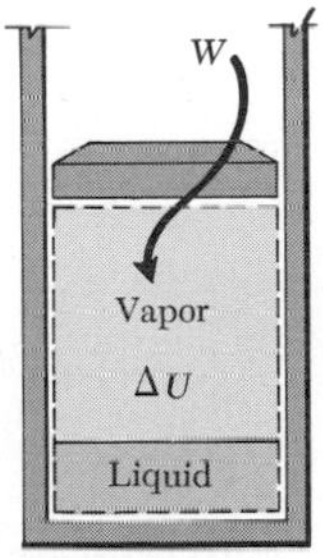

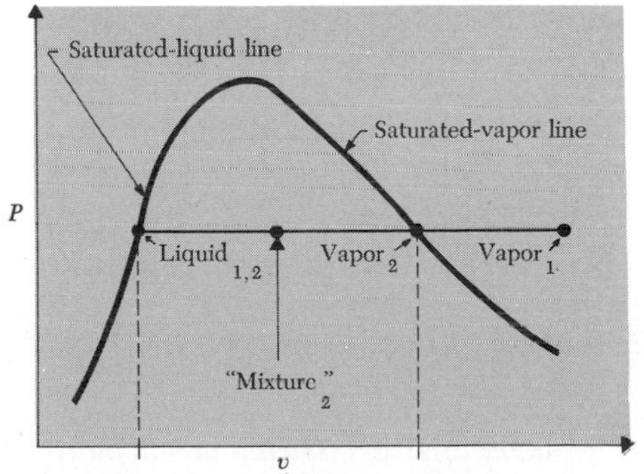

FIG. 5 · 4

(a) The control mass

(b) The process representation

where

$$\Delta U = U_2 - U_1$$

The work calculation is again made easy by the fact that the pressure is constant. When the piston moves in an amount dx, the energy transfer as work from the environment to the control mass is

$$đW = PA\,dx = -P\,dV$$

Integrating,

$$W = \int_1^2 -P\,dV = P(V_1 - V_2)$$

Combining with the energy balance,

$$U_2 + PV_2 = U_1 + PV_1 \tag{5·1}$$

To evaluate the initial terms we assume that the liquid is in an equilibrium state and the vapor is in an equilibrium state, even though they are not in equilibrium with one another. The graphical and tabular equations of state, Fig. B·10 and Table B·3, may then be employed for each phase. Since the available equation-of-state information is in terms of the enthalpy property, we express the right-hand side of Eq. (5·1) as

$$\begin{aligned} U_1 + PV_1 &= M_{l_1}u_{l_1} + M_{v_1}u_{v_1} + P(M_{l_1}v_{l_1} + M_{v_1}v_{v_1}) \\ &= M_{l_1}h_{l_1} + M_{v_1}h_{v_1} \end{aligned}$$

Now, from the tables, the initial liquid enthalpy is (saturated liquid at 1 psia, Table B·3)

$$\begin{aligned} h_{l_1} &= 13.96 \text{ Btu/lbm} \\ T_1 &= 457.7°\text{F} \end{aligned}$$

The initial vapor enthalpy is found from Fig. B·10 as

$$h_{v_1} = 164 \text{ Btu/lbm}$$

Substituting the numbers,

$$U_1 + PV_1 = 2 \times 13.96 + 4 \times 164 = 684 \text{ Btu}$$

The final state is a state of equilibrium, for which

$$U_2 + PV_2 = M(u + Pv)_2 = Mh_2$$

The enthalpy in the final state is therefore

$$h_2 = \frac{684 \text{ Btu}}{6 \text{ lbm}} = 114 \text{ Btu/lbm}$$

The final pressure and enthalpy may be used to fix the final state. Upon inspection of Fig. B·10 we see that the final state is a mixture of saturated liquid and vapor at 1 psia and that the "moisture" $(1 - x)$ is about 21 percent (0.79 quality). Alternatively, we could use the information in Table B·3:

$$114 = (1 - x_2) \times 13.96 + x_2 \times 140.7$$
$$x_2 = 0.79$$

A pneumatic lift. Air is used in a pneumatic lift (Fig. 5·5). The air is initially contained in a 10 ft³ steel tank at 80°F and 100 psia. When lifting is required, the valve is opened and air is bled out into the cylinder. The cylinder is initially filled with air at 1 atm, 60°F, has a cross-sectional area of 1 ft², and a lifting height of 3 ft. Its initial volume is 0.5 ft³. When the pressure in the cylinder reaches 50 psia the load begins to move upward, maintaining this cylinder pressure until the piston has traveled 3 ft. The load then stops, but air continues to flow into the cylinder. Eventually the pressures in the tank and cylinder are equal, and through energy transfer as heat all the air attains a temperature of 60°F. Calculate the final air pressure and the amount of energy transfer as heat from the tank walls to the air.

In making the energy balance we consider the time period from the start to the end, where the air is in equilibrium throughout the system, and the load is at its highest point. We take the air as the control mass, and consider the energy flows indicated in Fig. 5·5. The energy balance is

$$\underset{\substack{\text{energy}\\\text{input}}}{Q} = \underset{\substack{\text{energy}\\\text{output}}}{W} + \underset{\substack{\text{increase in}\\\text{energy storage}}}{\Delta U}$$

In order to calculate Q we must first evaluate ΔU and W. The work computation is facilitated by consideration of the process representation. Work will be done by the control mass on the piston only when the piston is moving, and during this period the cylinder pressure is assumed to remain at 50 psia. During this period the force exerted by the gas on the piston is $144 \times 50 = 7200$ lbf, and the piston moves a distance of 3 ft. Hence

$$W = 7200 \times 3 = 21{,}600 \text{ ft-lbf}/(778 \text{ ft-lbf/Btu})$$
$$= 27.8 \text{ Btu}$$

FIG. 5·5

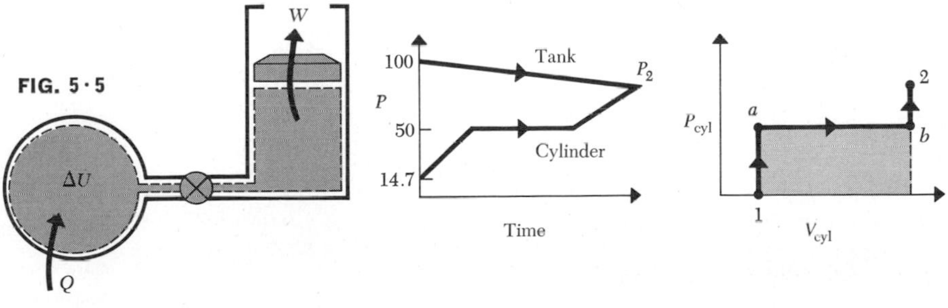

(a) *The control mass* (b) *The process representation*

Idealizing that the air behaves as a perfect gas, we have enough information to establish the initial and final air states completely. From Table B·6, we obtain the following constants for air:

$$c_v = 0.171 \text{ Btu/lbm-°R} \qquad R = 53.3 \text{ ft-lbf/lbm-°R}$$

Initial state

Tank air 80°F(=540°R), 100 psia

Using Eq. (4·16),

$$\rho = \frac{1}{v} = \frac{P}{RT} = \frac{100 \times 144}{53.3 \times 540} = 0.498 \text{ lbm/ft}^3$$

Hence

$$M_t = 10 \times 0.498 = 4.98 \text{ lbm}$$

Using Eq. (4·21), with $T_0 = 0°\text{F} = 460°\text{R}$,

$$u_t = 0.171 \times (540 - 460) = 13.7 \text{ Btu/lbm}$$

Hence

$$U_t = Mu = 4.98 \times 13.7 = 68.1 \text{ Btu}$$

Cylinder air 60°F (= 520°R), 14.7 psia

$$\rho = \frac{P}{RT} = \frac{14.7 \times 144}{53.3 \times 520} = 0.0764 \text{ lbm/ft}^3$$

$$M_c = 0.5 \times 0.0764 = 0.038 \text{ lbm}$$
$$u_c = 0.171 \times (520 - 460) = 10.3 \text{ Btu/lbm}$$
$$U_c = 0.038 \times 10.3 = 0.39 \text{ Btu}$$

So, the total mass and energy in the initial configuration are

$$M = 4.98 + 0.038 = 5.02 \text{ lbm}$$
$$U_1 = 68.1 + 0.39 = 68.5 \text{ Btu}$$

Final state All air at 60°F (520°R)

The total final volume is

$$V = 10.00 + 0.5 + 3.0 = 13.5 \text{ ft}^3$$

Hence the final density is

$$\rho_2 = \frac{M}{V} = \frac{5.02}{13.5} = 0.372 \text{ lbm/ft}^3$$

The final pressure is, from Eq. (4·16),

$$P_2 = \rho_2 R T_2 = 0.372 \times 53.3 \times 520 = 10{,}400 \text{ lbf/ft}^2$$
$$= 71.7 \text{ psia}$$

The final specific internal energy is [Eq. (4·21)]

$$u_2 = 0.171 \times (520 - 460) = 10.3 \text{ Btu/lbm}$$

So

$$U_2 = Mu_2 = 5.02 \times 10.3 = 52.0 \text{ Btu}$$

We now calculate the internal energy increase as

$$\Delta U = U_2 - U_1 = 52.0 - 68.5 = -16.5 \text{ Btu}$$

(The minus sign indicates that the internal energy actually decreases.) Substituting for W and ΔU in the energy balance,

$$Q = 27.8 + (-16.5) = 11.3 \text{ Btu}$$

The student should particularly note the manner in which we used the process representations to orient our thinking and to guide the analysis.

A steady-flow system. The previous examples of control-mass analysis have dealt exclusively with nonflow systems, for which the control-mass method is ideal. Flow systems are of great interest in engineering, and the control volume view is better suited to analysis of such systems. In a moment we are going to work out a proper energy equation for a control volume, and subsequently we shall consider all flow problems from the control-volume point of view. However, flow problems may be worked by the control-mass method, though this is somewhat awkward. In the interests of motivating the control-volume transformation and clarifying the physics involved, we shall now do a particular flow-system analysis by the *control-mass* method.

Consider a rather general "black-box" device, where fluid flows in one end and out the other. Energy is transferred as heat to the box, and power is transmitted into the device through a rotating shaft. We define the control mass to be the box and all its contents, and the fluid in the inlet and discharge pipes from section 1 through section 2 at time t. This control mass is indicated in Fig. 5·6.

The analysis will be made over an infinitesimal time interval dt. During this period the control mass will move, and its position at time $t + dt$ is indicated in Fig. 5·6. We shall assume that the inlet and discharge flows are *one-dimensional*, meaning that the velocities and thermodynamic properties are constant across the inlet and exit pipes. We also idealize this as a *steady-flow steady-state* situation, meaning that the velocities and thermodynamic properties *at each point in space* are unchanging in time.†

Let's illustrate the approach to be used in the energy analysis in a simpler analysis of the mass conservation. Applying the conservation-of-mass principle

† The state of a piece of fluid passing through the device does change; and the states of the fluid at various positions within the device may be different.

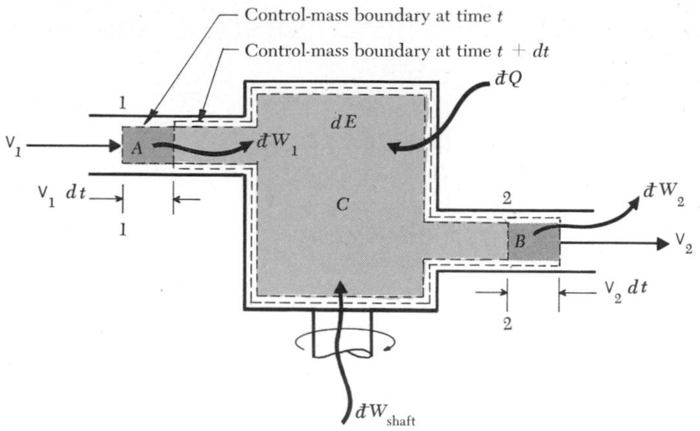

FIG. 5·6 *The control mass*

to the control mass, we obtain

$$dM = 0$$

where M is the mass of the control mass. This mass can be represented in terms of the spatial distribution of matter, that is, in terms of the mass in regions A, B, and C of Fig. 5·6. Using the steady-flow steady-state condition,

$$\begin{aligned} M(t) &= M_A + M_C \\ M(t + dt) &= M_B + M_C \\ dM &= M(t + dt) - M(t) = M_B - M_A \end{aligned}$$

The volumes of A and B are $(A\mathsf{V})_1\,dt$ and $(A\mathsf{V})_2\,dt$, where V_1 and V_2 are the velocities at sections 1 and 2. Hence the *mass balance* becomes

$$dM = (\rho A\mathsf{V})_2\,dt - (\rho A\mathsf{V})_1\,dt = 0$$

The term $(\rho A\mathsf{V})_1\,dt$ represents the amount of mass $đM$ which crosses section 1 in the time interval dt. The *rate of mass flow* $\dot{M}$ is defined as†

$$\blacktriangleright \qquad \dot{M} \equiv \frac{đM}{dt} = (\rho A\mathsf{V}) \qquad (5\cdot2)$$

Note that V is the velocity *normal* to the flow area A. The mass balance can now be interpreted as appling to the *space* C (the *control volume*),

$$\underset{\text{mass-inflow rate}}{\dot{M}_1} = \underset{\text{mass-outflow rate}}{\dot{M}_2}$$

This merely states that the rate of mass inflow *to the control volume* must equal the rate of mass outflow *from the control volume* under steady-flow steady-state conditions, which is obviously the proper control-volume mass balance. How-

† Note that $\dot{M} \neq dM/dt$. See the Nomenclature at the back of the book.

ever, the proper energy equation is not as obvious, and we must derive it carefully.

An energy balance on the control mass, made over the time period dt, yields

$$\underbrace{đW_1 + đW_{\text{shaft}} + đQ}_{\text{energy input}} = \underbrace{đW_2}_{\substack{\text{energy}\\\text{output}}} + \underbrace{dE}_{\substack{\text{increase in}\\\text{energy storage}}}$$

The work terms $đW_1$ and $đW_2$ represent energy transfers to and from the control mass due to normal motion of its boundaries in the pipes near sections 1 and 2. To evaluate these terms we assume that the pressure exerted by the fluid on the duct walls is the same as that exerted by the fluid immediately outside the control mass on the fluid just inside the boundary. In other words, the pressure *within the fluid* is presumed to be the same in all directions. Denoting the fluid pressures at sections 1 and 2 by P_1 and P_2 and assuming that these pressures act uniformly over the flow cross sections at those points, we have

$$đW_1 = (PA)_1\mathsf{V}_1\, dt$$
$$đW_2 = (PA)_2\mathsf{V}_2\, dt$$

The change in the energy of the control mass can be represented in terms of the energies of regions A, B, and C of Fig. 5·6. Using the steady-flow steady-state idealization, we obtain

$$E(t) = E_A + E_C$$
$$E(t + dt) = E_C + E_B$$
$$dE = E(t + dt) - E(t) = E_B - E_A$$

We denote the energy per unit of mass of fluid at 1 and 2 by e_1 and e_2. This represents the internal energy, plus kinetic energy due to motion, plus potential energy due to conservative force fields,

$$e = u + PE + KE$$

Then, the increase in energy within the control mass is

$$dE = e_2\rho_2(A_2\mathsf{V}_2\, dt) - e_1\rho_1(A_1\mathsf{V}_1\, dt)$$

and the energy balance becomes

$$(PA\mathsf{V})_1\, dt - (PA\mathsf{V})_2\, dt + đW_{\text{shaft}} + đQ = (eA\rho\mathsf{V})_2\, dt - (eA\rho\mathsf{V})_1\, dt$$

The *rates* of energy transfer as work and heat are defined as

$$\blacktriangleright \qquad \dot{W}_{\text{shaft}} \equiv \frac{đW_{\text{shaft}}}{dt} \qquad \dot{Q} \equiv \frac{đQ}{dt} \tag{5·3}$$

Dividing by dt and introducing the mass-flow rate $\dot{M} = A\rho\mathsf{V}$, the energy balance may be written as

$$\underbrace{[\dot{M}(e + Pv)]_1 + \dot{W}_{\text{shaft}} + \dot{Q}}_{\text{energy-input rate}} = \underbrace{[\dot{M}(e + Pv)]_2}_{\text{energy output rate}}$$

Note that the terms in this equation can be interpreted as applying to the *space C* (the *control volume*).

After a while the mass of fluid that we took for our control mass will have passed out of the device, and we are not really concerned about it subsequently. Of greater interest are the properties of and energy transfers to the device and whatever fluid happens to be in it at any given moment. The energy equation above relates the properties at sections 1 and 2 to the rates of energy transfer as heat and work to the device, and consequently is just what we need. Suppose we knew the temperature and pressure at states 1 and 2 and could thereby fix the thermodynamic states of the fluid. If, in addition, we could in some way determine the mass-flow rate and knew the rate of energy transfer as heat, the energy balance could be used to calculate the shaft-power output. This is a typical use for a first-law equation.

As we indicated, the control-mass point of view could be used to handle all flow problems. The analysis would always involve motion of the boundaries in the inlet and exit ducts and a representation of the energy of the control mass in terms of the distribution of energy through space. We might as well do a reasonably general analysis of this type once and then use it whenever it is applicable in flow-system analysis. This brings us now to the control-volume transformation.

5·3 THE CONTROL-VOLUME TRANSFORMATION

A *control volume* is any defined region in space. This region may be moving through space, and its shape and volume may be changing. However, most often we deal with control volumes that are of fixed shape and size and are fixed in the reference frame, so we shall consider this special case first.

Consider a control volume whose boundaries are fixed in space and stationary. Matter flows across the boundaries of this control volume, as indicated in Fig. 5·7. Following our previous analysis, we assume that the flow streams are one-dimensional at points where mass crosses the control-volume boundary.

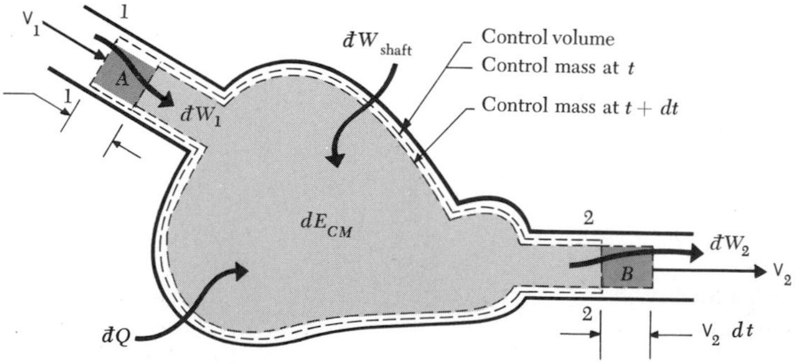

FIG. 5·7 *A control volume*

We again assume that the pressure exerted by the fluid on the duct walls is the same as the force per unit of area on an imaginary cut across the duct. This will be a good idealization, except in some cases where viscous shear is important, but there the one-dimensional idealization would be invalid anyway. We allow energy transfer as heat across the boundary of the control volume, but we must be careful in handling such energy transfer at points where mass enters the control volume, and to avoid confusion we shall assume that no energy is transferred as heat at the inlet and exit stations. We also presume that we can choose the control-volume boundaries such that we can neglect work arising from tangential shearing motions of the boundary, except for energy transfer as work through rotating shafts. Thus a number of important restrictions have been made, all of which can be removed by proper extension of the analysis. It is important to realize that our resulting control-volume energy equation will not be fully general, though it will be sufficiently general for most of our purposes.

To develop the proper control-volume energy-conservation expression, we shall consider two infinitesimally differing instants in time, t and $t + dt$, and apply the conservation-of-energy principle to the particular control mass whose boundaries at time t happen to correspond exactly to those of the control volume. Work will be done on the control mass by the rotating shaft and also by the normal motion of the control-mass boundary at the two points where matter flows into and out of the control volume. An energy balance on the control mass, made over the time period dt, gives

$$\underbrace{(PA)_1\mathsf{V}_1\,dt + đW_{\text{shaft}} + đQ}_{\text{energy input}} = \underbrace{(PA)_2\mathsf{V}_2\,dt}_{\text{energy output}} + \underbrace{dE_{CM}}_{\text{increase in energy storage}}$$

We want to express all terms in this energy balance in terms of properties of the control *volume* rather than the control mass. The energy contained within the control mass at time t is identical with the energy within the control volume at that instant. At time $t + dt$ the energy of the control mass is equal to the energy of the matter within the control-volume boundaries at $t + dt$, plus the energy of the matter within the shaded portion B, minus the energy of the matter within the shaded portion A. We therefore put

$$\begin{aligned} dE_{CM} &= E_{CM}(t + dt) - E_{CM}(t) \\ &= E_{CV}(t + dt) + (A_2\mathsf{V}_2\,dt)\rho_2 e_2 - (A_1\mathsf{V}_1\,dt)\rho_1 e_1 - E_{CV}(t) \\ &= dE_{CV} + (A\rho\mathsf{V}e)_2\,dt - (A\rho\mathsf{V}e)_1\,dt \end{aligned}$$

Here we have used e to represent the total energy of the matter per unit of mass. The terms $đW_{\text{shaft}}$ and $đQ$ represent energy transfers across the common boundaries, that is, across the control-volume boundary, which occur during the time interval dt. Substituting for dE_{CM} and regrouping terms,

$$đW_{\text{shaft}} + đQ + (A\rho\mathsf{V})_1\left(e + \frac{P}{\rho}\right)_1 dt = (A\rho\mathsf{V})_2\left(e + \frac{P}{\rho}\right)_2 dt + dE_{CV}$$

The term $A\rho \mathsf{V}\, dt$ represents infinitesimal mass transfer across the control-volume boundaries, which we denote by $đM$. Then

$$\blacktriangleright \quad \underbrace{đW_{\text{shaft}} + đQ + [(e + Pv)\, đM]_{\text{in}}}_{\text{energy input}} = \underbrace{[(e + Pv)\, đM]_{\text{out}}}_{\text{energy output}} + \underbrace{đE_{CV}}_{\substack{\text{increase in} \\ \text{energy storage}}} \tag{5·4}$$

This can be viewed as a conservation-of-energy equation *for the control volume,* expressed for a definite period of time. Alternatively, we could divide by dt and express the energy balance on a *rate basis* as

$$\blacktriangleright \quad \underbrace{\dot{W}_{\text{shaft}} + \dot{Q} + [\dot{M}(e + Pv)]_{\text{in}}}_{\text{energy-input rate}} = \underbrace{[\dot{M}(e + Pv)]_{\text{out}}}_{\substack{\text{energy-output} \\ \text{rate}}} + \underbrace{\left(\frac{dE}{dt}\right)_{CV}}_{\substack{\text{energy-storage} \\ \text{rate}}} \tag{5·5}$$

We see that the conservation-of-energy idea can be retained for the control volume, provided that we adopt a slightly modified picture of energy. When matter flows into a control volume, energy is *convected* in by the matter, and in addition, energy is transferred to the control volume as work. The amount of energy transfer as work associated with a unit of mass is Pv. In a sense, entering matter does work on the matter already within the control volume by "pushing it out of the way." The Pv product, when used in this context, is sometimes called *flow work*. It does not represent any energy contained by the fluid.

Note that the energy of matter is still designated by e. Only when matter crosses the boundaries of a control volume will the additional contribution of the Pv product occur in the energy-balance equation. Furthermore, care must be taken to distinguish between the $P\, dv$ work done by a control mass in expanding and the Pv work done by a unit of mass in flowing into a control volume (which may be of fixed size). Note that e, P, and v appearing in the flow terms are to be evaluated at the point where the matter crosses the boundary.

The energy per unit of mass of substance crossing the boundary is composed of internal energy, bulk potential energy, and bulk kinetic energy. We can therefore write

$$e + Pv = KE + PE + u + Pv$$

The appearance of the combination $h \equiv u + Pv$ suggests further utility for tabulations of the enthalpy property.

The kinetic energy of a unit of mass is simply $\mathsf{V}^2/2g_c$. The potential energy of a unit of mass in a uniform gravitational field may be shown to equal $(g_g/g_c)z$, where g_g is the local acceleration of gravity (ft/sec^2), g_c is the constant in Newton's law (32.17 ft-lbm/lbf-sec^2), and z is the height above some arbitrarily selected datum. The electrostatic potential energy of a unit of mass is simply $\mathcal{Q}\mathcal{E}$, where $\mathcal{Q}$ is the charge per unit of mass and $\mathcal{E}$ is the local value of the electrostatic potential above the (arbitrary) ground state. Hence,

$$e + Pv = h + \frac{\mathsf{V}^2}{2g_c} + \frac{g_g}{g_c} z + \mathcal{Q}\mathcal{E} + \cdots$$

For a control volume with matter flowing across the boundaries in several places, and with boundaries which may themselves be moving, the conservation-of-energy statement on the time-interval basis leads to

$$\blacktriangleright \quad \underbrace{\sum_{\text{in}} (e + Pv)\, đM + đW + đQ}_{\text{energy-input}} = \underbrace{\sum_{\text{out}} (e + Pv)\, đM}_{\text{energy-output}} + \underbrace{đE_{CV}}_{\text{energy-storage}} \tag{5·6}$$

and on the rate basis to

$$\blacktriangleright \quad \underbrace{\sum_{\text{in}} (e + Pv)\dot{M} + \dot{W} + \dot{Q}}_{\text{energy-input rate}} = \underbrace{\sum_{\text{out}} (e + Pv)\dot{M}}_{\text{energy-output rate}} + \underbrace{\left(\frac{dE}{dt}\right)_{CV}}_{\text{energy-storage rate}} \tag{5·7}$$

Here $\dot{W}$ is to be understood as being the sum of shaft-power *input* and power *input* due to normal motion of the control-volume boundaries. $\dot{Q}$ represents the sum of all heat transfer rates *to* the control volume. If the control-volume boundaries move, $\dot{M}$ must be calculated in terms of the velocity of the fluid *relative and normal to the control surface.*

It is sometimes necessary to replace the sums by integrals, and we then obtain

$$\blacktriangleright \quad \underbrace{-\int_{CS} (e + Pv)\rho \mathbf{V}_{\text{rel}} \cdot d\mathbf{A} + \dot{W} + \dot{Q}}_{\text{net energy-input rate}} = \underbrace{\frac{d}{dt}\int_{CV} \rho e\, dV}_{\text{energy-storage rate}} \tag{5·8}$$

The area integration is to be extended over the control surface CS, and $d\mathbf{A}$ represents an *outward* normal vector. The volume integration is extended over the entire control volume. Note that e appears in the energy-storage term, while $e + Pv$ appears in the energy-convection term. $\mathbf{V}_{\text{rel}}$ represents the *outward* velocity *relative to the boundary,* while the *absolute* velocity $\mathbf{V}$ must be used to compute the kinetic energy.

Two important idealizations frequently made in control-volume analysis are (1) that the flow is steady, so that no mass is accumulating within the control volume, and (2) that the state of the matter at each point in space is steady, that is, unchanging in time. This implies that the energy stored within the control volume is unchanging and thereby eliminates the term in the energy equation involving changes in the energy storage. It is therefore not necessary to know the details of what is going on within the control volume. This is very important, because it allows us to analyze intricate systems by examining only the transfers of energy across the control-volume boundary.

The methodology introduced for the control mass may readily be applied in setting up the control-volume energy balance. We shall now illustrate the methodology by examples. In each case it will be necessary to make idealizations in order to render the problem tractable. Such idealizations are usually based on experience, but engineering analysis is both a science and an art and can be learned only by imitation and practice. Thus, careful study of the examples will provide the student's first bit of experience and something to imitate. One can often verify the validity of an idealization by making appropriate estimates and should make every attempt to do so whenever a particular assumption is questionable. The examples serve to bring out many important features of systematic control-volume energy analysis and are typical of the simpler types of problems in engineering thermodynamics.

5·4 EXAMPLES OF CONTROL-VOLUME ENERGY ANALYSIS

Flow through a nozzle. Steam enters the nozzle of a steam turbine with a velocity of 10 ft/sec at a pressure of 500 psia and a temperature of 1000°F. At the nozzle discharge the pressure and temperature are measured and found to be 300°F and 1 atm. What is the discharge velocity? See Fig. 5·8.

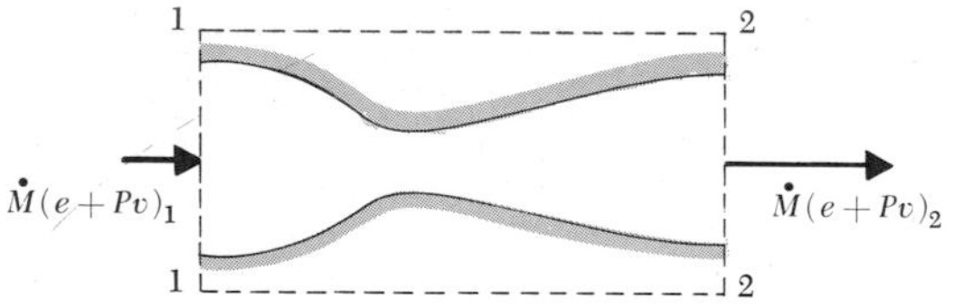

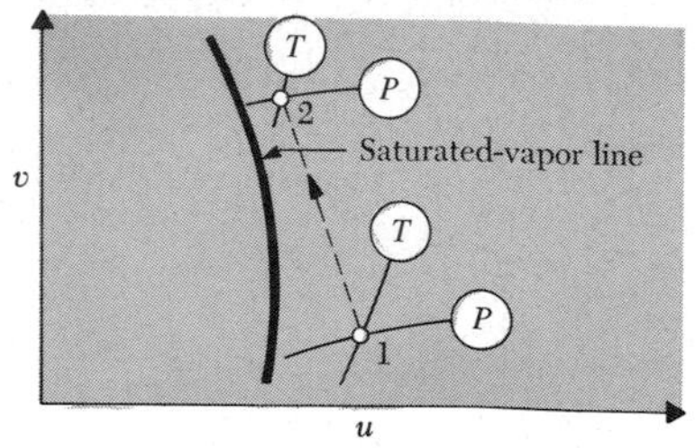

FIG. 5·8

(*a*) *The control volume* (*b*) *The process representation*

In any such nozzle frictional effects between the fluid and the walls might be important, but by choosing the boundaries as indicated in Fig. 5·8*a* these effects become internal. Then, idealizing the flow as steady and assuming that the state at each point in the control volume is invariant in time (steady state), we do not need to know what is going on within the control volume. We also idealize that the control volume is adiabatic, so that no energy transfer as heat takes place across the control-volume boundaries (this is a reasonable simplifying idealization for most nozzles). This does not mean that no energy transfer as heat takes place within the control volume, but any such transfer would not be involved in a steady-flow steady-state analysis.

The conservation-of-mass principle implies that the flow rate is the same at sections 1 and 2. In applying this principle we assume that the flow is one-dimensional at 1 and 2, which means that the properties are uniform across the sections. The energy per unit of mass is taken as

$$e = u + \frac{V^2}{2g_c}$$

In evaluating u as a function of the temperature and pressure we shall assume that the motion in no way alters the thermodynamic equations of state. In microscopic terms, even though the fluid is accelerating, the molecules behave locally as if there were no bulk motion. Satisfactory results are obtained with this idealization, and this experimental support is sufficient justification for its use. We shall also neglect any differences in the potential energy of position of the entering and emergent flows.

The internal process is quite complicated. However, only the states of the fluid at 1 and 2 need to be known, and we can indicate our ignorance of the intermediate states by showing the process as a dotted line (Fig. 5·8*b*).

Several important simplifying idealizations have been made, and it is a good idea to begin any analysis by listing these:

Steady flow steady state
Adiabatic control volume
One-dimensional flow at 1 and 2 (but not necessarily internally!)
Equation of state the same as for a simple compressible substance
Changes in the potential energy of position negligible

With these idealizations, application of the conservation-of-energy principle to the control volume gives, on a rate basis,

$$\underbrace{\dot{M}\left(u + Pv + \frac{V^2}{2g_c}\right)_1}_{\text{energy-inflow rate}} - \underbrace{\dot{M}\left(u + Pv + \frac{V^2}{2g_c}\right)_2}_{\text{energy-outflow rate}} = \underbrace{0}_{\substack{\text{energy-}\\\text{storage}\\\text{rate}}}$$

Solving for the discharge kinetic energy per unit of mass,

$$\frac{V_2^2}{2g_c} = \frac{V_1^2}{2g_c} + [(u + Pv)_1 - (u + Pv)_2]$$

The intensive thermodynamic states are fixed by the temperature and pressure measurements (see Fig. B·1):

$T_1 = 1000°F$	$T_2 = 300°F$
$P_1 = 500$ psia	$P_2 = 14.7$ psia
$u_1 = 1360$ Btu/lbm	$u_2 = 1110$ Btu/lbm
$v_1 = 1.7$ ft^3/lbm	$v_2 = 31$ ft^3/lbm

Hence

$$h_1 = (u_1 + P_1v_1) = 1520 \text{ Btu/lbm}$$
$$h_2 = (u_2 + P_2v_2) = 1193 \text{ Btu/lbm}$$

Then

$$\frac{V_1^2}{2g_c} = \frac{10^2}{2 \times 32.2} (\text{ft}^2/\text{sec}^2)/(\text{ft-lbm/lbf-sec}^2)$$

$$= 1.55 \text{ ft-lbf/lbm} = 2 \times 10^{-3} \text{ Btu/lbm}$$

$$\frac{V_2^2}{2g_c} = 2 \times 10^{-3} + 1520 - 1193 = 327 \text{ Btu/lbm} = 254{,}000 \text{ ft-lbf/lbm}$$

$$V_2 = \sqrt{2 \times 32.2 \text{ ft-lbm/lbf-sec}^2 \times 254{,}000 \text{ ft-lbf/lbm}} = 4100 \text{ ft/sec}$$

Note that the enthalpies could have been more conveniently found in Table B·2 or on Fig. B·2. Note also that the inlet kinetic energy is very small and could have been neglected.

A mercury turbine. Mercury enters the turbine of a high-temperature auxiliary power system at 1200°F and 30 psia and emerges as a mixture of liquid and vapor of 0.95 quality at 1 psia. What must the flow rate be if the power output is to be 10 kw? See Fig. 5·9.

A typical turbine consists of (1) a nozzle, which accelerates the flow, converting internal energy and flow work to kinetic energy; (2) a rotor, which slows down the fluid, extracting energy from the fluid as work; and (3) a diffuser, which slows the fluid down again, with a resulting rise in pressure. The internal workings of such a device are quite complicated. However, by judicious selection of the control-volume boundaries and the idealizations of steady flow and steady state, one need worry only about the conditions at the points where the flow crosses the boundaries. This is a great advantage of the control-volume approach to steady-flow steady-state problems.

We take the boundary as shown above and make the following idealizations:

Steady flow steady state
Adiabatic control volume
One-dimensional flow at 1 and 2
Kinetic and potential energy negligible at 1 and 2 (but certainly not inside!)
Mercury in thermodynamic equilibrium at 1 and 2

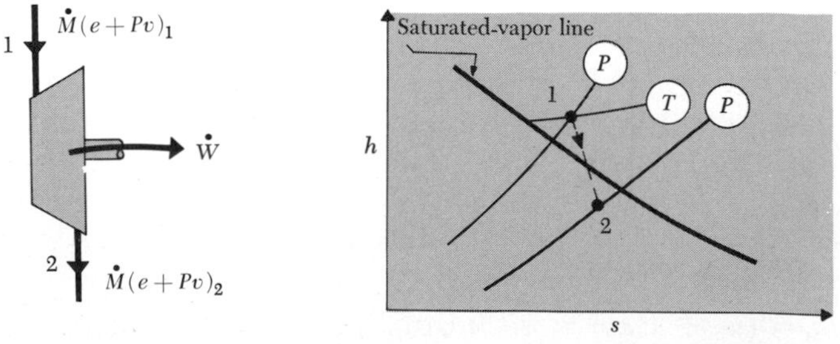

FIG. 5·9

(a) *The control volume* (b) *The process representation*

Under these idealizations, application of the conservation-of-energy principle to the control volume gives

$$\underbrace{\dot{M}(u + Pv)_1}_{\text{energy-inflow rate}} - \underbrace{[\dot{M}(u + Pv)_2 + \dot{W}_{\text{shaft}}]}_{\text{energy-outflow rate}} = \underbrace{0}_{\text{energy-storage rate}}$$

The shaft-energy output per unit of mass is then

$$W_{\text{shaft}} = \frac{\dot{W}_{\text{shaft}}}{\dot{M}} = h_1 - h_2$$

The enthalpies may be found directly on Fig. B·10, and we then have

$$W_{\text{shaft}} = (159 - 134) \text{ Btu/lbm} = 25 \text{ Btu/lbm}$$

The power requirement of 10 kw is equivalent to 34,130 Btu/hr, so the required mass-flow rate is

$$\dot{M} = 34{,}130/25 = 1360 \text{ lbm/hr} = 0.378 \text{ lbm/sec}$$

If the mercury is moving at 100 ft/sec (typical for the inlet of a small mercury turbine), the required flow area can be computed from the relation $\dot{M} = A\rho\mathsf{V}$, provided the inlet density is known. The density does not appear on Fig. B 10. However, we can make an estimate of the density by assuming that the vapor behaves like a perfect gas, for which

$$\frac{\rho}{\rho_0} = \frac{P/T}{P_0/T_0}$$

The zero denotes any selected reference state, which we take to be saturated vapor at 20 psia. Then, using the data in Table B·3, we estimate the density at 1 as

$$\rho_1 = \frac{1 \text{ lbm}}{3.09 \text{ ft}^3} \frac{30/(1200 + 460)}{20/(706 + 460)} = 0.34 \text{ lbm/ft}^3$$

At 100 ft/sec the inlet-flow area would be

$$A = \frac{0.378}{0.34 \times 100} = 0.0111 \text{ ft}^2 = 1.6 \text{ in.}^2$$

We can evaluate the validity of our idealization that the kinetic-energy changes are negligible by some typical numbers. Suppose the discharge velocity is 200 ft/sec, with the inlet velocity as 100 ft/sec. The difference in the inflow and outflow kinetic energies, per unit of mass, would then be

$$\frac{\mathsf{V}_2^2 - \mathsf{V}_1^2}{2g_c} = \frac{200^2 - 100^2}{2 \times 32.2} = 465 \text{ ft-lbf/lbm} = 0.6 \text{ Btu/lbm}$$

This represents an error of about 2 percent when compared to the enthalpy difference of 25 Btu/lbm, and our idealization was therefore quite reasonable for first analysis. The analyst is frequently in a position to make such quantitative estimates of the inaccuracies introduced by his simplifying assumptions and should do so whenever he can.

It is indeed interesting that the size of the system did not enter the thermodynamic calculation, nor did the particular internal configuration of the device. This is typical of thermodynamic energy analysis, in which important system parameters can be set without the need for detailed knowledge of the design.

Liquefaction of oxygen. Oxygen enters a turboexpander at 200°K and 60 atm. The expander discharges into a separator, from which saturated liquid and saturated vapor at 1 atm emerge as separate streams. The system is heavily insulated. The turboexpander shaft-power output is 1700 watts, and the total oxygen-flow rate is 15 g/sec. What percentage of liquefaction is achieved, and what is the net liquid-oxygen-production rate? See Fig. 5·10.

The idealizations are as follows:

Steady flow steady state
Adiabatic control volume
One-dimensional flow at 1, 4, and 3
Potential and kinetic energies at 1, 4, and 3 negligible
Thermodynamic equilibrium states at 1, 4, and 3

With these idealizations, an energy balance on the control volume gives, on a rate basis,

$$\underbrace{\dot{M}_1(u + Pv)_1}_{\text{energy-inflow rate}} - \underbrace{[\dot{M}_4(u + Pv)_4 + \dot{M}_3(u + Pv)_3 + \dot{W}]}_{\text{energy-outflow rate}} = \underbrace{0}_{\text{energy-storage rate}}$$

A mass balance will also be required; for the control volume,

$$\underbrace{\dot{M}_1}_{\text{mass-inflow rate}} - \underbrace{(\dot{M}_4 + \dot{M}_3)}_{\text{mass-outflow rate}} = \underbrace{0}_{\text{mass-storage rate}}$$

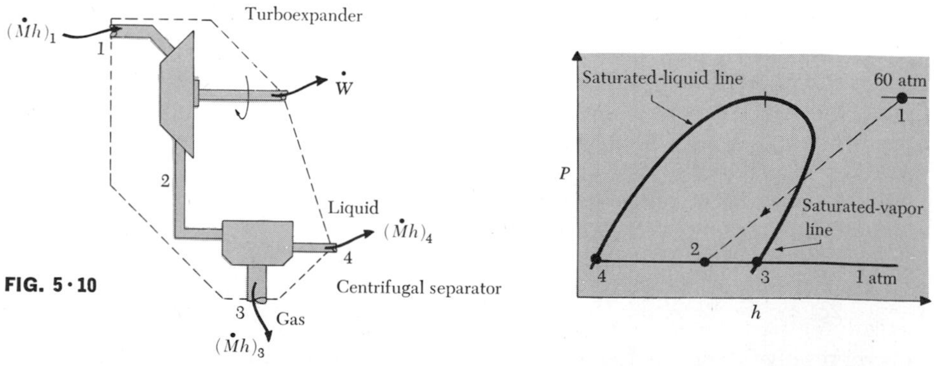

FIG. 5·10

(a) *The control volume* (b) *The process representation*

The problem will be solved if we can establish the relative flow rates. We put $f = \dot{M}_3/\dot{M}_1$ and the energy balance becomes an equation for f,

$$h_1 - [(1 - f)h_4 + fh_3] - \frac{\dot{W}}{\dot{M}_1} = 0$$

The enthalpies are evaluated with the aid of Fig. B·5, and we find (using $\ddot{M} = 32.00$ g/gmole)

$$h_1 = \frac{2320}{32.00} = 72.4 \text{ cal/g}$$

$$h_4 = \frac{160}{32.00} = 5.0 \text{ cal/g} \qquad \text{(saturated liquid)}$$

$$h_3 = \frac{1780}{32.00} = 55.7 \text{ cal/g} \qquad \text{(saturated vapor)}$$

The shaft-work output per unit of mass is

$$\frac{\dot{W}}{\dot{M}_1} = \frac{1700 \text{ joule/sec}}{15 \text{ g/sec}} = 1.13 \times 10^2 \text{ joule/g} \times \frac{1 \text{ cal}}{4.18 \text{ joule}} = 27.2 \text{ cal/g}$$

Solving for f and substituting the numbers,

$$f = \frac{27.2 + 5.0 - 72.4}{5.0 - 55.7} = 0.79$$

The system therefore achieves 21 percent liquefaction and delivers saturated liquid oxygen at 1 atm at the rate of 3.1 g/sec.

Do not be led to believe that liquid oxygen can be made "for nothing" in a process from which useful electrical power is obtained. Energy is required to separate oxygen from air, to compress it to 60 atm, and to run the refrigerator which precools it to 200°K. Only a portion of this would be recovered from the turboexpander.

CO_2 evaporator. Three hundred lbm/hr of CO_2 (liquid) will enter a heat exchanger as a saturated liquid at 100 psia and emerge at 75 psia and 20°F. This evaporation and superheating process is to be accomplished by passing dry air through the other side of the exchanger. The air will enter at 70°F, slightly above atmospheric pressure, and must emerge at 50°F at atmospheric pressure. Specify the air-flow rate required and the heat-transfer rate within the exchanger. See Fig. 5·11.

We make the following idealizations:

Steady flow steady state
Adiabatic control volume (energy transfer as heat occurring inside, and neglecting energy transfer as heat across the boundaries indicated)
One-dimensional flow at 1, 2, 3, and 4

Kinetic and potential energy changes negligible
Equilibrium states at 1, 2, 3, and 4 with properties related by thermodynamic equations of state

With these idealizations, the energy balance, on a rate basis, is

$$\underbrace{\dot{M}_1 h_1 + \dot{M}_3 h_3}_{\text{energy-inflow rate}} - \underbrace{(\dot{M}_2 h_2 + \dot{M}_4 h_4)}_{\text{energy-outflow rate}} = \underbrace{0}_{\text{energy-storage rate}}$$

By conservation of mass, $\dot{M}_1 = \dot{M}_2$ and $\dot{M}_3 = \dot{M}_4$.

The enthalpies are found from the given states using Figs. B·6 and B·8:

$h_3 = 137$ Btu/lbm (saturated liquid at 100 psia, $-55°$F)
$h_4 = 299$ Btu/lbm
$h_1 = 5.5$ cal/g (21.5°C, ≈ 1 atm)
$h_2 = 2.5$ cal/g (10°C, 1 atm)

The enthalpy differences are then

$$h_4 - h_3 = 299 - 137 = 162 \text{ Btu/lbm}$$
$$h_1 - h_2 = 5.5 - 2.5 = 3.0 \text{ cal/g} = 5.4 \text{ Btu/lbm}$$

The required air-flow rate is therefore

$$\dot{M}_{\text{air}} = \frac{162}{5.4} \times 300 \text{ lbm/hr} = 9000 \text{ lbm/hr}$$

To determine the heat-transfer rate within the exchanger, a second energy balance is required. Either side of the exchanger may be used. Having the

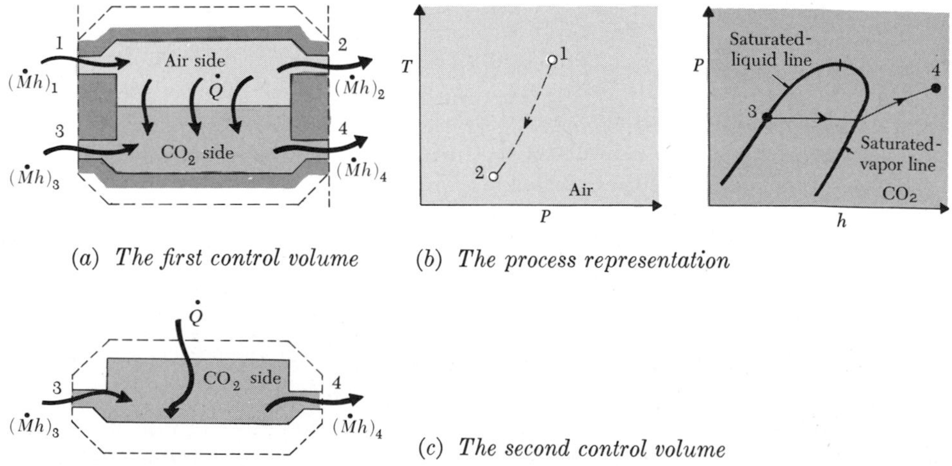

(a) *The first control volume* (b) *The process representation*

(c) *The second control volume*

FIG. 5·11

most accurate enthalpy-difference information for the CO_2, we select this side (Fig. 5·11c) and idealize as follows:

Steady flow steady state
One-dimensional flows at 3 and 4
Kinetic and potential energy changes negligible
Thermodynamic equilibrium at 3 and 4

The energy balance, on a rate basis, is

$$\underbrace{\dot{Q} + \dot{M}_{CO_2}h_3}_{\text{energy-input rate}} = \underbrace{\dot{M}_{CO_2}h_4}_{\text{energy-output rate}}$$

Substituting the numbers,

$$\dot{Q} = \dot{M}_{CO_2}(h_4 - h_3) = 300 \times 162 = 48{,}600 \text{ Btu/hr}$$

Determination of the physical dimensions of a heat exchanger which could transfer energy from one stream to the other at this rate over the temperature differences involved is a problem for the heat-transfer analyst and requires more than thermodynamics.

A thermoelectric generator. A thermoelectric generator consists of a series of semiconductor elements, heated on one side and cooled on the other. Electric-current flow is produced as a result of energy transfer as heat. A schematic diagram of a typical device is shown in Fig. 5·12. In a particular experiment the current was measured to be 0.5 amp and the electrostatic potential at 3 was 0.8 volt above that at 4. Energy transfer as heat to the hot side of the generator was taking place at a rate of 5.5 watts. Determine the rate of energy transfer as heat from the cold side and the energy-conversion efficiency.

We shall treat this problem by the control-volume method, since mass (electrons) flows across the indicated control surface. The electrons flowing possess electrostatic potential energy and kinetic energy. In addition, the electrons within the "electron gas" passing through the conductors execute randomly oriented motions, giving the "gas" internal energy in exactly the same

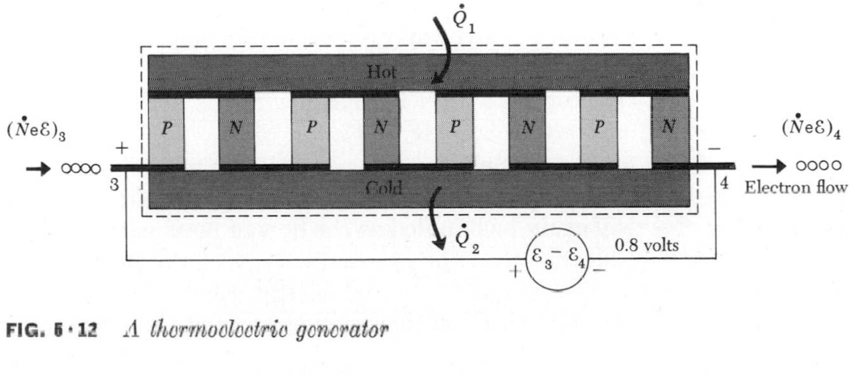

FIG. 5·12 *A thermoelectric generator*

way that molecules of a gas give it internal energy. Moreover, the electron gas will have a pressure and a specific volume, so it will have an enthalpy. The randomly oriented motions of the electrons within the gas are responsible in part for "noise" in electronic circuits. We shall assume that there is no noise in this system, or in other words, that the internal energy of the electron gas is insignificant compared to the electrostatic potential energy. The kinetic energy is also negligible, since electrons in metallic conductors move at very slow "drift velocities." Therefore only the electrostatic potential energy of the electrons will be considered. Idealizations are as follows:

Steady flow steady state
One-dimensional flows
Only electron potential energy important

Denoting the number of electrons crossing the boundary per unit of time by $\dot{N}$ and the charge of an electron by e, an energy balance, made on a rate basis, gives

$$\underbrace{[(\dot{N}e\mathcal{E})_3 + \dot{Q}_1]}_{\text{energy-inflow rate}} - \underbrace{[(\dot{N}e\mathcal{E})_4 + \dot{Q}_2]}_{\text{energy-outflow rate}} = \underbrace{0}_{\text{energy-storage rate}}$$

In terms of the current $i = -\dot{N}e$,

$$i(\mathcal{E}_4 - \mathcal{E}_3) + \dot{Q}_1 - \dot{Q}_2 = 0$$

Solving for $\dot{Q}_2$ and substituting the numbers,

$$\dot{Q}_2 = 5.5 \text{ watts} + 0.5 \text{ amp} \times (-0.8 \text{ volt}) \times 1 \text{ watt/volt-amp} = 5.1 \text{ watts}$$

The term $i(\mathcal{E}_3 - \mathcal{E}_4)$ represents the useful power output of the device; it is equal to 0.4 watt. The *energy-conversion efficiency* is then

$$\eta = \frac{i(\mathcal{E}_3 - \mathcal{E}_4)}{\dot{Q}_1} = \frac{0.4}{5.5} = 0.073$$

This low efficiency is typical of such solid-state direct-energy converters.

An arc heater. Air is to be heated to 8000°K in a steady-flow electric-arc device. The air will enter at 10^{-2} atm at atmospheric temperature and will emerge at the same pressure. Cooling water is provided to maintain low electrode temperatures, and it is estimated that half the electrical-energy input will be transferred as heat to the cooling water. The air-flow rate is to be 10,000 lbm/hr. Specify the required arc power. See Fig. 5·13.

The air will be ionized but electrically neutral. We assume that thermodynamic equilibrium has been obtained by the time that the air emerges. The electric-current flow will again be handled as the flow of mass with electrostatic potential energy. We idealize that the internal energy of the flowing electron "gas" is small compared to its bulk potential energy. Electrons move through solids at very low "drift velocities," so the kinetic energy of the electrons at the

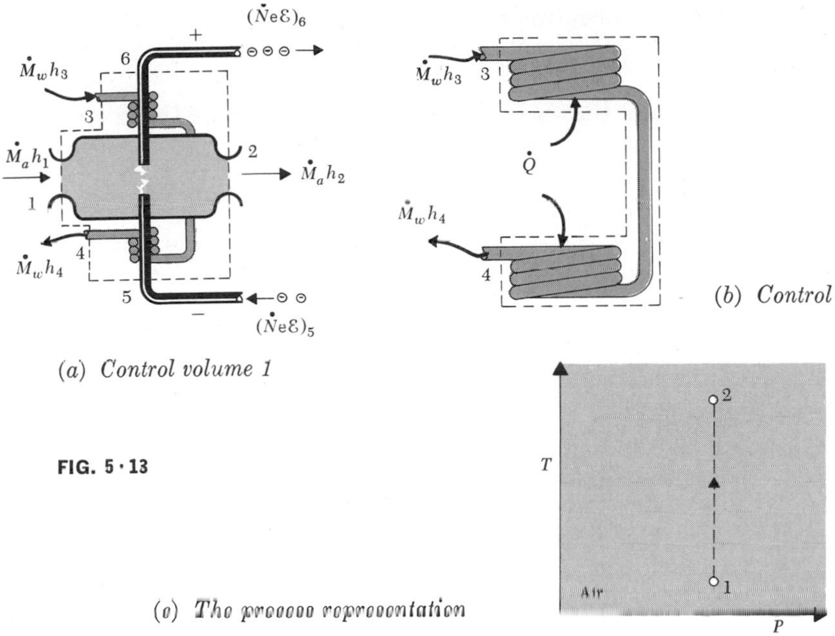

(a) *Control volume 1*

(b) *Control volume 2*

FIG. 5 · 13

(c) *The process representation*

points at which we draw the control-volume boundaries will be neglected. (It should be noted that the kinetic energy of the electrons striking the anode will be extremely high and could not be neglected were we to make our boundary cut through the air immediately adjacent to the anode.) We make the following idealizations:

Steady flow steady state
One-dimensional flows
Kinetic energy of air and water negligible
Only electrostatic potential energy of electrons important
Control volume 1 adiabatic
Air in thermodynamic equilibrium at 1 and 2
Water in thermodynamic equilibrium at 3 and 4

We again denote the number of electrons flowing per unit of time as $\dot{N}$ and their charge as e. The energy balance, made on a rate basis on control volume 1, gives

$$\underbrace{(\dot{N}e\mathcal{E}_5 + \dot{M}_a h_1 + \dot{M}_w h_3)}_{\text{energy-inflow rate}} - \underbrace{(\dot{N}e\mathcal{E}_6 + \dot{M}_a h_2 + \dot{M}_w h_4)}_{\text{energy-outflow rate}} = \underbrace{0}_{\text{energy-storage rate}}$$

In terms of the current $i = -\dot{N}e$,

$$i(\mathcal{E}_6 - \mathcal{E}_5) = \dot{M}_a(h_2 - h_1) + \dot{M}_w(h_4 - h_3)$$

The first term should be recognized as the electrical-power input.

An energy balance on control volume 2 leads to

$$\dot{Q} = \dot{M}_w(h_4 - h_3)$$

Using the design estimate that $\dot{Q} = i(\mathcal{E}_6 - \mathcal{E}_5)/2$, we combine the energy balances and obtain

$$\text{Power} = i(\mathcal{E}_6 - \mathcal{E}_5) = 2\dot{M}_a(h_2 - h_1)$$

The enthalpy at state 2 is obtained from the equation of state, Fig. B·9, as 19,000 Btu/lbm. This value is relative to the enthalpy at absolute zero of a gas obeying the equation of state $h = c_P T$ at low temperatures. For air $c_P \approx 0.24$ Btu/lbm-°R, so an estimate of the enthalpy at state 1 might be $0.24 \times 500 = 120$ Btu/lbm. This is negligible in comparison to the enthalpy of the highly energetic air at state 2. Our power calculation then yields

$$\begin{aligned}\text{Power} &= 2 \times 10{,}000 \text{ lbm/hr} \times (19{,}000 - 120) \text{ Btu/lbm} \\ &= 38 \times 10^7 \text{ Btu/hr} = 1.11 \times 10^5 \text{ kw} = 111 \text{ Mw}\end{aligned}$$

The total power output of a large central power station would be required to power this arcjet heater!

Charging of a high-pressure tank. A gas is pumped into a tank having volume V. The gas in the tank is initially at pressure P_0 and temperature T_0. The inlet temperature is T_1, and the inflow rate $\dot{M}_1$ is constant. Using the perfect-gas equation of state, derive an expression for the temperature in the tank as a function of time, assuming that the gas inside is perfectly mixed and in a state of thermodynamic equilibrium and that no energy transfer as heat takes place from the tank to the gas. See Fig. 5·14.

Our idealizations are as follows:

The gas may be treated as a perfect gas with constant specific heats
Steady inflow (but not steady state!)
Uniform state inside the tank (perfect internal mixing)
Adiabatic control volume
Equilibrium state within tank at every instant, equilibrium state at 1
Kinetic energy of inflow gas negligible
Inlet state steady (but not the internal state!) and one-dimensional flow at the inlet

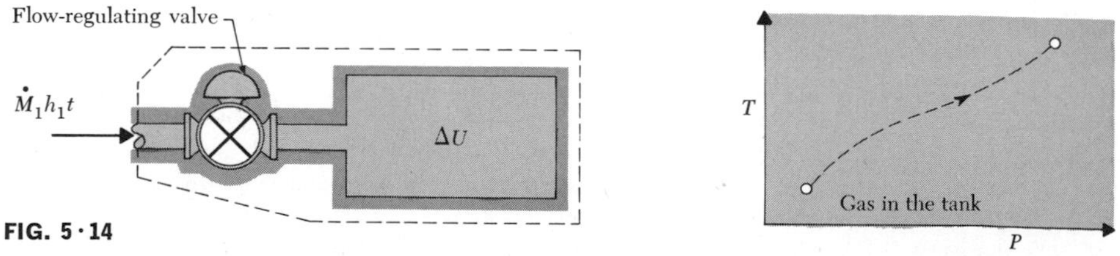

FIG. 5·14

(a) *The control volume* (b) *The process representation*

The energy balance, made over the time interval from the start of filling (time zero) to some later time t, is

$$\underbrace{\dot{M}_1(u_1 + P_1v_1)t}_{\text{energy inflow}} - \underbrace{0}_{\substack{\text{energy}\\\text{outflow}}} = \underbrace{\Delta U}_{\substack{\text{increase}\\\text{in energy}\\\text{storage}}}$$

Then,

$$\Delta U = Mu - M_0u_0$$

A mass balance on the control volume is also needed. Over the same time period,

$$\underbrace{\dot{M}_1t}_{\text{mass inflow}} - \underbrace{0}_{\substack{\text{mass}\\\text{outflow}}} = \underbrace{M - M_0}_{\substack{\text{increase in}\\\text{mass storage}}}$$

Solving for M and substituting into the energy balance,

$$\dot{M}_1h_1t = (M_0 + \dot{M}_1t)u - M_0u_0 \tag{5·9}$$

Note that the enthalpy property is involved in the energy-inflow term, while only the internal energy is involved in the energy-storage term.

The Pv product does not represent energy of matter; it is simply an extra term in the energy balance necessitated by our taking the control-volume rather than control-mass point of view.

We next bring in the equation of state. With the datum at 0° R in Eqs. (4·21) and (4·22), we introduce these into Eq. (5·9), obtaining

$$\dot{M}_1c_PT_1t = (M_0 + \dot{M}_1t)c_vT - M_0c_vT_0$$

The temperature T of the gas in the tank can be computed from this equation as a function of time. It is interesting that for very large t the temperature will approach the value

$$T_{\text{lim}} = \frac{c_P}{c_v}T_1 = kT_1$$

Since the ratio k is greater than unity, the limiting internal temperature will be somewhat greater than the temperature of the incoming gas.

A hydroelectric power plant. Suppose we wish to assess the capabilities of a foreign hydroelectric power plant, and have acquired the following field data.

Estimated water flow, 40 ft^3/sec
River inlet 1 atm, 40°F
Discharged at 1 atm, 40.5°F, 800 ft below the intake

We know from experience that the energy transfer as heat to such a power plant is negligible. The enthalpy of water is given approximately by

$$h_2 - h_1 = c_v(T_2 - T_1) + \frac{1}{\rho}(P_2 - P_1)$$

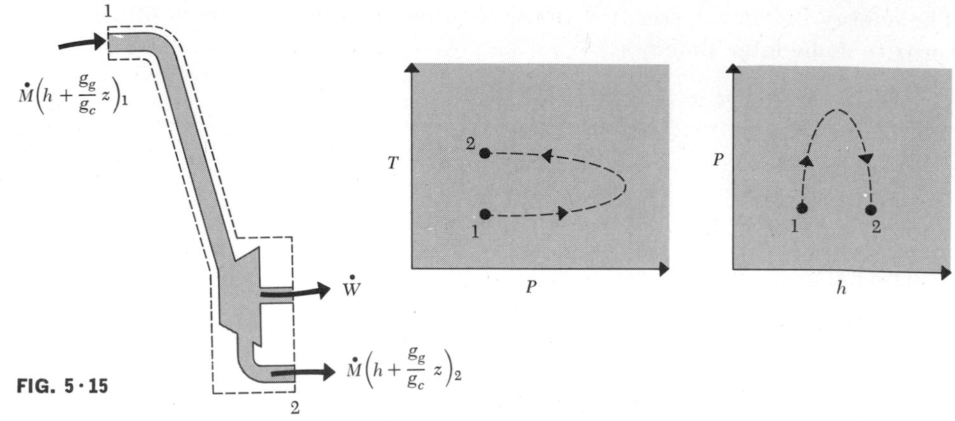

FIG. 5·15

(a) *The control volume* (b) *The process representation*

where $c_v = 1$ Btu/lbm-°R and $\rho = 62.4$ lbm/ft^3. We also estimate that the inlet and discharge ducts have the same flow area, so that the kinetic energy of the water entering the plant is essentially the same as that leaving. With this information, what is our estimate of the power output? See Fig. 5·15.

We make the following idealizations:

Change in kinetic energy of flow streams is negligible
Steady flow steady state
Adiabatic control volume

Note there is no assumption about friction or turbulence or "losses" within the control volume; these are all internal effects, and need not be considered explicitly in a steady-flow, steady-state analysis. They are implicitly considered through their effect on state 2. We would have to make some such assumption if we wanted to *predict* state 2. The energy balance, on a rate basis, is

$$\underbrace{\dot{M}\left(h_1 + \frac{g_g}{g_c} z_1\right)}_{\text{energy-input rate}} = \underbrace{\dot{W} + \dot{M}\left(h_2 + \frac{g_g}{g_c} z_2\right)}_{\text{energy-output rate}}$$

If we take the discharge state 2 as the elevation datum, then $z_2 = 0$ and $z_1 = 800$ ft. The various terms in the energy balance are then

$$\frac{g_g}{g_c} z_1 = \frac{32.2 \text{ ft/sec}^2}{32.2 \text{ ft-lbm/lbf-sec}^2} \times 800 \text{ ft} = 800 \text{ ft-lbf/lbm} = 1.02 \text{ Btu/lbm}$$

$$h_2 - h_1 = c_v(T_2 - T_1) + \frac{1}{\rho}(P_2 - P_1) = 1 \times (40.5 - 40) = 0.5 \text{ Btu/lbm}$$

Hence,

$$\frac{\dot{W}}{\dot{M}} = \frac{g_g}{g_c} z_1 - (h_2 - h_1) = 1.02 - 0.5 = 0.52 \text{ Btu/lbm}$$

Then,

$$\dot{W} = 0.52 \times 62.4 \times 40 = 1298 \text{ Btu/sec} = 1370 \text{ kw} = 1.37 \text{ Mw}$$

A heat pump. The heat pump shows promise of becoming a common household heating system; a simple heat pump consists of the components shown in Fig. 5·16. In an experiment with freon-12 as the working fluid, the following measurements were recorded:

$P_2 = P_3 = 140$ psia
$P_4 = P_1 = 10$ psia
$T_2 = 260°F$
$T_1 = -20°F$
Saturated liquid at 3
$\dot{W} = 10$ kw

Determine the condenser and evaporator rates of energy transfer as heat and the flow rate of the freon-12.

In this experiment no pressure drop through the heat exchangers was measurable. This is frequently true, and a good idealization is that the process undergone by a fluid in passing through a heat exchanger is one of *constant pressure.* We begin our analysis of this rather complicated problem by a process representation (Fig. 5·16*b*) to orient our thinking. The reason for the positioning of state 4 will be evident momentarily.

We have enough information to establish the condenser heat-transfer rate per unit of mass. For control volume 1 we idealize

Steady flow steady state
Kinetic and potential energies negligible
Equilibrium states at 2 and 3
One-dimensional flows at 2 and 3

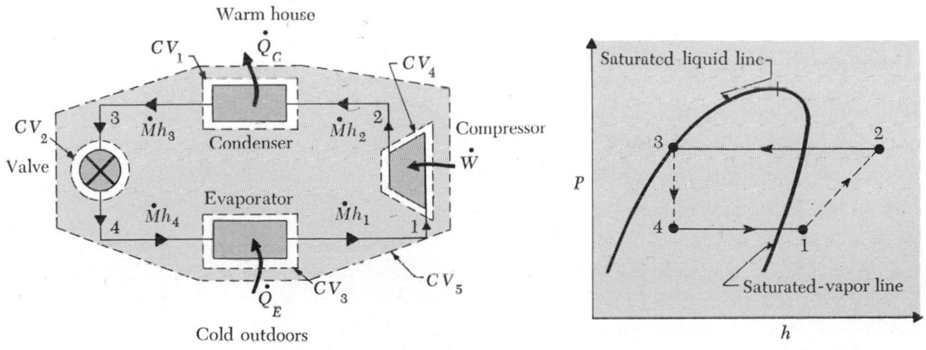

FIG. 5·16 (*a*) *The heat pump* (*b*) *The process representation*

The energy balance for $CV1$, made on a rate basis, gives

$$\underbrace{\dot{M}h_2}_{\substack{\text{energy-input}\\\text{rate}}} = \underbrace{\dot{M}h_3 + \dot{Q}_C}_{\substack{\text{energy-output}\\\text{rate}}}$$

Then, using Fig. B·7,

$$\frac{\dot{Q}_C}{\dot{M}} = h_2 - h_3 = 115 - 31 = 84 \text{ Btu/lbm}$$

We next analyze the valve (control volume 2), with the idealizations

Steady flow steady state
Kinetic and potential energies negligible
Adiabatic control volume
Equilibrium states at 3 and 4
One-dimensional flows at 3 and 4

The energy balance for $CV2$, on a rate basis, then is simply

$$\underbrace{\dot{M}h_3}_{\substack{\text{energy-input}\\\text{rate}}} = \underbrace{\dot{M}h_4}_{\substack{\text{energy-output}\\\text{rate}}}$$

or

$$h_3 = h_4 = 31 \text{ Btu/lbm}$$

Note that the energy balance here tells us something about the end states of a process; with these idealizations the enthalpy of the fluid emerging from a valve will be the same as the enthalpy of the entering fluid (though the enthalpy of the fluid within the valve may be quite different).

An energy balance (rate basis) on control volume 3, with idealizations as for control volume 1, yields

$$\underbrace{\dot{Q}_E + \dot{M}h_4}_{\substack{\text{energy-input}\\\text{rate}}} = \underbrace{\dot{M}h_1}_{\substack{\text{energy-output}\\\text{rate}}}$$

So the amount of energy transferred as heat to each lbm of freon-12 passing through the evaporator is

$$\frac{\dot{Q}_E}{\dot{M}} = h_1 - h_4 = 76 - 31 = 45 \text{ Btu/lbm}$$

Now for control volume 4 (the compressor) we idealize

Steady flow steady state
Kinetic and potential energies negligible
Adiabatic control volume
Equilibrium states at 1 and 2
One-dimensional flows at 1 and 2

The energy balance for $CV4$, on a rate basis, then gives

$$\underbrace{\dot{W} + \dot{M}h_1}_{\text{energy-input rate}} = \underbrace{\dot{M}h_2}_{\text{energy-output rate}}$$

So the compressor work per lbm of fluid which it handles is

$$\frac{\dot{W}}{\dot{M}} = h_2 - h_1 = 115 - 76 = 39 \text{ Btu/lbm}$$

We can check our calculations by an overall energy balance (control volume 5), made on a rate basis, assuming steady flow steady state:

$$\underbrace{\dot{W} + \dot{Q}_E}_{\text{energy-input rate}} = \underbrace{\dot{Q}_C}_{\text{energy-output rate}}$$

$$\dot{M}(39 + 45 - 84) = 0$$

The *coefficient of performance (cop) of a heat pump* is defined as

$$\text{cop} = \frac{\text{rate of energy transfer to house}}{\text{compressor shaft power}}$$

For our system

$$\text{cop} = \frac{\dot{Q}_C}{\dot{W}} = \frac{\dot{M}\ (84 \text{ Btu/lbm})}{\dot{M}\ (39 \text{ Btu/lbm})} = 2.15$$

Note that the rate of energy transfer into the house is more than twice the electrical power which must be paid for to obtain this heating rate. Note also that the cop could be evaluated without reference to the amount of flow or the total energy-transfer rates. We now compute these from the measured shaft power:

$$\dot{M} = \frac{10 \text{ kw} \times 3413 \text{ Btu/kw-hr}}{39 \text{ Btu/lbm}}$$
$$= 870 \text{ lbm/hr}$$

The rates of energy transfer as heat are therefore

$$\dot{Q}_E = 870 \times 45 = 39{,}100 \text{ Btu/hr}$$
$$\dot{Q}_C = 870 \times 84 = 73{,}000 \text{ Btu/hr}$$

The figure 39,100 Btu/hr is comparable with that of a small commercial freezer. The energy pumped into the house (73,000 Btu/hr) is comparable to that provided by a household furnace.

Heat pumps and refrigerators are sometimes rated in terms of their "tonnage." One ton of refrigeration is defined as 12,000 Btu/hr and is roughly the rate of energy transfer as heat required to freeze 1 ton of ice in a day. Considered as a heat pump, this unit would have a rating of $73{,}000/12{,}000 \approx 6$ "tons."

SELECTED READING

Jones, J. B., and G. A. Hawkins, *Engineering Thermodynamics*, secs. 2.7–2.13, John Wiley & Sons, Inc., New York, 1960.

Mooney, D. A., *Introduction to Thermodynamics and Heat Transfer*, chap. 6, Prentice-Hall, Inc., Englewood Cliffs, N.J., 1955.

Van Wylen, G. J., and R. E. Sonntag, *Fundamentals of Classical Thermodynamics*, secs. 5.4–5.10, John Wiley & Sons, Inc., New York, 1965.

QUESTIONS

5·1 What is the difference between a control mass and a control volume?

5·2 How would you distinguish between positive and negative energy transfers?

5·3 Why, in calculus, does dx represent an increase in x? What is the meaning of Δx?

5·4 In the first control-mass example, why was it necessary to idealize that states 1 and 2 were states of thermodynamic equilibrium, and where was this idealization actually used? Why was it not necessary to make a similar idealization about intermediate states?

5·5 What is a process representation?

5·6 In the first control-mass example, why was it necessary to idealize that the alteration in molecular behavior introduced by the gravitational field is negligible, and where was this idealization actually used? What change in the center of mass of the H_2O would produce a change in the potential energy of position equal in magnitude to the change in the internal energy for the process? What is the difference between the idealization that the bulk potential-energy change for the process is negligible and the idealization that the gravitational field does not alter the molecular behavior?

5·7 Why is the enthalpy change equal to the energy transfer as heat to a unit of mass undergoing a constant-pressure process, but not for other processes?

5·8 What is the "latent heat of vaporization" as related to thermodynamic properties?

5·9 Why do the conversion factors between gauss and coul/sec-m differ for $\mathbf{H}$ and $\mathbf{M}$?

5·10 Explain the last statement of the thermal-magnetization example.

5·11 What was assumed about the state of the paramagnetic material *during* the thermal-magnetization process?

5·12 Why does the term Pv appear in the control-volume energy balance and not in that for the control mass?

5·13 Explain why Pv is not energy stored in matter.

5·14 What is the difference between Pv and $P\,dv$, and when do terms of these types appear in energy-conservation equations?

5·15 Why is the enthalpy a useful property to have tabulated?

5·16 Derive the continuity equation $\dot{M} = A\rho\mathsf{V}$.

·17 Why is the control-volume transformation useful?

5·18 What is steady state? What is steady flow? Why do these idealizations greatly simplify control-volume analysis?
5·19 What is a one-dimensional flow?
5·20 In the first control-volume example, why was it necessary to idealize that the bulk motion does not alter the molecular behavior as seen by an observer riding with the fluid, and where was this idealization actually used?
5·21 What is a rate basis for an energy balance?
5·22 In the nozzle example, the energy stored in the fluid changes as it passes through the control volume. Why, then, is the term marked "energy-storage rate" equal to zero?
5·23 In the turbine example, why is it not necessary to know the state of the fluid inside the turbine?
5·24 Do the idealizations for the oxygen-liquefaction example rule out the possibility of any energy transfer as heat taking place to the fluid inside the control volume?
5·25 Why is the control volume of Fig. 5·11*a* idealized as adiabatic, while that of Fig. 5·11*c* is not?
5·26 At what speed do electrons move in a copper wire (see your physics book)?
5·27 Why do we handle electron-flow problems by the control-volume method?
5·28 In the tank-charging example, why is the idealization made that the gas in the tank is in equilibrium at every instant, and where is it used?
5·29 Explain the statement immediately following Eq. (5·9).
5·30 What can you say about the house and outdoor temperatures in the heat-pump example?
5·31 Outline a good energy-analysis methodology.
5·32 Why does it pay to be judicious in selecting a control volume or control mass? Is there sometimes more than one choice?

PROBLEMS

5·1 Two lbm of copper at 300°K are cooled to 250°K at 1 atm. How much energy is transferred as heat, and how much work is done on the copper (Table B·7)?
5·2 How much energy transfer as heat is required to completely evaporate 1 lbm of nitrogen for a constant-temperature process, with $T = 161.09$°R (Fig. B·4)?
5·3 Nitrogen in a 1-ft³ container is heated from the saturated-vapor state at 50 psia to 300°R. How much energy transfer as heat is involved (Fig. B·4)?
5·4 Three lbm of nitrogen is heated at constant pressure from the saturated-liquid state at 100 psia to a temperature of 400°R. How much energy transfer as heat is required? How much work is done by the nitrogen, if any, and on what (Fig. B·4)?
5·5 One lbm of freon-12 is heated in a constant-volume container from the critical point to 700°F. How much energy is transferred as heat to the freon, and from where (Fig. B·7)?
5·6 Iron-ammonium alum is magnetized at 1°K by increasing the external field **H** slowly from zero to 10,000 gauss. How much energy is transferred as heat for this process, and in which direction? How much work is done on the alum, and by what (Fig. B·12)?
5·7 One lbm of copper and 0.5 lbm of saturated H_2O vapor at 1 atm pressure are initially in equilibrium. The water is then heated at constant pressure and held

at 400°F until equilibrium between the copper and the water is again obtained. How much energy transfer as heat takes place between the water and its vessel, and how much between the water and the copper (Figs. B·1–B·3, Table B·7)?

5·8 One lbm of CO_2 is expanded adiabatically in a piston-cylinder system from 400 psia and 100°F to the saturated-vapor state at 100 psia. How much work is done by the CO_2 and on what (Fig. B·6)?

5·9 One lbm of O_2 is compressed adiabatically in a piston-cylinder system from the saturated-vapor state at 36.6 psia to a pressure of 17.5 atm and a temperature of 175°K. How much work is done on the O_2 and by what (Fig. B·5)?

5·10 One-half lbm of CO_2 is heated in a 0.5-ft^3 vessel from 0 to 200°F. Determine the initial and final states, and the amount of energy transfer as heat to the CO_2.

5·11 One-half lbm of CO_2 is heated at constant pressure from the saturated-vapor state at 100 psia to 200°F. Determine the amounts of energy transfer as heat and work involved in this process.

5·12 An adiabatic piston-cylinder system contains a 1000-watt immersion heater and 2 lbm of H_2O initially at 14.7 psia and 96 percent quality. The heater is operated for 7 minutes, during which the pressure is held constant. Find the final volume of the system.

5·13 A simple engine uses a perfect gas as the working fluid in a piston-cylinder system. The gas is first heated at constant pressure from state 1 to state 2, then cooled at constant volume to state 3 where $T_3 = T_1$, and then cooled at constant temperature, thereby returning to state 1. Derive expressions for the amounts of energy transfer as work and heat (per lbm of gas) for each process in terms of the temperatures and pressures at each state and the constants of the gas. Suppose $T_1 = 500°R$, $P_1 = 20$ psia, $T_2 = 1000°R$, and $k \equiv c_P/c_v = 1.4$. Calculate the cycle efficiency (*net* work output/energy *input* as heat).

5·14 A simple engine uses a perfect gas as the working fluid in a piston-cylinder system. The gas is first heated at constant volume from state 1 to state 2, then heated at constant temperature to state 3 where $P_3 = P_1$, and then cooled at constant pressure, returning to state 1. Derive expressions for the amounts of energy transfer as heat and work (per lbm of gas) for each process in terms of the temperatures and pressures at each state and the constants of the gas. Assuming $T_1 = 500°R$, $P_1 = 20$ psia, $T_2 = 1000°R$, and $k \equiv c_P/c_v = 1.4$, calculate the cycle efficiency (*net* work output/energy *input* as heat).

5·15 When the engine of Prob. 5·13 is reversed it becomes a refrigeration device. Calculate the amount of energy transfer as heat from the cold space for this cycle (per lbm of gas), and the cycle cop (energy transfer as heat from cold space/net work input).

5·16 Do Prob. 5·15 for the engine cycle of Prob. 5·14.

5·17 A low-temperature refrigeration cycle uses iron-ammonium alum (Fig. B·12) as the working substance. The alum is first heated at constant $\mathbf{H} = 3000$ gauss from state 1 where $\mathbf{M}_1 = 90$ gauss to state 2, where $\mathbf{M}_2 = 70$ gauss. It is then heated at constant $\mathbf{M}$ until $\mathbf{H} = 10{,}000$ gauss at state 3, and then cooled at constant $\mathbf{H}$ to state 4 where $\mathbf{M}_4 = \mathbf{M}_1$. A final cooling process at constant $\mathbf{M}$ returns the alum to state 1. Calculate the amounts of energy transfer as heat for the four processes (erg/g), and the cycle cop (energy transfer as heat from cold space/net energy input as work).

5·18 An engine operating on the reverse cycle to that described in Prob. 5·17 is proposed for use in a deep space probe which can have no part at greater than 2°K. Calculate the net work output per g of alum, the cycle efficiency (net work output/energy input as heat), and the required amount of alum for 1 watt of power if the cycle can be repeated every 22 seconds.

5·19 Consider the piston-cylinder-spring system shown below.

Piston area 1 in.²
Vacuum in spring chamber
Spring force F = ka, k = 300 lbf/in.

The cylinder initially contains CO_2 at 80°F, and a is initially 2 in. The cylinder walls are then slowly cooled, and the piston moves to the left until a = ½ in. Calculate the energy transfer as heat from the gas for this process.

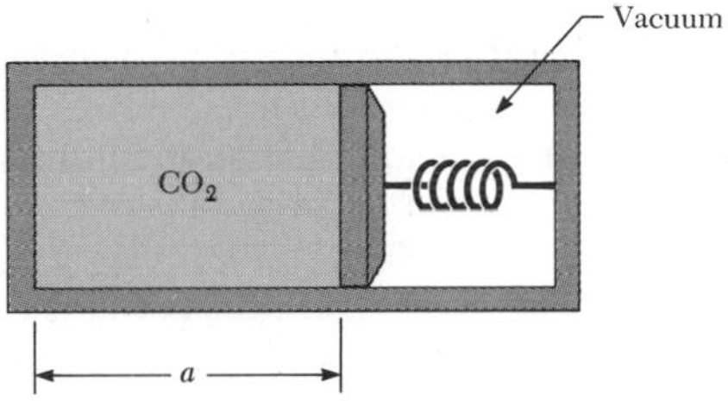

5·20 Twenty lbm/min of mercury vapor enters a condenser at 800°F, 0.5 psia. The mercury emerges as a saturated liquid at 0.4 psia. Calculate the rate of energy transfer as heat from the mercury side of the condenser (Fig. B·10, Table B·3).

5·21 Oxygen passes through an adiabatic steady-flow compressor at the rate of 1000 lbm/hr, entering as a saturated vapor at 36.6 psia and emerging at 17.5 atm and 175°K. Determine the shaft work per unit of mass of O_2 (compare Prob. 5·9) and the required motor hp.

5·22 Five hundred lbm/min of CO_2 passes through an adiabatic steady-flow turbine, entering at 400 psia and 100°F and emerging as a saturated vapor at 100 psia. What is the shaft-work output per lbm of CO_2 (compare Prob. 5·8), and what is the power (kw) delivered by the turbine?

5·23 Ten lbm/min of mercury enters a small turbine at 30 psia and 1400°F and emerges at 2 psia and 800°F. What is the shaft-power output if the "heat losses" (energy transfer as heat from the turbine casing) are negligible? What is the shaft-power output if the "heat losses" amount to 20 percent of the power output for the adiabatic device (Fig. B·10)?

5·24 Steam flows through a small steam turbine at the rate of 10,000 lbm/hr, entering at 600°F and 200 psia and emerging at 2 psia with 4 percent moisture. The flow enters at 250 ft/sec at a point 6 ft above the discharge and leaves at 140 ft/sec. Compute the shaft-power output, assuming that the device is adiabatic but considering kinetic and potential energies. How much error would be made were these secondary terms neglected? What are the diameters of the inlet and discharge pipes (Fig. B·2, Tables B·1, B·2)?

5·25 If the state at the discharge of the nozzle in the turbine of Prob. 5·24 is 8 percent moisture and 10 psia, what is the velocity at this point?

5·26 Air enters an adiabatic nozzle at 3 atm pressure and 100°F and emerges at 1 atm and 30°F. The inlet velocity is negligible, and the nozzle is adiabatic. What is the discharge velocity (Fig. B·8)?

5·27 The collecting panels of a solar boiler receive energy as heat at the rate of approximately 300 Btu/hr per square foot of collecting surface during the day. How many square feet of collector would be required for a small desert power plant producing 10 kw of electrical power if the electric power output is 8 percent of the collected solar energy? (This is a typical energy-conversion efficiency for such a system.)

5·28 Oxygen flows at the rate of 100 lbm/sec through a line to a large booster rocket. The lox enters the line as a saturated liquid at 2 atm, and the pressure drop is negligible. Specify the maximum permitted heat-transfer rate ("heat leak in") to the lox if a maximum of 0.5 percent vapor can be tolerated at the booster end of the line (Fig. B·5).

5·29 The throttling calorimeter is a device for measuring the state of a liquid-vapor mixture. The procedure is to bleed off a little of the mixture, throttle it through a valve, and make the measurements shown. Explain why P_1 and T_1 do not fix the state of the "wet" mixture, and how P_2 and T_2 measurements allow one to determine state 1. How much throttling is necessary for this scheme to work? Compute the quality at state 1 for the measurements below, assuming the fluid is water (Tables B·1 and B·2).

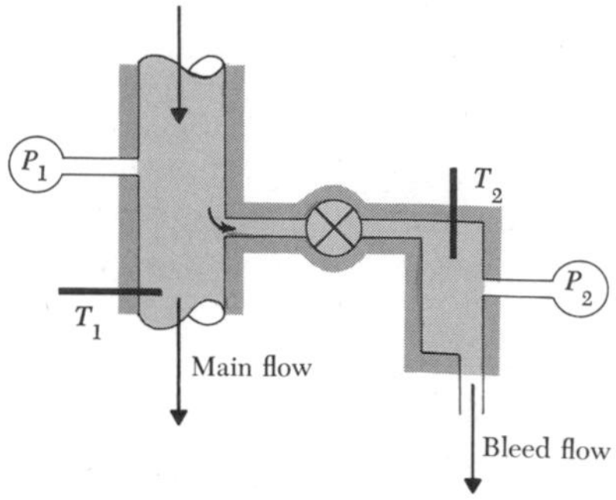

P_1 = 100 psia $\quad$ P_2 = 5 psia
T_1 = 327.81°F $\quad$ T_2 = 200°F

5·30 A valve in an insulated liquid-oxygen fuel line causes a pressure drop of 3 psia. The inlet state is saturated liquid at 2 atm. What is the discharge quality, and how much is the temperature reduced (Fig. B·5)?

5·31 Mercury emerges from the nuclear boiler of a space power system at 500 psia and 0.95 quality and is "flashed" by passing through a flow restriction (valve) into the superheat region to a pressure of 50 psia. What is the temperature of the mercury in this superheated state (Fig. B·10, Table B·3)?

5·32 Determine the air-flow rate that could be used in the air-CO_2-exchanger example if the CO_2 states and the inlet air state are as given but the air emerges as cold as possible.

5·33 A mixture of CO_2 containing 20 percent solid by mass, 20 percent liquid, and 60 percent vapor enters a pipe and emerges all vapor at the inlet pressure and 0°F. The flow rate is 4 lbm/sec. What is the rate at which energy is transferred as heat to the pipe?

5·34 Work the nozzle example using the control-mass approach.

5·35 Work the mercury-turbine example using the control-mass approach.

5·36 Work the tank-charging example using the control-mass approach.

5·37 Ten lbm/min of saturated-liquid mercury at 415°F and 2 lbm/min of mercury vapor at 700°F and 1 psia enter an adiabatic mixing device; the mercury emerges mixed in a single stream at 0.3 psia. What is the temperature of the emergent stream, and (if it is a mixture) what is its quality (Fig. B·10)?

5·38 Oxygen is used in a low-temperature refrigerator. The hardware is similar to that of the heat-pump example. The condenser pressure is 20 atm and the O_2 is evaporated at 2 atm. Liquid emerges from the condenser in the saturated state and vapor from the evaporator at a temperature of 100°K. The compressor outlet temperature is 225°K. Determine the coefficient of performance of this refrigerator, where

cop = (rate of energy removal from cold space)/(compressor power input)

What is the required oxygen-flow rate for a total cooling rate $\dot{Q}_E$ of 10,000 Btu/hr?

5·39 A small solar engine for desert water pumping uses steam as the working fluid. The hardware is shown in the figure. Water enters the pump as a saturated liquid at 120°F and is pumped up to 30 psia by a small centrifugal pump. The boiler evaporates the water at 30 psia, and saturated vapor at this pressure enters the small turbine. The steam leaves the turbine with 6 percent moisture at 120°F and is subsequently condensed. The flow rate is 300 lbm/hr, and the pump is driven by a ½-hp motor operating at full load. Making suitable idealizations, determine the power output of this plant (net hp), the energy-conversion efficiency (net shaft-work output/energy transfer to fluid in boiler), and estimate the number of square feet of solar collectors that would be required, assuming that the collectors can pick up 250 Btu/hr per square foot of exposed surface.

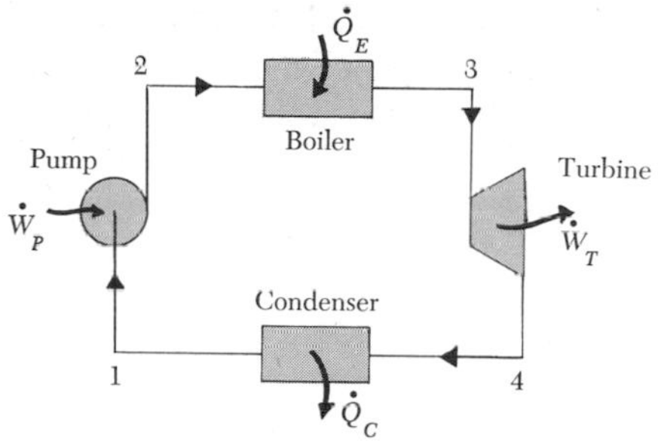

5·40 A proposed nuclear power system for space use employs mercury as the working fluid, using hardware similar to that in Prob. 5·39 above, except that a nuclear reactor replaces the sun as the energy source. The mercury enters the pump as a saturated liquid at 800°F, is compressed, and is then evaporated at 400 psia and superheated to 1400°F in the reactor-boiler. The turbine discharge is at 800°F with 3 percent moisture; pressure drops through the reactor and condenser may be neglected for this thermodynamic analysis. The power required to operate the pump will be 2 percent of the turbine-shaft power. Determine the energy-conversion efficiency for this system (net shaft power/reactor-power input), and the mercury-flow rate and reactor power required for 10 kw of net electrical power, assuming a 95-percent-efficient electrical generator will be employed (Fig. B·10, Table B·3).

5·41 Consider an electrical resistor through which flows a steady current i. The resistor is cooled in order to maintain a steady state. From thermodynamic considerations, show that the rate at which energy must be transferred from the resistor as heat is $\dot{Q} = i\,\Delta\mathcal{E}$, where $\Delta\mathcal{E}$ is the voltage drop across the resistor. What are the restrictions on this result imposed by the idealizations?

5·42 In a linear accelerator electrons are accelerated until their kinetic energy is 10 Mev per electron. If the beam is accidentally diverted it will strike the ⅛-in.-thick copper walls of the cavities and can cause serious damage. Assuming that a beam carrying 10^{18} (electrons/sec)/cm² moving at right angles to the wall strikes the wall and all electrons are stopped, what cooling rate (Btu/hr-ft²) must be provided to prevent a rise in the temperature of the wall? The electrostatic potential energy of the electrons at the point of impact is negligible compared to their kinetic energy.

5·43 Freon-12 will be used as the propellant for a small portable jet rocket for maneuvering parts during the assembly of a space station. The device will consist of a small spherical tank containing saturated freon-12 at 80°F, a valve, and a nozzle. The user will attach the jet to the package, open the valve momentarily, and let some gas escape through the nozzle. Energy transfer as heat from the walls to the freon-12 will keep the pressure constant in the cylinder during a short burst, and the flow through the nozzle may be considered steady. The valve will throttle the freon-12 to 20 psia, and the nozzle discharge state will be 2 psia and −80°F. The thrusting force is approximately given by $F = \dot{M}V/g_c$, where $\dot{M}$ is the mass-flow rate and V the exit velocity. Use requirements call for a thrust of 10 lbf. Determine the specific impulse of this device, $SI = F/\dot{M}$, in lbf/(lbm/sec). By comparison, a good chemical rocket has an SI of the order of 250 lbf/(lbm/sec). Specify the size of tank required to hold enough freon-12 for 1000 sec of operation, assuming that the heat-transfer rate is sufficient to keep the pressure constant for short-duration bursts. Compute the total amount of energy which must be transferred from the walls to the freon-12 during this 1000 sec of operation in order to maintain the pressure (Fig. B·7, Table B·5). This requires a careful energy analysis.

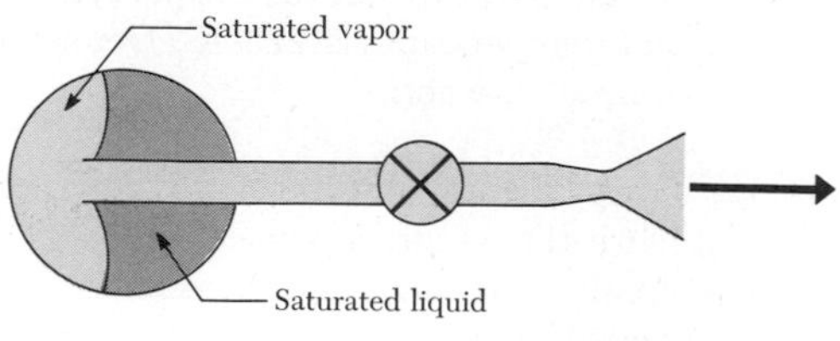

5·44 A small power system proposed for use in the arctic has the hardware of Prob. 5·39 and uses CO_2 as the working fluid. However, a supercritical cycle is employed; condensation occurs underground at −60°F, and saturated CO_2 liquid leaves the condenser at this temperature. The pump raises the pressure to 1600 psia, and the liquid emerges from the pump at −40°F. A solar collector is used to heat the CO_2 to 160°F, and the pressure drop through the "supercritical boiler" is 200 psia. The CO_2, at 1400 psia and 160°F, then enters the turbine and emerges at −40°F and 0.90 quality. Find the energy-conversion efficiency (net shaft-energy output/solar-energy input) for this system. Specify the pump power, turbine power, and solar-energy-collection rate required for a 10-kw plant, assuming that the electric generator has an efficiency of 92 percent. Make appropriate idealizations to allow solutions (Fig. B·6).

5·45 The hardware for a proposed SNAP system for generation of electrical power for space vehicles is shown on the facing page.

The boiler is a nuclear reactor in which the working fluid is heated by passage over the nuclear fuel elements. $\dot{Q}_B$ represents the rate of energy transfer as heat from the rods to the fluid, and is equal to the reactor power. The condenser is a heat exchanger in which energy transferred as heat from the fluid is radiated away to space at the rate $\dot{Q}_C$. Pressure drop through the boiler, condenser, ducting are negligible, and the pump, valve, turbine, and ducting are adiabatic devices.

Mercury is proposed as the working fluid. The mercury will leave the condenser as a saturated liquid at 30 psia. The pump will raise the pressure to 400 psia, where evaporation will occur. The mercury will leave the reactor at 95 percent quality (at 400 psia). The valve provides pressure drop for load control.

The manufacturer of the electromagnetic pump says he can provide a pump that will do the job for a work input of about 0.5 Btu/lbm of mercury pumped. The turbine manufacturer feels he can build a turbine with an "isentropic efficiency" of 60 percent for the range of flows probably involved. The isentropic efficiency is

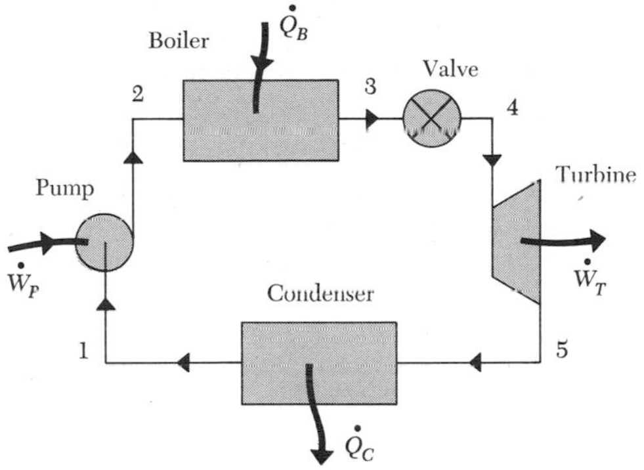

$$\eta_s = \frac{h_4 - h_5}{h_4 - h_{5s}}$$

where h_4 and h_5 are the enthalpies entering and leaving the actual turbine, and h_{5s} is the enthalpy at a hypothetical reference state fixed by the inlet entropy (s) and outlet pressure.

(*a*) Suppose the component manufacturers can indeed deliver as they promise. Determine the component energy flows per lbm of mercury assuming that the valve is wide open so that $P_3 = P_4$. Determine the *net* work output per unit of mass and the overall system efficiency (efficiency of conversion of the reactor power to mechanical shaft power). Then, specify the required mass flow rate if the net shaft power is to be 10 kw. Calculate the pump power, reactor power, turbine power, and condenser cooling rate (kw) for this flow; discuss briefly the distribution of the input reactor energy.

(*b*) Suppose the velocity of the stream at section 5 is limited to a maximum of 100 ft/sec. Calculate the required duct diameter at this point.

(*c*) Suppose the valve is partially closed such that the turbine inlet pressure is reduced to 100 psia, while the same evaporating and condensing pressures, and flow, are maintained. Determine the net power output in this configuration, the condenser cooling rate, and the overall system efficiency.

5·46 A geothermal power plant in California uses steam produced underground by natural sources. Steam enters the adiabatic turbine at 362°F and 80 psia, and emerges at 2 psia with 8 percent moisture (92 percent quality). It is then condensed at 2 psia, and then pumped back up to atmospheric pressure. The plant produces 12.5 Mw of electric power. Assuming an electric generator efficiency of 0.95, and neglecting the pump power, determine the steam flow rate and the condenser heat-transfer rate. Why do you think the system has the condenser? Why does it need the pump?

5·47 It is desired to reduce the pressure of cesium vapor from 50 psia at 2400°R to 1.9 psia. Suggest a means for doing this in a steady-flow device without any energy transfer as heat or shaft work to or from the system. For your device, what is the exit temperature at 1.9 psia?

5·48 You are required to determine the state of a mixture of liquid and vapor mercury used in a power plant for a space application. Only P and T measurements can be made. Design a system to fix the mixture state. The system must be reliable, inexpensive, and simple.

5·49 Freon-12 vapor flows at 10 ft/sec at 300 psia and 360°F. It is desired to accelerate the flow to 500 ft/sec at a pressure of 200 psia in a steady-flow device. What hardware is required and what is the exit temperature?

5·50 Consider the steady, one-dimensional, adiabatic, frictionless flow of an ideal gas in a passage of variable area. Suppose that the gas emerges from a chamber at temperature T_0 with negligible kinetic energy, and is accelerated to velocity V in a passage of appropriate design. At this point it now has temperature T, sound speed a, and Mach number $M \equiv \mathsf{V}/a$. For the ideal gas, $a^2 = g_c kRT$. Show that

$$\frac{T_0}{T} = 1 + \frac{k-1}{2} M^2$$

CHAPTER SIX

ENTROPY AND THE SECOND LAW

6·1 THE ESSENCE OF THE SECOND LAW

The central idea of all science is that nature behaves in a manner which in principle is predictable. The concepts of energy and its conservation are used in order to make these predictions quantitative. We have seen how energy-balance analysis is used to predict the change in state of a system due to transfers of energy as heat and work or by spontaneous internal changes. Experience indicates that it is sometimes ideally possible to reverse the directions of energy transfer as heat and work, and thereby reverse the change of state. The energy analyses of the forward and backward processes differ only in the change of sign for each term; that is, the energy analysis is insensitive to the direction of time. But we also know from experience that, while certain spontaneous changes of state can occur in isolated systems, the reverse changes are never observed. Oxygen and hydrogen readily react to form water; but who has ever seen water spontaneously separate into its two basic elements? By itself, first-law analysis cannot reveal the possibility or impossibility of a process; it cannot point the direction of time. The ability to rule out impossible processes is clearly essential to any complete predictive theory of nature. The *second law of thermodynamics* provides the necessary structure for this second type of analysis.

Every system is considered to have a property called its *entropy*. Entropy, like energy, is a *conceptual* property. Part of the concept of entropy is that it is an *extensive* property; the entropy of a system is the sum of the entropies of all its parts. This extensive feature makes it easy to evaluate the entropy of a complex system by hypothetically dissecting it into simpler parts. Another aspect of entropy is the idea that the entropy of an *isolated* system can *never decrease*. This *postulate* is the second law of thermodynamics; it permits entropy to serve as a "signpost of time." Any process that would increase the entropy of an isolated system is possible; any process that would decrease the entropy of an isolated system is impossible; any process that would keep the entropy of an isolated system constant is possible in either the forward or backward direction.

For example, with these second-law ideas we shall be able to predict what chemical reactions can and cannot occur. If we compute the entropy of H_2 and O_2, then the entropy of a system containing 2 moles of H_2 and 1 mole of O_2 can be computed using the extensive feature of entropy. We imagine the H_2 and O_2 reacting in an isolated system, and compute the entropy of the resulting 2 moles of H_2O. It is larger than the sum of the entropies of the 2 moles of H_2 and 1 mole of O_2, and hence the reaction does not violate the second law. However, the reverse reaction would lead to a *decrease* in entropy within the isolated system; this violates the second law, and hence the *reverse* reaction is *impossible*.

As with energy, the understanding of entropy can be greatly enhanced by consideration of the microscopic nature of matter. An analogy will be helpful in grasping the microscopic concepts underlying the second law. Suppose we have a large tray containing a large number of "educated jumping beans," half red and half white. Imagine that we have taught the beans to jump in pairs, thereby trading places, and we set up the tray initially with the white beans on one side and red on the other. An observer viewing the tray from a great distance could not see individual beans; he would say, "That object is white on one side and red on the other." Now we let the beans start jumping; soon our observer might comment, "The red stuff is diffusing through the white; and the system is becoming pink." After a while the tray would appear to our observer a uniform pinkish hue, and he would think that all changes had stopped. From our closer proximity we would see continual change, with the red and white beans relatively evenly distributed. Occasionally we would see momentary concentrations of one color in various spots, but these would disappear quickly and would not be noticed by the sluggish eye of our distant observer. We could repeat this experiment many times; each time the observer would note that the red diffused through the white, and after a while an equilibrium condition was reached. If he noticed this reproducibility, he might attempt to construct a mathematical theory that would explain the diffusion and perhaps even predict its rate. Even in his ignorance of the beans, he might make a rather good theory. But certainly consideration of the beans would allow a better and more understandable theory.

We might permit our observer to experiment on the tray. He could enlarge it, distort it, shake it, but we would allow him to have no permanent control over the behavior of *individual* beans. They would remain free to act as they pleased, jumping randomly from spot to spot. Learning of the existence of the beans, our observer might try to make a statistical theory by postulating that, left to themselves, the bean arrangement tends to become more and more random. As a consequence he would be uncertain about the instantaneous arrangement of the beans, and as time went on any uncertainty he had would surely increase. To make these ideas quantitative he would need some *numerical measure* of the "randomness" or of his "uncertainty" about the detailed bean arrangement when the tray is viewed from afar. When the tray looked half white and half red the beans were relatively well organized and our observer could be relatively certain as to the bean arrangement. As time passed and the tray became pink, the bean arrangements would be more disorganized, and our distant observer would be much less certain about the instantaneous detailed state. The bean randomness or disorder, and his uncertainty, would have increased, and his theory could be based on the postulate that the value of the randomness-uncertainty measure could never decrease.

This analogy has many points of contact with the notions of entropy and the second law of thermodynamics. We can replace the beans by atoms of argon and helium, the tray by an isolating wall, and the observer by ourselves. The same sort of diffusion process would be observed. The quantitative measure of the microscopic randomness, of our uncertainty as to the exact microscopic state when we know only the macroscopic state, is the entropy; we find we can explain the directions of all processes observed in nature with theory developed from the postulate that the microscopic randomness of an *isolated* system, that is, the *entropy* of an isolated system, can never decrease.

In order to use this postulate in an analysis we must be able to evaluate quantitatively the entropy of systems. In statistical thermodynamics the entropy is defined in terms of "probabilities" of the microscopic states. The entropy can then be computed from this definition if the probabilities can be found. In macroscopic thermodynamics the basic concepts of what entropy is and does are employed in order to learn how to evaluate entropy. The microscopic interpretations of entropy are more easily grasped, and consequently we have chosen to start with statistical concepts and definition of entropy. This development is the main theme of this chapter. While the microscopic ideas greatly assist understanding, most practical analysis does not require consideration of the microscopic view. In fact, the entropy can be evaluated from macroscopic laboratory data without any explicit consideration of microscopic states. We shall see how this is done in Chap. Seven. Our combined microscopic-macroscopic approach is designed to help the student understand the concepts and strengthen his ability to work successfully with practical second-law analysis. The objective of this chapter is therefore understanding of the statistical meaning of entropy and the plausibility of the second law. We emphasize that the ability to work quantitatively with the statistical ideas is *not* required now.

6·2 ALLOWED QUANTUM STATES

What are the possible microscopic states of a system? A key idea that we take from quantum mechanics is that the states which atoms, molecules, and entire systems have are *discretely quantized*. For example, a photon associated with radiation of a particular frequency ν can have but one energy. This is given by the Einstein-Planck equation,

$$\epsilon = h\nu \tag{6·1}$$

The constant h is *Planck's constant,* 6.625×10^{-34} joule-sec. The energy traveling with radiation is therefore said to be *quantized.*

Electrons having a given energy can be used to bombard a sample of a gas, and the emitted radiation can be examined in a spectroscope. At low bombardment energies no radiation is emitted, but when a certain threshold is reached light suddenly appears. With mercury, for example, when the energy of the electrons passes 4.86 ev a bright line at 2537 Å suddenly appears in the spectroscope. The interpretation given this line is that it is produced by the decay of atoms of mercury from an "excited state" to the normal or "ground state." Electrons with energies greater than 4.86 ev are required to produce this excitation, which we view as an increase in the energy of electrons orbiting the nucleus as a result of interactions with the bombarding electrons. The excited state appears to be a definite repeatable level above the ground state. The energy jump between the two states of the atom is calculated assuming that energy is conserved in the decay and that the energy of the emitted radiation is equal to the decrease in the energy of the atom. It is further assumed that a single photon is emitted per decay. The energy-level difference is then given by the Einstein-Planck equation as

$$\epsilon_1 - \epsilon_0 = h\nu$$

When this calculation is made using the measured wavelength of 2537 Å, the energy-level difference is found to be 4.86 ev.

The single line remains as the energy of the impinging electrons is increased, until at about 7 ev a new line appears at 1849 Å, corresponding to an energy change from 6.67 ev to the ground state. At 8.4 ev new lines appear, corresponding to transitions from 7.8 ev to the ground state and to the other excited states. Lines continue to appear, until at 10.4 ev the impinging electrons possess sufficient energy to remove an electron from orbit, ionizing the mercury atom. It appears that the ejected electrons can have any energy, so that the ionized atom can accept any parcel of energy greater than the "ionization potential" of 10.4 ev.

At low temperatures practically all the atoms of mercury exist in the ground state, and bombardment by electrons or other particles is necessary to produce excited states. However, at higher temperatures collisions between the rapidly translating mercury atoms can have the same effect, and as the temperature increases, the excitations and decays become more and more frequent. High temperatures, electron collisions, and every other way of producing emission of light from gas atoms are all means of promoting the atoms to excited states. The skilled spectroscopist can examine the spectrum of a substance and from it enumerate the "allowed quantum states" of its atoms or molecules. The

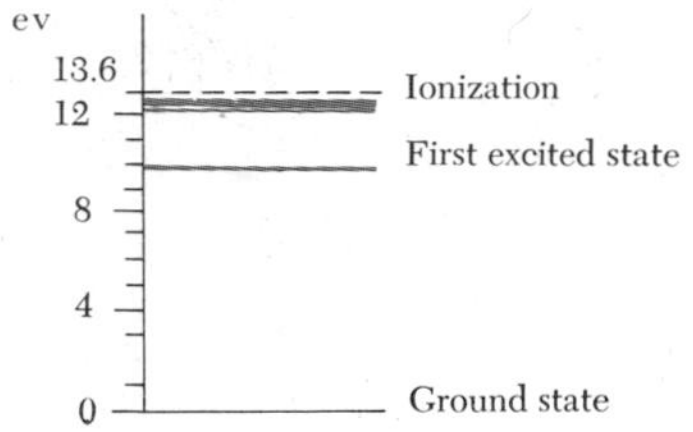

FIG. 6·1 *Electronic quantum states for a hydrogen atom*

electronic quantum states determined in this manner for the simplest atom, hydrogen, are shown in Fig. 6·1.

The quantum theory of matter and energy seemingly meets every test man has been able to devise. By postulating that any particle or system of particles constrained in some manner (such as being required to orbit a nucleus, being in a magnetic field, or being in a box of specified size) can exist only in certain *allowed quantum states*, we obtain amazingly complete and precise descriptions of all natural phenomena. The allowed states are determined by the nature of the particles and the circumstances in which they find themselves; an equation, known as the *Schrödinger equation*, has been postulated as the basis for calculation of the allowed quantum states. For the present we need only the idea that the allowed states of a system are quantized, and it is not necessary to be able to evaluate these states.

It is important to appreciate that quantization refers to very detailed *microscopic* descriptions of state. At any instant a piece of matter must be in one of its allowed quantum states. Macroscopic instruments, which average over time, will reflect averages over the sequence of quantum states; hence macroscopic descriptions of state are very much less detailed. For example, a microscopic description of state might require values for the energy and position of *each particle*, while macroscopic descriptions might involve only the total energy, volume, the temperature, pressure, and of course the entropy.

6·3 QUANTUM-STATE PROBABILITIES

Systems of many interacting molecules undergo continual change in their quantum state. Macroscopic instruments are unable to follow these rapid changes, and hence tend to average over a long sequence of quantum states. Since we have essentially no control over individual molecules, it is really quite impossible for us to force the system to be in a particular quantum state at the start of an experiment; hence if we repeat the experiment a number of times a different initial quantum state will be involved in each repetition. Consequently a different sequence of quantum states will be traced out in each experiment. A large set of such repetitions (real or hypothetical) is called an *ensemble* of experiments.

Traces of the quantum-state numbers (no one has ever measured these in a real experiment) might look something like those in Fig. 6·2. The sequences

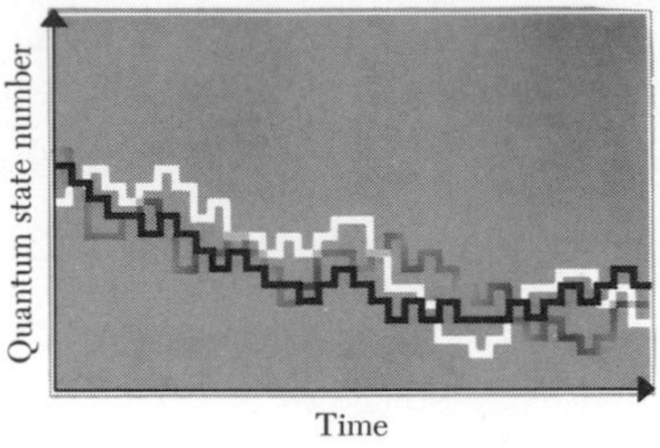

(*a*) *There is little difference between experiments in this ensemble*

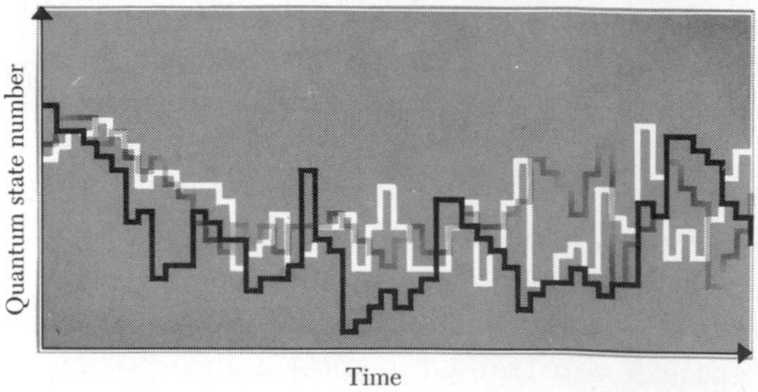

(*b*) *There is much more variation between experiments in this ensemble*

FIG. 6·2 *Quantum-state sequences; each trace represents a different experiment*

of Fig. 6·2*a* are nearly identical; at each time a narrow band of quantum states is found. In contrast, the sequences of Fig. 6·2*b* are much more random; at each instant there is a wide variation in quantum states between experiments. Consequently, a guess about the instantaneous quantum state in a particular experiment might be quite close for sequence (*a*), but may be way off for sequence (*b*). A *quantitative* measure of the *likelihood* of a particular quantum state existing at some time would be useful. The *quantum-state probability* $p_i(t)$ provides this measure. $p_i(t)$ is defined as the fraction of the ensemble of experiments in which quantum state i would be realized at time t. If the realized quantum states (those which actually occur) are few, the p_i will be high. If the realized quantum states are many, the p_i will be low. If in every experiment the same quantum state exists at time t, the probability of that quantum state will be unity and the probability of all other quantum states will be zero. The set of all the p_i's is called the *distribution;* it reflects the relative likelihood of particular quantum states. Since the sum of the probabilities of all the allowed quantum states must be unity,

$$\sum_i p_i = 1$$

Suppose we allow a system to reach equilibrium with its environment. Thereafter there are no macroscopic changes, though the microscopic state is undergoing continual change. In equilibrium there is nothing special about any point in time, and consequently the p_i's must be independent of time. The resulting distribution is called the *equilibrium distribution.* In equilibrium p_i can be taken as the fraction of *time* that a single system spends in the ith allowed quantum state. The time-fraction definition of probability is valid only in equilibrium; for nonequilibrium the ensemble-fraction definition must be used.

The system properties used in macroscopic analysis are averages over the continuous sequence of microscopic states. Since in equilibrium the p_i represent the fraction of time spent in each state, if we know any property G_i of each quantum state we can calculate the average G as

$$\langle G \rangle \equiv \sum_i p_i G_i \tag{6·2}$$

Thus, for example, if ϵ_i is the energy of the ith quantum state, the average energy is

$$\langle E \rangle = \sum_i p_i \epsilon_i \tag{6·3}$$

This type of average is also used for systems that are not in equilibrium, that is, where the p_i depend upon time. The average can then be interpreted as an average over an ensemble (real or hypothetical) of experiments; the ensemble average reflects the "expected" value of a property in any particular experiment, and hence ensemble averages are sometimes called "expectation values."

The probabilities indicate the "randomness" of the equilibrium quantum states. For example, suppose we have a system that can exist in one of three quantum states. If the equilibrium distribution is

$$(a)\quad p_1 = 1 \qquad p_2 = 0 \qquad p_3 = 0$$

we know that the system is always in quantum state 1; the randomness is zero. If asked to guess the instantaneous quantum state, we could say "one" with absolute certainty. Suppose that the equilibrium distribution is

$$(b)\quad p_1 = 0.8 \qquad p_2 = 0.2 \qquad p_3 = 0$$

This says that 80 percent of the time the system is in quantum state 1, and 20 percent of the time it is in quantum state 2. Asked to guess the instantaneous state we would again say "one," and in the long run we would be correct 80 percent of the time. This distribution shows more randomness than case (*a*) above. Our uncertainty as macroscopic observers about the instantaneous microscopic state is certainly greater in (*b*) than in (*a*). If the equilibrium distribution is

$$(c)\quad p_1 = 0.8 \qquad p_2 = 0.1 \qquad p_3 = 0.1$$

or

$$(d)\quad p_1 = 0.1 \qquad p_2 = 0.8 \qquad p_3 = 0.1$$

the quantum-state sequence will show even more variation or randomness, and we shall be even more uncertain about the instantaneous quantum state. However, the same uncertainty will apply to both (*c*) and (*d*). The most randomness is indicated by the distribution

$$(e)\quad p_1 = p_2 = p_3 = 1/3$$

Here each allowed quantum state is equally likely, and we can only guess the instantaneous state with 33 percent chance of being correct. Note that the "broader" the distribution is the more uncertain we must be about the instantaneous quantum state.

We have seen that the distribution conveys a qualitative impression of the randomness of the sequence of quantum states, that is, of our uncertainty as to the instantaneous microscopic state. A list of all the p_i would convey a very good picture of the randomness and uncertainty. This list would be far too long to be usable; it would be much more convenient if we could use a *single number* to measure the amount of randomness and uncertainty reflected by the entire list of p_i. The *entropy* provides this measure.

6·4 ENTROPY

Since the entire set of p_i reflect the quantum-state randomness, it would seem appropriate to look for some function of all the p_i that would serve as a single measure of randomness. We shall call this randomness measure the *entropy*, and denote it by S.

For operational convenience we shall define S such that it is *extensive*. That is, the entropy of system C, composed of parts A and B, must be given by

$$S_C = S_A + S_B \tag{6·4}$$

The randomness measure should also give greater values of S when the system is more random; that is, it should agree with the qualitative ideas about randomness. We are now going to use these ideas to discover an appropriate definition of S in terms of the probability distribution.

Now, we ask what function of the p_i might be useful as a single numerical measure of the randomness? The product of the probabilities $p_1 \times p_2 \cdot \cdot \cdot \times p_n$ won't do, because it will be zero when *any* one of the p_i is zero. The sum of the p_i won't do either because it always has the value unity. The *average* probability is sometimes used in statistics as a measure of randomness, so let's see if it will work. The average probability is [see Eq. (6·2)]

$$\langle p \rangle = \sum_i p_i p_i = \sum_i p_i^2$$

When $\langle p \rangle$ is high only a few quantum states are realized, and there is little randomness. When it is low many quantum states are realized and there is much randomness and uncertainty. Hence the average probability does seem to fit the qualitative requirements of a randomness measure. Is it extensive? To investigate this we first make use of Eq. (6·4). Suppose there are n allowed states for system A and m allowed states for system B. If the allowed states in each part are independent of those in the other, the quantum state for the combined system C can be described by specifying the quantum states of A and B; we denote these by i and j, respectively, and suppose that they are numbered such that $i = 1, 2, \ldots, n$, $j = 1, 2, \ldots, m$. The allowed states for C can then be denoted by the number pair i, j. For example, C-state 2,6 is the state where part A is in its state $i = 2$ and part B is in its state $j = 6$. There are $n \cdot m$ allowed states for C, corresponding to the $n \cdot m$ points in Fig. 6·3.

The probability of each C state can be computed from the individual probabilities for A and B states. If p_i is the probability of A-state i, and p_j the probability of B-state j, then

$$p_{ij} = p_i \cdot p_j \tag{6·5}$$

is the probability of the C-state i, j. This follows from a basic part of the concept of probability, namely, that probabilities are such that the joint probability of two independent events (the realization of A-state i and the realization of B-state j) is the *product* of their individual probabilities.†

Now, the average probabilities of A and B are

$$\langle p \rangle_A = \sum_{i=1}^{n} p_i^2 \qquad \langle p \rangle_B = \sum_{j=1}^{m} p_j^2$$

and the average probability of C is

$$\langle p \rangle_C = \sum_{i=1}^{n} \sum_{j=1}^{m} p_{ij}^2 = \sum_{i=1}^{n} \sum_{j=1}^{m} (p_i p_j)^2$$

Rearranging the sums,

$$\langle p \rangle_C = \sum_{i=1}^{n} \left[p_i^2 \left(\sum_{j=1}^{m} p_j^2 \right) \right] = \sum_{i=1}^{n} p_i^2 \langle p_B \rangle = \langle p_A \rangle \langle p_B \rangle$$

† For example, if there is only an 0.2 chance that A-state 2 will exist, and only an 0.3 chance that B-state 6 will exist, then there is only an 0.06 chance of them both existing at the same time, that is, C-state 2,6 has a probability of 0.06.

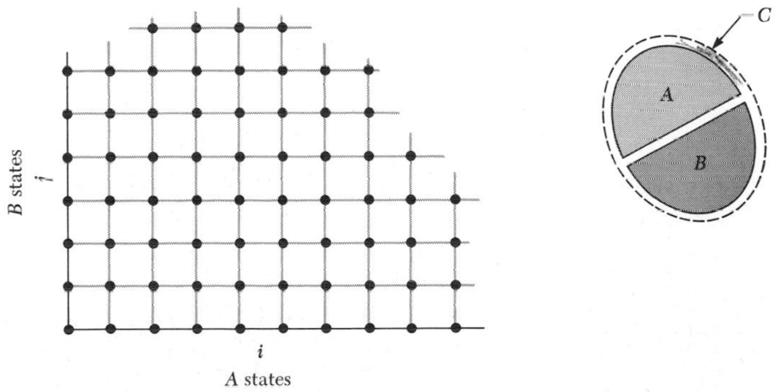

FIG. 6·3 *The allowed states of C are determined from all possible combinations of allowed states of A and B. Each point represents a C state*

Noting that

$$\langle p \rangle_C \neq \langle p \rangle_A + \langle p \rangle_B$$

we conclude that the average probability is *not* extensive; as yet we have not found an appropriate definition for entropy.

Let's be more systematic and ask, "What function of the probability *does* have an average which is extensive?" This leads us to look for a definition of entropy S in the form

$$S = \langle f \rangle = \sum_i p_i f(p_i) \tag{6·6}$$

The function $f(p_i)$ remains to be found. Then

$$S_A = \sum_{i=1}^{n} p_i f(p_i) \qquad S_B = \sum_{j=1}^{m} p_j f(p_j)$$

$$S_C = \sum_{i=1}^{n} \sum_{j=1}^{m} p_{ij} f(p_{ij}) = \sum_{i=1}^{n} \sum_{j=1}^{m} p_i \cdot p_j f(p_i \cdot p_j)$$

Applying Eq. (6·4),

$$\sum_{i=1}^{n} \sum_{j=1}^{m} p_i p_j f(p_i \cdot p_j) = \sum_{i=1}^{n} p_i f(p_i) + \sum_{j=1}^{m} p_j f(p_j) \tag{6·7}$$

f must be such that this is true regardless of the values of the p_i and p_j. A function that will work is $f(\quad) = \ln(\quad)$. With this choice, the left-hand side of Eq. (6·7) becomes (recall that $\ln(a \cdot b) = \ln a + \ln b$)

$$\sum_{i=1}^{n} \sum_{j=1}^{m} p_i p_j \ln p_i + \sum_{i=1}^{n} \sum_{j=1}^{m} p_i p_j \ln p_j$$

Rearranging the sums, this becomes

$$\sum_{i=1}^{n} \left[p_i \ln p_i \left(\sum_{j=1}^{m} p_j \right) \right] + \sum_{j=1}^{m} \left[p_j \ln p_j \left(\sum_{i=1}^{n} p_i \right) \right]$$

since

$$\sum_{i=1}^{n} p_i = 1 \qquad \sum_{j=1}^{m} p_j = 1$$

the left-hand side of Eq. (6·7) may be expressed as

$$\sum_{i=1}^{n} p_i \ln p_i + \sum_{j=1}^{m} p_j \ln p_j$$

Hence Eq. (6·7) is precisely satisfied for *any* p_i, p_j, n, and m with this choice for f. It may be shown that† the most general $f(p_i)$ whose average is an extensive property is $f = C \ln p_i$, where C is an arbitrary constant; since p_i is less than unity, we choose the constant to be negative to make the entropy positive. Our definition of entropy, the extensive randomness-uncertainty measure, is therefore

$$\blacktriangleright \quad S = -\mathsf{k} \sum_i p_i \ln p_i \tag{6·8}$$

The constant k is chosen as the *Boltzmann* constant,

$$\mathsf{k} = 1.380 \times 10^{-23} \text{ joule/°K}$$

This choice makes the thermodynamic temperature (defined in Chap. Seven) the same as the empirical temperature used in previous chapters.

We must now become convinced that the entropy has the proper qualitative features of a randomness or uncertainty measure. Arguments in support of this contention will now be given.

† To show this, consider the special case where $p_i = 1/n$ and $p_j = 1/m$. Then Eq. (6·7) becomes

$$\sum_{i=1}^{n} \sum_{j=1}^{m} \frac{1}{n} \frac{1}{m} f\left(\frac{1}{n} \frac{1}{m}\right) = \sum_{i=1}^{n} \frac{1}{n} f\left(\frac{1}{n}\right) + \sum_{j=1}^{m} \frac{1}{m} f\left(\frac{1}{m}\right)$$

Carrying out the sums

$$f\left(\frac{1}{n} \cdot \frac{1}{m}\right) = f\left(\frac{1}{n}\right) + f\left(\frac{1}{m}\right)$$

The function $f(\;)$ must therefore satisfy the *functional equation*

$$f(xy) = f(x) + f(y)$$

Functional equations are usually solved by obtaining a differential equation which the function must satisfy. To do this, we differentiate the functional equation with respect to x, obtaining

$$y \frac{df(xy)}{d(xy)} = \frac{df(x)}{dx}$$

Differentiating this with respect to y,

$$\frac{df(xy)}{d(xy)} + (xy) \frac{d^2f(xy)}{d(xy)^2} = 0$$

Letting $z = xy$, this is

$$z \frac{d^2f}{dz^2} + \frac{df}{dz} = 0$$

The general solution of this linear second-order differential equation is

$$f(z) = C_1 + C_2 \ln (z)$$

The functional equation will not be satisfied unless $C_1 = 0$. Hence, the most general solution to the functional equation is indeed $f(z) = C \ln (z)$

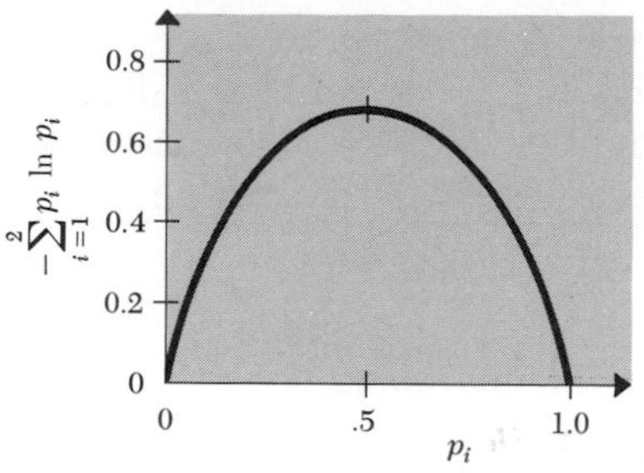

FIG. 6·4 *Note that S is greatest when there is the most randomness*

Since the uniform probability distribution reflects the greatest randomness, no system with n allowed states should ever have a greater entropy than when each state is equally likely ($p_i = 1/n$). Indeed, the maximum value of S occurs for this case. We can see this easily for $n = 2$. Then

$$S = -\mathsf{k}(p_1 \ln p_1 + p_2 \ln p_2)$$

Since

$$p_1 + p_2 = 1$$

p_1 and p_2 cannot both be varied independently. Figure 6·4 shows the variations of S with p_1. Note that S is indeed maximum where $p_1 = p_2 = \frac{1}{2}$. One may indeed show that for any n the uniform distribution has the greatest entropy.

Next, consider that class of distributions where each quantum state is equally likely. Suppose there are Ω equally likely quantum states, so $p_i = 1/\Omega$,

$$S = -\mathsf{k} \sum_{i=1}^{\Omega} \frac{1}{\Omega} \ln \frac{1}{\Omega} = -\mathsf{k}\Omega \left(\frac{1}{\Omega} \ln \frac{1}{\Omega} \right) = -\mathsf{k} \ln \frac{1}{\Omega}$$

$$= \mathsf{k} \ln \Omega \qquad (6 \cdot 9)$$

Hence, the larger the number of possible states, the greater is the entropy. This would seem to be a proper qualitative feature of a randomness-uncertainty measure.

Consider the probability distributions (*a*), (*b*), (*c*), and (*d*) used as examples in Sec. 6·3. These distributions, and their entropies, are

(*a*) $p_1 = 1 \quad p_2 = 0 \quad p_3 = 0$
$S = -\mathsf{k}(1 \ln 1 + 0 \ln 0 + 0 \ln 0) = 0$
(*b*) $p_1 = 0.8 \quad p_2 = 0.2 \quad p_3 = 0$
$S = -\mathsf{k}[0.8 \ln 0.8 + 0.2 \ln 0.2 + 0 \ln 0] = 0.5002\mathsf{k}$
(*c*) $p_1 = 0.8 \quad p_2 = 0.1 \quad p_3 = 0.1$
(*d*) $p_1 = 0.1 \quad p_2 = 0.8 \quad p_3 = 0.1$
$S = -\mathsf{k}[0.8 \ln 0.8 + 0.1 \ln 0.1 + 0.1 \ln 0.1] = 0.6390\mathsf{k}$
(*e*) $p_1 = p_2 = p_3 = \frac{1}{3}$
$S = -\mathsf{k}[\frac{1}{3} \ln \frac{1}{3} + \frac{1}{3} \ln \frac{1}{3} + \frac{1}{3} \ln \frac{1}{3}] = \mathsf{k} \ln 3 = 1.099\mathsf{k}$

Distribution (*a*) reflects no randomness or uncertainty. Distribution (*b*) suggests we know for sure that state 3 is never realized; the higher entropy of distributions (*c*) and (*d*) suggests slightly greater randomness and uncertainty about the state than distribution (*b*). Note that distributions (*c*) and (*d*) have the same entropy. Distribution (*e*), which reflects the greatest randomness and uncertainty, yields the greatest entropy. These all seem to be proper qualitative aspects of a randomness-uncertainty measure; Eq. (6·8) seems to be a plausible definition of entropy.

To summarize, we define the entropy, or microscopic randomness-uncertainty measure, as

$$\blacktriangleright \quad S \equiv -\mathsf{k} \sum_i p_i \ln p_i \tag{6·8}$$

The p_i are the probabilities of individual system quantum states. If all quantum states are equally likely, and there are Ω such equally probable states, it happens that

$$\blacktriangleright \quad S = \mathsf{k} \ln \Omega \tag{6·9}$$

This expression is sometimes taken as the basic definition of entropy. It should be noted that Eq. (6·9), the *Boltzmann* definition of entropy, is appropriate only if each quantum state is equally likely. This is the case for some statistical models of matter, and Eq. (6·9) is widely used in elementary texts on statistical thermodynamics. We shall also make some use of it in subsequent chapters. Equation (6·8), the *Gibbs* definition of entropy, is more general, and hence is preferable as the fundamental definition. The Gibbs definition applies equally well for both equilibrium and nonequilibrium; the Boltzmann definition is only applicable to isolated systems in equilibrium.†

6·5 APPROACH TO EQUILIBRIUM

We have shown that the entropy as defined by Eq. (6·8) is extensive, and has its greatest value when the system quantum state is most random, that is, when we are most uncertain about the instantaneous quantum state. As time passes, we expect the disorder, randomness, and uncertainty, that is, the entropy, of an *isolated* system to increase, and to approach a constant as the isolated

† For an excellent discussion of the virtues of Eq. (6·8), see R. C. Tolman, *The Principles of Statistical Mechanics*, p. 562, Oxford University Press, London, 1938. See also L. D. Landau and E. M. Lifshitz, *Statistical Physics*, p. 25, Pergamon Press, New York, 1958; J. H. Keenan and G. N. Hatsopoulos, *Principles of General Thermodynamics*, p. 606, John Wiley & Sons, Inc., New York, 1965; F. Reif, *Fundamentals of Statistical and Thermal Physics*, p. 219, McGraw-Hill Book Company, New York, 1965; M. Tribus, *Thermostatics and Thermodynamics*, p. 84, D. Van Nostrand Company, Inc., Princeton, N.J., 1961.

system approaches equilibrium. The *second law of thermodynamics* is the *postulate* that:

The entropy of an isolated system can never decrease.

In terms of the microscopic notions we have discussed, this seems very plausible. It also works; a vast superstructure of theory has been built upon this postulate, and this theory has never failed to meet the test of a laboratory experiment.

The experiments cited above usually employ macroscopic means to evaluate the entropy, and not the fundamental definition Eq. (6·8). A direct test of the increase in entropy as defined by Eq. (6·8) is difficult to perform in the laboratory, but easy to perform on a computer. We shall now describe such an experiment on an interesting, but nonphysical, system.

Consider a system of 10 particles, each of which can exist in one of 5 states. We denote the particles by A, B, C, . . . , J, and the particle states by their energies 0, 1, 2, 3, and 4. Suppose the system is isolated and has total energy 30. We shall first examine the allowed states of the system. There are many possible system states, some of which are shown in Fig. 6·5. Any state in which the total energy is 30 is possible. All possible combinations were considered with the help of a high-speed computer, and it was found that there are 72,403 possible quantum states. We could not hope to list these here; however, they can be collected into groups of states where the states in each group have the same number of particles in each particle state. For example, quantum states 2 and 3 of Fig. 6·5 would fall in the same group (22). There are only 23 different groups and these are given in Table 6·1.

We can assign probabilities p_i to the 72,403 quantum states. The distribution that maximizes the entropy has each $p_i = 1/72{,}403$, and this is the equilibrium distribution that should be approached in any experiment. Corresponding to any set of $72{,}403 p_i$ is a set of 23 *group* probabilities p_k, each of which is simply the sum of the p_i in that group. Thus, for example, for the equilibrium distribution the probability that the system is in *one* of the 90 states of group 22 is 90/72,403, while the probability that it is in one of the 12,600 states of group 1 is much higher, namely 12,600/72,403. The group probabilities corresponding to the equilibrium distribution are shown in Table 6·1.

Now, suppose the system is in some state in a particular group. We consider changes in state resulting from 2-particle interactions. For example, sup-

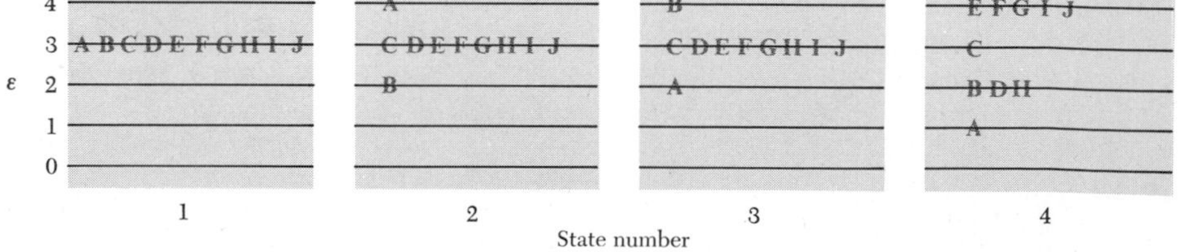

FIG. 6·5 *Some of the allowed states; note each state has a total energy of 30*

TABLE 6·1 THE ALLOWED STATES†

Group k	*Number of particles with each energy*					*Number of quantum states*	*Equilibrium group probability* p_k
	$\varepsilon = 0$	1	2	3	4		
1	0	1	2	3	4	12,600	0.1740
2	0	2	1	2	5	7,560	0.1044
3	1	0	2	2	5	7,560	0.1044
4	1	0	1	4	4	6,300	0.0870
5	0	1	1	5	3	5,040	0.0696
6	0	1	3	1	5	5,040	0.0696
7	1	1	0	3	5	5,040	0.0696
8	1	1	1	1	6	5,040	0.0696
9	0	0	3	4	3	4,200	0.0580
10	0	0	4	2	4	3,150	0.0435
11	0	2	0	4	4	3,150	0.0435
12	0	0	2	6	2	1,260	0.0174
13	0	2	2	0	6	1,260	0.0174
14	2	0	0	2	6	1,260	0.0174
15	1	0	0	6	3	840	0.0116
16	1	0	3	0	6	840	0.0116
17	0	3	0	1	6	840	0.0116
18	0	1	0	7	2	360	0.0050
19	1	2	0	0	7	360	0.0050
20	2	0	1	0	7	360	0.0050
21	0	0	5	0	5	252	0.0035
22	0	0	1	8	1	90	0.0012
23	0	0	0	10	0	1	$0.0_4 14$

† Total number of quantum states = 72,403.

pose the system is in quantum state 1 (state-group 23) of Fig. 6·5. Two particles come together, interact, and may or may not change the system state. There are 45 possible particle pairs for this interaction, and we assume that each pair is equally likely to interact. For each pair there are two interactions that take the system to state 22, and one that leaves the system in state 23. We assume that, for a given particle pair, the possible transitions are equally likely. Hence, the probability that a given pair-interaction will take the system to state 22 is $\frac{2}{3}$, while the probability that a pair interaction will leave the system in state 23 is $\frac{1}{3}$. The transitions from the other state groups are more complicated, but can be computed according to the transition model (equal probability for pair selection, equal probability for the possible transitions for a given pair). Analysis of all pair-interactions permits us to develop a table of

TABLE 6·2 TRANSITION PROBABILITIES

Initial group	*Final group*										
	1	2	3	4	5	6	7	8	9	10	11
1	0.7052	0.0667	0.0267	0.0222	0.0593	0.0444	0.0089	0	0.0444	0.0133	0.0089
2	0.1111	0.7244	0.0148	0	0	0.0178	0.0222	0.0356	0	0	0.0370
3	0.0444	0.0148	0.7452	0.0741	0	0.0222	0.0089	0.0444	0	0.0222	0
4	0.0444	0	0.0889	0.7319	0.0356	0	0.0444	0	0.0178	0	0.0074
5	0.1482	0	0	0.0444	0.6630	0	0	0	0.0222	0	0.0556
6	0.1111	0.0267	0.0333	0	0	0.7000	0	0.0267	0	0.0556	0
7	0.0222	0.0333	0.0133	0.0556	0	0	0.7600	0.0444	0	0	0.0444
8	0	0.0533	0.0667	0	0	0.0267	0.0444	0.7548	0	0	0
9	0.1333	0	0	0.0267	0.0267	0	0	0	0.6578	0.0889	0
10	0.0533	0	0.0533	0	0	0.0889	0	0	0.1185	0.6711	0
11	0.0356	0.0889	0	0.0148	0.0889	0	0.0711	0	0	0	0.7007
12	0	0	0	0	0.1333	0	0	0	0.2222	0	0
13	0	0.0889	0	0	0	0.1333	0	0.0444	0	0	0
14	0	0	0.0533	0	0	0	0.1067	0.0444	0	0	0
15	0	0	0	0.2222	0.0667	0	0	0	0	0	0
16	0	0	0.1333	0	0	0.0533	0	0.0267	0	0	0
17	0	0.2000	0	0	0	0	0	0.0444	0	0	0
18	0	0	0	0	0.3111	0	0	0	0	0	0
19	0	0	0	0	0	0	0	0.1556	0	0	0
20	0	0	0	0	0	0	0	0.1244	0	0	0
21	0	0	0	0	0	0.0889	0	0	0	0.1852	0
22	0	0	0	0	0	0	0	0	0	0	0
23	0	0	0	0	0	0	0	0	0	0	0

Initial group	Final group											
	12	13	14	15	16	17	13	19	20	21	22	23
1	0	0	0	0	0	0	0	0	0	0	0	0
2	0	0.0148	0	0	0	0.0222	0	0	0	0	0	0
3	0	0	0.0089	0	0.0148	0	0	0	0	0	0	0
4	0	0	0	0.0296	0	0	0	0	0	0	0	0
5	0.0333	0	0	0.0111	0	0	0.0222	0	0	0	0	0
6	0	0.0333	0	0	0.0089	0	0	0	0	0.0044	0	0
7	0	0	0.0267	0	0	0	0	0	0	0	0	0
8	0	0.0111	0.0111	0	0.0044	0.0074	0	0.0111	0.0089	0	0	0
9	0.0667	0	0	0	0	0	0	0	0	0	0	0
10	0	0	0	0	0	0	0	0	0	0.0148	0	0
11	0	0	0	0	0	0	0	0	0	0	0	0
12	0.5970	0	0	0.0089	0	0	0.0089	0	0	0	0.0296	0
13	0	0.7007	0	0	0.0148	0.0089	0	0.0089	0	0	0	0
14	0	0	0.7807	0	0	0	0	0	0.0148	0	0	0
15	0.0133	0	0	0.6711	0	0	0.0237	0	0	0	0	0
16	0	0.0222	0	0	0.7111	0	[illegible]	0	0.0267	0.0267	0	0
17	0	0.0133	0	0	0	0.7156	[illegible]	0.0267	0	0	0	0
18	0.0311	0	0	0.0622	0	0	0.5733	0	0	0	0.0222	0
19	0	0.0311	0	0	0	0.0622	[illegible]	0.7363	0.0148	0	0	0
20	0	0	0.0519	0	0.0622	0	[illegible]	0.0148	0.7467	0	0	0
21	0	0	0	0	0.0889	0	[illegible]	0	0	0.6370	0	0
22	0.4148	0	0	0	0	0	0.0889	0	0	0	0.4889	0.0074
23	0	0	0	0	0	0	0	0	0	0	0.6667	0.3333

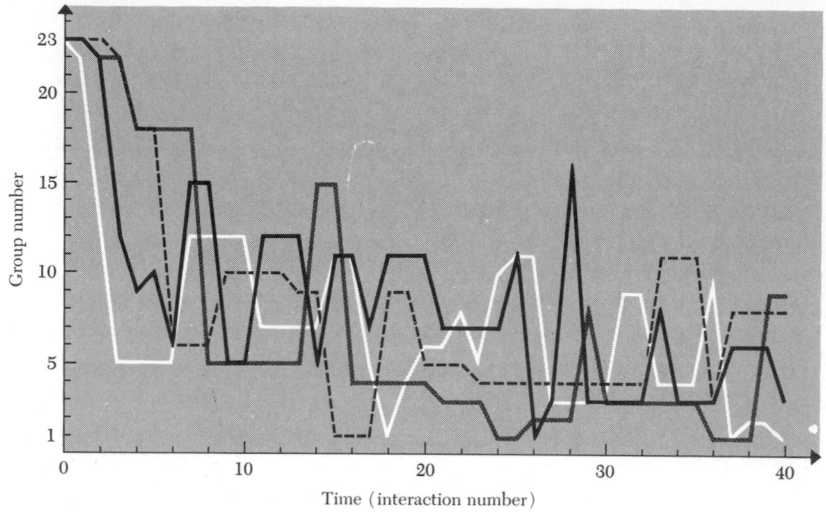

FIG. 6·6 *Four members of the ensemble of experiments*

"transition probabilities" for passage from one quantum state group to another. The results are shown in Table 6·2.†

In the computer experiments we started the system out in state 23, and then followed a long series of interactions chosen randomly in accordance with the transition probabilities of Table 6·2. The experiment was repeated 10,000 times, with a different group history being traced each time. The fraction of the experiments in which each group occurred at time t was used to calculate the group probabilities $p_k(t)$ at each time. The entropy at each time was calculated for the group distribution p_k. The results are shown in Figs. 6·6–6·8. Since the energy of the system was fixed, these results correspond to experiments in an isolated system.

Figure 6·6 shows four members of the ensemble of 10,000 experiments. Each time unit corresponds to one interaction. Note that there is initially no randomness, with all systems in group 23. After the first interaction some remain in group 23 (one third) and some have moved to group 22 (two thirds). At this time there is a slightly greater randomness. The randomness rapidly increases,

† The number of possible particle pairs from a particular pair of energy levels, divided by the total number of particle pairs, gives the "particle selection probabilities" for interaction of two particles from those particular energy levels. Then, all possible movements of two particles from those energy levels must be counted to find the "movement probabilities" for particles chosen from particular levels. The product of the particle selection and movement probabilities gives the probability of transition from one group to another by a particular particle selection-movement combination. Summing over all possible selection-movement combinations that take the system from one quantum state group to another, the total probability of passing from the first to the second group is obtained. Table 6.2 was calculated in this manner.

and before long there are some systems in each state at each time. After many interactions the equilibrium condition is reached, and the quantum-group sequence for any particular experiment becomes quite random.

Figure 6·7 shows the evolution of some of the $p_k(t)$. Note that p_{23} drops rapidly, while p_{22} and p_{12} first increase and then relax toward their equilibrium values. Note that after the first interaction p_{22} was up to 0.6666, and p_{23} had dropped to 0.3333. This is indeed in accordance with the transition probabilities.

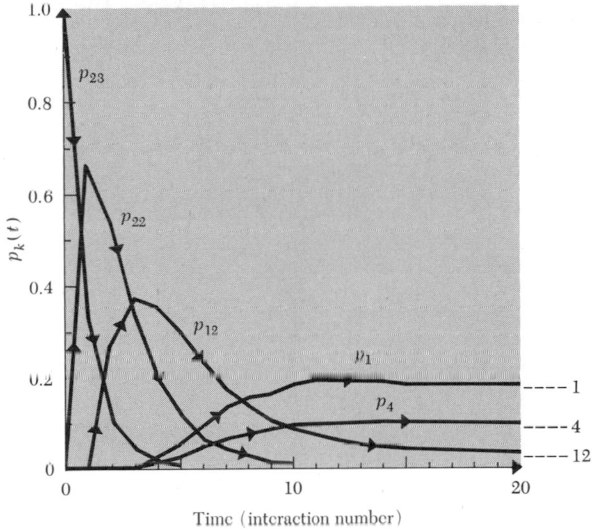

FIG. 6·7 *Some of the $p_k(t)$ for the ensemble of 10,000 experiments*

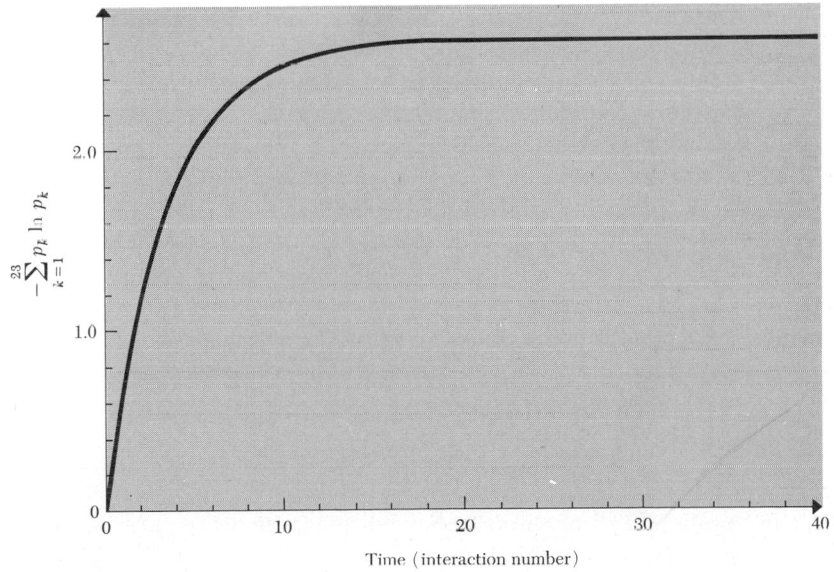

FIG. 6·8 *Group-distribution entropy for the ensemble of 10,000 experiments*

Figure 6·8 shows the group-distribution entropy as a function of time. If our postulate about the natural tendency for the microscopic randomness of an isolated system to increase is correct, the group-distribution entropy should increase. Indeed, the entropy did increase as time went on, and finally approached the equilibrium value computed from the p_k of Table 6·1.

Another interesting calculation can be made using the table of transition probabilities. Since the probability of a transition sequence is the product of the individual step transition probabilities, the transition

23 22 12 9 1

has the probability

$$0.6667 \times 0.4148 \times 0.2222 \times 0.1333 = 0.82 \times 10^{-2}$$

On the other hand, the reverse transition,

1 9 12 22 23

has the probability

$$0.0444 \times 0.0667 \times 0.0296 \times 0.0074 = 0.67 \times 10^{-6}$$

We see that there is a tremendous probability that the system will move toward and persist in the quantum-state groups having high equilibrium probabilities. Once a system has moved from group 23 to group 1 there is only a very slight chance it will ever return to group 23. This overwhelming likelihood of particular tendencies is exhibited even more dramatically by systems of very many particles. The probability is extremely small that a system of 10^{20} particles will move from a quantum state having a broad distribution of particle energies to a quantum state where all particles have the same energy. Such an event would probably not occur even once in the lifetime of the observer, and is far too rare to be useful in an engineering system.

6·6 SUMMARY

The major points we wish to get across in this chapter are the basic microscopic concepts of entropy and the plausibility of the second law.

Entropy is an *extensive property* of matter. The statistical definition of entropy is

$$\blacktriangleright \quad S \equiv -\mathsf{k} \sum_i p_i \ln p_i \qquad (6\cdot 8)$$

where p_i is the "probability" of the ith allowed quantum state. The constant k is chosen as the Boltzmann constant, $\mathsf{k} = 1.380 \times 10^{-23}$ joule/°K, to make the thermodynamic temperature scale (Chap. Seven) correspond to the empirical temperature.

Entropy is defined in terms of the p_i because the set of p_i reflect the microscopic randomness and the resulting uncertainty about the microscopic state when given only macroscopic data. The entropy is a *single number* which measures this randomness and uncertainty. The logarithm appears because $\ln p_i$ is the *only* function of p_i whose average is an extensive property.

The entropy of two systems considered as one is the sum of their individual entropies, provided that the allowed quantum states of each system are independent from those of the other.

The *second law of thermodynamics* is the postulate that:

The entropy of an isolated system can never decrease.

Expressed algebraically, the second law is

$$\left.\begin{array}{ll} & dS \geq 0 \\ \text{or} & \\ & \Delta S \geq 0 \end{array}\right\} \text{for an isolated system}$$

The second law says that we can never know more about the microscopic details of an isolated system than we know at the moment of isolation. Future measurement might reveal more information, but getting this information would require termination of the isolation. As long as the system remains isolated, our uncertainty as to microscopic detail can never decrease.†

Evaluation of entropy of different substances by Eq. (6·8) is an objective

† It is sometimes said that entropy is a measure of microscopic "disorder." Disorder, like beauty, is in the eye of the beholder. Any system that looks random because we are uncertain about the details would look "disordered." Interpreted in this way, the "disorder" concept of entropy is valid.

Sometimes the entropy concept is tied to ideas of the "availability" of energy. The spontaneous changes that take place in an isolated system approaching equilibrium tend to make the distribution of internal energy more random, and hence make it more difficult to extract energy as work (useful "organized" energy transfer). Hence it is sometimes said that the entropy is a measure of the "unavailability of internal energy." An analogy will be helpful in tying this concept of entropy to the uncertainty concepts discussed previously. Suppose you stand facing a baseball pitcher who throws balls at you one at a time. You can see where the balls are headed, and consequently can catch each one, thereby extracting all of its kinetic energy. Since you know precisely where each ball is headed, you can move your glove around and thereby "capture" all of the energy of each ball. Now, turn around, and attempt to catch the balls without being able to see them. With luck you may catch some, and extract all of their kinetic energy. But you will miss many more; without the full knowledge of their trajectories you cannot extract all of their energy as useful work. The greater your uncertainty as to their trajectories, the more "unavailable" is their energy. So it is with the energy associated with the microscopic structure of matter; if the entropy is large, your uncertainty as to the precise microscopic state (given only macroscopic data) is large, and consequently you cannot fully harness the energy of the hidden microscopic modes. Thus, in a very real sense the entropy is indeed a measure of the "unavailability of internal energy."

of statistical thermodynamics. More often the entropy is evaluated by purely macroscopic means, to be discussed in the next chapter.

SELECTED READING

Fast, J. D., *Entropy*, introduction, McGraw-Hill Book Company, New York, 1963.

Goldman, S., *Information Theory*, sec. 1.8, Prentice-Hall, Inc., Englewood Cliffs, N.J., 1953.

Reif, F., *Fundamentals of Statistical and Thermal Physics*, secs. 3.1–3.4, 6.1–6.6, McGraw-Hill Book Company, New York, 1965.

———, *Statistical Physics*, Berkeley Physics Course, vol. 5, secs. 1.1–1.4, 2.1, 2.2, 2.4, McGraw-Hill Book Company, New York, 1967.

Sonntag, R. E., and G. J. Van Wylen, *Fundamentals of Statistical Thermodynamics*, sec. 4.3, John Wiley & Sons, Inc., New York, 1966.

Zemansky, M. W., and H. C. Van Ness, *Basic Engineering Thermodynamics*, sec. 15.6, McGraw-Hill Book Company, New York, 1966.

QUESTIONS

6·1 Why do we need a "second law" of thermodynamics?
6·2 What is the fundamental conceptual property underlying the second law?
6·3 Does the first law rule out the possibility of water spontaneously becoming hydrogen and oxygen in an isolated container?
6·4 How do allowed quantum states differ from macroscopic states?
6·5 What is the "probability" of a quantum state?
6·6 What role does the concept of quantization play in the development of the entropy?
6·7 What is an ensemble-average property?
6·8 What is entropy?
6·9 Is entropy an intensive or extensive property?
6·10 Why is the logarithm involved in the definition of entropy?
6·11 Can the entropy of a system ever decrease?
6·12 What do concepts of uncertainty have to do with thermodynamics?
6·13 How would you explain entropy to your mother?
6·14 Look up entropy in a nontechnical dictionary. Can you reconcile this definition with your concept of entropy?
6·15 When did you first learn about energy? When did you first begin to really understand the concept of energy? Do you understand the concept of entropy?

PROBLEMS

6·1 Consider the following sets of quantum-state probabilities for a system with five allowed states.
(*a*) 0, 0.1, 0.2, 0.3, 0.4
(*b*) 0.2, 0.2, 0.2, 0.2, 0.2

(*c*) 0.5, 0.5, 0, 0, 0
(*d*) 0.3, 0.2, 0.3, 0.2, 0
(*e*) 0.3, 0.3, 0.1, 0.1, 0.3
(*f*) 1, 0, 0, 0, 0
(*g*) 0.1, 0.2, 0.4, 0.3, 0

One of these is not proper as a probability set. Which one, and why not? Assuming that the others represent the distributions at six consecutive moments in an ensemble of experiments on an isolated system, which was the initial distribution and which was the final? Rank the others properly between the initial and final distributions.

6·2 Consider a rectangular box containing N molecules. Suppose that each molecule can be on either side of the box with equal probability. What is the probability that all N molecules are on one side? Compute this number for $N = 1, 2, 20$, and 10^{20}.

6·3 Set up a system of 20 molecules as described in Prob. 6·2, using any suitable markers for the molecules. Place them all initially on the left side of the box. Flip a coin and move one particle to right or left (if possible), depending on whether the coin shows heads or tails, respectively. Record the system state during a sequence of such flips. Discuss the outcome of this experiment. What would be the meaning of entropy here, and how would it be calculated?

6·4 Write a digital computer program to perform 10,000 experiments of the type described in Prob. 6·3. Use a random-number generator instead of the coin. Record the number of molecules on each side after each toss, and compute the entropy evolution over the first 100 tosses.

6·5 Repeat the experiment of Prob. 6·3, this time starting the system with 10 molecules on each side. Record the number on the left after each flip. Continue until all molecules are on one side; if you become worn out before then, compute the fraction of the time that such a state would be observed over a very long run of experiments. Does the second law say that such a state could never happen?

6·6 Consider a system of four atoms (A, B, C, and D) that can exist with nuclear spin "up" or "down" (u or d). List all the possible spin states of this system. Group them according to the number of atoms with spin up. Assuming that each spin state is equally likely, determine the probability of each spin-state group. Calculate the entropy of the group probability distribution (take $k = 1$ for simplicity) and compare to $\ln \Omega$, where Ω is the total number of system spin states, and to $\ln \Omega_g$, where Ω_g is the number of spin-state groups. Why do these three "entropies" differ? (In which description do you know most about the system?)

6·7 Consider a system of three indistinguishable molecules, each of which can have energy 0, 1, 2, 3, or 4. Find all system states having a total energy of 6 (one is shown in the figure). Assuming that each system state is equally likely, calculate the probability p_k that energy level k is occupied by at least one particle. Why do these probabilities not add up to unity? Suppose we define a property, g, as the sum of the squares of the energies of the three molecules. What is the ensemble-average g?

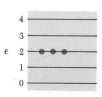

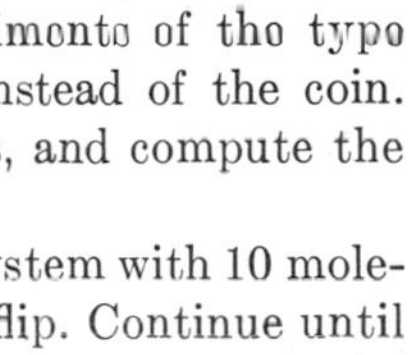

6·8 Suppose that in the system of Prob. 6·7 two-particle interactions take the system to other states (or leave the system in the same state) with equal probability for all possible transitions from a given initial state. Make up a table of transition probabilities similar to Table 6·2. If the system is started in the state shown in Prob. 6·7, what is the probability of being in each state after 1, 2, 3, and 4 interactions? Compute the entropies (with $k = 1$) of the probabilities after 0, 1, 2, 3, and 4 interactions for an ensemble of such experiments, and compare with the "equilibrium" entropy.

6·9 Write a digital computer program to repeat the experiment of Prob. 6·8 1000 times, carrying each experiment through 10 interactions. Use a random-number generator and the transition probability table to find the state sequence in each experiment. Plot the experimentally determined evolution of the probability distribution and the entropy history; compare with the analytical predictions of Prob. 6·8.

6·10 Suppose you have a coin on a table, heads up. Imagine an experiment in which you roll a die and turn the coin over if the die shows a 1 but leave the coin as it stands if 2 to 6 is rolled. What is the probability of turning the coin over on the first roll? On the second roll? What is the probability that the coin will be tails up after the second roll of the die? Compute the probability distribution for the two coin states (H or T) after each of the first 10 rolls of the die. Calculate the entropy of the distribution that would be obtained after each of the first 10 tosses (take $k = 1$ for simplicity). What distribution is obtained after a large number of tosses, and what is its entropy?

6·11 Perform 100 of the experiments as described in Prob. 6·10 (stop after three rolls) and compare the experimental evolution of the distribution to that predicted theoretically.

6·12 Write a digital computer program to carry out an ensemble of 10,000 experiments as described in Prob. 6·10. Use a random-number routine instead of the die. Compare the experimentally determined evolution of the distribution and entropy to that predicted theoretically.

6·13 Calculate the entropy of a gmole of gas assuming that there are as many system quantum states as there are particles, and that each state is equally likely.

6·14 Repeat Prob. 6·13 assuming there are 10^{20} times as many system quantum states as particles.

6·15 The entropy of 1 gmole of O_2 at 600°R and 1 atm is 49.7 cal/°K. Assuming each quantum state is equally likely, calculate the number of system quantum states for 1 gmole and the ratio of this number to the number of molecules.

6·16 Repeat Prob. 6·15 at 5000°R and 1 atm where the entropy of 1 gmole of O_2 is 67.2 cal/°K. What happens to the number of allowed states as the temperature of O_2 increases?

6·17 The entropy of 1 g of H_2O changes by 1.445 cal/°K when it is evaporated at 1 atm. Assuming that in either the saturated liquid or saturated vapor states the allowed quantum states have equal probability, calculate the ratio of the number of allowed states in the vapor state to that for the liquid.

6·18 How much does the entropy of 1 lbm of mercury change when it is condensed at 415°F? Why does this not violate the second law?

6·19 A two-compartment tank contains saturated water vapor at 100 psia on one side and water vapor at the same temperature but at 1 psia in the other compartment. Each compartment has a volume of 1 ft³. A valve connecting the two compartments is opened, and the water is allowed to come to equilibrium adiabatically.

Calculate the entropy change for this isolated system, using the equation-of-state information in Appendix B (Table B·1 will be especially helpful). Give a microscopic explanation of why the entropy increases.

6·20 A two-compartment tank contains saturated water vapor at 100 psia on one side and water vapor at 100 psia and 1000°F on the other side. Each volume is 1 ft^3. Energy is transferred as heat through the dividing wall, and the system is allowed to reach equilibrium in an isolated manner. Compute the final steam states in the two compartments and determine the change in entropy for this isolated system.

CHAPTER SEVEN

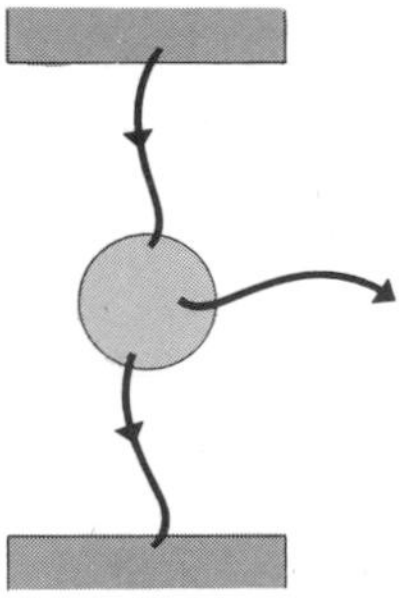

SOME CONSEQUENCES OF THE SECOND LAW

7·1 INTRODUCTION

In the last chapter we developed the concepts and definition of entropy and the second law of thermodynamics. It is indeed very helpful to view entropy as a measure of the randomness in, or uncertainty about, the microscopic state of a system. But it is equally clear that the calculation of entropy from its statistical definition [Eq. (6·8)] is rather involved and requires physical input about the microscopic nature of the system. Such calculations fall in the domain of statistical thermodynamics. Before getting involved in such calculations, we should see what we can find out about entropy from purely *macroscopic* considerations. This is the central theme of the present chapter. We shall see that it is possible to relate differences in entropy between two thermodynamic states to other macroscopically measurable properties. This allows us to determine the entropy of a substance as a function of state (relative to an arbitrary datum). The entropy per unit of mass can then be tabulated, graphed, or stored in a computer with the other thermodynamic properties for use in engineering calculations. Our first objective in this chapter is the development of the framework required for the macroscopic evaluation of entropy.

In the initial discussion we shall develop the thermodynamic definition of temperature mentioned in earlier chapters, and a thermodynamic definition of pressure. We shall see that these are equivalent to the empirical temperature and mechanical pressure used earlier. The thermodynamic temperature scale is independent of any arbitrary choice of thermometric substance, and hence the thermodynamic definition of temperature places the temperature concept on really firm ground.

Once we have established the macroscopic basis for entropy evaluation we shall turn to discussion of the role played by entropy and the second law in engineering analysis. We shall see that the postulate that the entropy of an isolated system will never decrease provides a very powerful tool for practical analysis.

7·2 ENTROPY AS A FUNCTION OF STATE

The statistical definition of entropy [Eq. (6·8)] is in terms of the probability of allowed quantum states and is valid in both equilibrium and nonequilibrium situations. Of most interest is the entropy of matter in equilibrium states, where the equilibrium probability distribution is attained. The equilibrium entropy is a thermodynamic property of the substance, and from the state postulate we know that it is a function of only a few macroscopic properties. For example, the equilibrium entropy of a given amount of a simple compressible substance is some function of the energy and volume,

$$S = S(U, V) \tag{7·1}$$

If in addition the substance can be electrically polarized, the equilibrium entropy will also depend on the total dipole moment,

$$S = S(U, V, \mathbf{P}V)$$

Our goal here is to find some *macroscopic* means to determine these functions, thereby eliminating the need to compute entropy from Eq. (6·8).

The entropy is an extensive property, which means that the entropy of a system composed of two parts is the sum of the entropies of the individual parts,

$$S_{A+B} = S_A + S_B \tag{7·2}$$

Recall from Chap. Six that this holds only if the allowed quantum states of parts A and B are independent. Equation (7·2) is useful when we want to compute the entropy of a complex system. For example, the entropy of a two-phase mixture (say liquid water and ice) is computed as the sum of the individual entropies of the two phases,

$$S_{\text{mixt}} = S_{\text{solid}} + S_{\text{liquid}}$$

Just as tabulation of internal energy is facilitated by considering the internal energy per unit of mass, it is convenient to "intensify" the entropy. For example, for a simple compressible substance we can use the "specific entropy," or entropy per unit of mass; the symbol s is usually used for the intensified entropy, while S is used for the total (extensive) entropy;

$$s \equiv \frac{S}{M}$$

Then, for a simple compressible substance,

$$s = s(u, v)$$

The dimensions of S are energy/temperature, and those of s are energy/mass-temperature; that is, cal/°K or Btu/°R for S and cal/g-°K or Btu/lbm-°R for

s. These dimensions result from the choice of the Boltzmann constant in the definition of entropy [Eq. (6·8)], which in turn results from the desire to make the thermodynamic temperature scale agree with the empirical ideal-gas temperature scale.

The specific entropy of a liquid-vapor mixture can be expressed in terms of the quality and the specific entropies of the liquid and vapor,

$$s = (1 - x)s_f + xs_g \tag{7·3}$$

The student may derive this equation following the steps used in obtaining Eq. (4·1).

In the next few sections we shall examine the nature of the functional relationships among entropy, energy, and volume for a simple compressible substance. Treatment of more general substances follows exactly these lines of argument, and the details will be omitted here. The first step is to establish a basic thermodynamic definition of temperature.

7·3 THE THERMODYNAMIC DEFINITION OF TEMPERATURE

Let us first review the concepts of temperature that we have used implicitly. If we bring two masses into contact, and there is some energy transfer as heat between them, we say that their temperatures were different. We also view the energy as passing from the "hotter" mass to the "colder" one. We say that the masses are in thermal equilibrium if they are at the same temperature, and no energy transfer as heat will occur when they are brought together. These notions show that temperature is basically thought of as an indicator of the direction of energy transfer as heat. Differences in temperature reflect lack of equilibrium, and this suggests that we might be able to make a basic definition of temperature through considerations about thermal equilibrium. Indeed, temperature is conceived as a property that two systems have in common when they are in thermal equilibrium.

Our approach will be to consider two masses, each in a thermodynamic equilibrium state. If we bring them together, and any energy transfer as heat takes place between them, then they were not initially at the same temperature. We then shall look for conditions under which *no* energy transfer as heat takes place when they are brought together, and try to find a *property* that has the same value for both masses under this condition of thermal equilibrium. The temperature is just such a property, and this approach will therefore lead us to the basic definition of temperature.

Consider two control masses, A and B, each initially in a state of thermodynamic equilibrium (Fig. 7·1), though A and B are not necessarily in equilibrium with each other. For simplicity assume that each mass is a simple compressible substance.

We shall let C denote the combined system A and B. Assuming that the allowed quantum states of A and B are independent, the entropy of the com-

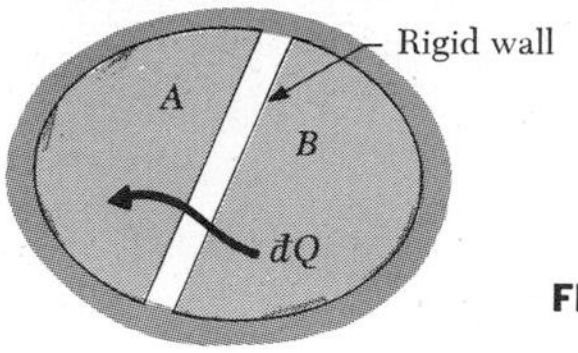

FIG. 7·1 *The combined system C is isolated*

bined system C is simply

$$S_C = S_A + S_B \tag{7·4}$$

Now, since A and B are each in some equilibrium state,

$$S_C = S_A(U_A, V_A) + S_B(U_B, V_B) \tag{7·5}$$

This expression holds as long as A and B are each in some equilibrium state, even when A and B are not in equilibrium with each other. Note that the individual masses of A and B are also specified and fixed.

We now imagine letting A and B interact through a rigid wall, which prevents changes in V_A and V_B. This rules out the possibility of any energy transfer as work between A and B, and any energy transfer must take place as heat. We also imagine isolating the combined system C, so that the only interactions are between A and B internal to C. Since system C is isolated, its entropy must not decrease; any interaction between A and B will serve to increase the entropy of C. S_C will attain its largest value when A and B are finally in thermal equilibrium, that is, when they are at the same temperature. Hence, the state of C that maximizes S_C is the equilibrium state we need in order to discover the thermodynamic definition of temperature.

Since C is isolated, the total internal energy $U = U_A + U_B$ must be "shared" by A and B. If we define r to be the fraction of the total internal energy contained by A, then

$$U_A = rU \qquad U_B = (1 - r)U \tag{7·6}$$

Since for a given isolation U, V_A, and V_B are fixed, the only free parameter left to vary S_C is r [see Eq. (7·5)]. For given U, V_A, and V_B, the value of r which maximizes S_C determines the distribution of internal energy between A and B in the equilibrium state. Figure 7·2 shows the variation of S_C with r schematically.

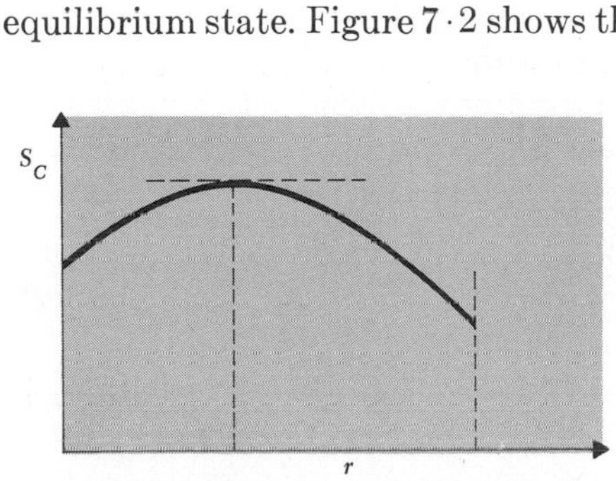

FIG. 7·2 *The entropy of the combined isolated system is a maximum when A and B are in equilibrium*

The point of maximum S is found by setting $dS_C/dr = 0$. Using the chain rule of differentiation, we differentiate Eq. (7·5),

$$\frac{dS_C}{dr} = \left(\frac{\partial S_A}{\partial U_A}\right)_{V_A} \frac{dU_A}{dr} + \left(\frac{\partial S_B}{\partial U_B}\right)_{V_B} \frac{dU_B}{dr}$$

or,

$$\frac{dS_C}{dr} = \left(\frac{\partial S_A}{\partial U_A}\right)_{V_A} U + \left(\frac{\partial S_B}{\partial U_B}\right)_{V_B} (-U) \tag{7·7}$$

This vanishes only when

$$\left(\frac{\partial S_A}{\partial U_A}\right)_{V_A} = \left(\frac{\partial S_B}{\partial U_B}\right)_{V_B} \tag{7·8}$$

Equation (7·8) fixes the state of maximum S_C, that is, the condition under which A and B will be in thermal equilibrium. Note that the derivatives in Eq. (7·8) are *properties* of A and B, respectively; the derivative on the left depends only on the state (U, V) of A, and that on the right depends only on the state of B.

When the *property* $(\partial S/\partial U)_V$ of A is equal to that for B, A and B are in thermal equilibrium. This suggests that we should define temperature in terms of this property. Any function of this property would have the qualitative feature that two systems in equilibrium had the same value of the function. What function should we choose? A choice which retains the other conceptual aspect of temperature, namely, that energy transfer as heat should take place from the warmer body to the cooler one, is†

▶ $$T \equiv \frac{1}{(\partial S/\partial U)_V} \tag{7·9}$$

As we shall show, this choice also makes the thermodynamic temperature scale coincide with the perfect-gas temperature scale, and hence makes the thermodynamic temperature equivalent to what we have been using for temperature all along. Equation (7·9) is the *thermodynamic definition of temperature* for a simple compressible substance. Since both S and U are extensive, their ratio, and hence T, is *intensive*. Note also that T is defined in terms of the equilibrium equation of state $S(U, V)$, and hence T does not have any meaning for a system not in a thermodynamic equilibrium state.

Let us next establish that energy transfer as heat takes place from the hotter to the cooler body. Equation (7·7) can be written as

$$dS_C = U \cdot dr \left(\frac{1}{T_A} - \frac{1}{T_B}\right) \tag{7·10}$$

† Noting that the dimensions of S are energy/temperature, the derivative $\partial S/\partial U$ must have dimensions 1/temperature.

Now, if in the initial state $T_B \neq T_A$, then S_C must increase as a result of the interaction, and $dS_C > 0$. If $T_B > T_A$, this requires $dr > 0$, which corresponds to an increase in U_A and a decrease in U_B. Hence, the energy indeed flows from the warmer body (B) to the cooler one (A).

We can learn still more about the thermodynamic temperature from the analysis of the condition for equilibrium between A and B (Fig. 7·1). In order for the point at which $dS_C/dr = 0$ to be a *maximum*, and not a minimum or inflection point in the $S_C(r)$ curve, the *second* derivative d^2S_C/dr^2 must be negative. Differentiating Eq. (7·7) again with respect to r, we have

$$\frac{d^2S_C}{dr^2} = \left[\left(\frac{\partial^2 S}{\partial U_A{}^2}\right)_{V_A} U^2 + \left(\frac{\partial^2 S_B}{\partial U_B{}^2}\right)_{V_B} U^2\right] < 0 \tag{7·11}$$

Suppose A and B are identical systems. Then, the necessary condition for a maximum yields

$$\left(\frac{\partial^2 S}{\partial U^2}\right)_V < 0 \qquad \text{for } A \text{ or } B \tag{7·12}$$

This derivative is merely the first derivative of $1/T$, and hence $T(U, V)$ must be such that

$$\left(\frac{\partial(1/T)}{\partial U}\right)_V < 0$$

or

$$\left(\frac{\partial T}{\partial U}\right)_V > 0 \tag{7·13}$$

Equation (7·13) says that the temperature must be a monotone increasing function of the energy (Fig. 7·3); increasing the energy at fixed volume must increase the temperature. This is in accordance with experience cited previously.

A physical interpretation of temperature in terms of the microscopic concepts of entropy discussed in the last chapter is quite helpful. The reciprocal of temperature describes the sensitivity of the entropy to internal energy changes at fixed volume. If a small increase in internal energy greatly changes the microscopic randomness and the uncertainty about the microscopic state, the

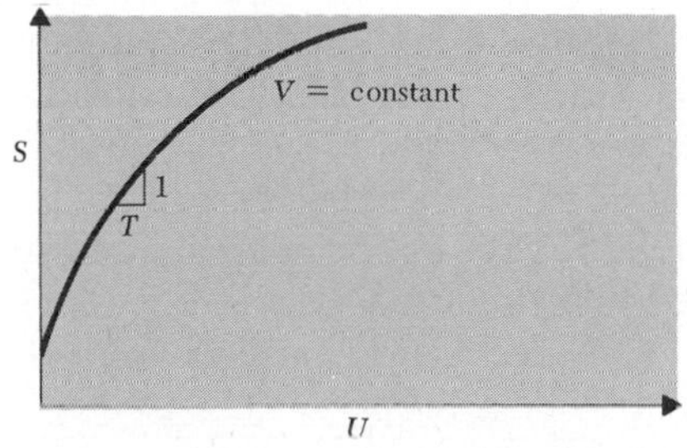

FIG. 7·3 *Temperature is a monotonically increasing function of internal energy*

quantity $1/T$ is large, and T is small. Absolute zero T corresponds to a state in which any infinitesimal increase in internal energy will make a finite increase in the microscopic randomness. At higher and higher temperatures $1/T$ becomes smaller and smaller, and hence the amount of additional microscopic randomness or uncertainty produced by adding some energy at constant volume becomes less and less at high temperatures. For simple compressible substances only positive absolute temperatures are of interest; if $T > 0$, any increase in internal energy (at constant volume) will result in an increase in entropy, that is, in an increase in the microscopic randomness and uncertainty. This seems quite reasonable, indeed.

We started with the idea that the entropy of a given amount of a simple compressible substance can be expressed as some function of its internal energy and volume, $S = S(U, V)$. If we take the differential of this function we obtain

$$dS = \left(\frac{\partial S}{\partial U}\right)_V dU + \left(\frac{\partial S}{\partial V}\right)_U dV \qquad (7 \cdot 14)$$

We now know that the derivative coefficient of dU in Eq. $(7 \cdot 14)$ is $1/T$, which we know as a function of state (presuming that the thermodynamic and empirical temperatures are indeed equivalent as we have stated and will shortly prove). If we can determine the derivative coefficient of dV in Eq. $(7 \cdot 14)$ as a function of measurable properties, Eq. $(7 \cdot 14)$ would become a differential equation for the entropy of a function of state. Then, by integration of this equation by appropriate analytical, numerical, or graphical means, we could determine the entropy as a function of the state of the substance, relative to the entropy in some arbitrary datum state. Our next task is therefore to examine $(\partial S/\partial V)_U$, which brings us to the thermodynamic definition of pressure.

7·4 THE THERMODYNAMIC DEFINITION OF PRESSURE

What is "the pressure" of a piece of matter? We think of pressure in mechanical terms as the force per unit area exerted by the matter on its boundaries. A microscopic interpretation of gas pressure in terms of molecular collisions with a wall is very vivid, even though we can't really see the molecules. Thermodynamics provides an entirely different way to define pressure, and in many ways this definition is more fundamental. Fortunately, the thermodynamic and mechanical pressures are equivalent under certain circumstances, so we can use force-measuring instruments to determine the thermodynamic pressure.

We discovered the thermodynamic definition of temperature by examining the conditions of thermal equilibrium. Following this line of thought, the thermodynamic definition of pressure is obtained from considerations of *mechanical* equilibrium. Pressure is conceived to be a property that two systems have in common when they are in mechanical equilibrium.

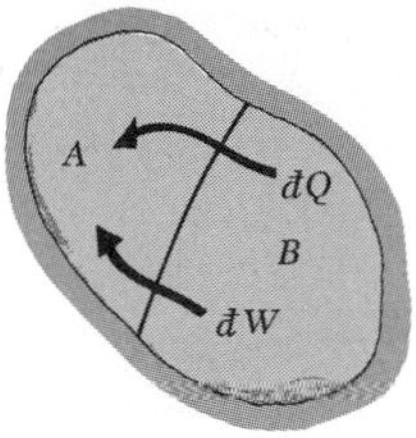

FIG. 7·4 *The combined system C is isolated*

Consider two control masses A and B, which together form an isolated system C. We presume A and B are free to expand or contract, thereby exchanging energy as work, and that they can also exchange energy as heat. The sign conventions for our analysis of these interactions are defined in Fig. 7·4. We again treat only the case of simple compressible substances.

The conditions of isolation require that the energy and volume of the combined system C remain fixed,

$$U_C = U_A + U_B = \text{constant} \tag{7·15a}$$
$$V_C = V_A + V_B = \text{constant} \tag{7·15b}$$

Assuming that A and B are each in some thermodynamic state, that the masses of A and B are fixed, and that their allowed quantum states are independent, the entropy of the combined system is again given by

$$S_C = S_A(U_A, V_A) + S_B(U_B, V_B) \tag{7·16}$$

Upon isolation of C, systems A and B will interact, exchanging both energy and volume. This interaction will lead to a state of equilibrium within C; for mechanical equilibrium the pressures of A and B must be equal, and for thermal equilibrium the temperatures must be equal. The conditions of equilibrium are obtained by seeking the state that maximizes the entropy of the isolated system C.

Since the total energy and volume are fixed, we cannot independently vary U_A, U_B, V_A, and V_B in seeking the maximum of S_C. It is therefore convenient to define the fraction of the energy and volume contributed by part A as r_U and r_V, respectively. Then,

$$U_A = r_U U \qquad U_B = (1 - r_U)U \tag{7·17a,b}$$
$$V_A = r_V V \qquad V_B = (1 - r_V)V \tag{7·17c,d}$$

The fractions r_U and r_V can be considered the two free variables to be adjusted in the maximization of S_C. $S_C(r_U, r_V)$ can be thought of as a *surface* above the $r_U - r_V$ plane; the form of this surface is shown in Fig. 7·5.

The state of maximum S_C is determined by the two conditions

$$\left(\frac{\partial S_C}{\partial r_U}\right)_{r_V} = 0 \qquad \left(\frac{\partial S_C}{\partial r_V}\right)_{r_U} = 0 \tag{7·18a,b}$$

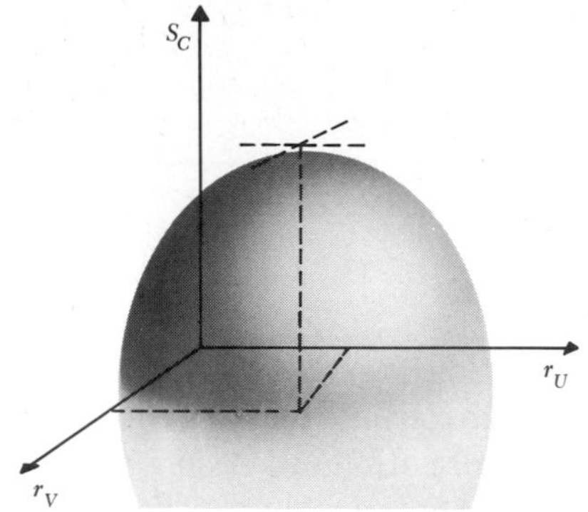

FIG. 7·5 *The S_C surface*

Using Eqs. (7·17), these two conditions give

$$\left(\frac{\partial S_A}{\partial U_A}\right)_{V_A} U - \left(\frac{\partial S_B}{\partial U_B}\right)_{V_B} U = 0 \tag{7·19a}$$

$$\left(\frac{\partial S_A}{\partial V_A}\right)_{U_A} V - \left(\frac{\partial S_B}{\partial V_B}\right)_{U_B} V = 0 \tag{7·19b}$$

Noting that the derivatives in Eq. (7·19*a*) are the reciprocal temperatures of A and B, Eq. (7·19*a*) is simply the requirement of thermal equilibrium, that is, that the temperatures of A and B must be equal. Equation (7·19*b*) is the condition of mechanical equilibrium, and these derivatives must somehow be related to the pressure. Noting that the dimensions of entropy are energy/temperature, the derivative $\partial S/\partial V$ has the dimensions of energy/volume-temperature = force-length/length³-temperature = pressure/temperature. Hence, this derivative must be either plus or minus the pressure divided by T. The proper choice for sign can be obtained by noting that if A and B are not in equilibrium the system with the larger pressure should expand, and the entropy of C should thereby increase. The infinitesimal change in S_C associated with an infinitesimal dr_V is, when $T_A = T_B$,

$$dS_C = \left[\left(\frac{\partial S_A}{\partial V_A}\right)_{U_A} - \left(\frac{\partial S_B}{\partial V_B}\right)_{U_B}\right] V\, dr_V \geq 0$$

Hence, if $dr_V > 0$, which corresponds to expansion of A,

$$\left(\frac{\partial S_A}{\partial V_A}\right)_{U_A} > \left(\frac{\partial S_B}{\partial V_B}\right)_{U_B}$$

Since for $dV_A > 0$, $P_A > P_B$, the plus sign must be chosen. The thermodynamic definition of pressure is therefore given by

$$\blacktriangleright \quad \frac{P}{T} \equiv \left(\frac{\partial S}{\partial V}\right)_U \tag{7·20}$$

Since both S and V are extensive, P/T and hence P is *intensive*. Note that the thermodynamic pressure is defined in terms of the *equilibrium* equation of state $S = S(U, V)$, and hence P has no meaning for a substance not in a thermodynamic state.

Following the thoughts of our microscopic interpretation of temperature, we can interpret the pressure as a measure of the sensitivity of the entropy to volume changes at fixed internal energy. If a system of gas molecules expands at fixed internal energy, we become more uncertain about the locations of individual molecules, for they can roam over a larger space. Hence $(\partial S/\partial V)_U$ and P should always be positive, as is indeed the case for a gas. In a solid, an expansion at fixed energy may be accompanied by an ordering of the molecular structure, which reduces the randomness and uncertainty about the microscopic state. Hence in solids the pressure can be negative (which corresponds to tension).

The thermodynamic pressure P has the qualitative aspects of the mechanical pressure, but it is not obvious that they are identical. We shall show that they are identical shortly.

7·5 INTENSIVE REPRESENTATIONS AND SOME EXTENSIONS

We developed the definitions of T and P in terms of the extensive properties S, U, and V. Since the mass M is fixed for any piece of matter, we can divide numerators and denominators in these defining ratios by M, and thereby express T and P in terms of the intensive properties s, u, and v. The definitions of T and P in terms of $s(u, v)$ become

$$\blacktriangleright \quad \frac{1}{T} \equiv \left(\frac{\partial s}{\partial u}\right)_v \tag{7·21}$$

$$\blacktriangleright \quad \frac{P}{T} \equiv \left(\frac{\partial s}{\partial v}\right)_u \tag{7·22}$$

The differential of the specific entropy is therefore

$$\blacktriangleright \quad ds = \frac{1}{T}\,du + \frac{P}{T}\,dv \tag{7·23}$$

This is a very important equation; it provides the means for evaluation of the entropy of substances from macroscopic laboratory data. It is called the *Gibbs equation* for a simple compressible substance.

The definitions above apply for simple compressible substances only, but extension to other classes of substances is quite straightforward. For example, the thermodynamic definition of temperature for a simple magnetic substance is

$$\blacktriangleright \quad \frac{1}{T} \equiv \left(\frac{\partial s}{\partial u}\right)_{\mathbf{M}} \tag{7·24}$$

while for a simple dielectric substance it is

$$\blacktriangleright \quad \frac{1}{T} \equiv \left(\frac{\partial s}{\partial u}\right)_{\mathbf{P}} \tag{7·25}$$

Following the development of the thermodynamic pressure, thermodynamic definitions for the electric and magnetic fields can be developed. The Gibbs equations for these substances can then be used to calculate the entropy as a function of state. For example, the Gibbs equation for a simple magnetic substance is, in intensive form,

$$\blacktriangleright \quad ds = \frac{1}{T}\,du - \mu_0 \frac{v\mathbf{H}}{T} \cdot d\mathbf{M} \tag{7·26}$$

The development of this and other Gibbs equations are left as problems for the student.

The temperature T as used here is the "absolute" temperature, which would be measured as the Rankine (°R) or Kelvin (°K) scales. The relative temperatures (°F, °C) can be used when temperature differences are involved, but must not be used when temperature *levels* are needed [such as in Eqs. (7·21 to 7·26)].

Let's consider for a moment the possibility that the absolute temperature T might be negative for some system. Since $1/T$ measures the sensitivity of the entropy to energy changes at fixed "constraints" (fixed volume, magnetic moment, and so on), a negative temperature state would be one for which an increase in energy would reduce the entropy; by adding energy we could make the system become more ordered, that is, we could become less uncertain about the microscopic state. Most systems have more allowed quantum states at high energy than at low energy, and hence do not exhibit the peculiarity of negative absolute temperature. However, imagine a system for which there is an upper limit on the energy of allowed quantum states for individual particles. As the system energy is increased, more and more particles must occupy the state of greatest energy until finally at the system-state of maximum energy all of the particles are in their maximum energy state. This is a highly ordered condition; if we know that the total (macroscopic) energy is this highest possible amount, we know the microscopic state with no uncertainty. The entropy must therefore be zero in this state. Hence, as we add energy in approaching this state, the entropy would decrease, which corresponds to a situation of negative absolute temperature. Note that the negative temperatures would occur at higher energies than positive temperatures! Nuclear spin systems in crystals exhibit this negative temperature behavior. The spin state adjusts rapidly to changes in comparison to the lattice vibration, and hence the spin states can be treated as a separate thermodynamic system. The operation of solid-state masers depends upon the existence of such spin-system states of negative T.†

† A. E. Siegman, *Microwave Solid-State Masers,* McGraw-Hill Book Company, New York, 1964.

7·6 MACROSCOPIC EVALUATION OF ENTROPY

Later in this chapter we shall show that the thermodynamic and empirical temperatures are identical, and that the thermodynamic and mechanical pressures are identical for a substance in an equilibrium state. Let's accept these equivalences for the moment, and begin to do something quantitatively useful with the second law and entropy ideas. This will help the student to get his feet on the ground, and will make it easier for him to see where we are going and why.

Accepting these equivalences, we see that the coefficients of du and dv in the Gibbs equation [Eq. (7·23)] are directly measurable in the laboratory. The Gibbs equation therefore provides a differential equation from which the entropy of a substance can be quantitatively evaluated as a function of thermodynamic state, relative to an arbitrarily chosen reference state. Integration of this equation between any two states 1 and 2 yields

$$s_2 - s_1 = \int_1^2 \frac{du}{T} + \int_1^2 \frac{P}{T}\,dv \tag{7·27}$$

The integrations can be carried out along any path connecting the two states. For example, suppose we take the path shown in Fig. 7·6*a*. We imagine plotting $1/T$ versus u and P/T versus v along this path as shown in Figs. 7·6*b* and 7·6*c*. The integrals under these curves can be computed numerically or graphically, and the difference $s_2 - s_1$ thereby evaluated from Eq. (7·27). If state 1 is the datum state, we set $s_1 = 0$, and s_2 then is the entropy relative to the datum state. It is *not* the *absolute entropy* as defined by Eq. (6·8). It is possible to evaluate the absolute entropy from macroscopic data with the help of an additional postulate about the limit of the entropy of a pure substance as $T \to 0$ (Chap. Eleven), or using statistical thermodynamics (Chap. Twelve). However, only entropy *differences* and *changes* are required for most second-law analysis, and hence as long as we work with a single substance we can use its entropy as evaluated relative to the datum state.

As an example of this type of entropy evaluation, let's compute the entropy

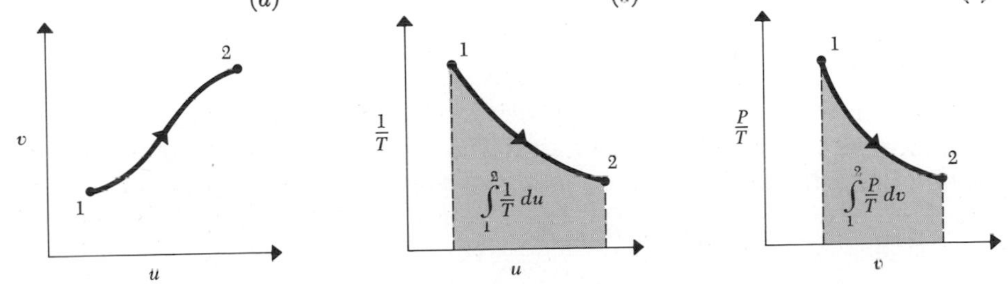

FIG. 7·6 *Computing an entropy difference from the Gibbs equation*

of saturated water vapor at 1 atm taking the saturated liquid at 1 atm as the datum state. The necessary u-v-P-T data are taken from Table B·1*b* (note we use the absolute temperature °R)

State 1 saturated liquid at 1 atm

$T = 671.59°R\ (212.00°F)$
$v = 0.01672\ \text{ft}^3/\text{lbm}$
$u = 180.02\ \text{Btu/lbm}$
$P = 14.696\ \text{lbf/in.}^2$

State 2 saturated vapor at 1 atm

$T = 671.59°R\ (212.00°F)$
$v = 26.80\ \text{ft}^3/\text{lbm}$
$u = 1077.5\ \text{Btu/lbm}$
$P = 14.696\ \text{lbf/in.}^2$

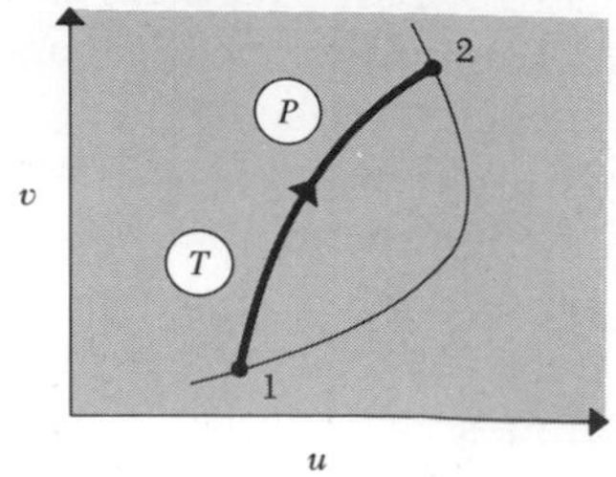

FIG. 7·7 *The path of integration (see also Fig. B·1)*

We could take any path of integration connecting two states. The path of constant pressure is easiest, for along this path both the temperature and pressure are constant (Fig. 7·7). The two integrals are then

$$\int_1^2 \frac{du}{T} = \frac{1}{T}(u_2 - u_1) = \frac{1077.5 - 180.02}{671.59} = 1.3363\ \text{Btu/lbm-°R}$$

$$\int_1^2 \frac{P}{T}\,dv = \frac{P}{T}(v_2 - v_1) = \frac{14.696 \times 144}{671.59}(26.80 - 0.01672)$$
$$= 84.4\ \text{ft-lbf/lbm-°R} = 0.1083\ \text{Btu/lbm-°R}$$

Hence,†

$$s_2 - s_1 = 1.4446\ \text{Btu/lbm-°R}$$

(Note that this is precisely the "entropy of vaporization" s_{fg} given in Table B·1*b*.) Hence, the specific entropy of saturated water vapor at 1 atm, relative to the saturated liquid at 1 atm, is 1.4446 Btu/lbm-°R. In Table B·1*b* we give the value of 1.7566 Btu/lbm-°R for the entropy at this state. This difference is due to a different choice of datum state; either would be correct, as long as we were consistent in any one analysis. Taking the entropy of state 1, relative to the triple-point datum, from Table B·1*b* as $s_1 = 0.3120$ Btu/lbm-°R, the entropy at state 2, relative to the triple point, would be

$$0.3120 + 1.4446 = 1.7566\ \text{Btu/lbm-°R}$$

Evaluation of the *absolute* entropy requires material from Chap. Eleven. But to complete the picture here, we state that the absolute entropy of state 1 is about 1.16 Btu/lbm-°R, and hence the absolute entropy of state 2 is

$$1.16 + 1.44 = 2.60\ \text{Btu/lbm-°R}$$

† Since the intervals are the same on the °R and °F scales, 1 Btu/lbm-°R = 1 Btu/lbm-°F; the latter units are often used.

This is essentially the value that would be computed from statistical thermodynamics using the basic definition of entropy.

The graphs and tables in Appendix B give the specific entropy, relative to some datum state, for a variety of substances. Most of these values were obtained by the type of integration outlined here. For some of the more exotic substances, such as cesium vapor (Fig. B·11) and the paramagnetic salt iron-ammonium alum (Fig. B·12), the entropy is based on a combination of statistical thermodynamics and macroscopic thermodynamic equations of the sort discussed in the next chapter.

With this background about the source of the entropy data given in Appendix B, we can begin to use these data in some simple quantitative second-law analyses. We shall want to study processes, and hence shall first discuss some important ideas about the nature of various processes.

7·7 REVERSIBLE AND IRREVERSIBLE PROCESSES

Processes that do not violate the second law can be classed as reversible or irreversible. The concept of a reversible process is very important in thermodynamics, and the ability to recognize, evaluate, and reduce irreversibilities in a process is essential to a competent engineering thermodynamicist.

Suppose the system of interest is an isolated system. The second law says that any process that would reduce the entropy of the isolated system is impossible. Suppose a process takes place within the isolated system in what we shall call the forward direction. If the change in state of the system is such that the entropy increases for the forward process, then for the backward process (that is, for the reverse change of state) the entropy would decrease. The backward process is therefore impossible, and hence we say that the forward process is *irreversible*. If the entropy is unchanged by the forward process, then it will be unchanged by the reverse process, and the process could go in either direction without violating the second law; such a process is called *reversible*. The key idea of a reversible process within an isolated system is that it does not "produce" any entropy.

Since a reversible process does not produce any entropy, the total molecular disorganization within the isolated system remains constant. It is impossible to tell which state in a reversible process came first; the reversible process leaves no "footprints in the sands of time." The reversible process is an idealization, like frictionless pulleys and resistanceless wires. It can be approached to a very high degree, and in fact there is some evidence that at very low temperatures electric current flow can become exactly reversible. Currents started in loops of superconducting materials have been observed to persist for very long times without measurable decay. These experiments are perhaps the closest man has come to truly realizing a reversible process, and may even be fully reversible. Some other processes that the student has probably idealized as being reversible in other courses are shown in Fig. 7·8. Note that each of the isolated systems of

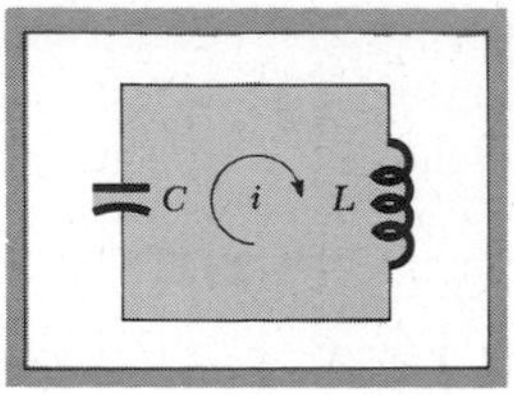

(*a*) *Resistanceless current flow*

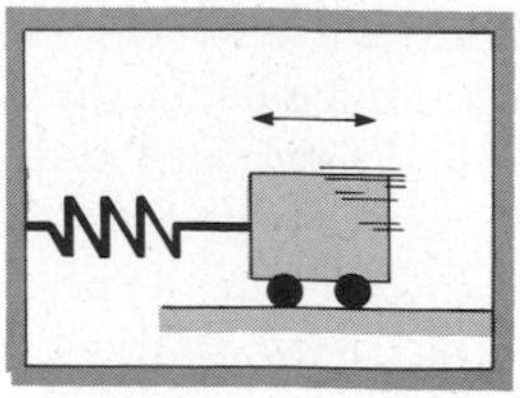

(*b*) *Frictionless motion*

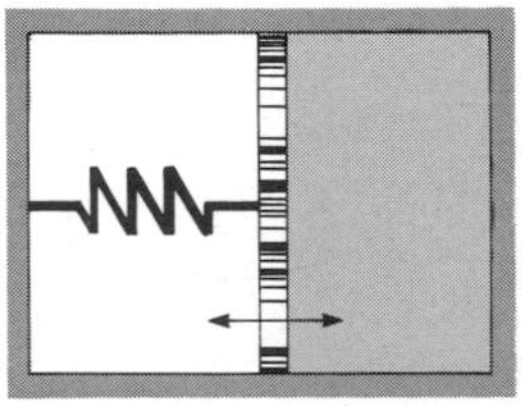

(*c*) *Pneumatic spring*

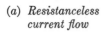

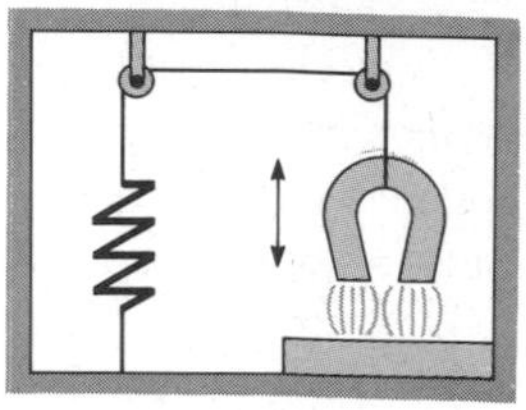

(*d*) *Magnetic spring*

FIG. 7·8 *Some familiar reversible processes*

Fig. 7·8 happens to be an oscillator in which the oscillations persist indefinitely. At the end of each cycle the system is returned to its initial state, thereby "undoing" the state change of the first half cycle. Hence, if the entropy increased during a portion of the cycle, it would have to decrease during another portion in order to return to its initial value. But this would violate the second law, and thus we conclude that the entropy remains constant during each process. The processes are therefore (ideally) reversible.

An irreversible process is one that is not reversible, that is, one that *produces* entropy. All real processes (with the possible exception of superconducting current flows) are in some measure irreversible, though many processes can be analyzed quite adequately by assuming that they are reversible. Some processes that are clearly irreversible include mixing of two gases, spontaneous combustion, friction, and the transfer of energy as heat from a body at high temperature to a body at low temperature. These and some other obviously irreversible processes are shown in Fig. 7·9. Each process of Fig. 7·9 results in some increase in the entropy of the isolated system, that is, in some "entropy production." Qualitative microscopic interpretations of this entropy production will now be given.

In Fig. 7·9*a* an electric current flows through a resistance following the closing of a switch. We know from experience that the capacitor eventually becomes completely discharged, the wires become warmer, and finally the current flow ceases entirely. The electrons, which initially were concentrated on the plates of the capacitor, are now distributed throughout the system, and the dielectric in the capacitor has lost the molecular organization which gave it a net dipole moment. This randomization accounts for the entropy increase.

The spring-mass system in Fig. 7·9*b* oscillates at smaller and smaller amplitudes, until finally friction brings the mass to rest. Our experience tells us that the temperature of the system increased during the decay of the oscillation. The highly directed kinetic energy of the mass has been converted into randomly oriented motion of the molecules, and this extra randomness accounts for the entropy increase.

In Fig. 7·9*c* we see gas leaving a high-pressure container and flowing into one of lower pressure. The entropy increase required by the second law is reflected by the increased positional uncertainty.

Energy transfer as heat from a hot system to a cooler one is also irreversible (Fig. 7·9*d*). If this were not the case, we could expect to watch an isothermal system and eventually observe an energy transfer that would produce a nonuniformity of temperature. This would indeed be handy, for we could get hot water from ice for nothing. The energy transfer as heat tends to spread the energy over the system, and this increases the uncertainty about the microscopic state.

The system in Fig. 7·9*e* initially has oxygen on one side and nitrogen on the other. The molecules diffuse through one another, and eventually we have a homogeneous mixture. The mixing increases the randomness and uncertainty about the microscopic state, and this is reflected in the increase of entropy.

The spontaneous chemical reaction within the system of Fig. 7·9*f* is irreversible. Oxygen and hydrogen might explode in an isolated container and form water, but the reverse process never takes place. The spontaneous com-

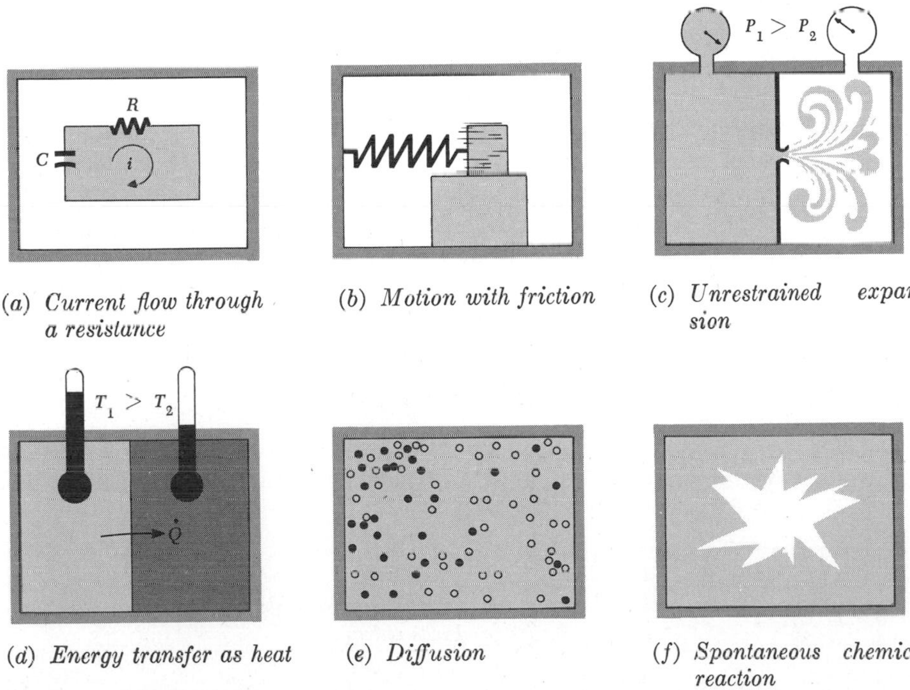

(*a*) *Current flow through a resistance*

(*b*) *Motion with friction*

(*c*) *Unrestrained expansion*

(*d*) *Energy transfer as heat*

(*e*) *Diffusion*

(*f*) *Spontaneous chemical reaction*

FIG. 7·9 *Some irreversible processes*

bustion process converts electron and molecular binding energy into randomly oriented translational energy, and this randomization is evidenced by the increase in entropy.

Recognition of the irreversibilities in a real process is especially important in engineering. Irreversibility, or departure from the ideal condition of reversibility, reflects an increase in the amount of disorganized energy at the expense of organized energy. The organized energy (such as that of a raised weight) is easily put to practical use; disorganized energy (such as the random motions of the molecules in a gas) requires "straightening out" before it can be used effectively. And since we are always somewhat uncertain about the microscopic state, this straightening can never be perfect. Consequently the engineer is constantly striving to reduce irreversibilities in his systems in order to obtain better performance.

To summarize:

Processes that are usually idealized as *reversible* include

- Frictionless movement
- Restrained compression or expansion
- Energy transfer as heat due to infinitesimal temperature nonuniformity
- Magnetization, polarization
- Electric current flow through a zero resistance
- Restrained chemical reaction
- Mixing of two samples of the same substance at the same state

Processes that are *irreversible* include

- Movement with friction
- Unrestrained expansion
- Energy transfer as heat due to large temperature nonuniformities
- Magnetization or polarization with hysteresis
- Electric current flow through a nonzero resistance
- Spontaneous chemical reaction
- Mixing of matter of different composition or state

7·8 AN EXAMPLE OF A SECOND-LAW ANALYSIS

Let's now make these second-law ideas concrete by an example. Consider the isolated system shown in Fig. 7·10. Initially the system consists of 1.84 lbm

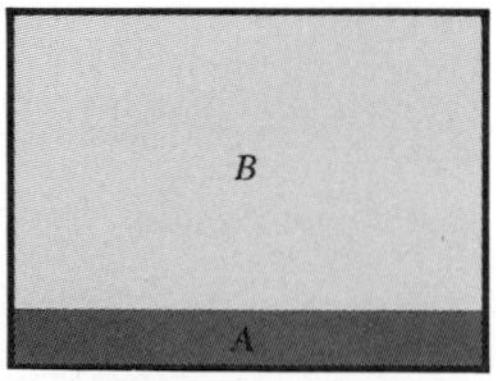

FIG. 7·10 *The system is isolated; the irreversible process produces entropy*

of saturated water vapor at 95 psia and 8.16 lbm of saturated liquid water at 10 psia. This system is clearly not in equilibrium initially, for there are severe pressure and temperature variations inside. The interactions that will occur spontaneously within the isolated system will smooth out these temperature and pressure differences; some of the vapor will condense, and this will drop the pressure and vapor temperature. The liquid will warm up, and finally the system will come to rest with a uniform temperature and pressure inside. Calculation of the final state requires only the ideas of equilibrium and a first-law analysis. The second law can be applied to see if the entropy increases within the isolated system; if it does, the process is irreversible, and the reverse process would be impossible. Intuition tells us that this is the case; indeed, so does the second law, which is really just a generalization of this kind of intuition. We shall carry out the first- and second-law analyses in some detail to illustrate the computation of entropy from the tabular and graphical equations of state and to confirm the expectation that the process does produce entropy.

Let's first evaluate the initial state. We assume that the liquid A and the vapor B are each in equilibrium states, and hence we can use the tables for the thermodynamic properties of water (Table B·1*b*) to evaluate their properties.

Liquid A 8.16 lbm of saturated liquid at 10 psia

$T = 653°\text{R} \ (193°\text{F})$

$u = 161.14 \ \text{Btu/lbm}$

$v = 0.01659 \ \text{ft}^3/\text{lbm}$

$s = 0.2835 \ \text{Btu/lbm-°R}$

Vapor B 1.84 lbm saturated vapor at 95 psia

$T = 784°\text{R} \ (324°\text{F})$

$u = 1104.5 \ \text{Btu/lbm}$

$v = 4.652 \ \text{ft}^3/\text{lbm}$

$s = 1.6068 \ \text{Btu/lbm-°R}$

The total energy, volume, and entropy of the system in its initial state are therefore

$$U_1 = 8.16 \times 161.14 + 1.84 \times 1104.5 = 3350 \ \text{Btu}$$
$$V_1 = 8.16 \times 0.01659 + 1.84 \times 4.652 = 8.67 \ \text{ft}^3$$
$$S_1 = 8.16 \times 0.2835 + 1.84 \times 1.6068 = 5.26 \ \text{Btu/°R}$$

The next job is to determine the final state (2) using a first-law analysis. Assuming that the system is isolated, the energy balance gives

$$U_2 = U_1$$

Also, the volume is fixed and hence

$$V_2 = V_1$$

We assume that the entire system is in an equilibrium state at the end of the process. The internal energy and volume will therefore fix state 2. The specific internal energy and specific volume in the final state will be

$$u_2 = \frac{U_2}{M} = \frac{3350}{10} = 335 \text{ Btu/lbm}$$

$$v_2 = \frac{V_2}{M} = \frac{8.67}{10} = 0.867 \text{ ft}^3\text{/lbm}$$

Looking at Fig. B·1, we see that the final state is approximately 50 psia, $x = 0.1$. Returning to Table B·1*b* for more accurate data, we find

At 50 psia

$u_f = 249.9$ Btu/lbm $u_g = 1095.3$ Btu/lbm
$v_f = 0.0173$ ft^3/lbm $v_g = 8.515$ ft^3/lbm
$s_f = 0.4110$ Btu/lbm-°R $s_g = 1.6585$ Btu/lbm-°R

Then, if the quality x is 0.1, the final energy, volume, and entropy are

$$U_2 = 10(0.9 \times 249.9 + 0.1 \times 1095.3) = 3350 \text{ Btu}$$
$$V_2 = 10(0.9 \times 0.0173 + 9.1 \times 8.515) = 8.67 \text{ ft}^3$$
$$S_2 = 10(0.9 \times 0.4110 + 0.1 \times 1.6585) = 5.36 \text{ Btu/°R}$$

Note that the energy and volume are maintained as the first-law analysis requires (this checks the final state read from Fig. B·1).

Finally, the second law states that the entropy of this isolated system should increase, or remain constant if the process is reversible, that is, the amount of entropy production $\mathcal{P}_S$ cannot be negative,

$$\mathcal{P}_S \equiv S_2 - S_1 \geq 0$$

Noting that $S_2 > S_1$ from the calculations above, we are assured that the process is *irreversible*. The amount of entropy production for this process is†

$$\mathcal{P}_S = 5.36 - 5.26 = 0.1 \text{ Btu/°R}$$

7·9 TWO IDEALIZED SYSTEMS

Often the system of interest is not isolated. In order to investigate the reversibility, irreversibility, or impossibility of processes within the system, we can imagine that the system interacts with a hypothetical environment in which all processes are reversible. The system under study and this hypothetical environment then form an isolated system, and any increase in the entropy within the combined isolated system must be due to irreversibilities within the system under study. The amount by which the entropy of the combined system increases during the process is then the entropy production due to irreversibilities within the system under study. This type of irreversibility test requires elements from which the hypothetical reversible environment can be con-

† The fact that $\mathcal{P}_S$ is small compared to either S_1 or S_2 has no particular significance since the entropy datum of Fig. B·1 was arbitrarily chosen.

structed. Since the interactions between the system and its environment include heat and work, we need to conceive of two "reservoirs" to or from which energy can be transferred reversibly as work or heat.

We shall conceive of a *thermal energy reservoir* (TER) as some system of fixed mass that can undergo only heat interactions with its environment. Any energy transferred into the TER as heat will appear as an increase in its internal energy. The TER is further idealized as having a uniform internal temperature; a TER is always in an equilibrium state. We usually conceive of the TER as being very large, so that the temperature remains constant for the interactions we consider. Internal energy represents "disorganized" molecular energy, and energy transfer as heat can be viewed as "disorganized microscopic work." The TER can therefore be thought of as a source or sink for "disorganized energy."

In contrast, the *mechanical energy reservoir* (MER) is some system that possesses energy only in some fully organized mechanical form, such as in a raised weight. The only energy-transfer mode for a MER is reversible *work;* whatever force acts on the MER is independent of the direction or rate of change of the energy. The force on the MER is conceived to be adjustable by design to fit the analysis at hand. All motions within a MER are assumed to be frictionless, so that any energy put into the MER as work can be completely recovered as work. The MER can be thought of as a source or sink for "fully organized energy." A MER can have but one state for a given energy; given its energy, we know the position of the weight *exactly*, without uncertainty.

These two conceptual systems would be difficult to build exactly, but can be closely approximated and hence are reasonable concepts. A block of copper can be a good approximation to a TER; it has a large capacity to store internal energy, and can be idealized as being incompressible. A dead weight on the end of a frictionless pulley and a dead mass for the weight to gravitate toward forms a reasonable conceptualization for a MER (Fig. 7·11).

The MER and TER are useful concepts because they are two nonisolated systems for which we can easily compute the entropy change. The TER is a

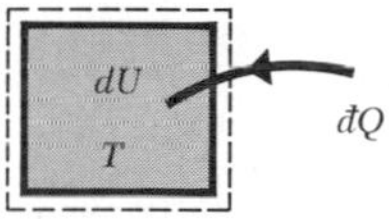

(a) The TER is a reservoir for "disorganized" energy

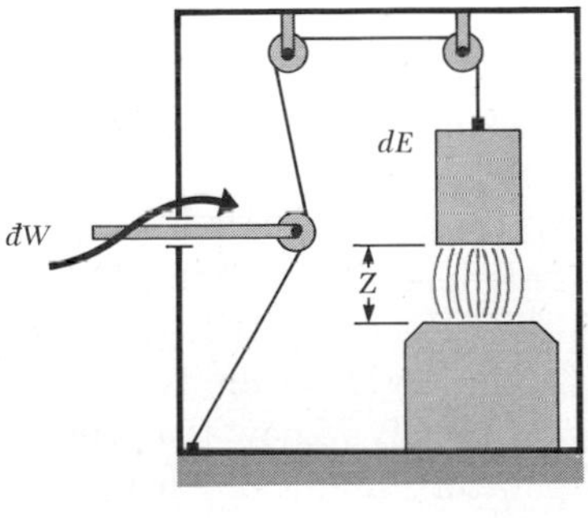

FIG. 7·11 *Two conceptual systems*

(b) The MER is a reservoir for "organized" energy

chunk of matter held at fixed volume. The infinitesimal increase in its entropy associated with an infinitesimal increase in its internal energy is, from Eq. (7·23),

$$dS = \frac{1}{T}\,dU \qquad \text{for a TER} \tag{7·28}$$

An energy balance (Fig. 7·11*a*) reveals that the internal energy change is due solely to the energy transfer as heat *to* the TER

$$dU = đQ$$

and hence the entropy change of a TER can be calculated from

▶ $$dS = \frac{đQ}{T} \qquad \text{for a TER, } đQ \text{ is energy input} \tag{7·29}$$

Thus, the disorganized transfer of energy to a TER will result in an increase in the randomness inside, that is, in an increase in our uncertainty about its microscopic state. The entropy of a TER can be decreased by removal of energy as heat ($đQ < 0$). This will reduce the randomness inside and hence the entropy will decrease ($dS < 0$).

In contrast, the MER is conceptually a *perfectly organized* system. It has *one* microscopic state for each energy; given the energy, the microscopic state of the MER is *precisely* known without any uncertainty. The probability of its single microscopic state is therefore exactly one and its entropy is therefore always exactly zero. Hence

▶ $$dS = 0 \qquad \text{for a MER} \tag{7·30}$$

An energy balance on the MER (Fig. 7·11*b*) reveals that the energy transfer to the MER as work appears as an increase in the fully organized mechanical energy stored inside. This organization makes the energy fully recoverable as work.

Imagine an isolated system composed of two interacting MERs (they must be properly balanced to exert the same forces). If any change occurs in the state of the isolated system, the entropy will remain unchanged because the entropies of the subsystems comprising the isolated system remain unchanged. Hence a MER is clearly a reversible device.

Consider now an isolated system composed of two interacting TERs (Fig. 7·12). We know that energy transfer as heat will not take place "up the temperature hill," and hence heat transfer "down the temperature hill" is irreversible. However, in the limit where the temperature difference vanishes, the energy transfer process can be treated as reversible. To show this, let the

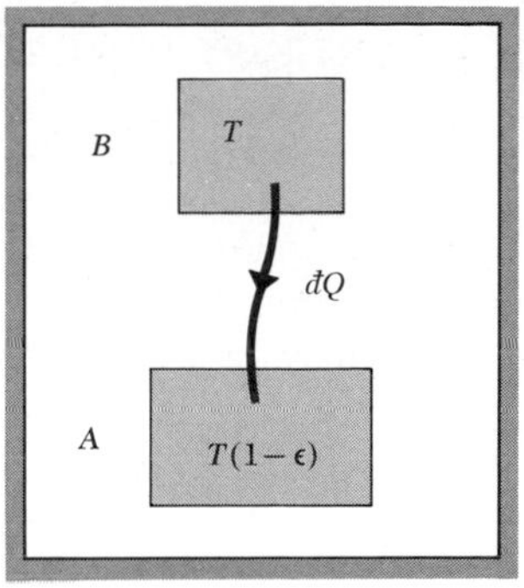

FIG. 7·12 *As $\epsilon \to 0$ the process approaches reversibility*

temperature of TER B be T, and that of TER A be $T(1 - \epsilon)$, where ϵ is a small number. The increase in entropy of the combined system C as a result of the transfer of an amount of energy as heat $đQ$ from B to A is

$$dS_C = d(S_A + S_B) \geq 0 \tag{7·31}$$

and, considering the signs for positive energy transfer in Figs. 7·12 and 7·11, the entropy changes of A and B are

$$dS_A = + \frac{đQ}{T(1 - \epsilon)} = + \frac{đQ}{T}(1 + \epsilon + \epsilon^2 + \cdots) \tag{7·32a}$$

$$dS_B = - \frac{đQ}{T} \tag{7·32b}$$

Adding, we have

$$dS_C = \epsilon \frac{đQ}{T} + \cdots \geq 0 \tag{7·33}$$

Now, when the temperatures of A and B are very nearly equal ϵ will be very small, and we see that the entropy production, that is, dS_C, becomes very small in magnitude in comparison to dS_A or dS_B, and vanishes in the limit $\epsilon \to 0$. Hence, while the transfer of energy as heat across a finite temperature difference is irreversible and produces entropy, in the limit of zero temperature difference the process produces no entropy and hence becomes reversible. By reducing the temperature difference, the amount of entropy production can be made as small as one desires. Hence, we can consider the process of energy transfer as heat between a system at some temperature T and another (say a TER) at some infinitesimally different temperature to be a reversible process.

We shall next use the TER and MER to form ideal reversible environments in order to study the entropy production due to processes within a control mass.

7·10 ENTROPY CHANGE AND PRODUCTION FOR A CONTROL MASS

We can now derive an expression for the amount of entropy production as a result of an irreversible process within a control mass. Suppose the system A receives energy as heat and work during the process; we imagine that these energies come from a TER and a MER, respectively. In order to ensure the reversibility of all processes within the hypothetical environment, the temperature difference between the TER and the point on the control mass where the energy is received as heat must be infinitesimal. The control mass and its hypothetical environment form an isolated system, shown in Fig. 7·13.

Denoting the control-mass entropy by S, we have

$$dS_C = d(S_{\text{TER}} + S_{\text{MER}} + S) \geq 0$$

Now, the entropy of the MER does not change. Noting the difference in the direction of positive energy transfer as heat in Figs. 7·11 and 7·13, the entropy change for the TER is

$$dS_{\text{TER}} = \frac{-đQ}{T}$$

Therefore,

$$dS_C = dS - \frac{đQ}{T} \geq 0 \qquad (7\cdot34)$$

Hence the entropy change of the control mass must satisfy

$$\blacktriangleright \quad dS \geq \frac{đQ}{T} \qquad \textit{control mass, } đQ \textit{ is energy input} \qquad (7\cdot35)$$

The equality holds for the reversible process, the inequality for the irreversible process. Since the process within the ideal environment is reversible, any irreversibility must be due to the process within control mass A.

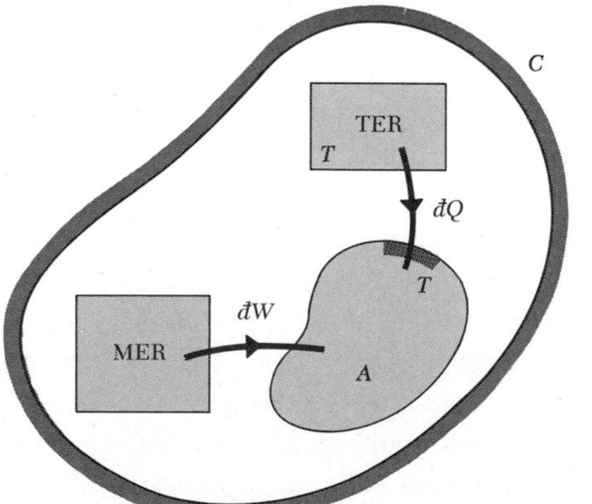

FIG. 7·13 *The combined system C is isolated, and the processes in the environment of A are all reversible*

In the special case where the process within A is reversible, the equality in Eq. (7·35) gives

$$\blacktriangleright \quad dS = \frac{đQ}{T} \qquad \begin{array}{l}\textit{reversible process,}\\ \textit{control mass, } đQ\\ \textit{is energy input}\end{array} \tag{7·36a}$$

Integrating between an initial state 1 and a final state 2,

$$\blacktriangleright \quad \Delta S = \int_1^2 \frac{đQ}{T} \qquad \begin{array}{l}\textit{reversible process,}\\ \textit{control mass, } đQ\\ \textit{is energy input}\end{array} \tag{7·36b}$$

The restrictions are listed because they are important and often forgotten. This equation is very important in thermodynamics, for it provides a means for evaluating the entropy change from laboratory measurements of temperature and energy transfer, provided that the experimental process can be made sufficiently close to reversible that dS_C is small compared to dS. Equation (7·36a) is taken as the definition of entropy in many classical macroscopic thermodynamic treatments.

A reversible process of special importance is the *reversible adiabatic process* ($đQ = 0$). Applying Eqs. (7·36) we see that the entropy of a control mass undergoing a reversible adiabatic process will not change; such a process of constant entropy is called an *isentropic process*.

$$\blacktriangleright \quad dS = 0 \tag{7·37a}$$

or

$$\blacktriangleright \quad \Delta S = 0 \tag{7·37b}$$

for any control mass, reversible adiabatic process

In a reversible adiabatic process the only energy-transfer mechanism is work. Reversible work constitutes perfectly ordered energy transfer, and will not increase the molecular randomness. For example, the process of gas compression in a piston-cylinder system can be made very nearly reversible and adiabatic, and this process is often treated as an isentropic process. As the gas is compressed its energy is increased. If the volume were not also reduced, this increased energy would increase the randomness and our uncertainty about the microscopic state. However, the reduction in volume means that we are more certain about the location of the molecules, and the constancy of the entropy can be regarded as a balance between the increased uncertainty due to the greater energy and the reduced uncertainty due to the more concentrated volume.† Another example of a (nearly) reversible adiabatic process is the rapid demagnetization of a paramagnetic salt at low temperatures. (This process is often used to produce very low temperatures.) Idealizing this process

† These arguments are not quite correct, but are made in the proper spirit. Actually, the quantum theory says that compression of the gas reduces the number of allowed states, and it is this which really compensates for the uncertainty increase due to energy addition.

as reversible and adiabatic, the reduction in uncertainty due to the removal of energy in the demagnetization process can be viewed as being balanced by the increase in uncertainty due to the disalignment of the magnetic dipoles. The second law says that the net effect is to maintain constant entropy during the reversible adiabatic demagnetization.

If the process within A is irreversible the entropy increase dS_C is directly chargeable to irreversibilities within A, and we call it the *entropy production*, due to the process within A. Hence, the amount of entropy production $đ\mathcal{P}_S$ within system A of Fig. 7·13 is

$$đ\mathcal{P}_S \equiv \underset{\substack{\text{increase in}\\ \text{entropy}\\ \text{storage}}}{dS} - \underset{\substack{\text{entropy}\\ \text{inflow}}}{\frac{đQ}{T}} \tag{7·38}$$

Since the entropy production is a function of the process and not a function of the system states, the notation $đ$ is appropriate. Note that the entropy production represents the strength of the inequality in the second law. The second law says that the entropy production cannot be negative; the entropy production is zero for a reversible process:

$$\begin{aligned} &đ\mathcal{P}_S > 0 \quad \text{irreversible process}\\ &đ\mathcal{P}_S = 0 \quad \text{reversible process}\\ &đ\mathcal{P}_S < 0 \quad \text{impossible process} \end{aligned} \tag{7·39}$$

Since a transfer of energy as heat from the TER to the control mass results in a reduction of the entropy of the TER and an increase in the entropy of the control mass, it is convenient and logical to think of entropy "flowing" between the two as a result of their interaction. This is quite analogous to our concept of heat as energy flowing between the two. The magnitude of the entropy decrease for the TER is $đQ/T$, which would be the entropy increase of the control mass were the process reversible. Hence we call the term $đQ/T$ the amount of *entropy transfer with heat* into the control mass. This allows us to focus only on the control mass in making future second-law analyses; wherever energy enters a control mass as heat, we consider there to be an entropy *inflow* with heat in the amount $đQ/T$, where T is the temperature of the control mass at the point where the energy $đQ$ is received as heat. If energy is transferred *out* of the control mass, then we think of an entropy *outflow* with heat in the amount $đQ/T$, where T is the temperature of the control mass at the point where the energy $đQ$ is removed as heat. If there is a net inflow of entropy with heat, the entropy of the control mass must increase by at least this amount. The excess of the actual control-mass entropy increase over the net entropy-inflow to the control mass represents the entropy that must have been "produced" within the control mass by irreversible action.

The microscopic view is very helpful in grasping the idea of entropy transfer with heat. We view heat as energy transfer that takes place as work on the microscopic scale, but in a random, disorganized way. We are very uncertain about the microscopic details of energy transfer as heat, and consequently do not know where or exactly when the wall molecules are going to push on system molecules in order to effect this energy transfer. Consequently, as a result of our uncertainty about exactly how the energy transfer takes place we become even more uncertain about the instantaneous microscopic state of the system. The entropy, the measure of our uncertainty as to microscopic detail, increases as a result of the disorganized energy-addition process.

7·11 EXAMPLES OF CONTROL-MASS SECOND-LAW ANALYSIS

Irreversible compression. Consider the control mass of Fig. 7·14*a*. The cylinder initially contains 0.2 lbm of freon-12 vapor at −20°F (440°R) with an initial volume of 1.0 ft³. The piston is suddenly pushed in very rapidly, causing shock waves to propagate through the freon; after a short period of adjustment, the freon comes to equilibrium at the new volume (0.2 ft³). The process is sufficiently rapid that we can neglect any energy transfer as heat to the freon. Find the possible terminal states for this process.

There is no entropy flow with heat for this adiabatic process, and hence any increase in the freon entropy must be due to irreversible effects within the freon. Denoting the initial and final states by 1 and 2, respectively, the second law, as applied to the control mass, is

$$\mathcal{P}_S \equiv \underbrace{S_2 - S_1}_{\substack{\text{increase in} \\ \text{entropy storage}}} = M(s_2 - s_1) \geq 0$$

Thus, any state with specific entropy greater than the initial state will be a possible final state. From Fig. B·7,

$$T_1 = 440°\text{R} \ (-20°\text{F}) \qquad v_1 = 1.0/0.2 = 5 \text{ ft}^3/\text{lbm}$$
$$P_1 = 7.6 \text{ psia} \qquad s_1 = 0.184 \text{ Btu/lbm-°R}$$

Following up a line of constant entropy to the final specific volume of 0.2/0.2 = 1.0 ft³/lbm, we find the state 2 corresponding to no entropy produc-

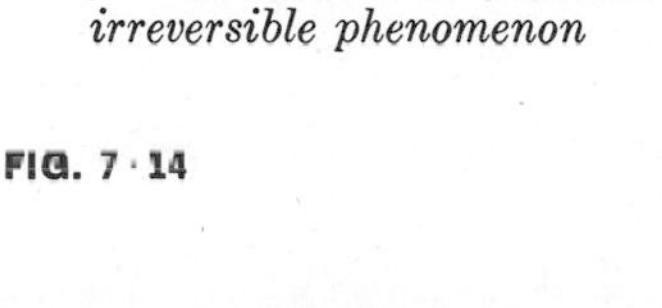

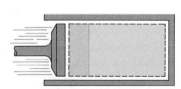

(*a*) *The rapid compression process forms a shock wave, which is an irreversible phenomenon*

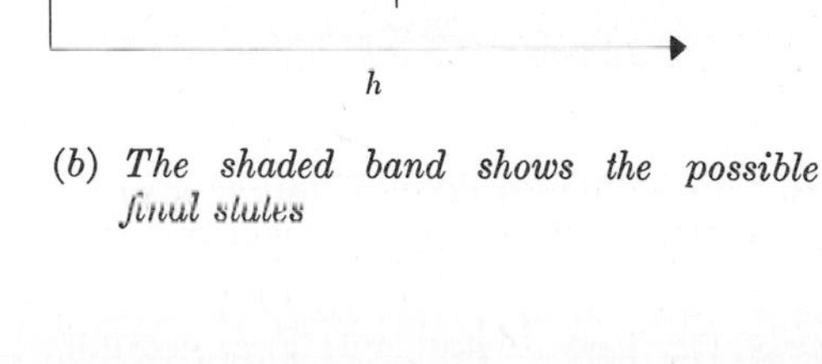

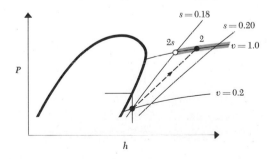

(*b*) *The shaded band shows the possible final states*

FIG. 7·14

tion (reversible compression, isentropic process) as

$$T_{2s} = 93°F \qquad v_2 = 1.0 \text{ ft}^3/\text{lbm}$$
$$P_{2s} = 47 \text{ psia} \qquad s_{2s} = 0.184 \text{ Btu/lbm-°R}$$

The other possible final states lie along the line of final specific volume, as shown in Fig. 7·14*b*. Note that we can conclude that the pressure obtained by this process will be at least 47 psia, and possibly greater if the process is irreversible. A first-law analysis could be used to calculate the work required for the compression if state 2 is known. One would find that the *least* amount of work is required when state 2 is state 2*s*, that is, when the compression process is reversible. This conclusion would be of obvious importance in the design of a freon compressor for a large refrigeration system.

Adiabatic demagnetization. Iron-ammonium alum is placed in a magnetic field **H** of 10,000 gauss at 1°K. The magnetic field is suddenly removed. What is the lowest temperature that can be attained?

We assume the process is adiabatic. Therefore

$$\mathcal{P}_S \equiv S_2 - S_1 \geq 0$$

Looking at Fig. B·13, we see that the final state (2) must lie on the line $\mathbf{H} = 0$ to the right of the point where $s = 2.8 \times 10^5$ erg/g-°K. The lowest temperature is therefore obtained with isentropic demagnetization, and is 0.04°K. The actual value of T_2 would be greater (Fig. 7·15).

7·12 EQUIVALENCE OF THE MECHANICAL AND THERMODYNAMIC PRESSURES

We can now show the conditions under which the mechanical and thermodynamic pressures are equal. Consider the control mass of Fig. 7·16. The entropy change of the control mass can be related to the energy and volume changes using the Gibbs equation (7·23), which in extensive form is

$$dS = \frac{1}{T} dU + \frac{P}{T} dV \tag{7·40}$$

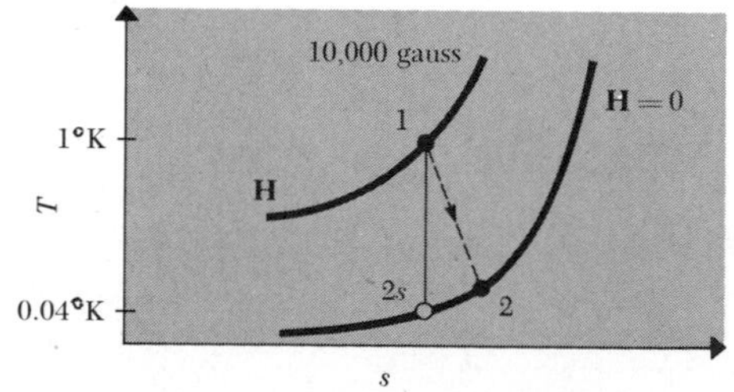

FIG. 7·15 *Adiabatic demagnetization is an effective way to obtain very low temperatures*

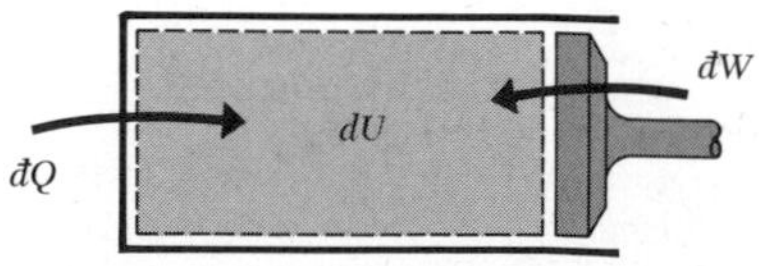

FIG. 7·16 *The control mass is a simple compressible substance*

An energy balance on the control mass of Fig. 7·16 gives

$$dU = đQ + đW \tag{7·41}$$

In Chap. Two we derived an expression for the energy transfer as work for fluid compression; there we used the mechanical pressure, which we denote for the moment as P_m. The work done *on* the substance is

$$đW = -P_m \, dV \tag{7·42}$$

Finally, the entropy production is, from Eq. (7·38),

$$đ\mathcal{P}_S = \underset{\substack{\text{increase in}\\ \text{entropy}\\ \text{storage}}}{dS} - \underset{\substack{\text{entropy}\\ \text{inflow}}}{\frac{đQ}{T}} \tag{7·43}$$

Using Eq. (7·40) to substitute for dS in Eq. (7·43), and Eq. (7·41) to substitute for $đQ$, we have

$$đ\mathcal{P}_S = \frac{1}{T}\,dU + \frac{P}{T}\,dV - \frac{dU}{T} + \frac{đW}{T} = \frac{P\,dV + đW}{T}$$

Then, using Eq. (7·42), the second law requires

$$đ\mathcal{P}_S = \left(\frac{P - P_m}{T}\right) dV \geq 0 \tag{7·44}$$

Now, if the process is reversible the amount of entropy production $đ\mathcal{P}_S$ will be zero, and hence we conclude that $P = P_m$ *for a reversible process.* During any such reversible process the control mass must always be in an equilibrium state (otherwise there would be some irreversibility associated with the relaxation toward equilibrium). We conclude that the thermodynamic and mechanical pressures are identical *in any equilibrium state.*

If the process is irreversible, then $đ\mathcal{P}_S > 0$, and hence

$$(P - P_m)\,dV > 0$$

If the substance is expanding, doing work, $dV > 0$, and hence $P > P_m$. The pressure measured during an irreversible expansion would therefore be less than the pressure that the system would have in equilibrium at the same energy and volume. Hence less work is done by the system than might be. In contrast, if the substance is being compressed, $dV < 0$, and $P < P_m$. The pressure exerted during compression is therefore greater than the equilibrium pressure. Hence more work must be done on the system than for the reversible process.

A microscopic interpretation will be helpful. Consider the compression of a gas in a piston-cylinder system. If the compression process is very rapid, the molecules will bunch up near the piston, exerting a larger pressure (P_m) than if they were distributed uniformly over the cylinder (P). Hence more

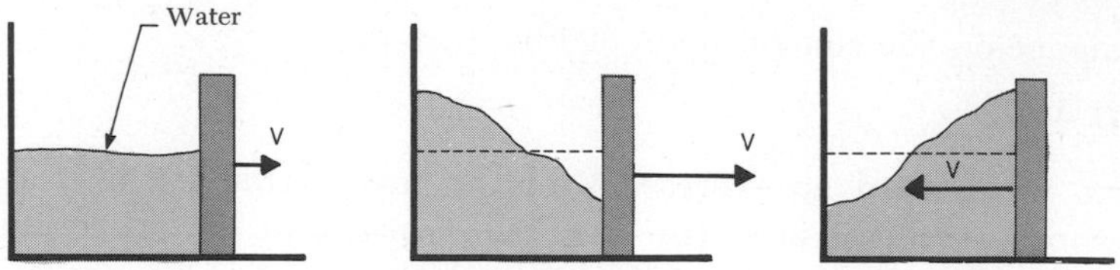

FIG. 7·17 *Work in reversible and irreversible processes*

work will be required for the rapid than for the slow compression. If the piston moves rapidly away from the gas, there will be fewer molecules near the piston than for a slower expansion ($P_m < P$), and less work will be done by the gas. Figure 7·17 shows an hydraulic analogy that is helpful in grasping these ideas.

7·13 EQUIVALENCE OF THE THERMODYNAMIC AND EMPIRICAL TEMPERATURES

Now that we know $P = P_m$ in any equilibrium state, we can use the fact that the entropy is a function of state, together with certain experimental observations, to establish the correspondence between the thermodynamic and empirical temperature scales. The experimental evidence required is that the gases used in empirical thermometers apparently have the property that at very low pressures their internal energies u and their pressure-volume products depend solely on temperature (they behave like a "perfect gas"). This behavior is also predicted by quantum-statistical thermodynamic theory. The fact that the internal energy becomes a function only of temperature at very low pressures is nicely shown in Figs. B·1 and B·4. Conversely, at low pressures, specification of the internal energy is sufficient to determine the temperature, or the temperature is a function only of the internal energy. Consequently, for gases at sufficiently low pressures, we put

$$T = T(u)$$

Here T denotes the thermodynamic temperature. For the Pv product,

$$Pv = f(T) \tag{7·45}$$

where $f(T)$ represents some unknown function of the thermodynamic temperature.

In an equilibrium state the specific entropy is a function only of the specific internal energy and the specific volume,

$$s = s(u, v)$$

Then, from the calculus

$$\left\{\frac{\partial[(\partial s/\partial u)_v]}{\partial v}\right\}_u = \left\{\frac{\partial[(\partial s/\partial v)_u]}{\partial u}\right\}_v$$

Expressed in terms of the thermodynamic temperature and pressure,

$$\left[\frac{\partial(1/T)}{\partial v}\right]_u = \left[\frac{\partial(P/T)}{\partial u}\right]_v$$

Since the temperature of the low-pressure gas is independent of volume along a line of constant internal energy, the term on the left is zero, and consequently

$$\left[\frac{\partial(P/T)}{\partial u}\right]_v = 0$$

We see that P/T is independent of u along a line of constant v. However, since u depends only on T, the ratio P/T must be independent of T along this line. Therefore, we conclude that low-density gases have the property that

$$\left[\frac{\partial(P/T)}{\partial T}\right]_v = 0 \qquad (7\cdot46)$$

Using Eq. (7·45) in Eq. (7·46), we obtain

$$\frac{1}{v}\left[\frac{\partial(f/T)}{\partial T}\right]_v = \frac{1}{v}\frac{d(f/T)}{dT} = 0$$

The ratio $f(T)/T$ must therefore be *a constant*, which means that $f(T)$ must be of the form

$$Pv = f(T) = \text{constant} \times T$$

This is exactly the form that was arbitrarily selected for the empirical temperature; the empirical and thermodynamic temperature scales therefore must coincide, apart from a multiplicative constant. By judicious selection of the constant in the defining equation for the entropy, the two scales can be made identical. Henceforth we shall consider that the thermodynamic and empirical absolute temperatures† are exactly the same.‡

7·14 APPLICATIONS OF THE SECOND LAW TO ENERGY-CONVERSION SYSTEMS

We now have in hand all the tools necessary to study the possibility or limitations of any process imposed by the second law. One of the important areas of application of thermodynamics is in the study of energy-conversion systems. Nature has been generous in providing large sources of energy, but she managed to keep most of it tied up in randomly oriented microscopic forms and left man with the task of devising means for converting this energy to usable macroscopic forms. However, the second law places certain limitations

† On the Kelvin or Rankine scales.

‡ A more accurate experimental test of this could be made using the *Clapeyron equation*. This experiment will be discussed in the next chapter.

on the performance of energy-conversion systems; for example, we find that it is not possible to convert all the energy obtained from a nuclear reaction into useful mechanical work. The second law can be used to derive an expression for the maximum possible energy-conversion efficiency for any continuously operating converter, and the same limit holds for both steam power plants and thermoelectric converters. Such sweeping generality is indeed impressive, and very characteristic of thermodynamic theory.

We shall define a *heat engine* as any control mass to and from which energy is transferred as heat and from which energy is transferred as work. We further require that the processes undergone by the matter within the engine be cyclic, or continuous, such that after some period all the matter within the engine has been returned to its initial state.

A special type of heat engine is useful. Any heat engine to which energy is transferred as heat at one temperature and from which energy is transferred at a lower temperature is called a *2T engine* (Fig. 7·18).

There are many ways by which one can devise a $2T$ engine, and it would be well to illustrate one at this point. Suppose we have a piston-cylinder system filled with a gas. By causing this system to excute the four-process cycle, shown schematically in Fig. 7·19, we can obtain work as a result of transfers of energy as heat to and from the engine. The process representation shows the temperature of the gas as a function of the piston position. Observe the cyclic nature of this process. By proper control of the piston displacement, the processes can in principle be carried out in such a way that the gas temperature is constant while energy is being transferred as heat. The processes inside the engine can in principle be made reversible. However, if we tried to reverse the engine (this is then called a heat pump), $T_{A'}$ would have to rise above T_A for there to be a transfer of heat to environment A. But if the process is carried out slowly enough $T_{A'}$ need be only an infinitesimal bit lower than T_A, and $T_{B'}$ only an infinitesimal bit higher than T_B, so that the heat-pump process can, in the limit, be made the exact reverse of the heat-engine process (Fig. 7·20); this we call a *reversible 2T engine* (R$2T$). This particular engine operates on a Carnot cycle and is thus called a *Carnot engine.* The reversible $2T$ engine is, of course, only an idealization, but it is fully as useful in thermodynamic theory as is the frictionless pulley in mechanics.

The *energy-conversion efficiency* of a heat engine is defined as the ratio of the useful work output to the energy input as heat,

$$\blacktriangleright \qquad \eta \equiv \frac{W}{Q_A} \qquad (7\cdot 47)$$

This ratio will not remain constant when the engine is reversed, except for a reversible $2T$ engine (see Fig. 7·21). Note that no energy-storage terms have been shown in any of these figures. The symbols Q and W are to be interpreted as being "for a cycle," and since the engines operate cyclicly, there is no change in the energy within an engine over a cycle.

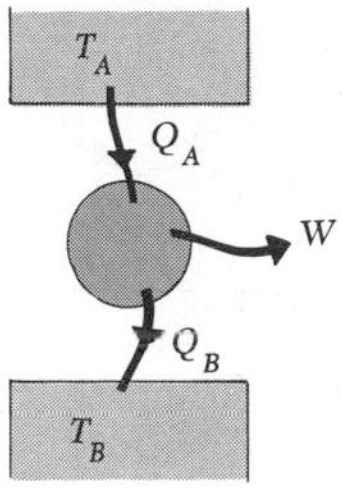

FIG. 7·18 *A 2T heat engine*

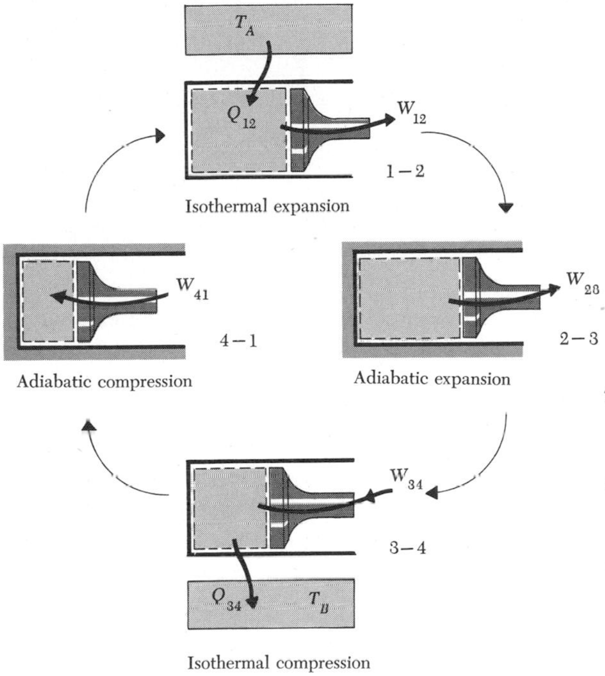

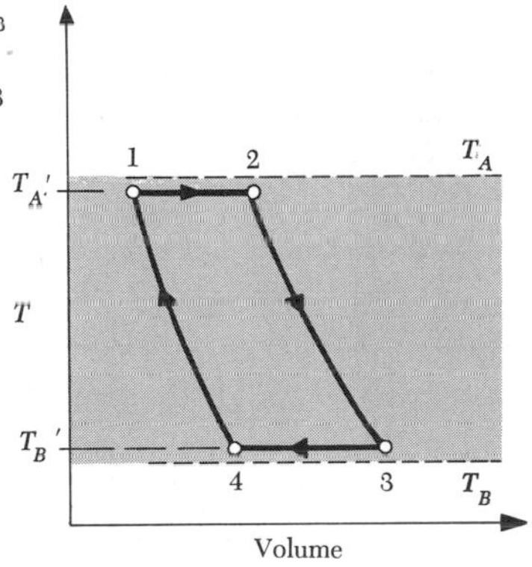

FIG. 7·19 *A 2T-heat-engine cycle*

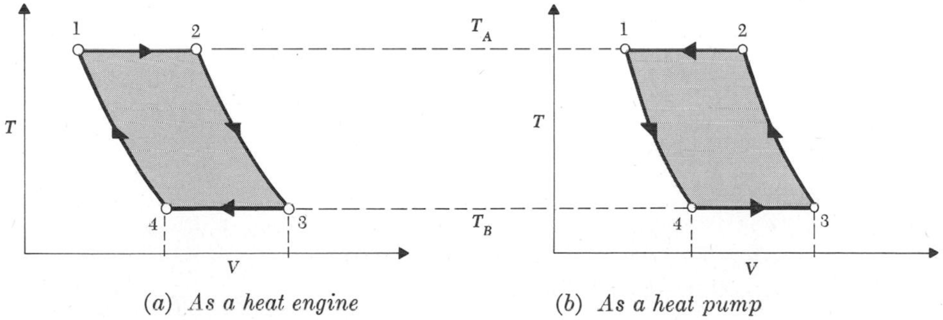

FIG. 7·20 *A reversible 2T engine*

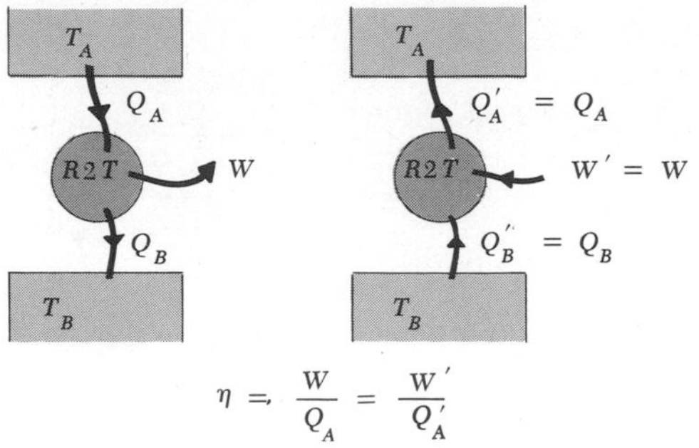

FIG. 7·21 *The efficiency of a reversible 2T heat engine is independent of the direction of operation*

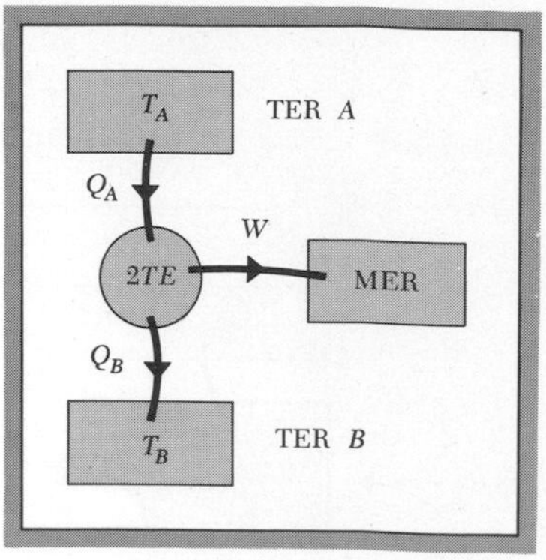

FIG. 7·22 *Determining the efficiency of a 2T engine*

A simple expression for the limiting efficiency of a $2T$ engine can be derived by considering the system of Fig. 7·22. The engine receives energy as hêat from a thermal energy reservoir at temperature T_A, and rejects energy as heat to a second TER at T_B. The energy output as work is stored in a mechanical energy reservoir. The combined system is isolated, and the second law says that the entropy of this isolated system can never decrease. Now, since the engine executes a cycle, all matter in the engine returns to its initial state, and hence its entropy is unchanged over one cycle. The MER undergoes no change in entropy. The entropy increases of the two TERs are

$$\Delta S_A = \frac{-Q_A}{T_A} \qquad \Delta S_B = \frac{Q_B}{T_B}$$

and hence the entropy produced when the engine executes one cycle is

$$\mathcal{P}_S = \left(\frac{Q_B}{T_B} - \frac{Q_A}{T_A}\right) \geq 0 \tag{7·48}$$

The equality holds only if the processes within the isolated system are reversible, that is, if the engine is an R$2T$.

▶ $$\frac{Q_A}{Q_B} = \frac{T_A}{T_B} \quad \text{for a reversible } 2T \text{ engine} \tag{7·49}$$

Applying the first law over the period of a cycle, we find

$$W = Q_A - Q_B \tag{7·50}$$

so that

▶ $$\eta_{R2T} = \frac{Q_A - Q_B}{Q_A} = \frac{T_A - T_B}{T_A} \quad \text{for } \textit{any} \text{ reversible } 2T \text{ engine} \tag{7·51}$$

It is common practice to call this the *Carnot efficiency,* since the Carnot engine is one type of reversible $2T$ engine. However, we have said nothing at all about the nature of the engine, so the expression actually holds for *any* reversible $2T$ engine.

The inequality in Eq. (7·48) pertains to irreversible processes within the engine, that is, to an *irreversible* $2T$ engine, for which

$$\frac{Q_B}{Q_A} > \frac{T_B}{T_A} \qquad \text{for } Q_A > 0$$

Thus

$$\eta_{\text{irrev}} = \left(1 - \frac{Q_B}{Q_A}\right) < \left(1 - \frac{T_B}{T_A}\right) = \eta_{\text{Carnot}} \tag{7·52}$$

The Carnot efficiency is therefore an upper limit for the performance of any real heat engine. Highest efficiencies will be obtained when the ratio T_B/T_A is as small as possible; one would like to add the energy as heat at as high a temperature as possible and reject energy as heat at the lowest possible temperature. However, nature places physical limitations on man's capabilities. The energy which is rejected as heat must flow to an environment which is cooler than T_B; this means that we are limited to T_B of the order of 520°R (60°F). The energy transfer as heat must come into the engine from a region at a temperature greater than T_A. Temperatures of the order of 3500°R can be obtained by combustion reactions, but metallurgical considerations normally require that the device be kept much cooler. Modern steam power plants operate at about 1100°F (not on the Carnot cycle). Advanced nuclear power systems are being designed and tested in the range of 1500–2500°F. These high-temperature systems employ exotic metals and are not intended for long life or for production of low-cost electrical power. At 1500°F the Carnot-cycle efficiency is

$$1 - {}^{520}\!/_{1960} = 0.735$$

Even under such extreme conditions this most ideal cycle could convert only 73.5 percent of the energy transferred in as heat to useful work. Realistic devices of present technology operate in the range of 15–40 percent, and a heat engine having a thermal energy-conversion efficiency of even 50 percent has yet to be built.

It is evident that it would be impossible to devise a 100 percent efficient heat engine even if we really had reversible processes at our disposal. This can be seen by setting $Q_B = 0$ in Eq. (7·48), for we then find that Q_A must also be zero or negative for any cyclicly operating device. A $1T$ engine is therefore impossible, though it is not at all difficult to dream up a continuously operating device to which energy is transferred as work and from which energy is transferred as heat. It is also possible to make a system which will receive energy as heat, converting all this energy to work, but which will

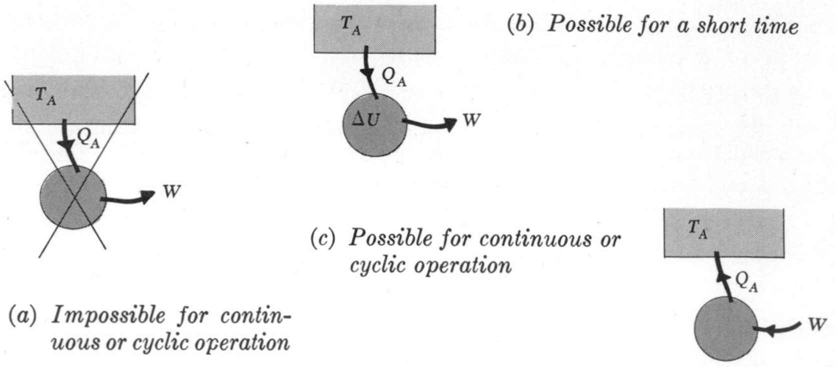

(*a*) *Impossible for continuous or cyclic operation*

(*b*) *Possible for a short time*

(*c*) *Possible for continuous or cyclic operation*

FIG. 7·23 *A 1T heat engine is impossible*

not operate indefinitely. For example, we can heat the gas in a piston-cylinder system and allow it to expand, removing the same amount of energy we put in, but eventually we would run out of cylinder, the piston would fall out, and the device would cease to operate. A short-lived converter with 100 percent efficiency is possible, but a continuously operating one is not. The statement that a continuously operating $1T$ engine is impossible is known as the *Kelvin-Planck statement* and is taken as the starting point in many classical developments of the second law. The restrictions placed on heat engines by the second law are illustrated in Fig. 7·23.

The second law also places limitations on systems that continuously transfer energy as heat from a region of low temperature to one of higher temperature (a refrigerator, or a heat pump). In particular, it may easily be shown

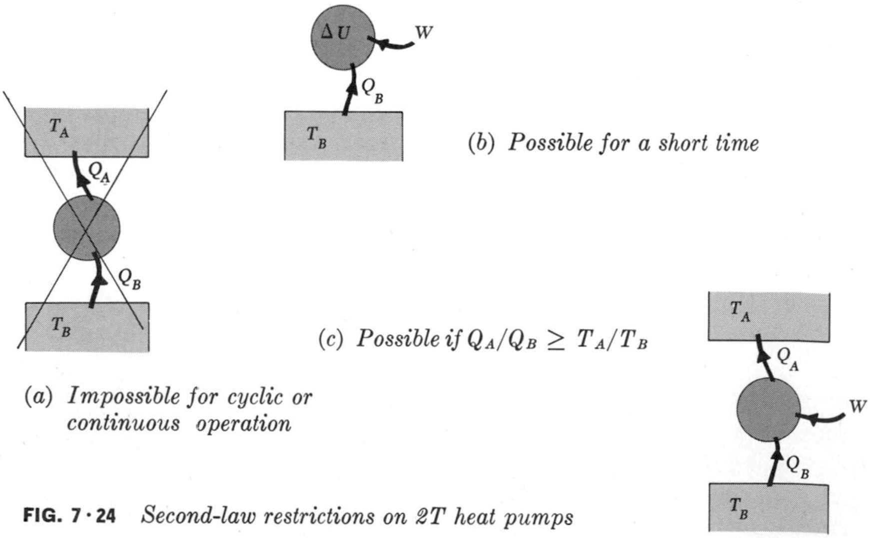

(*a*) *Impossible for cyclic or continuous operation*

(*b*) *Possible for a short time*

(*c*) *Possible if* $Q_A/Q_B \geq T_A/T_B$

FIG. 7·24 *Second-law restrictions on 2T heat pumps*

that it is impossible to devise any system that will do this cyclicly or continuously without any energy input as work. Such a device would constitute a refrigerator which requires no input power, and it certainly seems reasonable that this is an impossibility. However, it is possible to devise a system that will do this for a short time, or to have energy flow through a device from high temperature to low temperature without power input. The restrictions imposed by the second law on heat pumps are illustrated in Fig. 7·24. The statement that a zero-work heat pump is impossible is called the *Clausius statement*, and it too is often taken as the starting point for the development of the second law in classical thermodynamics. Its proof from entropy-production considerations is left as an exercise.

7·15 A REMARK ON THE THERMODYNAMIC TEMPERATURE

The fact that all reversible $2T$ engines operating between the same two temperatures have the same efficiencies can be used in principle to obtain a direct measurement of the thermodynamic temperature. We imagine using any reversible $2T$ engine as a thermometer and letting it operate between the unknown temperature T_A and the H_2O triple-point temperature $T_B = 273.16°K$. We measure the energy transfers Q_A and Q_B and then use Eq. (7·49) to calculate the thermodynamic temperature of the test environment. It is important to appreciate that the thermodynamic temperature scale is independent of the nature of any thermometric substance; we can now look upon the gas thermometer as a means for measuring the thermodynamic temperature rather than as a means for defining an empirical temperature scale.

7·16 THE SECOND LAW FOR A CONTROL VOLUME

We began our discussions of the second law in the last chapter with a postulate that the entropy of an isolated system must never decrease. From this postulate we introduced the notions of entropy inflow and outflow with heat and of entropy production, and showed that the entropy production caused by processes within a control mass could never be less than zero. The entropy of a control mass can, of course, decrease, but only if some energy is removed as heat. We shall now extend these ideas to a control volume, for it is in this form that the second law is most often applied in engineering.

Consider the control volume of Fig. 7·25. We permit energy transfer as heat to take place at various points on the boundary, except where mass crosses the control surface. Energy transfer as work may also occur. For simplicity we assume that there are only the two mass flows shown and that they are one-dimensional at sections 1 and 2. To make the control-volume transformation we consider a control mass which occupies the control volume at time t and examine this control mass over an infinitesimal time interval dt. The change

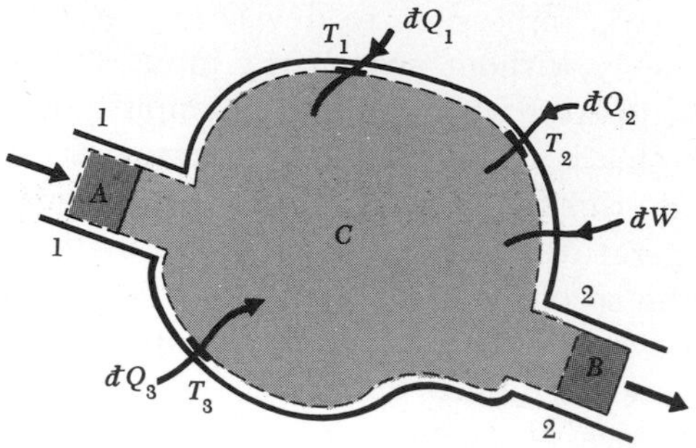

FIG. 7·25 *The control volume*

in its entropy is

$$dS_{CM} = S_{CM}(t + dt) - S_{CM}(t)$$

The entropy within the control mass at time t is exactly the entropy within the control volume at that time, since the two then coincide. The value of $S_{CM}(t + dt)$ can be expressed in terms of the entropy within the control volume at $t + dt$ and the entropies of the shaded portions A and B as

$$S_{CM}(t + dt) = S_{CV}(t + dt) + S_B - S_A$$

The entropies within A and B may be expressed in terms of the specific entropies of the substances flowing across the control surface, and we have

$$S_A = (A\rho V\,dt)_1 s_1 \qquad S_B = (A\rho V\,dt)_2 s_2$$

However, the terms $A\rho V\,dt$ represent the elemental additions and removals of mass from the control volume at the respective sections. Thus

$$dS_{CM} = dS + (s\,đM)_2 - (s\,đM)_1$$

where $dS = S_{CV}(t + dt) - S_{CV}(t)$. The energy transfers as heat $đQ_i$ may now be considered as going to either the control mass or the control volume. The entropy production *for the control mass* is

$$đ\mathcal{P}_S \equiv \Bigg\{ \underbrace{\Big[dS + (s\,đM)_2 - (s\,đM)_1 \Big]}_{\text{increase in entropy within the control mass}} - \underbrace{\sum_{\text{in}} \frac{đQ_i}{T_i}}_{\text{entropy inflow}} \Bigg\}$$

Note that this equation is written in terms of the properties of the control volume, and hence can be viewed as an expression for the entropy production *for the control volume.*

$$\blacktriangleright \quad đ\mathcal{P}_S \equiv \Bigg\{ \underbrace{dS}_{\text{increase in entropy within the control volume}} + \underbrace{(s đM)_2}_{\text{entropy outflow}} - \underbrace{\Big[(s đM)_1 + \sum_{\text{in}} \frac{đQ_i}{T_i} \Big]}_{\text{entropy inflow}} \Bigg\} \tag{7·53}$$

Note that T_i should be interpreted as the temperature of the control surface at the point where $đQ_i$ enters the control volume. The terms $s\,đM$ represent *convective entropy flow* associated with mass transfer across the boundaries of the control volume. The second law requires that the entropy production be positive,

$$đ\mathcal{P}_S \geq 0 \tag{7·54}$$

For a control volume with several inflows and outflows, the definition of entropy production can readily be extended and expressed on a *rate* basis as

$$\blacktriangleright \quad \dot{\mathcal{P}}_S = \left\{ \underbrace{\frac{dS}{dt}}_{\substack{\text{rate of}\\\text{entropy}\\\text{storage}}} + \underbrace{\left[\sum_{\text{out}} (s\dot{M}) + \sum_{\text{out}} \frac{\dot{Q}_i}{T_i}\right]}_{\substack{\text{rate of}\\\text{entropy}\\\text{outflow}}} - \underbrace{\left[\sum_{\text{in}} (s\dot{M}) + \sum_{\text{in}} \frac{\dot{Q}_i}{T_i}\right]}_{\substack{\text{rate of}\\\text{entropy inflow}}} \right\} \tag{7·55}$$

Here $\dot{\mathcal{P}}_S$ is the *rate of entropy production* within the control volume. The terms $s\dot{M}$ represent *rates of convective entropy transfer*, and the terms $\dot{Q}/T$ represent *rates of entropy transfer with heat.* The second law requires that the rate of entropy production be positive,

$$\dot{\mathcal{P}}_S \geq 0 \tag{7.56}$$

The equality is again associated with reversible processes within the control volume, and the inequality with irreversible processes.

7·17 EXAMPLES OF SECOND-LAW ANALYSIS

A solar engine. It is proposed that solar energy be used to warm a large "collector plate"; this energy would, in turn, be transferred as heat to a fluid within a heat engine, and the engine would reject energy as heat to the atmosphere. Experiments indicate that about 200 Btu/hr-ft² of energy can be "collected" when the plate is operating at 190°F. Estimate the minimum collector area that would be required for a plant producing 1 kw of useful shaft power.

We first estimate the maximum energy-conversion efficiency of this system, using the Carnot efficiency as an upper limit. The atmospheric temperature is assumed to be 70°F. Then

$$\eta_{\max} = 1 - \frac{70 + 460}{190 + 460} = 0.184$$

The efficiency of any real heat engine operating between the collector place and atmospheric temperature would be less than this, owing to irreversibilities in real devices. The minimum rate at which energy must be collected is related to the required power output and maximum energy-conversion efficiency,

$$\dot{Q}_{\min} = \frac{\dot{W}}{\eta_{\max}} = \frac{1 \text{ kw}}{0.184} = 5.44 \text{ kw} = 18{,}600 \text{ Btu/hr}$$

so the minimum area required is

$$A_{\min} = \frac{18{,}600}{200} = 93 \text{ ft}^2$$

A real system might be expected to need twice or three times this area, since its efficiency would probably be considerably less than 18.4 percent.

A compressor. Freon-12 enters an adiabatic compressor at 30 psia and 40°F and is compressed to 140 psia. What is the shaft-work input per lbm of freon-12 for the best adiabatic compressor which might be devised? See Fig. 7·26.

We make the following idealizations:

Steady flow steady state
Kinetic and potential energy changes negligible

An energy balance allows us to relate the work input per unit of mass W to the enthalpy rise across the compressor,

$$W = h_2 - h_1$$

The second law requires that the entropy production be positive. Since we have assumed that steady-flow steady-state conditions prevail, the entropy within the control volume is not changing, and because of our adiabatic idealization, no entropy flows with heat across the boundary. Only the convected entropy flows are involved, so we have

$$\dot{\mathcal{P}}_S = \underbrace{\dot{M}(s_2 - s_1)}_{\text{net rate of entropy outflow}} \geq 0$$

which yields

$$s_2 - s_1 \geq 0$$

The entropy of the fluid must increase as it passes through the device. This means that the outlet state must lie to the right of state 2s on the P-h diagram

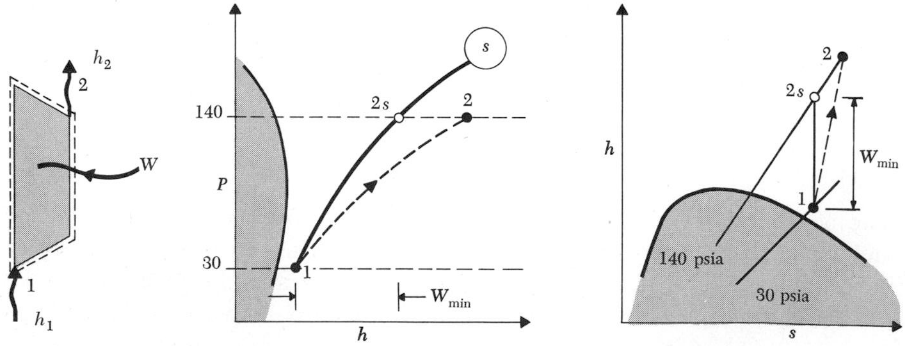

(a) *The control volume* (b) *The process representation*

FIG. 7·26 *Compressor analysis*

of Fig. 7·26*b* (see Fig. B·7). It is evident that the least enthalpy change, that is, the least work input, is required by a device in which there is no entropy production. This work is $h_{2s} - h_1$, and its magnitude can be fixed with the aid of Fig. B·7. Denoting the work required by this ideal isentropic compressor by W_s, we find

$$W_s = h_{2s} - h_1 = 96 - 83 = 13 \text{ Btu/lbm}$$

The work required by a real irreversible adiabatic compressor would be greater than W_s. It is customary to define the *isentropic efficiency* of a compressor as

$$\blacktriangleright \quad \eta_s = \frac{\text{work required by ideal isentropic compressor}}{\text{work required by actual compressor}} = \frac{W_s}{W_{act}}$$

Note that the isentropic efficiency compares an actual process to an ideal process and is not an energy-conversion efficiency. Both the actual and ideal devices are assumed to have the same inlet state and the same discharge pressure. A typical value for η_s might be 0.90. Then

$$W_{act} = \frac{W_s}{\eta_s} = \frac{13}{0.90} = 14 \text{ Btu/lbm}$$

The actual discharge enthalpy would be

$$h_2 = h_1 + W_{act} = 83 + 14 = 97 \text{ Btu/lbm}$$

This value, together with the discharge pressure, suffices to determine the discharge state.

An inventor's claim. An inventor claims to have devised a steady-flow compressor which requires no shaft-power input. He claims that CO_2 at 200 psia and 120°F can be compressed to 300 psia, where it will emerge at 20°F, simply by a transfer of energy as heat from his device. His patent application states that the device will handle 2 lbm of CO_2 per sec and is driven by a "cold

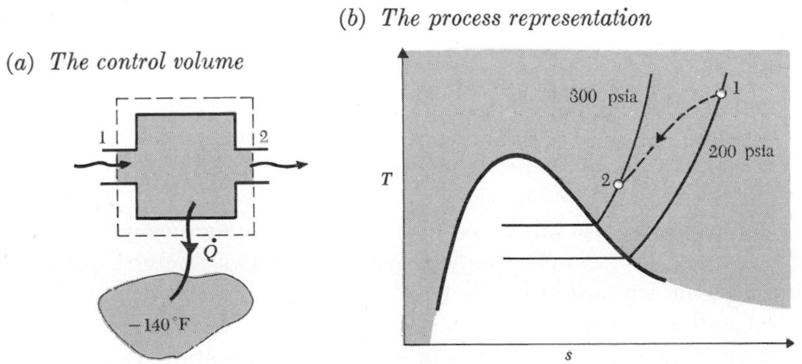

FIG. 7·27 *Analysis of the inventor's claim*

source" at −140°F. Energy is transferred as heat from this device to the cold space at the rate of 60 Btu/sec. He further states that the CO_2 enters and leaves the device at very low velocity, and that no significant elevation changes are involved. Could his claims be valid?

The device will be impossible if it violates either the first or second laws of thermodynamics. According to his claims, we may neglect kinetic and potential energies in the fluid streams and assume that steady-flow steady-state conditions prevail. We further assume that the flows are one-dimensional at the inlet and exit and that the CO_2 is in equilibrium states at these points. From Fig. B·6 we read the following:

$T_1 = 120°\text{F}$	$T_2 = 20°\text{F}$
$P_1 = 200$ psia	$P_2 = 300$ psia
$h_1 = 318$ Btu/lbm	$h_2 = 288$ Btu/lbm
$s_1 = 1.315$ Btu/lbm-°R	$s_2 = 1.240$ Btu/lbm-°R

An energy balance on the control volume, on a rate basis, gives

$$\dot{M}(h_2 - h_1) + \dot{Q} = 2 \times (288 - 318) + 60 = 0 \text{ Btu/sec}$$

His device is not an energy producer, so it does not violate the first law.

The entropy-production rate for the control volume is

$$\dot{\mathcal{P}}_S = \underbrace{\dot{M}(s_2 - s_1)}_{\substack{\text{net convective}\\ \text{entropy-outflow}\\ \text{rate}}} + \underbrace{\frac{\dot{Q}}{T_c}}_{\substack{\text{rate of}\\ \text{entropy outflow}\\ \text{with heat}}}$$

where T_c is the temperature of the cold space (−140°F = 320°R). Then

$$\dot{\mathcal{P}}_S = 2 \times (1.240 - 1.315) + \frac{60}{320} = -0.150 + 0.188 = +0.038 \text{ Btu/°R-sec}$$

The rate of entropy production is indeed positive, so his device does not violate the second law. We conclude that it is theoretically possible.

The availability of energy in a steady-flow device. A fluid enters a device at state 1 and emerges at state 2. The device can communicate with a large environment at temperature T_0, from which it can obtain energy as heat. What is the maximum available power output from this device?

This type of problem falls in the general area of *availability analysis*, a technique of great interest in advanced applied thermodynamics courses. The general approach here is to apply the first and second laws, thereby obtaining an upper limit on the amount of power which could be obtained from a device, given the inlet and discharge states.

The system we consider is shown in Fig. 7·28. We allow it to extract energy as heat from the environment at the rate $\dot{Q}_0$, and presume that it puts

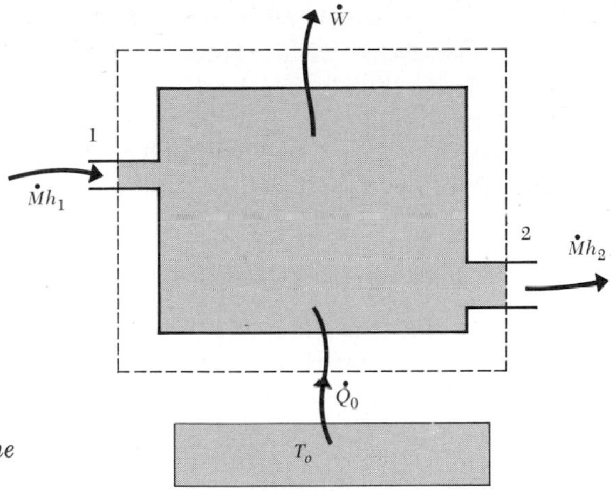

FIG. 7·28 *The control volume for the availability analysis*

out useful work at the rate $\dot{W}$. Assuming steady flow, steady state, and neglecting kinetic or potential energy of the flow streams, the first law analysis yields

$$\underbrace{\dot{M}h_1 + \dot{Q}_0}_{\text{energy-inflow rate}} = \underbrace{\dot{M}h_2 + \dot{W}}_{\text{energy-outflow rate}}$$

The entropy-production rate for the control volume is

$$\dot{\mathcal{P}}_S = \underbrace{\dot{M}s_2}_{\substack{\text{entropy-}\\ \text{outflow}\\ \text{rate}}} - \underbrace{\left(\dot{M}s_1 + \frac{\dot{Q}_0}{T_0}\right)}_{\text{entropy-inflow rate}}$$

and the second law requires that $\dot{\mathcal{P}}_S \geq 0$. Combining the first and second equations, we have

$$\dot{M}(s_2 - s_1) - \frac{1}{T_0}[\dot{M}(h_2 - h_1) + \dot{W}] \geq 0$$

So,

$$\dot{W} \leq \dot{M}[(h - T_0s)_1 - (h - T_0s)_2]$$

The function $h - T_0s$ is called the *steady-flow availability function;* note that it is a function of both the fluid and the environment. The availability analysis tells us that the work output per lbm of fluid, $\dot{W}/\dot{M}$, cannot exceed the decrease in the availability function. If the equality holds, the processes within the control volume must all be reversible, including the energy-transfer process between the device and the environment at T_0. The maximum work output is therefore obtained for a *reversible* process.

The difference between the maximum possible useful work output and the actual work output is sometimes called the *irreversibility* of the process. In the analysis of complex engineering systems one can locate the primary sources of irreversibility, which all cost money, by calculating the amount of irreversibility associated with each component in the system or each step in the process. Efforts to improve performance can then be concentrated in areas where the greatest gains stand to be made. The student who goes on to more advanced courses in applied thermodynamics will likely find considerable use for this sort of availability-irreversibility analysis.

7·18 A SUMMARY OF THE FIRST AND SECOND LAWS

At this point it would be a good idea to summarize the working expressions for the basic laws, lest there be any confusion about what is applicable only to an isolated system or only to a control mass. The formalism of production is convenient and easy to recall; in general, *production* is defined as follows:

Production equals the increase in the amount stored within the system plus the excess of amount which flows out over that which flows in.

Similarly, the *rate of production* of something is defined as follows:

Rate of production equals the rate of increase in the amount stored within the system plus the excess of the outflow rate over the inflow rate.

We applied the production concept in formulating the mathematics of the second law; we stated that entropy can be produced but never destroyed. The formalism is equally useful in stating the ideas of the first law, for energy can be neither produced nor destroyed. We can therefore state the first and second laws of thermodynamics in a very compact and physically appealing way; for an infinitesimal process,

$$\blacktriangleright \quad đ\mathcal{P}_E = 0 \tag{7·57}$$

$$\blacktriangleright \quad đ\mathcal{P}_S \geq 0 \tag{7·58}$$

Alternatively, on a rate basis,

$$\blacktriangleright \quad \dot{\mathcal{P}}_E = 0 \tag{7·59}$$

$$\blacktriangleright \quad \dot{\mathcal{P}}_S \geq 0 \tag{7·60}$$

Table 7·1, a summary of these ideas for an isolated system, a control mass, and a control volume, uses the notation $\mathcal{K}$ for entropy transfer with heat,

$$\blacktriangleright \quad đ\mathcal{K} \equiv \frac{đQ}{T} \tag{7·61}$$

Here $đQ$ is an energy transfer as heat to the system under study and is received by the system at a point on the boundary where its temperature is T. The notation $đ$ is used, since $đ\mathcal{K}$ represents an infinitesimal amount of entropy transfer with heat and does not, in general, represent the change of a property.

TABLE 7·1 SUMMARY OF THE WORKING FORMS OF THE FIRST AND SECOND LAWS

	First law	*Second law*
Basic principle	$đ\mathcal{P}_E = 0$ $\dot{\mathcal{P}}_E = 0$	$đ\mathcal{P}_S \geq 0$ $\dot{\mathcal{P}}_S \geq 0$
Isolated system 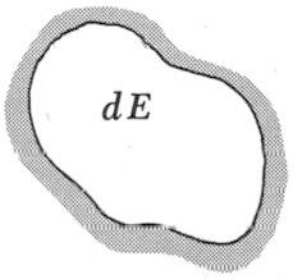 	$đ\mathcal{P}_E = dE$	$đ\mathcal{P}_S = dS$
Control mass 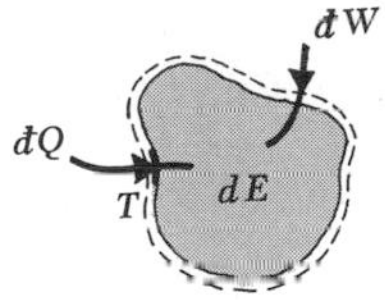 	$đ\mathcal{P}_E = dE - đQ - đW$	$đ\mathcal{P}_S = dS - đ\mathcal{K}$
Control volume 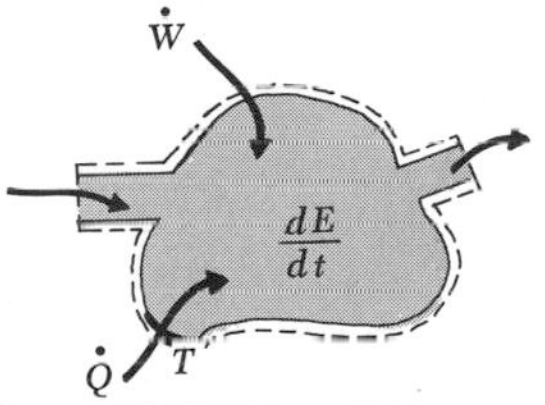 	$\dot{\mathcal{P}}_E = \dfrac{dE}{dt} - \dot{W} - \dot{Q} + \sum_{\text{out}} (e + Pv)\dot{M} - \sum_{\text{in}} (e + Pv)\dot{M}$	$\dot{\mathcal{P}}_S = \dfrac{dS}{dt} - \sum_{\text{in}} \dot{\mathcal{K}} + \sum_{\text{out}} s\dot{M} - \sum_{\text{in}} s\dot{M}$

Note: $e \equiv u + \dfrac{V^2}{2g_c} + \dfrac{g_g}{g_c} z + \mathcal{Q}\mathcal{E} + \cdots$ $\quad đ\mathcal{K} \equiv \dfrac{đQ}{T}$ $\quad \dot{\mathcal{K}} \equiv \dfrac{\dot{Q}}{T}$

SELECTED READING

Callen, H. B., *Thermodynamics*, secs. 1.1, 1.9, 2.4, 2.5, 2.7, John Wiley & Sons, Inc., New York, 1960.

Reif, F., *Fundamentals of Statistical and Thermal Physics*, secs. 3.5, 3.6, 3.10–3.12, McGraw-Hill Book Company, New York, 1965.

Tribus, M., *Thermostatics and Thermodynamics*, chap. 5, D. Van Nostrand Company, Inc., Princeton, N.J., 1961.

Van Wylen, G. J., and R. E. Sonntag, *Fundamentals of Classical Thermodynamics*, secs. 6.4, 6.7, 7.8, 7.9, 7.12, 7.13, chap. 8, John Wiley & Sons, Inc., New York, 1965.

QUESTIONS

7·1 What is the conceptual basis and definition of the thermodynamic temperature?

7·2 Is $-10°F$ a negative thermodynamic temperature?

7·3 Which have meaning in nonequilibrium states, which do not, and why: temperature, energy, entropy?

7·4 Suppose a substance could exist in equilibrium at negative temperatures; what would this mean with regard to the energy and entropy (on a microscopic scale)?

7·5 What is the thermodynamic definition of pressure?

7·6 What is a reversible process?

7·7 How is heat different from work?

7·8 What is an irreversible process?

7·9 One reversible $2T$ engine uses mercury as the working fluid, and another uses steam. When operating between the same two temperatures, how will their efficiencies compare?

7·10 Think of a device which receives energy as heat, rejects energy as work (these are the only energy transfers), yet does not violate the Kelvin-Planck statement.

7·11 Does a $1T$ engine violate the first law, the second law, or both?

7·12 What is entropy production? What is entropy inflow with heat?

7·13 Under what conditions will the entropy change of matter undergoing an adiabatic process be zero?

7·14 Suppose the thermodynamic temperature had been defined as $(\partial s/\partial u)_v$. Which way would heat flow, and would positive or negative temperatures be of most interest?

7·15 Give a qualitative microscopic explanation for the entropy change of a gas which undergoes reversible adiabatic expansion.

7·16 Give a qualitative microscopic explanation for the entropy change of a paramagnetic salt which undergoes reversible adiabatic magnetization.

7·17 What will happen to the entropy, energy, and temperature of a gas which is polarized reversibly and adiabatically at constant volume?

7·18 Under what circumstances would measurements of energy transfer as heat and temperature allow you to deduce the change in entropy of a control mass?

7·19 What happens to the entropy produced in a steady-flow steady-state system?

7·20 What is entropy?

PROBLEMS

7·1 Calculate the thermodynamic temperature of saturated water vapor at 100 psia from the u-s-v data in Appendix B and compare the result with the empirical temperature at this state.

7·2 Using the data on Fig. B·12, calculate the thermodynamic temperature for the paramagnetic substance iron-ammonium alum when $M = 70$ gauss and $H = 1000$ gauss and compare your result with that given by Fig. B·12.

7·3 Calculate the thermodynamic pressure for saturated water vapor at 100°F and compare your result with the tabulated saturation pressure at this state.

7·4 Derive the analog of Eq. (7·13) for a simple magnetic substance.

7·5 Using the method of Lagrange multipliers, show that the conditions for equilibrium for N interacting but independent pieces of simple compressible substances are that their temperatures and pressures all be identical.

7·6 Consider a control mass which executes a cycle, returning to its initial state. Prove that if $đQ$ inflow is positive,

$$\oint \frac{đQ}{T} \leq 0$$

(This is the *inequality of Clausius*, and is an important intermediate theorem in classical developments of the second law.)

7·7 Consider two interacting systems, one at a negative T and the other at a positive T. Show that any energy transfer as heat will take place from the system at negative T to the one at positive T, and hence the negative T state is "hotter."

7·8 Consider two interacting systems at negative T. Show that any energy transfer as heat will take place from the system at the least negative value of T to the one at a more negative value of T. Which state is the "hotter"?

7·9 It has been proposed that energy be taken as heat from the atmosphere around Chicago and used to run a power plant. Energy would be rejected as heat to Lake Michigan. Estimate the maximum efficiency of conversion of thermal energy to electrical power which could be obtained in such a plant.

7·10 An inventor claims to have perfected an engine which will produce power from energy transferred as heat from a 1000°F flame. Energy will be rejected as heat to the ground at 60°F. He claims a 75 percent energy-conversion efficiency. As chief patent officer, would you issue him a patent, and if so, would you invest money in his operation?

7·11 An inventor claims his device is able to convert to work all energy transferred to it as heat, but he makes no claims as to how long his device will work. Could it work at all?

7·12 An inventor claims to have a device which receives 1000 watts of energy as heat but puts out only 750 watts of electrical power. The rest of the energy is put out as mechanical work and dissipated outside his device by friction. Discuss the validity of these claims.

7·13 Thermal power systems for use in space normally reject energy as heat by radiating to space. Since fluid-filled radiators are generally quite heavy, it has been suggested that this energy be converted to electricity and the current run through lighter resistors to dissipate the energy as heat. What do you think of this idea? Energy transfer as heat from a space vehicle must take place by radiation. The weight of a space radiator is proportional to its area, which is determined by the rate at which the energy must be radiated as heat; the rate of energy radiation is proportional to the product of area and the fourth power of the radiator temperature. Consider a reversible $2T$ engine giving a fixed amount of power and operating with fixed source temperature. Show that the least radiator weight is obtained when the radiator temperature is 0.75 times the source temperature.

7·14 The amount of solar energy received at the earth's surface is approximately 420 Btu/hr-ft². Not all of this energy can be used in a solar power plant because of the reradiation of energy by the collector surface. Assume that the reradiation is described by $\dot{Q} = A\sigma\epsilon T^4$, where A is the collector area, $\epsilon = 0.5$, and $\sigma = 1.71 \times 10^{-9}$ Btu/hr-ft^2-°R^4 is the Stefan-Boltzmann constant. Find the maximum collector surface temperature (at which all the incident solar energy is reradiated). Suppose the power plant has the Carnot efficiency. If T_0 is the environmental temperature to which energy is rejected as heat, and T_c is the collector temperature, at what temperature of T_c should the system operate to achieve the most power output with a collector of fixed size ($T_0 \approx 80$°F)?

7·15 Examine the examples in Sec. 5·2. Indicate which processes might be reasonably idealized as reversible and which are inherently irreversible.

7·16 Determine the amount of entropy production by the control mass of the thermal-mixing example in Sec. 5·2.

7·17 Calculate the entropy-production rate for the control volume of the nozzle example in Sec. 5·4 if $\dot{M} = 10{,}000$ lbm/hr.

7·18 Calculate the rate of entropy production for the heat-exchanger example in Sec. 5·4.

7·19 Mercury flows through an adiabatic device. At one end the mercury is a saturated vapor at 400°F, and at the other end it is a mixture of 0.30 quality at 40 psia. The flow rate is 10 lbm/sec. Determine the rate at which energy is transferred to the device as work (power input or output) and the direction of flow. Kinetic and potential energies are negligible.

7·20 Calculate the maximum possible output power (kw) from an adiabatic steam turbine handling 10 lbm/sec, where the inlet state is 100 psia at 500°F and the discharge pressure is 1 atm.

7·21 Mercury enters a small adiabatic turbine as a saturated vapor at 1200°F and is discharged at 100 psia. Determine the minimum possible quality of the discharge stream.

7·22 Determine the lowest temperature that could be obtained by adiabatic demagnetization of iron-ammonium alum (Fig. B·12) if the applied field **H** were suddenly dropped from 10,000 gauss to zero, assuming that the initial temperature is 2°K.

7·23 Devise a Carnot power cycle to operate with iron-ammonium alum, receiving energy at 2°K and rejecting energy at 1°K. State the processes that make up this cycle, and give a symbolic energy analysis of each process. What is the cycle efficiency?

7·24 Steam enters an adiabatic diffuser at 1200 ft/sec as a saturated vapor at 60 psia. What is the maximum possible discharge pressure?

7·25 Freon-12 enters an adiabatic nozzle at 100 psia, 120°F, and emerges at 10 psia. What is the maximum possible discharge velocity?

7·26 Compute the maximum amount of work that could be obtained from each lbm of freon-12 if the valve of Fig. 5·16 were replaced by an adiabatic turbine. Why is the valve usually used?

7·27 Compute the maximum percent liquifaction (by mass) of O_2 that can be achieved by expanding it adiabatically in a piston-cylinder system from the saturated vapor state at 10 atm to twice the volume.

7·28 Compute the minimum amount of power required by an adiabatic compressor that handles 10 lbm/min of freon-12, compressing it from −20°F, 10 psia to 60 psia.

7·29 Calculate the amount of useful power output which could be obtained from each component of the heat pump system of Fig. 5·16, assuming that the components were replaced by devices which keep the inlet and discharge states the same, and that the replacement components can interact with an environment at 60°F. Which components are the most costly in terms of the available energy which they "waste?" Where do you think that efforts should be spent on design improvements in order to realize the most appreciable gain?

CHAPTER EIGHT

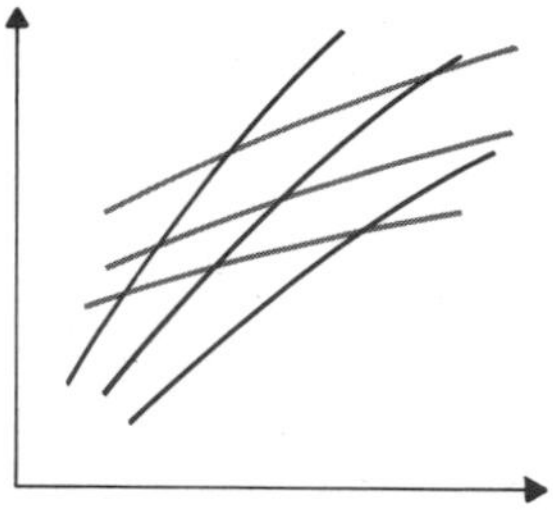

THE THERMODYNAMICS OF STATE

8·1 INTRODUCTION

The first and second laws provide the basis for analysis of thermodynamic systems, but little quantitative work can be done if the equations of state of the working substances are not known. Over the years a considerable body of equation-of-state information has been obtained by careful laboratory measurements, and these data are extremely important to the analyst. However, experiments are time-consuming and costly, and frequently we cannot wait for the availability of extensive data on a substance of interest. The first and second laws themselves can be extremely helpful in constructing a complete equation of state from a limited amount of data. Furthermore, thermodynamic theory is needed to provide relationships between the properties, so that those which are not directly measurable can be deduced. In this chapter we shall develop some of the more important relations between the intensive thermodynamic properties of some simple substances and indicate how these are used in the construction of equations of state from basic laboratory data.

Equations of state can also be obtained from microscopic theories, such as those of quantum-statistical mechanics, if a correct model is employed.† Relationships between the properties, derived by applications of the first and second laws, are essential in order to connect the results of these theories with measurable quantities. In Chap. Twelve we give some examples of equation-of-state development by this method. Included in this chapter is a very simple example in which part of the equation of state for a monatomic gas is obtained from an idealized model with the help of some thermodynamic relations.

It is important to appreciate that thermodynamics is very general and is not restricted solely to simple compressible substances. In this chapter we shall also discuss application of thermodynamics to magnetic substances and radiation in order to emphasize this point.

† Figure B·12 was obtained in this manner.

8·2 THERMODYNAMIC PROPERTIES OF A SIMPLE COMPRESSIBLE SUBSTANCE

We have introduced a number of intensive thermodynamic properties; some are purely conceptual, and others are defined. The state postulate tells us that any intensive thermodynamic state of a simple compressible substance is completely determined by the specification of any two independent properties, such as the specific internal energy and volume; all the other properties can then be viewed as functions of the two independent properties. A list of the important properties for any simple compressible substance is given in Table 8·1. In this table we introduce the *Helmholtz function*, *a*, and the *Gibbs function*, *g*, two

TABLE 8·1 INTENSIVE THERMODYNAMIC PROPERTIES OF A SIMPLE COMPRESSIBLE SUBSTANCE

Property	*Definition*
Conceptual	
Internal energy u	Energy associated with molecular and atomic motions and forces
Entropy s	A measure of the microscopic randomness or disorder, of our uncertainty as to the microscopic state knowing only the macroscopic state
Defined	
Temperature T	$T \equiv 1/(\partial s/\partial u)_v$, equal to the empirical temperature
Pressure P	$P \equiv T(\partial s/\partial v)_u$, equal to the mechanical pressure
Specific volume v	Volume per unit of mass
Density ρ	Mass per unit of volume
Enthalpy h	$h \equiv u + Pv$
Helmholtz function a	$a \equiv u - Ts$
Gibbs function g	$g \equiv h - Ts$
Isobaric compressibility β	$\beta \equiv \dfrac{1}{v}\left(\dfrac{\partial v}{\partial T}\right)_P$
Isothermal compressibility κ	$\kappa \equiv -\dfrac{1}{v}\left(\dfrac{\partial v}{\partial P}\right)_T$
Isentropic compressibility α	$\alpha \equiv -\dfrac{1}{v}\left(\dfrac{\partial v}{\partial P}\right)_s$
Specific heat at constant volume c_v	$c_v \equiv \left(\dfrac{\partial u}{\partial T}\right)_v$
Specific heat at constant pressure c_P	$c_P \equiv \left(\dfrac{\partial h}{\partial T}\right)_P$

thermodynamic properties whose importance will be made clear in Chaps. Ten and Eleven. The fact that a and g are properties, that is, functions of state, is itself very important, as we shall show in the present chapter. The isentropic compressibility, a derivative property relating volume changes to pressure changes for an isentropic process, is also defined in Table 8·1. The isentropic compressibility is related to the speed at which pressure waves (sound) travel through a substance, and is consequently of considerable importance.

8·3 EVALUATING THE ENTROPY OF A SIMPLE COMPRESSIBLE SUBSTANCE

The equations of state may be expressed functionally in terms of the properties considered to be independent. In particular, for the simple compressible substance we can put

$$s = s(u, v)$$

Taking the differential,

$$ds = \left(\frac{\partial s}{\partial u}\right)_v du + \left(\frac{\partial s}{\partial v}\right)_u dv$$

Then, using the thermodynamic definitions of temperature and pressure, we find

$$\blacktriangleright \qquad ds = \frac{1}{T}\,du + \frac{P}{T}\,dv \tag{8·1}$$

This is the *Gibbs equation*, which we derived in the same manner in the previous chapter. It is a differential equation of state which is extremely important in the thermodynamic theory of simple compressible substances. Since it relates the difference in the entropy between any two infinitesimally separated states to the infinitesimal differences in internal energy and volume between those states, the difference in entropy between two states can be found by integration,

$$s_2 - s_1 = \int_{u_1}^{u_2} \frac{du}{T} + \int_{v_1}^{v_2} \frac{P}{T}\,dv \tag{8·2}$$

In analyses not involving chemical reaction only the differences in entropy are involved. Consequently, we can select some state arbitrarily and refer the entropy for that substance to its value in this datum state. The charts and tables in Appendix B employ a variety of datum states. Having selected the datum state, we may perform the integrations of Eq. (8·2) from that point to any other state along any convenient path in the u-v plane. An illustration showing one simple integration is included in the examples presented in the previous chapter. Graphical or numerical integrations are usually employed, and we must, of course, know T and P as functions of u and v in order to per-

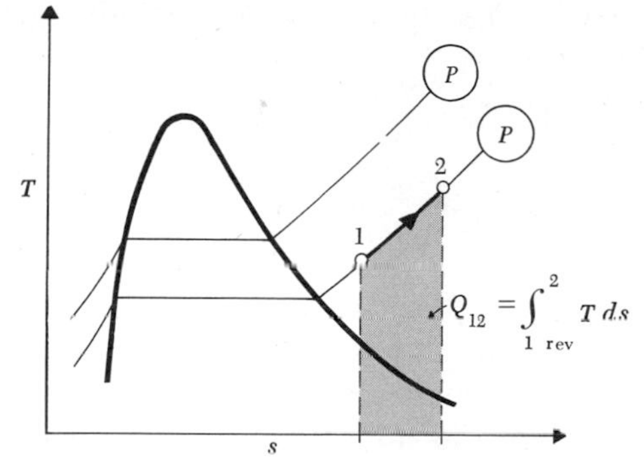

FIG. 8·1 *The area under a curve on the T-s plane represents reversible energy transfer as heat*

form the integration. In this manner we can determine the entropy of any substance, relative to the datum state.

Knowing the specific entropy of a substance as a function of the thermodynamic state, we can put lines of constant entropy on the graphical equations of state and enter values for the entropy in the tables. We can also use the entropy as a coordinate on a graphical equation of state; such graphs are particularly convenient in engineering analysis, especially where reversible adiabatic (isentropic, or constant-entropy) processes are involved. The temperature-entropy diagram is of special importance, for the area under a curve tracing out a reversible process on a T-s plane represents the energy transfer as heat to a unit of mass of the substance for the process (Fig. 8·1). Extensive use is made of T-s planes in engineering for both quantitative analysis and qualitative portrayal.

8·4 OTHER DIFFERENTIAL EQUATIONS OF STATE

The Gibbs equation may be written in another form which is convenient for deriving useful relationships among the properties,

$$du = T\,ds - P\,dv \tag{8·3}$$

Other differential equations of state can be obtained by combining the Gibbs equations with the differentials of the enthalpy, Helmholtz, and Gibbs functions. The enthalpy $h = u + Pv$ can be differentiated, yielding

$$dh = du + P\,dv + v\,dP$$

Combining with Eq. (8·3) results in a second differential equation of state,

▶ $$dh = T\,ds + v\,dP \tag{8·4}$$

This expresses enthalpy differences between two infinitesimally separated states in terms of the infinitesimal differences in the entropy and pressure. Moreover, we see that the coefficients T and v are merely partial derivatives of $h(s, P)$,

$$\blacktriangleright \quad \left(\frac{\partial h}{\partial s}\right)_P = T \tag{8·5a}$$

$$\blacktriangleright \quad \left(\frac{\partial h}{\partial P}\right)_s = v \tag{8·5b}$$

Since $v > 0$, an isentropic increase in pressure will always result in an increase in the enthalpy. In other words, adiabatic compressors require work.

In a similar manner the Gibbs equation can be combined with the differential of the Helmholtz function $a = u - Ts$ to give

$$\blacktriangleright \quad da = -P\,dv - s\,dT \tag{8·6}$$

The coefficients $-P$ and $-s$ are the partial derivatives of $a(v, T)$, so

$$\blacktriangleright \quad \left(\frac{\partial a}{\partial v}\right)_T = -P \tag{8·7a}$$

$$\blacktriangleright \quad \left(\frac{\partial a}{\partial T}\right)_v = -s \tag{8·7b}$$

Similarly, using the Gibbs function $g = h - Ts$, we may show that

$$\blacktriangleright \quad dg = v\,dP - s\,dT \tag{8·8}$$

Consequently,

$$\blacktriangleright \quad \left(\frac{\partial g}{\partial P}\right)_T = v \tag{8·9a}$$

$$\blacktriangleright \quad \left(\frac{\partial g}{\partial T}\right)_P = -s \tag{8·9b}$$

The importance of the Gibbs equation cannot be overemphasized. As an aid in being able to rederive it from first principles, we shall now make an alternative derivation. Consider a system consisting of a unit of mass of a simple compressible substance undergoing a reversible process, as shown in Fig. 8·2. Applying the first law over an infinitesimal part of the process, we have

$$du = đW + đQ$$

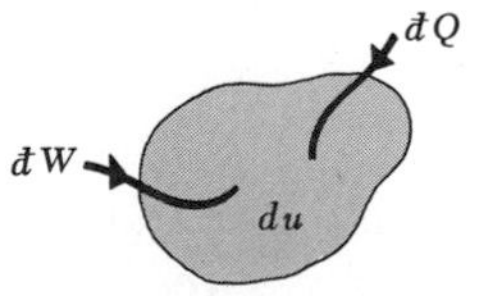

FIG. 8·2 *Rederivation of the Gibbs equation*

Since the process is reversible, the second law gives

$$đQ = T\,ds$$

Moreover, the work is given by

$$đW = -P\,dv$$

Combining, we again obtain the Gibbs equation,

$$du = T\,ds - P\,dv$$

It should be easy to recall that $đQ = T\,ds$ for a reversible process, from which the Gibbs equation can be rederived if needed, or developed for other classes of substances.

8·5 SOME IMPORTANT PROPERTY RELATIONS

The four differential equations of state developed in Sec. 8·4 provide the basis for numerous important relationships among the thermodynamic properties of a simple compressible substance. Note that each is of the form

$$dz(x, y) = M\,dx + N\,dy$$

where

$$M = \left(\frac{\partial z}{\partial x}\right)_y \qquad N = \left(\frac{\partial z}{\partial y}\right)_x$$

Mathematically we would say that dz is an exact differential, which simply means that z is a continuous function of the two independent variables x and y. Since the order in which a second partial derivative is taken is unimportant, it follows that

$$\left(\frac{\partial M}{\partial y}\right)_x = \left(\frac{\partial N}{\partial x}\right)_y$$

This result may be applied to each of the four differential equations of state, giving

▶ $$\left(\frac{\partial T}{\partial v}\right)_s = -\left(\frac{\partial P}{\partial s}\right)_v \qquad \text{from Eq. (8·3)} \qquad (8·10a)$$

▶ $$\left(\frac{\partial T}{\partial P}\right)_s = \left(\frac{\partial v}{\partial s}\right)_P \qquad \text{from Eq. (8·4)} \qquad (8·10b)$$

▶ $$\left(\frac{\partial P}{\partial T}\right)_v = \left(\frac{\partial s}{\partial v}\right)_T \qquad \text{from Eq. (8·6)} \qquad (8·10c)$$

▶ $$\left(\frac{\partial v}{\partial T}\right)_P = -\left(\frac{\partial s}{\partial P}\right)_T \qquad \text{from Eq. (8·8)} \qquad (8·10d)$$

Equations (8·10) are known as the *Maxwell relations*. They are relations between the derivatives of the thermodynamic properties that must hold for any simple compressible substance; similar relations may be derived for other types of substances.

The internal energy of a simple compressible substance is generally expressible as

$$u = u(T, v)$$

Differentiating and bringing in the definition of the specific heat at constant volume, we find

$$du = c_v\, dT + \left(\frac{\partial u}{\partial v}\right)_T dv \tag{8·11}$$

Equating Eqs. (8·3) and (8·11) and solving for ds,

$$ds = \frac{c_v}{T}\, dT + \frac{1}{T}\left[\left(\frac{\partial u}{\partial v}\right)_T + P\right] dv \tag{8·12}$$

Thinking of the entropy as a function of temperature and volume, we take its differential,

$$ds = \left(\frac{\partial s}{\partial T}\right)_v dT + \left(\frac{\partial s}{\partial v}\right)_T dv$$

and comparing this with Eq. (8·12), we see that

$$\left(\frac{\partial s}{\partial T}\right)_v = \frac{c_v}{T} \tag{8·13}$$

Using the third Maxwell relation, Eq. (8·10*c*), and Eq. (8·12),

$$\left(\frac{\partial s}{\partial v}\right)_T = \left(\frac{\partial P}{\partial T}\right)_v = \frac{1}{T}\left[\left(\frac{\partial u}{\partial v}\right)_T + P\right]$$

From this we obtain

$$\blacktriangleright \quad \left(\frac{\partial u}{\partial v}\right)_T = T\left(\frac{\partial P}{\partial T}\right)_v - P \tag{8·14}$$

This important equation expresses the dependence of the internal energy on the volume at fixed temperature solely in terms of the measurables T, P, and v. Since these three properties are easily measured, Eq. (8·14) is very useful in the construction of equation-of-state information from laboratory data.

From the previous discussion it follows that

$$ds = \frac{c_v}{T}\, dT + \left(\frac{\partial P}{\partial T}\right)_v dv \tag{8·15}$$

By considering the entropy as a function of the temperature and pressure and bringing in the differential of h in the form of Eq. (8·4), it may similarly be shown that†

$$ds = \frac{c_P}{T}\,dT - \left(\frac{\partial v}{\partial T}\right)_P dP \tag{8·16}$$

Subtracting Eq. (8·15) from Eq. (8·16) and solving for dP,

$$dP = \frac{c_P - c_v}{T(\partial v/\partial T)_P}\,dT - \frac{(\partial P/\partial T)_v}{(\partial v/\partial T)_P}\,dv$$

Then, considering P as a function of T and v, we see that

$$\frac{c_P - c_v}{T(\partial v/\partial T)_P} = \left(\frac{\partial P}{\partial T}\right)_v$$

It may be shown from the calculus (see Eq. 4·9) that

$$\left(\frac{\partial P}{\partial T}\right)_v = \frac{(\partial v/\partial T)_P}{-(\partial v/\partial P)_T}$$

Combining and solving for the difference in the specific heats,

$$▶ \quad c_P - c_v = -\frac{T[(\partial v/\partial T)_P]^2}{(\partial v/\partial P)_T} \tag{8·17}$$

This is one of the more important equations of thermodynamics, and it tells us a great deal. For example, the derivative $(\partial v/\partial P)_T$ is negative for all stable substances, and consequently c_P can never be less than c_v. Furthermore, whenever the derivative $(\partial v/\partial T)_P = 0$, the two specific heats will be equal (for example, water at 4°C). Finally, experiments indicate that as T approaches absolute zero, $(\partial v/\partial P)_T$ does not vanish, and so the two specific heats must approach one another at very low temperatures.

Equation (8·17) can be expressed in terms of the isothermal and isobaric compressibilities,

$$▶ \quad c_P - c_v = \frac{Tv\beta^2}{\kappa} \tag{8·18}$$

It is difficult to measure c_v with any precision for a solid or liquid, and the above equation is quite useful for obtaining c_v from more easily measured quantities.

By manipulating with the previous equations, we may show that the ratio of specific heats is related to the isentropic and isothermal compressibilities by

$$▶ \quad k \equiv \frac{c_P}{c_v} = \frac{\kappa}{\alpha} \tag{8·19}$$

† This requires use of a Maxwell relation. The development is left for an exercise.

The isentropic compressibility is related to the speed at which sound waves travel in the substance, and such speed measurements have been used as a means for determining the ratio of the specific heats.

A useful expression describing the variation of saturation pressure with saturation temperature can be derived with the help of Eq. (8·8). Since the liquid and vapor phases of a mixture in equilibrium have the same temperature and pressure, integration of Eq. (8·8) along an isotherm (a line of constant temperature) from the saturated-liquid line to the saturated-vapor line indicates that the two phases also have the same Gibbs function,† that is, $g_f = g_g$. Since g_f and g_g are functions of the saturation temperature only, it then follows that along the saturated liquid and vapor lines

$$\frac{dg_f}{dT_{\text{sat}}} = \frac{dg_g}{dT_{\text{sat}}}$$

Again using Eq. (8·8), we find

$$v_f\left(\frac{dP}{dT}\right)_{\text{sat}} - s_f = v_g\left(\frac{dP}{dT}\right)_{\text{sat}} - s_g$$

or

$$\left(\frac{dP}{dT}\right)_{\text{sat}} = \frac{s_g - s_f}{v_g - v_f} = \frac{s_{fg}}{v_{fg}} \tag{8·20}$$

This expresses the change in the saturation pressure with respect to changes in temperature in terms of the properties of the saturated liquid and vapor. Now, since $g_f = g_g$,

$$h_f - Ts_f = h_g - Ts_g$$

$$s_g - s_f = \frac{h_g - h_f}{T}$$

Combining with Eq. (8·20), we find

$$\blacktriangleright \quad \left(\frac{dP}{dT}\right)_{\text{sat}} = \frac{h_{fg}}{Tv_{fg}} \tag{8·21}$$

This is known as the *Clapeyron equation;* it relates the variation of pressure with temperature along the saturated-vapor (or liquid) line to the enthalpy and volume of vaporization. The Clapeyron equation is extremely useful in constructing a graphical or tabular equation of state from a minimum of experimental measurements. It also tells us that $(dP/dT)_{\text{sat}}$ is positive, since enthalpies of vaporization are always positive, as are the volume changes un-

† This is a condition for equilibrium between phases of a mixture, as we shall show in Chap. Ten.

dergone during the phase change. Consequently, the vapor pressure of any substance increases with temperature.

A Clapeyron equation for fusion may be derived in an analogous manner. Denoting the saturated-solid state by a subscript s, the result would be

$$\left(\frac{dP}{dT}\right)_{\text{sat sol}} = \frac{h_{sf}}{Tv_{sf}} \tag{8·22}$$

The enthalpy of melting $h_{sf} = h_f - h_s$ is positive for all known substances. The volume change $v_{sf} = v_f - v_s$ is positive for most substances, indicating that the freezing temperature increases with increasing pressure. However, water has the peculiar property that v_{sf} is negative and therefore has a fusion curve with a negative slope. Hence water will freeze at a lower temperature if the pressure is increased.

The Clapeyron equations provide a means for direct measurement of the thermodynamic temperature T, and this has been proposed (but never tried) as a means for testing the equivalence between the empirical (ideal gas) and thermodynamic temperatures. Integrating Eq. (8·21) along the saturation line,

$$\ln \frac{T_2}{T_1} = \int_1^2 \frac{v_{fg}}{h_{fg}}\, dP$$

The terms in the integrand can be determined by direct electrical and mechanical measurements, without any reference to temperature. The ratio of *thermodynamic* temperatures T_1/T_2 could then be computed, and this ratio compared to that given by the gas-thermometer measurements. Such a comparison would require accurate v_{fg} and h_{fg} data. Unfortunately the usual procedure is to use the Clapeyron equation to smooth, interpolate, and refine the experimental saturation data, and hence a test of this type based on the currently available tabulations may not be valid. Hopefully a careful experimental confirmation will someday be made along these lines.

Thermodynamic theory provides many additional relationships between the properties that must hold for any simple compressible substance, since no other particular restrictions as to the nature of the substance are made. These relations are frequently brought to bear in more specific analyses of substances, such as in quantum-statistical mechanics or kinetic theory, as means for filling in gaps in the theory and also as a check on the validity of the particular microscopic model employed.

Algebraic equations of state can be developed for a few idealized classes of substances. These equations must be considered approximations to real behavior, but they are nevertheless quite useful in quantitative analysis. Perhaps the most important of these is the algebraic equation of state for a perfect gas, which we introduced in Chap. Four. We shall next consider the perfect gas in greater detail.

8·6 ALGEBRAIC EQUATION OF STATE FOR THE PERFECT GAS

The *perfect gas* is defined as any gas whose P-v-T relationship is of the form

$$\blacktriangleright \quad Pv = RT \tag{8·23}$$

The gas constant R is related to the *universal gas constant* $\mathcal{R}$ and the molal mass $\hat{M}$ by

$$\blacktriangleright \quad R = \frac{\mathcal{R}}{\hat{M}} \tag{8·24}$$

$\mathcal{R}$ has the experimentally determined value

$$\blacktriangleright \quad \mathcal{R} = 1545 \text{ ft-lbf/lbmole-°R}$$

The Boltzmann constant k is defined in terms of $\mathcal{R}$ and Avogadro's number N_0 by

$$\blacktriangleright \quad \mathsf{k} = \frac{\mathcal{R}}{N_0} \tag{8·25}$$

Sometimes k is called the gas constant per molecule. Values of $\hat{M}$ and R for several gases are given in Table B·6. The idealization that a gas is perfect is reasonable only for relatively low densities, where the gas molecules are, on the average, quite far apart (compared to molecular spacing in solids or liquids). The student should review the perfect-gas discussions in Chap. Four at this point, and in particular the examples showing when the perfect-gas idealization is valid.

The defining equation $Pv = RT$ can be put in two other useful forms. If M is the mass of a sample of gas occupying volume V, multiplication by the mass yields

$$\blacktriangleright \quad PV = MRT \tag{8·26}$$

Denoting the number of moles of the gas by $\mathfrak{N}$ and observing that the mass M is related to the number of moles and the molal mass $\hat{M}$ by

$$\blacktriangleright \quad M = \mathfrak{N}\hat{M}$$

we can express Eq. (8·26) as

$$\blacktriangleright \quad PV = \mathfrak{N}\hat{M}RT = \mathfrak{N}\mathcal{R}T \tag{8·27}$$

In Chap. Seven we showed that the thermodynamic and empirical (perfect-gas) temperatures were identical, using the additional information that the internal energy of gases used in empirical thermometers depends only on temperature as P approaches zero. It may easily be shown that the internal energy u of any substance obeying Eq. (8·23) is a function only of temperature. One way is to apply Eq. (8·14) directly; doing so, we find

$$\left(\frac{\partial u}{\partial v}\right)_T = T\left(\frac{R}{v}\right) - P = \frac{TR}{v} - \frac{RT}{v} = 0$$

This means that the internal energy is independent of the specific volume and consequently depends only on the temperature,†

$$\blacktriangleright \quad u = u(T)$$

The differential of u is therefore expressible solely in terms of temperature changes [see Eq. (8·11)],

$$du = c_v\, dT \tag{8·28}$$

Since u depends only on T, c_v must be a function only of temperature,

$$c_v = c_v(T)$$

The enthalpy is also a function only of temperature, since

$$\blacktriangleright \quad h = u + Pv = u(T) + RT = h(T)$$

Following the previous line of argument, we can show that

$$\begin{aligned} dh &= c_P\, dT \\ c_P &= c_P(T) \end{aligned} \tag{8·29}$$

The differential equation for the entropy is the Gibbs equation,

$$ds = \frac{du}{T} + \frac{P}{T}\, dv = \frac{c_v}{T}\, dT + R\,\frac{dv}{v} \tag{8·30}$$

Alternatively, from Eq. (8·4),

$$ds = \frac{dh}{T} - \frac{v}{T}\, dP = \frac{c_P}{T}\, dT - R\,\frac{dP}{P} \tag{8·31}$$

We may now integrate these differential equations of state. Integrating Eq. (8·28),

$$\blacktriangleright \quad u_2 - u_1 = \int_{T_1}^{T_2} c_v(T)\, dT \tag{8·32}$$

† An alternate proof can be made starting directly from the Gibbs equation,

$$ds = \frac{1}{T}\, du + \frac{P}{T}\, dv$$

Then, since ds is exact,

$$\left(\frac{\partial\,(1/T)}{\partial v}\right)_u = \left(\frac{\partial\,(P/T)}{\partial u}\right)_v = \left(\frac{\partial\,(R/v)}{\partial u}\right)_v = 0$$

T is therefore independent of v along any line of constant u, and consequently $T = T(u)$, or $u = u(T)$.

Integrating Eqs. (8·29),

$$\blacktriangleright \quad h_2 - h_1 = \int_{T_1}^{T_2} c_P(T)\, dT \tag{8·33}$$

Equations (8·30) and (8·31) integrate to give

$$\blacktriangleright \quad s_2 - s_1 = \int_{T_1}^{T_2} \frac{c_v(T)}{T}\, dT + R \ln \frac{v_2}{v_1} \tag{8·34}$$

$$\blacktriangleright \quad s_2 - s_1 = \int_{T_1}^{T_2} \frac{c_P(T)}{T}\, dT - R \ln \frac{P_2}{P_1} \tag{8·35}$$

In order to carry the algebraic equations of state further it would be necessary to know how the specific heats varied with temperature. An important relation between the specific heats is

$$\blacktriangleright \quad c_P - c_v = R \tag{8·36}$$

which may easily be shown from Eqs. (8·23), (8·28), and (8·29). Alternatively, the general relation Eq. (8·17) may be used. It is therefore necessary to determine only one of the two properties c_v and c_P for any gas, and since c_P is more easily measured it is customary to work with c_P. We define a property ϕ by

$$\blacktriangleright \quad \phi(T) = \int_{T_0}^{T} \frac{c_P(T)}{T}\, dT \tag{8·37}$$

where T_0 is some selected reference temperature. Using Eq. (8·35), the entropy is then expressed as

$$\blacktriangleright \quad s_2 - s_1 = \phi_2 - \phi_1 - R \ln \frac{P_2}{P_1} \tag{8·38}$$

Values of the enthalpy and the property ϕ as functions of temperature have been obtained from measurements on many gases,† and a tabulation of these properties for air‡ is given in Table B·9. $T_0 = 0°\text{R}$ forms the datum for these compilations. The reduced pressures p_r and reduced volumes v_r appearing in these tables are defined by

$$\ln p_r \equiv \frac{\phi(T)}{R} \tag{8·39}$$

$$\ln v_r \equiv -\frac{1}{R} \int_{T_0}^{T} \frac{c_v}{T}\, dT \tag{8·40}$$

These are both dimensionless quantities.

† See, for example, J. Keenan and J. Kaye, *Gas Tables*, John Wiley & Sons, Inc., New York, 1950.

‡ Air at low pressures may be treated as a mixture of perfect gases. In Chap. Ten we shall show that any such mixture behaves like a perfect gas.

The reduced pressure is particularly useful in the analysis of isentropic processes. Setting the entropy difference to zero in Eq. (8·38), we obtain

$$\ln \frac{P_2}{P_1} = \frac{\phi_2 - \phi_1}{R} \qquad \text{for an isentropic process}$$

In terms of the reduced pressures, the right-hand side becomes

$$\ln p_{r_2} - \ln p_{r_1} = \ln \frac{p_{r_2}}{p_{r_1}}$$

and consequently we see that

$$\frac{P_2}{P_1} = \frac{p_{r_2}}{p_{r_1}} \qquad \text{for an isentropic process} \tag{8·41}$$

The reduced pressures are therefore useful in evaluating pressure changes for isentropic processes. Similarly, it may be shown that

$$\frac{v_2}{v_1} = \frac{v_{r_2}}{v_{r_1}} \qquad \text{for an isentropic process} \tag{8·42}$$

To illustrate the use of the reduced pressure, suppose we want to compress air at 60°F isentropically from 1 atm to 5 atm, and need to know the final temperature (see Fig. 8·3). From Table B·9, at 60°F $p_r = 1.215$. Then

$$\frac{p_{r_2}}{p_{r_1}} = \frac{P_2}{P_1} = \frac{5}{1}$$

$$p_{r_2} = 5 \times 1.215 = 6.08$$

Reading in Table B·9 for $p_r = 6.08$, we see that the final temperature is slightly greater than 360°F.

As we discussed in Chap. Four, it is often useful and sufficiently accurate to treat c_P and c_v as constants (see Fig. B·17). This approximation is valid

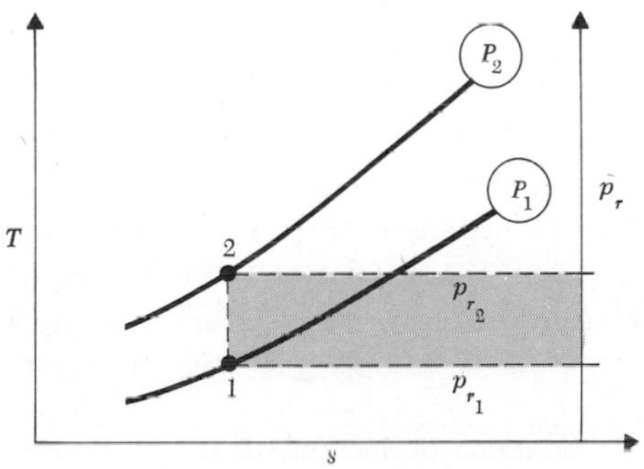

FIG. 8·3 *The reduced pressures relate to two states having the same entropy*

over remarkably wide temperature ranges, and permits great simplification of the equations of state. The equations of state are as follows for a perfect gas with constant specific heats†

$$\blacktriangleright \quad Pv = RT \tag{8·43}$$

$$\blacktriangleright \quad u_2 - u_1 = c_v(T_2 - T_1) \tag{8·44}$$

$$\blacktriangleright \quad h_2 - h_1 = c_P(T_2 - T_1) \tag{8·45}$$

$$\blacktriangleright \quad s_2 - s_1 = c_v \ln \frac{T_2}{T_1} + R \ln \frac{v_2}{v_1} \tag{8·46a}$$

$$\blacktriangleright \quad s_2 - s_1 = c_P \ln \frac{T_2}{T_1} - R \ln \frac{P_2}{P_1} \tag{8·46b}$$

$$\blacktriangleright \quad s_2 - s_1 = c_P \ln \frac{v_2}{v_1} + c_v \ln \frac{P_2}{P_1} \tag{8·46c}$$

$$\blacktriangleright \quad c_P - c_v = R \tag{8·47}$$

It is important to remember that equations (8·44–47) pertain only to a perfect gas with *constant* specific heats. They are especially useful in gas dynamics, where neat closed-form algebraic expressions for the properties of a one-dimensional gas-flow field can be derived.

A useful relation between the pressures and volumes at two states can be derived from Eq. (8·46c). Dividing by c_v, we have

$$\frac{s_2 - s_1}{c_v} = \ln \left[\left(\frac{v_2}{v_1} \right)^k \frac{P_2}{P_1} \right]$$

where k is the ratio of specific heats,

$$k \equiv \frac{c_P}{c_v}$$

Taking the antilog, we obtain

$$P_2 v_2^k = P_1 v_1^k \exp \left(\frac{s_2 - s_1}{c_v} \right) \tag{8·48}$$

From the equation above we see that two states of the same entropy will have the same values for their property Pv^k, provided that the idealizations we have made are satisfied. Only a *reversible* adiabatic process is isentropic, and this is an important restriction to bear in mind. Further, the gas must obey $Pv = RT$ and, in addition, have constant specific heats. If all these restrictions are met, that is, *for a perfect gas with constant specific heats undergoing a reversible*

† Equation (8·46c) follows from combination of Eqs. (8·46b) and (8·43).

adiabatic process,

$$Pv^k = \text{constant} \tag{8·49}$$

The equations of state given above allow calculation of the differences in internal energy, enthalpy, and entropy between any two states. Sometimes it is convenient to set the internal energy and entropy to be zero at some arbitrarily chosen datum state. In thermodynamic analyses not involving chemical reaction, we work exclusively with differences in internal energy, enthalpy, and entropy, so the use of a datum state is entirely permissible. However, entropy then differs from the true entropy by the value of the absolute entropy at the datum state. Since internal energy is relative anyway, no artificiality is introduced by the use of an internal energy datum. When chemical reactions are involved it becomes necessary to properly tie the internal energies and entropies of all elements and compounds together in a common way; we shall do this in Chap. Eleven.

Sometimes it is more convenient to select a datum state for enthalpy rather than for internal energy. Since the values of h and u differ by Pv at the datum temperature, it is not permissible to select datums for both enthalpy and internal energy; only one of these may be set as zero at the datum state.

The equations of state for a perfect gas may be represented graphically on several thermodynamic planes; some of which are shown qualitatively in Fig. 8·4. Note that lines of constant T, u, and h coincide, so an h-s diagram would differ from the T-s diagram only by a scale stretching. Familiarity with the general nature of these graphical representations is especially helpful in the analysis of engineering systems involving idealized gases.

It is possible to make a simple microscopic analysis that yields surprisingly accurate predictions for the specific heats of a monatomic gas. With a postulated extension, we can do a fair job of predicting the specific heats of polyatomic gases. In the interests of further understanding we shall now depart momentarily from thermodynamics to discuss the microscopic nature of a perfect gas.

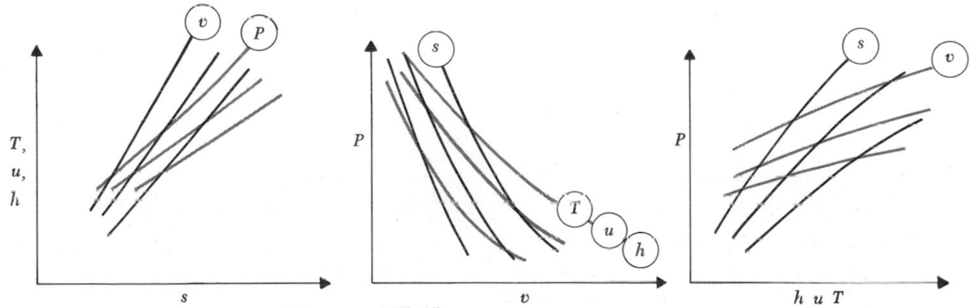

FIG. 8·4 *Graphical equation of state for a perfect gas*

8·7 A SIMPLE KINETIC MODEL OF A GAS

Our kinetic model of the monatomic gas will be that each particle behaves as a hard sphere in its interactions with the wall and that the only energy is due to the translation motion of the atoms. A collision of a typical particle with the wall is shown in Fig. 8·5.

Particles will have a spectrum of velocities and will be moving in different directions. We represent the velocity of a particle by its three components V_x, V_y, and V_z. The total velocity V is then given by

$$V^2 = V_x^2 + V_y^2 + V_z^2$$

The fraction of particles per unit of volume moving with x-velocity component having magnitude V_x will be denoted by f_{V_x}. Since there is no bulk motion, half of these will be going in the positive-x direction and the other half in the negative-x direction. The number of particles having velocity component V_x which strike an area A of the wall in the time interval δt is determined by the number of particles within the box of Fig. 8·6 and is

$$\tfrac{1}{2} n f_{V_x} A V_x \, \delta t$$

where n is the number of particles per unit of volume. Each of these particles will impart an impluse to the wall normal to the wall of magnitude

$$F_{V_x} \, \delta t = \frac{2mV_x}{g_c}$$

Here m is the particle mass. The 2 results from the reversal of direction in the elastic collision. The total impulse delivered to the wall in time δt by all the

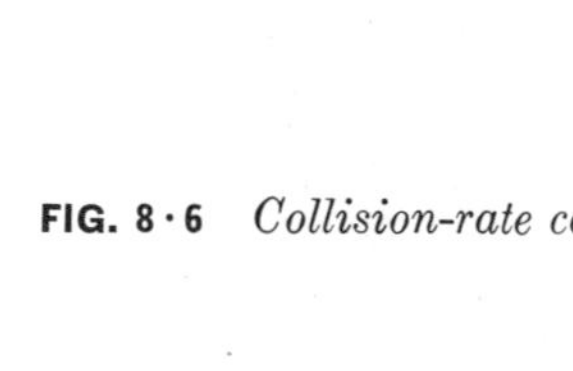

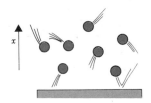

FIG. 8·5 *Collisions with the wall*

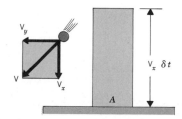

FIG. 8·6 *Collision-rate calculation*

particles which strike the wall is then

$$F\,\delta t = \sum (2mV_x)\frac{1}{2}nf_{V_x}\frac{AV_x}{g_c}\,\delta t$$

The summation is to be extended over all possible V_x's. The pressure is the average force per unit of area,

$$P = \frac{mn}{g_c}\sum f_{V_x}V_x^2$$

The summation term represents the average of the square of the magnitude of the x-velocity components, and we denote it by $(V_x^2)_{av}$. Because of the homogeneity of the gas, the average-square velocity is the same in every direction, so that

$$(V_x^2)_{av} = (V_y^2)_{av} = (V_z^2)_{av} = \tfrac{1}{3}(V^2)_{av}$$

We then have for the pressure

$$P = \frac{1}{3}\frac{nm}{g_c}(V^2)_{av} \tag{8·50}$$

Now we bring in the experimental equation of state $Pv = RT$. Noting that the specific volume v is merely $v = 1/nm$, Eq. (8·50) gives

$$Pv = \frac{1}{3g_c}(V^2)_{av}$$

Upon comparison we have

$$RT = \frac{1}{3g_c}(V^2)_{av} \tag{8·51}$$

The temperature of the perfect gas is therefore proportional to the average of the square of the velocity of the particles.

The kinetic energy of a single particle is $mV^2/2g_c$, so the internal energy of the gas is

$$U = \sum \frac{1}{2}\frac{m}{g_c}V^2 = \frac{nm}{2g_c}(V^2)_{av}$$

Combining with Eq. (8·51), we find†

$$u = \tfrac{3}{2}RT \tag{8·52a}$$

The internal energy per mole is called the *molal internal energy*. It is simply

$$\blacktriangleright \quad \hat{u} = \tfrac{3}{2}\mathcal{R}T \tag{8·52b}$$

† Note that $u = h = 0$ at the datum state $T = 0$.

Note that we arrive at the experimentally known result that the energy of the gas is a function of temperature only. Our model did not include energy associated with interatomic forces, which would depend on density. This partially explains why the perfect-gas approximation is restricted to low densities.

The specific heat at constant volume is

$$c_v \equiv \left(\frac{\partial u}{\partial T}\right)_v = \tfrac{3}{2}R \tag{8·53a}$$

or, on a molal basis,

▶ $$\hat{c}_v = \tfrac{3}{2}\mathcal{R} \tag{8·53b}$$

The molal specific heat of every monatomic gas is, by our theory, $\tfrac{3}{2}\mathcal{R}$. The enthalpy is

$$h = u + Pv = \tfrac{3}{2}RT + RT = \tfrac{5}{2}RT$$

The specific heat at constant pressure is then

$$c_P \equiv \left(\frac{\partial h}{\partial T}\right)_P = \tfrac{5}{2}R \tag{8·54a}$$

On a molal basis,

▶ $$\hat{c}_P = \tfrac{5}{2}\mathcal{R} \tag{8·54b}$$

Note that this simple kinetic theory predicts that the specific heats will be constants.

The ratio of specific heats given by our simple monatomic gas model is simply

▶ $$k = \frac{c_P}{c_v} = \frac{5}{3} = 1.6667 \tag{8·55}$$

It is surprising how well this simple theory compares with the measured specific-heat values given in Table B·6.

It is interesting to estimate the number of allowed quantum states for a typical situation. Using Eq. (8·46b), together with our predicted c_P, the entropy may be expressed as

$$s = \tfrac{5}{2}R \ln T - R \ln P + \text{constant}$$

The *molal entropy* $\hat{s}$ is then

$$\hat{s} = \mathcal{R} \ln T^{5/2} - \mathcal{R} \ln P + \text{constant} \tag{8·56}$$

If we isolate 1 mole of gas, the allowed quantum states will (at equilibrium) be equally probable (see Sec. 6·4). Hence we put

$$\hat{s} = \mathsf{k} \ln \hat{\Omega}$$

where $\hat{\Omega}$ represents the number of allowed quantum states for 1 mole of the gas. Since $k = \mathcal{R}/N_0$, where N_0 is Avogadro's number, we have

$$\hat{s} = \frac{\mathcal{R} \ln \hat{\Omega}}{N_0} \tag{8·57}$$

We cannot evaluate $\hat{\Omega}$ from our simple theory, but we can estimate the change in $\hat{\Omega}$ for a nominal change in state, and the value of $\hat{\Omega}$ must be more than this change. For states 1 and 2 we use Eqs. (8·56) and (8·57) and obtain

$$\hat{s}_2 - \hat{s}_1 = \mathcal{R} \ln \left[\left(\frac{T_2}{T_1}\right)^{5/2} \frac{P_1}{P_2}\right] = \frac{\mathcal{R}}{N_0}(\ln \hat{\Omega}_1 - \ln \hat{\Omega}_2)$$

Then,

$$\ln \frac{\hat{\Omega}_1}{\hat{\Omega}_2} \approx N_0 \ln \left[\left(\frac{T_2}{T_1}\right)^{5/2} \frac{P_1}{P_2}\right]$$

Suppose that T_1, T_2, P_1, and P_2 have reasonable values, such that the right-hand logarithm is of order unity. Then

$$\frac{\hat{\Omega}_1}{\hat{\Omega}_2} \sim e^{N_0} \sim e^{10^{23}}$$

This is an almost incomprehensibly large number; the number of quantum states available to a mole of gas is simply tremendous.

If we divide Eq. (8·52*b*) by Avogadro's number we obtain an expression for the average translational energy of an atom,

$$\blacktriangleright \quad \frac{\hat{u}}{N_0} = \epsilon_{av} = \frac{3}{2} kT \tag{8·58}$$

Since the atoms have velocity components in three directions, we can think of there being an energy $\frac{1}{2}kT$ associated with each degree of freedom; on the average, the energy is equally divided between the three translational modes. We can make a surprisingly accurate prediction for the specific heats of diatomic perfect gases by extending this idea and postulating that each independent energy mode contributes $\frac{1}{2}kT$ to the average energy of a molecule. This is known as the *equipartition principle;* it is not really a basic principle, as are the first and second laws of thermodynamics, but is merely a statement postulating a model from which the properties of polyatomic gases can be computed. It works very well for diatomic gases at moderate temperatures and is reasonably successful when applied to other simple gases.

A diatomic molecule can be modeled as a simple "dumbbell" (Fig. 8·7). The two atoms would have a total of six degrees of translational freedom were it not for the fact that they are constrained to move together. This reduces the number of independent motions to five (three translational, two rotational; spin about the axis is neglected). The equipartition model would then suggest

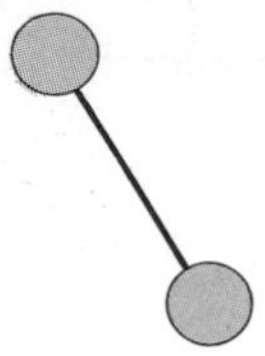

FIG. 8·7 *A simple model of a diatomic molecule*

that the average energy of a diatomic molecule is

$$\mathcal{E}_{av} = \tfrac{5}{2}kT \tag{8·59a}$$

The internal energy and specific heats for the diatomic gas are therefore predicted as

$$\blacktriangleright \quad \hat{u} = \tfrac{5}{2}\mathcal{R}T \tag{8·59b}$$
$$\blacktriangleright \quad \hat{c}_v = \tfrac{5}{2}\mathcal{R} \tag{8·59c}$$
$$\blacktriangleright \quad \hat{c}_P = \tfrac{7}{2}\mathcal{R} \tag{8·59d}$$
$$\blacktriangleright \quad k = \frac{\hat{c}_P}{\hat{c}_v} = \tfrac{7}{5} = 1.4 \tag{8·59e}$$

This is surprisingly accurate, as can be checked by comparison with the experimental values given in Table B·6.

A triatomic molecule, such as H_2O, could be modeled as three atoms held in a rigid triangular structure (see Fig. 8·8). There would be nine degrees of translational freedom minus three constraints, or six degrees of independent motion (three translational, three rotational). The equipartition model then predicts triatomic gas properties as

$$\blacktriangleright \quad \hat{u} = 3\mathcal{R}T \tag{8·60a}$$
$$\blacktriangleright \quad \hat{c}_v = 3\mathcal{R} \tag{8·60b}$$
$$\blacktriangleright \quad \hat{c}_P = 4\mathcal{R} \tag{8·60c}$$
$$\blacktriangleright \quad k = \frac{\hat{c}_P}{\hat{c}_v} = \tfrac{4}{3} = 1.33 \tag{8·60d}$$

This prediction also agrees well with the data in Table B·6.

At high temperatures polyatomic molecules seem to lose their rigidity, and a significant amount of energy is contributed by the vibrational energy modes. If we apply the equipartition idea to a vibrating diatomic molecule, assuming that the kinetic energies of the vibrating atoms (relative to their center of mass) and the potential energy of the molecular binding forces each contribute $\tfrac{1}{2}kT$,

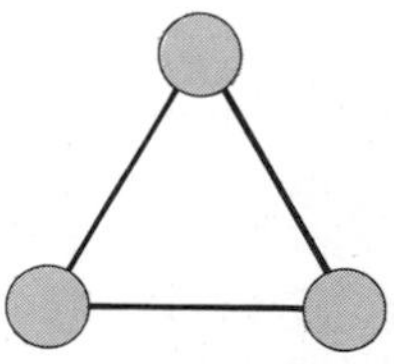

FIG. 8·8 *A simple model of a triatomic molecule*

we would predict specific heats for a diatomic gas at high temperatures as

$$\hat{c}_v = \tfrac{7}{2}\mathcal{R} \tag{8·61a}$$
$$\hat{c}_P = \tfrac{9}{2}\mathcal{R} \tag{8·61b}$$
$$k = \tfrac{9}{7} = 1.28 \tag{8·61c}$$

Although it is true that the specific heats of diatomic gases increase with increasing temperature, and the ratio of specific heats decreases, it is only at very high temperatures that the limiting values given above are approached. The equipartition model fails to predict adequately the behavior of gases at moderately elevated temperatures. In Chap. Twelve we shall indicate how the quantum-statistical approach can be applied to obtain valid predictions in the moderately elevated temperature range (see Fig. 12·10).

The simple molecular model is not accurate at high temperatures for other reasons as well. The vibrational motion can become so intense as to actually cause the atoms to dissociate from one another. Significant amounts of dissociation occur in many gases at temperatures of the order of 2000–3000°F, which are common in combustion systems. A large fraction of the atoms may be in excited states, where the electrons take more distant, more energetic orbits. At sufficiently high energies ionization occurs, and electrons leave the atom; a gas containing a significant fraction of ionized molecules and free electrons is called a *plasma*. Ionization in a plasma alters the specific heat in a peculiar way which cannot adequately be explained by the simple equipartition model but which can be properly taken into account by a quantum-statistical analysis of the type discussed in Chap. Twelve.

8·8 EQUATIONS OF STATE FOR DENSE GASES

The discussions in the section above apply only to low-density gases, where the average distance between molecules is large, so that energy associated with attractive forces between molecules can be neglected. While the perfect-gas idealization is a useful first approximation, it is often inadequate for more accurate thermodynamic analysis. The tabular and graphical equations of state can be used to handle nonideal gases, and approximate algebraic equations are very useful, especially for digital-computer applications, and a number have been suggested. We shall now examine two of the more important of these.

On the basis of molecular arguments, Van der Waals suggested a modification of the perfect-gas equation which helps to account for weakly attractive intermolecular forces. A molecule about to strike the wall will be attracted by molecules within the gas, and this will lessen the impulse which it delivers to the wall. The attractive force is proportional to the number of molecules per unit of volume, as is the number of particles which strike the wall in a unit of time. Thus the effect of intermolecular attraction should be to lessen the pressure by an amount roughly proportional to the square of the gas density. This suggests that we should replace P in the perfect-gas expression by $P + (a/v^2)$, where a

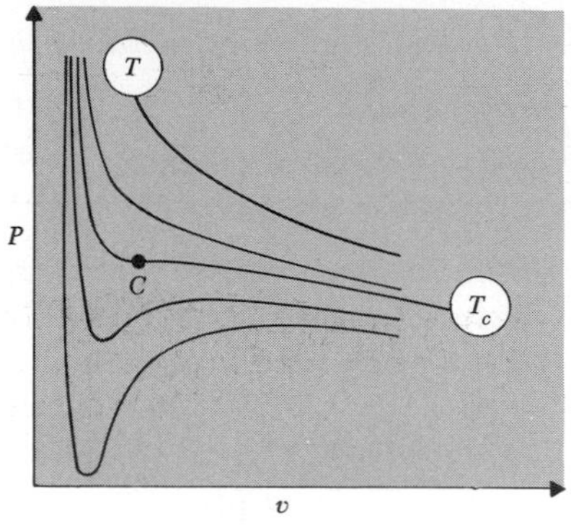

FIG. 8·9 *Van der Waals isotherms*

is a constant. In addition, the molecules of a dense gas occupy some volume, which suggests that v should be replaced by $v - b$, where b is a constant roughly indicative of the volume occupied by a unit of mass in a dense (liquid) state. With these qualitative considerations, Van der Waals was led to propose the approximate equation which bears his name,

$$\left(P + \frac{a}{v^2}\right)(v - b) = RT \tag{8·62}$$

The constants a and b have been determined for many gases as those which provide the best fit with experimental data. The fit is not very good over a wide range, and more accurate algebraic representations are usually employed where precise information is required.

The Van der Waals equation is a *cubic* in v, and consequently, to any given P and T there will correspond either one or three real values of v. When one plots the equation on a P-v plane, the isotherms are found to appear as shown in Fig. 8·9. Intuition tells us that the Van der Waals equation is not realistic in the region where the isotherms have a positive slope. However, there is one particular isotherm having an inflection point where $(\partial P/\partial v)_T = 0$; we might interpret this point as the *critical point*, and it can be determined very simply. We first rewrite Eq. (8·62) as

$$P = \frac{RT}{v - b} - \frac{a}{v^2}$$

Both the slope and curvature of the critical isotherm must vanish at the inflection point. Thus, denoting the critical point by the subscript c,

$$\left(\frac{\partial P}{\partial v}\right)_T = 0 = \frac{-RT_c}{(v_c - b)^2} + \frac{2a}{v_c^3}$$

$$\left(\frac{\partial^2 P}{\partial v^2}\right)_T = 0 = \frac{2RT_c}{(v_c - b)^3} - \frac{6a}{v_c^4}$$

$$a = \frac{27}{64}\frac{R^2T_c^2}{P_c} = \frac{9}{8}v_cRT_c$$

$$b = \frac{RT_c}{8P_c} = \frac{1}{3}v_c$$

$$Z_c = \frac{P_cv_c}{RT_c} = \frac{3}{8} = 0.375$$

We see that the Van der Waals equation predicts that the constants a and b are determined solely by the critical state, and that P_cv_c/RT_c has the same value for all substances. While this is not quite verified experimentally, it is true that Z_c has a value of the order of 0.25–0.3, as can be seen in Table B·8.

The Van der Waals equation of state may be rewritten in terms of the *compressibility factor* $Z \equiv Pv/RT$, a dimensionless thermodynamic property, and the *reduced pressure*† and *reduced temperature*

$$P^* = \frac{P}{P_c} \qquad T^* = \frac{T}{T_c}$$

The Van der Waals equation then becomes

$$\left(Z + \frac{1}{Z}\frac{27}{64}\frac{P^*}{T^{*2}}\right)\left(1 - \frac{1}{8Z}\frac{P^*}{T^*}\right) = 1$$

which suggests that a plot of the form

$$\blacktriangleright \qquad Z = Z(P^*, T^*)$$

might correlate the P-v-T equation of state for real gases. This brings us to the principle of corresponding states.

It is found experimentally that the compressibility factor Z is very nearly the same function of the reduced pressure and temperature for many gases. This fact is known as the *principle of corresponding states;* it is not a basic principle in the sense of the first and second laws, but merely a convenient approximation. Figure 8·10 shows the correlation for a number of gases. The Z-P^* plane is called a *generalized compressibility chart;* it is very useful in predicting the properties of substances for which more precise equation-of-state data have not yet been obtained. Note that at very low pressures Z approaches unity, the value appropriate for the perfect-gas approximation.

In the absence of better data, the enthalpy of a dense gas can be estimated using a combination of perfect-gas theory and the generalized compressibility correlation. Considering $h(T, P)$, we have

$$dh = \left(\frac{\partial h}{\partial T}\right)_P dT + \left(\frac{\partial h}{\partial P}\right)_T dP$$

† Not to be confused with the reduced pressure p_r used in the perfect-gas tables.

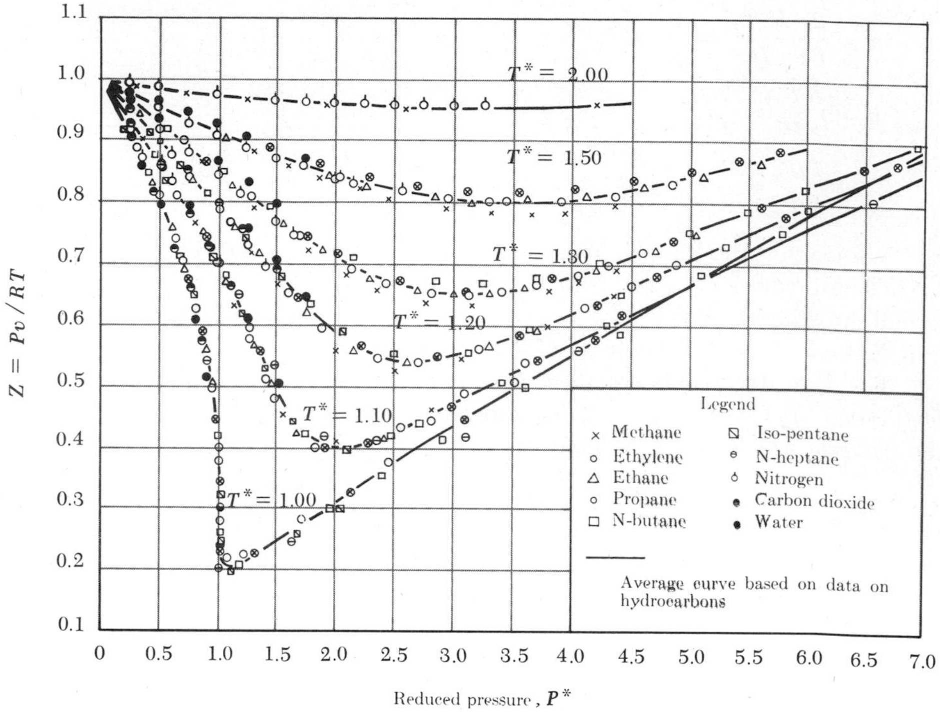

FIG. 8·10 *Correlation of P-v-T data*

The first partial derivative is simply c_P, and the second may be calculated solely from P-v-T data using an equation analogous to Eq. (8·14),

$$\left(\frac{\partial h}{\partial P}\right)_T = v - T\left(\frac{\partial v}{\partial T}\right)_P \tag{8·63}$$

The derivation of this important relation follows that of Eq. (8·14), and is left as an exercise. The enthalpy can therefore be determined from

$$dh = c_P(T, P)\,dT + \left[v - T\left(\frac{\partial v}{\partial T}\right)_P\right] dP \tag{8·64}$$

We emphasize that in general c_P depends upon both T and P. However, at low pressures the perfect-gas limit is approached. The enthalpy of a perfect gas can therefore be viewed as

$$h_{pg}(T) = \int_0^T c_P(T, 0)\,dT \tag{8·65}$$

Now, we imagine carrying out the integrations from the reference state $T = 0$, $P = 0$. The path of integration is shown in Fig. 8·11. On the first part $dP = 0$. The contribution to h from this path is precisely the perfect-gas term, Eq.

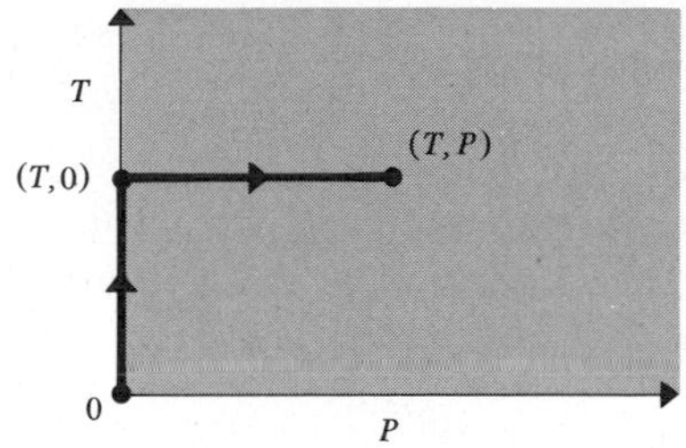

FIG. 8·11 *The path of integration*

(8·65). On the second part $dT = 0$, and the contribution to h can be evaluated solely from P-v-T data. Then,

$$h = h_{pg}(T) + \int_0^P \left[v - T\left(\frac{\partial v}{\partial T}\right)_P \right] dP \tag{8·66}$$

This integration could be performed numerically using tabulated P-v-T data. The temperature variation of c_P should of course be considered when evaluating h_{pg}.

The entropy can be found in a similar manner. We write Eq. (8·16) as

$$ds = \frac{c_P(T, P)}{T}\, dT - \left(\frac{\partial v}{\partial T}\right)_P dP$$

In the perfect-gas limit for small P,

$$ds_{pg}(T, P) = \frac{c_P(T, 0)}{T}\, dT - \frac{R}{P}\, dP$$

We now subtract these two equations, and again carry out the integrations along the path of Fig. 8·11. Since there is no contribution from the dT terms on the second path, and they precisely cancel on the first path, we have

$$s - s_{pg}(T, P) = \int_0^P \left[\frac{R}{P} - \left(\frac{\partial v}{\partial T}\right)_P \right] dP \tag{8·67}$$

Since the integrand approaches zero as $P \to 0$, the integral presents no problems near the lower limit, and the numerical integration of the P-v-T data is quite straightforward. Note that s_{pg} must be evaluated from Eq. (8·35).

A more complete compressibility chart has been included in Appendix B as Figs. B·14*a* and B·14*b*. The corresponding enthalpies and entropies can be read from the generalized enthalpy and entropy charts, Figs. B·15 and B·16. It should be emphasized that these charts are based on the principle of corresponding states, which is only an approximation. Whenever possible one should use equation-of-state data for the particular substance of interest; the generalized properties charts provide at least some way to work beyond the range of available data, which is often a necessity in modern engineering analysis.

Prior to the advent of high-speed digital computers, complex algebraic equations seemed too involved for most calculations, and graphs and tables were more popular. But as more and more thermodynamic analysis has been programmed for machine calculation, the algebraic equations have found revived importance. A number of algebraic *P-v-T* equations have been proposed, and perhaps the best known and most widely used is the *Beattie-Bridgeman equation,*

$$\blacktriangleright \quad P = \frac{\mathcal{R}T(1-\epsilon)}{\hat{v}^2}(\hat{v} + B) - \frac{A}{\hat{v}^2} \tag{8·68}$$

A, *B*, and ϵ are functions of state,

$$A = A_0\left(1 - \frac{a}{\hat{v}}\right) \qquad B = B_0\left(1 - \frac{b}{\hat{v}}\right) \qquad \epsilon = \frac{c}{\hat{v}T^3}$$

where A_0, B_0, a, b, and c are constants which must be determined experimentally for each gas. Table 8·2 gives these constants for a few gases.

TABLE 8·2 CONSTANTS IN THE BEATTIE-BRIDGEMAN EQUATION OF STATE

Gas	A_0, *atm-ft⁶/lbmole²*	*a*, *ft³/lbmole*	B_0, *ft³/lbmole*	*b*, *ft³/lbmole*	$10^{-4}\,c$, *ft³-°R³/lbmole*
He	5.6	0.958	0.224	0.0	0.37
H_2	50.57	−0.0811	0.336	−0.698	4.7
Air	334.1	+0.309	0.739	−0.0176	406
O_2	382.5	0.410	0.741	+0.0674	448
CO_2	1284.9	1.143	1.678	1.159	6165
NH_3	613.9	2.729	0.547	3.062	44,560

8·9 ALGEBRAIC EQUATION OF STATE FOR AN INCOMPRESSIBLE LIQUID

An algebraic equation of state can be developed for a liquid under the assumption that it is incompressible. This idealized equation of state is of particular utility in analysis of liquid pumps, nozzles, heaters, etc., operating well below the critical pressure or over limited pressure ranges. It is also applicable to a solid which is idealized as incompressible.

If the substance is incompressible, its pressure can be increased a finite amount by an infinitesimal decrease in volume, which would not result in a significant amount of energy transfer as work. The only means for *reversibly* changing the internal energy of such an idealized liquid is by transfer of energy as heat.† The incompressible liquid is therefore a degenerate case in which there are no reversible work modes, and consequently only *one* independent

† The internal energy can also be changed by viscous friction, but this is not a reversible work mode. The fluid can also have kinetic energy due to its bulk motion and potential energy due to its position in a gravitational field.

thermodynamic property. While the pressure is involved in energy transfers to the bulk fluid (flow work), which show up in increased bulk kinetic and potential energy, it is not involved in energy transfer to the "hidden microscopic modes," and consequently is not a relevant thermodynamic property for this idealized liquid. The properties that are purely thermodynamic in nature include the internal energy, entropy, and temperature; from the state postulate we see that specification of any one of these suffices to fix the thermodynamic state.

We may express internal energy as

$$u = u(T)$$

Differentiating and defining a specific heat for the liquid,

$$du = c\,dT$$

where

$$c = \frac{du}{dT} = c(T) \tag{8·69}$$

Integrating between two states,

$$▶ \quad u_2 - u_1 = \int_1^2 c(T)\,dT \tag{8·70}$$

To determine the entropy, imagine heating a unit of mass of the incompressible liquid reversibly. Application of the first and second laws then yields

$$đQ = du \qquad đQ = T\,ds$$

so that the Gibbs equation for an incompressible substance is

$$ds = \frac{du}{T}$$

as expected. Substituting for du and integrating,

$$▶ \quad s_2 - s_1 = \int_1^2 \frac{c(T)}{T}\,dT \tag{8·71}$$

If it is reasonable to assume that c is constant, Eqs. (8·70) and (8·71) further reduce to

$$▶ \quad u_2 - u_1 = c \cdot (T_2 - T_1) \tag{8·72}$$

$$▶ \quad s_2 - s_1 = c \ln \frac{T_2}{T_1} \tag{8·73}$$

We shall illustrate the use of these equations in a moment.

In control-volume analysis of engineering systems involving fluids, the enthalpy invariably arises. In the case of this idealized liquid the enthalpy is a mixture of thermodynamic and mechanical properties,

$$h = u + Pv$$

For an incompressible liquid with constant specific heat, we find

$$h_2 - h_1 = c \cdot (T_2 - T_1) + (P_2 - P_1)v \tag{8·74}$$

The enthalpy of an incompressible liquid, unlike the enthalpy of a perfect gas, is seen to be a function of both temperature and pressure.

Equations (8·72) to (8·74) are useful for estimating the properties of subcooled liquids when tabulations of the real thermodynamic properties are not available. Since the internal energy is a function only of temperature, the value of u for a subcooled liquid at T will be the same (idealizing the liquid as incompressible) as for the saturated liquid at the same temperature. A similar statement can be made for the entropy. The enthalpy can be computed in a number of ways, two of which we now describe.

Suppose we wish to estimate the values of u, h, and s for H_2O at 80°F and 1 atm pressure, liquid state 1 on Fig. 8·12. From Table B·1a we read

$$h_3 = 48.02 \text{ Btu/lbm} \qquad v_3 = 0.01608 \text{ ft}^3\text{/lbm}$$
$$s_3 = 0.0932 \text{ Btu/lbm-°R} \qquad P_3 = 0.5069 \text{ psia}$$

Therefore, our estimate of s_1 is

$$s_1 = s_3 = 0.0932 \text{ Btu/lbm-°R}$$

For the internal energy,

$$u_1 = u_3 = h_3 - P_3v_3 = 47.6 \text{ Btu/lbm}$$

The enthalpy at 1 is estimated by

$$h_1 - h_3 = v(P_1 - P_3) = 0.01608 \times (14.7 - 0.5) \times \frac{144}{778} = 0.042 \text{ Btu/lbm}$$

$$h_1 = 48.02 + 0.04 = 48.06 \text{ Btu/lbm}$$

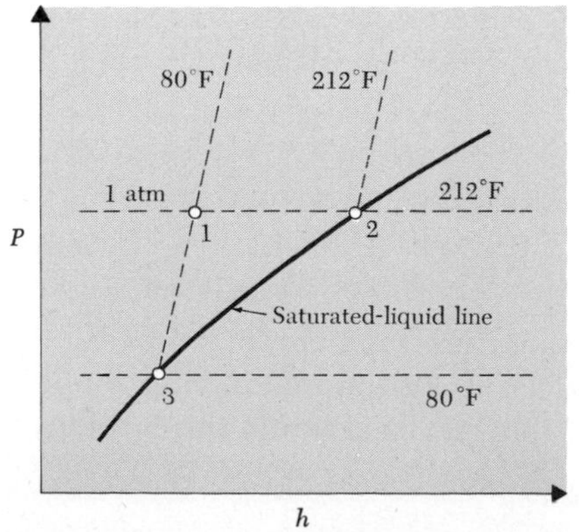

FIG. 8·12 *Estimating the properties of subcooled liquid*

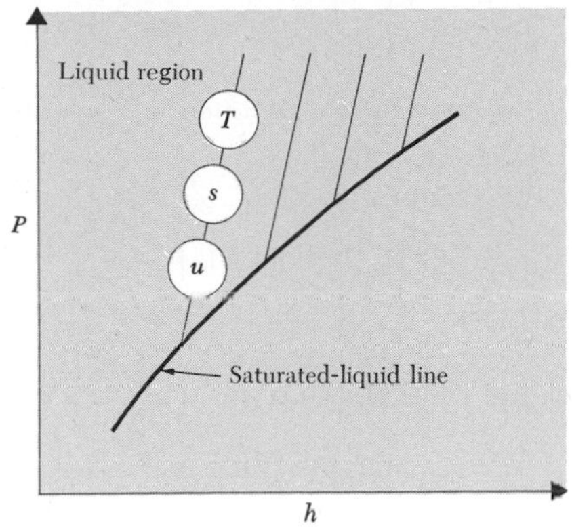

FIG. 8·13 *Graphical equation of state for an incompressible liquid*

Alternatively, we could have read from Table B·1*b*

$$h_2 = 180.07 \text{ Btu/lbm}$$

and then computed h_1 from

$$h_1 - h_2 = c(T_1 - T_2) = 1 \times (80 - 212) = -132 \text{ Btu/lbm}$$
$$h_1 = 180.07 - 132 = 48.07 \text{ Btu/lbm}$$

Since our first calculation involves the least extrapolation, we would probably consider it the better estimate if the disagreement had been significant.

The equations of state for an incompressible liquid must be portrayed graphically on a mixed plane, since there is only one independent thermodynamic property. The *P*-*h* plane is usually used, and a typical example is shown in Fig. 8·13.

8·10 THERMODYNAMICS OF THE SIMPLE MAGNETIC SUBSTANCE

Thermodynamics is not restricted to simple compressible substances. In fact, some of the most interesting and important uses of thermodynamics involve other kinds of substances; we shall examine the simple magnetic substance to illustrate again the manner in which thermodynamics is used to obtain information about the properties of matter.

For a simple magnetic substance the state postulate tells us that there are only two independent intensive thermodynamic properties; we may take these as the internal energy and dipole moment per unit of mass, $v\mathbf{M}$. The magnetic Gibbs equation may be obtained by considering a unit of mass of the material undergoing a reversible process between two infinitesimally separated thermodynamic states (Fig. 8·14). An energy balance gives

$$du = đQ + đW$$

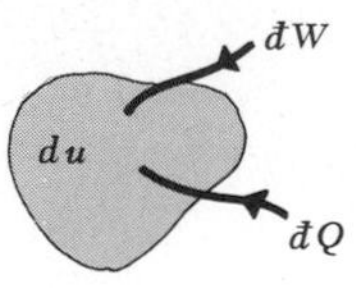

FIG. 8·14 *Deriving the magnetic Gibbs equation*

The energy transfer as work per unit of mass [see Eq. (2·17)] is†

$$đW = \mu_0 v \mathbf{H} \cdot d\mathbf{M}$$

Since the process is reversible, the second law requires that

$$ds = \frac{đQ}{T}$$

Combining, the Gibbs equation is found to be

$$\blacktriangleright \quad du = T\,ds + \mu_0 v \mathbf{H} \cdot d\mathbf{M} \tag{8·75}$$

Inspecting the coefficients, it follows that

$$\blacktriangleright \quad \mu_0 v \mathbf{H} = \left(\frac{\partial u}{\partial \mathbf{M}}\right)_s \tag{8·76}$$

$$\blacktriangleright \quad T = \left(\frac{\partial u}{\partial s}\right)_{\mathbf{M}} = \frac{1}{(\partial s/\partial u)_{\mathbf{M}}} \tag{8·77}$$

The latter is merely the thermodynamic definition of temperature for magnetic systems.

It is convenient to define a magnetic enthalpy and a magnetic Gibbs function as

$$\blacktriangleright \quad \mathrm{h} \equiv u - \mu_0 v \mathbf{H} \cdot \mathbf{M}$$

$$\blacktriangleright \quad \mathrm{g} \equiv \mathrm{h} - Ts$$

Specific heats at constant **M** and **H** are the analogs of c_v and c_P; they are defined as

$$\blacktriangleright \quad c_{\mathbf{M}} \equiv \left(\frac{\partial u}{\partial T}\right)_{\mathbf{M}}$$

$$\blacktriangleright \quad c_{\mathbf{H}} \equiv \left(\frac{\partial \mathrm{h}}{\partial T}\right)_{\mathbf{H}}$$

A set of Maxwell relations for magnetic substances can be obtained. For example, the analog of Eq. (8·10*c*) is

$$\blacktriangleright \quad \mu_0 v \left(\frac{\partial \mathbf{H}}{\partial T}\right)_{\mathbf{M}} = -\left(\frac{\partial s}{\partial \mathbf{M}}\right)_T \tag{8·78}$$

† The rationalized mksc system is employed throughout this section (see Appendix A). However, the equation-of-state information of Fig. B·12 is in the absolute magnetostatic system.

An expression relating the difference in specific heats may be found by the methods used in obtaining Eq. (8·17),

$$c_{\mathbf{H}} - c_{\mathbf{M}} = \frac{T\mu_0 v[(\partial \mathbf{M}/\partial T)_{\mathbf{H}}]^2}{(\partial \mathbf{M}/\partial \mathbf{H})_T} \qquad (8\cdot 79)$$

If $(\partial \mathbf{M}/\partial \mathbf{H})_T$ is positive for any substance, as seems always to be the case, $c_{\mathbf{H}}$ must be larger than $c_{\mathbf{M}}$.

Superconductors are known to undergo a transition from superconducting to normally conducting states at well-defined values of the applied field. This "threshold field" is a function of temperature, and experimental data suggest that the equation of state might appear as shown in Fig. 8·15.

It may be shown from energy considerations that the energy which must be transferred as heat to effect a constant-T constant-$\mathbf{H}$ transition is equal to the difference in the magnetic enthalpies,

$$\mathrm{h}_{sn} \equiv \mathrm{h}_n - \mathrm{h}_s$$

Here we use the subscripts n and s to denote the normal and superconducting states, respectively. Following the development of the Clapeyron equation, it may be shown that the threshold field is related to the temperature and to the enthalpy of transformation h_{sn} by

$$\left(\frac{d\mathbf{H}}{dT}\right)_{\text{threshold}} = -\frac{\mathrm{h}_{sn}}{T\mu_0 v(\mathbf{M}_n - \mathbf{M}_s)}$$

In normally conducting states the magnetic moment $\mathbf{M}$ is zero. Superconduction occurs when the magnetization exactly cancels the applied field $\mathbf{H}$, so that electrons passing through the material experience no magnetic field. Setting $\mathbf{M}_n = 0$ and $\mathbf{M}_s = -\mathbf{H}$, the above equation reduces to

$$\left(\frac{d\mathbf{H}}{dT}\right)_{\text{threshold}} = \frac{-\mathrm{h}_{sn}}{T\mu_0 v\mathbf{H}} \qquad (8\cdot 80)$$

We see that the threshold field decreases with increasing temperature, which is indeed found to be the case.

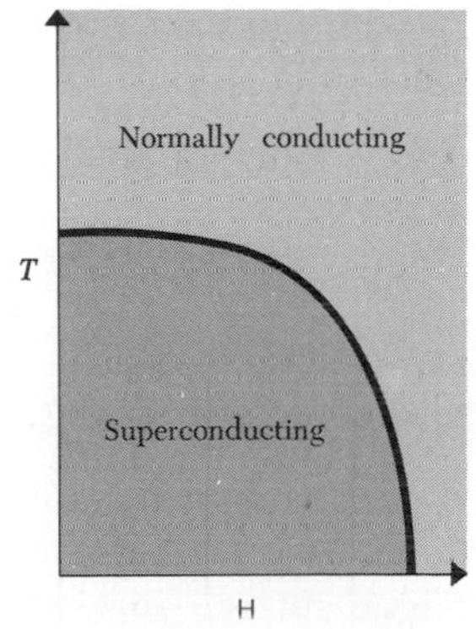

FIG. 8·15 *Typical superconducting and normally conducting phases*

8·11 ALGEBRAIC EQUATION OF STATE FOR THE CURIE SUBSTANCE

The Curie substance is any simple magnetic substance obeying the equation of state

$$\blacktriangleright \quad \mathbf{M} = C\frac{\mathbf{H}}{T} \tag{8·81}$$

Paramagnetic salts at temperatures which are not too low and in fields which are not too strong behave in this general manner.

It may be shown that the internal energy is a function only of temperature for any simple magnetic substance for which $\mathbf{H}/T = f(\mathbf{M})$. Consider the magnetic Gibbs equation (8·75), written in the form

$$ds = \frac{1}{T}\,du - \mu_0 v \left(\frac{\mathbf{H}}{T}\right) d\mathbf{M}$$

If $\mathbf{H}/T = f(\mathbf{M})$, then since ds is exact,

$$\left[\frac{\partial(1/T)}{\partial \mathbf{M}}\right]_u = -\mu_0 v \left[\frac{\partial(\mathbf{H}/T)}{\partial u}\right]_{\mathbf{M}} = 0$$

T is therefore independent of $\mathbf{M}$ along a line of constant u, and $T = T(u)$. Inverting this relationship, we have $u = u(T)$. It must be emphasized that this holds only for the special circumstances where $\mathbf{H}/T = f(\mathbf{M})$ and is not true for paramagnetics in general.

The energy of a Curie substance is therefore given by

$$du = c_{\mathbf{M}}(T)\,dT$$

The entropy may be found from the magnetic Gibbs equation, which for the Curie substance is

$$ds = \frac{c_{\mathbf{M}}}{T}\,dT - \frac{\mu_0 v}{C}\,\mathbf{M}\cdot d\mathbf{M}$$

For a Curie substance with constant $c_{\mathbf{M}}$ the above equations integrate to give

$$\blacktriangleright \quad u_2 - u_1 = c_{\mathbf{M}}(T_2 - T_1) \tag{8·82}$$

$$\blacktriangleright \quad s_2 - s_1 = c_{\mathbf{M}} \ln\frac{T_2}{T_1} - \frac{\mu_0 v}{2C}(\mathsf{M}_2{}^2 - \mathsf{M}_1{}^2) \tag{8·83}$$

8·12 THERMODYNAMICS OF THERMAL RADIATION

Consider an evacuated cavity in which the wall temperature is uniform, as shown in Fig. 8·16. Some of the atoms within the solid walls will be in excited electronic states, from which they may drop into the normal, or "ground,"

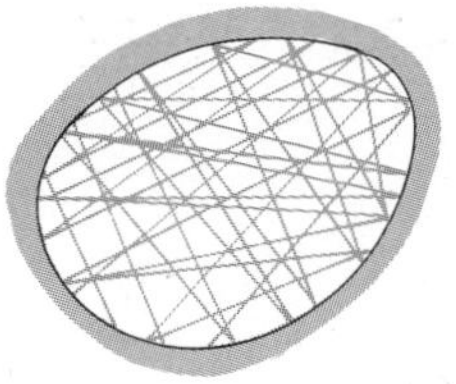

FIG. 8·16 *A cavity filled with radiation*

state by emission of radiation. These photons travel across the cavity, strike the opposite wall, and can be absorbed by other atoms while promoting them to excited states. The emission and absorption goes on continuously, and hence the cavity may be thought of as being filled with radiation. Thermodynamics helps us to determine how the energy of this radiation is related to temperature.

As the photons impinge upon the wall they deliver an impulse, which gives rise to *radiation pressure*. The solar sail has been proposed as a means for utilizing the pressure of the radiation from the sun for long interplanetary flight. The amount of radiation pressure can be related to the radiant energy per unit of volume by electromagnetic theory; we obtain the same result with a simple kinetic argument. Suppose the number of photons per unit of volume is n and that the momentum of a single photon is p. Photons move with the speed of light c and have energy cp. The energy per unit of volume is therefore

$$\blacktriangleright \quad \mathrm{u} = n\mathsf{cp}$$

The contribution to the pressure of a reflected photon may be assumed to be the same as that of one which is captured plus one which is emitted. Following the development leading to Eq. (8·50), we find that the radiation pressure P is given by

$$\blacktriangleright \quad P = \tfrac{1}{3}n\mathsf{cp} = \tfrac{1}{3}\mathrm{u} \tag{8·84}$$

The number of atoms in excited states will depend primarily on the temperature and will be virtually independent of density. Consequently, we assume that the energy per unit of volume of the radiation is a function only of its temperature.†

$$\blacktriangleright \quad \mathrm{u} = \mathrm{u}(T) \tag{8·85}$$

Equations (8·84) and (8·85) will now be used in conjunction with thermodynamics. Equation (8·14) applies here, provided it is written in an extensive form,‡

$$\left(\frac{\partial U}{\partial V}\right)_T = T\left(\frac{\partial P}{\partial T}\right)_V - P$$

† The temperature of the radiation is the temperature of the matter with which it is in equilibrium.

‡ The extensive form is required because the mass of a photon system is not conserved.

For the radiation, $U = \mathrm{u}V$. This equation then yields

$$\mathrm{u} = \frac{T}{3}\frac{d\mathrm{u}}{dT} - \frac{1}{3}\mathrm{u}$$

which reduces to

$$\frac{d\mathrm{u}}{\mathrm{u}} = 4\frac{dT}{T}$$

Integrating,

$$\ln \mathrm{u} = \ln T^4 + \ln b$$

or

$$\blacktriangleright \qquad \mathrm{u} = bT^4 \tag{8·86}$$

where b is a constant. This is the well-known *Stefan-Boltzmann law*. The rate at which thermal radiation is emitted is found to be proportional to the fourth power of the absolute temperature, and here we see that this particular power has some thermodynamic basis.

Unlike organized radiation from a radio transmitter, thermal radiation is disorganized, and consequently has a nonzero entropy. The extensive Gibbs equation (7·14) applies, and hence

$$dS = \frac{dU}{T} + \frac{P}{T}\,dV \tag{8·87}$$

Substituting $U = \mathrm{u}V$, $\mathrm{u} = bT^4$, $P = \frac{1}{3}\mathrm{u}$, Eq. (8·87) can be written as

$$dS = 4bT^2V\,dT + \tfrac{4}{3}bT^3\,dV$$

Presuming that S vanishes at zero volume, we integrate and find

$$\blacktriangleright \qquad S = \tfrac{4}{3}bT^3V \tag{8·88}$$

Note that the radiation entropy vanishes as $T \to 0$.

8·13 GENERALIZATIONS

In Chap. Two we enumerated a number of reversible work modes (Table 2·1). In each case we found that the amount of energy transfer as work to a given control mass could be represented by a term of the form

$$đW = \mathsf{F}\,dX$$

In each case F was some intensive property of the system, and X was some extensive property. We called F a *generalized force* and dX a *generalized displacement*, and can call X a *generalized extensive constraint*. If there are a number of such work modes, their sum represents the total energy transfer as reversible work to the system. The reversible energy addition as heat is $T\,dS$, and hence the increase in energy for a reversible process is

$$dU = T\,dS + \sum_i \mathsf{F}_i\,dX_i \tag{8·89}$$

Since we can imagine passing from any one state to another by some reversible process, Eq. (8·89) can be viewed as a differential equation of state; it is in fact the *generalized Gibbs equation.*

All of the formal theory outlined above can be extended readily to systems with more than one work mode. For example, we see that

$$T = \left(\frac{\partial U}{\partial S}\right)_{X_1,X_2,\ldots} \tag{8·90}$$

$$\mathsf{F}_i = \left(\frac{\partial U}{\partial X_i}\right)_{S,X_1,X_2,X_{i-1},X_{i+1},\ldots} \tag{8·91}$$

which in effect represent the thermodynamic definitions of the intensive properties. Definition of the generalized (extensive) enthalpy as

$$H \equiv U - \sum_i \mathsf{F}_i X_i \tag{8·92}$$

allows the Helmholtz and Gibbs functions to be defined as before; in extensive form,

$$A \equiv U - TS \tag{8·93}$$

$$G \equiv H - TS \tag{8·94}$$

The fact that dH, dA, and dG are exact differentials is useful in deriving the Maxwell relations for any particular system.

SELECTED READING

Lee, J., and F. Sears, *Thermodynamics*, 2d ed., chap. 2, secs. 7.1–7.7, Addison-Wesley Publishing Co., Inc., Reading, Mass., 1962.

Van Wylen, G., and R. Sonntag, *Fundamentals of Classical Thermodynamics*, chaps. 3, 10, John Wiley & Sons, Inc., New York, 1965.

Wark, K., *Thermodynamics*, chap. 13, McGraw-Hill Book Company, New York, 1966.

Zemansky, M. W., *Heat and Thermodynamics*, 4th ed., chaps. 11, 13, 14, McGraw-Hill Book Company, New York, 1957.

QUESTIONS

8·1 What role do equations of state play in the analysis of engineering systems?
8·2 Of what value are the differential equations of state?
8·3 Explain how the entropy can be found (relative to some datum state) without enumerating the quantum states.
8·4 What is the Gibbs equation?
8·5 Starting from the fundamental definition of a partial derivative, can you derive the chain rule of calculus?

8·6 Why is it essential to put a subscript on a partial derivative to indicate the property held constant?
8·7 Of what utility is the Clapeyron equation?
8·8 Explain how c_v can be determined without ever being measured directly.
8·9 On what diagram is c_P the slope of a line, and what line?
8·10 Considering the Clapeyron equation, what peculiar characteristic of H_2O makes ice skating possible?
8·11 Is the specific heat of a substance obeying $Pv = RT$ necessarily constant? Is it necessarily a function only of temperature?
8·12 If c_v is constant for a perfect gas, must c_P also be constant?
8·13 What is the meaning and utility of p_r and v_r in the air tables (Table B·9)?
8·14 Under what conditions is Pv^k = constant?
8·15 What is the difference between c_v and $\hat{c}_v$?
8·16 What is the equipartition principle?
8·17 Why are the molal specific heats of two diatomic gases quite similar?
8·18 Why is k for SO_2 less than that for CO_2 (see Table B·6)?
8·19 Why would k for a complicated hydrocarbon gas be very close to unity?
8·20 When can $Pv = RT$ be expected to apply?
8·21 What is the approximate value of Pv/RT near the critical point?
8·22 Why is thermodynamics useful in the study of magnetic substances?
8·23 What is radiation pressure?
8·24 Could thermodynamics be useful in the study of the interior of stars?

PROBLEMS

8·1 The Joule-Kelvin coefficient μ is defined by $\mu = (\partial T/\partial P)_h$. Prove that

$$\mu = \frac{1}{c_P}\left[T\left(\frac{\partial v}{\partial T}\right)_P - v\right]$$

Discuss how this equation might be used.
8·2 Show that the Joule-Kelvin coefficient for a perfect gas is zero.
8·3 Show that

$$\left(\frac{\partial c_v}{\partial v}\right)_T = T\left(\frac{\partial^2 P}{\partial T^2}\right)_v \qquad \left(\frac{\partial c_P}{\partial P}\right)_T = -T\left(\frac{\partial^2 v}{\partial T^2}\right)_P$$

Discuss the use of these equations.
8·4 Prove that

$$\left(\frac{\partial u}{\partial P}\right)_T = -T\left(\frac{\partial v}{\partial T}\right)_P - P\left(\frac{\partial v}{\partial P}\right)_T$$

How might this be used?
8·5 Prove that

$$\left(\frac{\partial P}{\partial T}\right)_s = \frac{c_P}{Tv\beta}$$

Describe an experiment that would use this equation to determine c_P without any energy measurements.

8·6 Describe an experiment by which the latent heat of vaporization of a substance could be determined without any energy measurements.

8·7 Estimate the vapor pressure of mercury at 1600°F using the Clapeyron equation.

8·8 Using appropriate differential equations of state and taking the datum for entropy to be saturated liquid at 14.7 psia, determine the entropy of nitrogen at the following states, using that data of Fig. B·4 [graphical integrations are required for (*b*) and (*c*)]; use the most convenient differential equation of state: (*a*) saturated vapor, 14.7 psia; (*b*) 500°R, 14.7 psia; (*c*) the critical point.

8·9 Show that the isothermal compressibility is always greater than or equal to the isentropic compressibility.

8·10 The properties of ice at 1 atm may be found in the *Handbook of Chemistry and Physics*. Estimate the melting temperature of ice at 1000 psia.

8·11 Derive expressions for the slopes of constant-pressure and constant-volume lines on a T-s plane for a perfect gas with constant specific heats and show that the volume line is steeper.

8·12 Derive the complete algebraic equation of state for a perfect gas for which $c_P = a + bT$, where a and b are constants.

8·13 Compute the average-square velocity (ft/sec) in helium at 1 atm and 60°F.

8·14 Using the ideas of equipartition of energy, estimate $\hat{c}_v$, $\hat{c}_P$, c_v, c_P, and k for the following substances and compare with values given in Table B·6: (*a*) A, (*b*) CO, and (*c*) C_2H_2.

8·15 Show that c_v is a function only of temperature for a Van der Waals gas. Derive an expression for $c_P - c_v$ for the gas. Is c_P also a function only of temperature? Derive algebraic expressions for the internal energy and entropy of a Van der Waals gas with constant c_v as a function of temperature and specific volume. Compare these with the perfect-gas equations.

8·16 Calculate the pressure as a function of molal volume for CO_2 at 400°K using the Beattie-Bridgeman equation of state. Cover the range 0–100 atm. Compare the values that you calculated with values obtained from the generalized compressibility chart.

8·17 Derive the complete algebraic equation of state for an incompressible liquid for which $c = a + bT$, where a and b are constants.

8·18 Estimate the enthalpy and entropy of mercury at room conditions relative to the datum used in Table B·3.

8·19 Derive the analog of the Maxwell relations for a simple magnetic substance.

8·20 Sketch the equation of state of a Curie substance on a T-s plane; show lines of constant u, $\mathbf{H}$, and $\mathbf{M}$.

8·21 Derive the complete algebraic equation of state for a Curie substance for which $c_{\mathbf{M}} = aT^2$, where a is a constant.

8·22 Consider a simple dielectric substance for which the polarization is related to the electric field and temperature by $\mathbf{E} = AT\mathbf{P}$, where A is a constant. Show that the energy of this dielectric is a function only of temperature. Derive a complete algebraic equation of state for the case where the specific heat at constant polarization $c_{\mathbf{P}} \equiv (\partial u/\partial T)_{\mathbf{P}}$ is constant.

8·23 Consider a simple surface for which the only reversible work mode is surface extension. Derive the Gibbs equation $T\,dS = dU - \sigma\,dA$, where A is the surface area and σ is the surface tension. Derive the relation

$$\left(\frac{\partial U}{\partial A}\right)_T = \sigma - T\left(\frac{\partial \sigma}{\partial T}\right)_A$$

Show that if the surface tension is a function only of temperature, the energy per unit of area also depends only on temperature, and consequently that

$$\frac{U}{A} = \sigma - T\frac{d\sigma}{dT}$$

The surface tension is easily measured, but it is difficult to measure the surface energy directly. How else might it be determined?

8·24 Consider a thin metal wire for which the only work mode is a one-dimensional extension. Develop the Gibbs equation $T\,ds = du - \sigma\,dl$, where l is the length per unit mass and σ is the tensile stress. Derive an expression for $(\partial l/\partial s)_\sigma$ in terms of $(\partial T/\partial \sigma)_s$. Take a rubber band, stretch it rapidly, and hold it to your lip. Which way does the temperature change? Check your result by rapidly releasing the strain. On the basis of your theory and experiment, will the elongation of a rubber rod under fixed stress increase or decrease when the rod is heated? (You might try to verify this prediction experimentally.) Unstressed metal rods normally expand when heated. What will happen to the temperature of a metal rod when it is rapidly stretched?

8·25 If the strain in the thin wire of Prob. 8·24 is small, it is convenient to put $l = l_0(1 + \epsilon)$, where l_0 is the unstretched length of the wire and ϵ is the strain (extension per unit length). The isothermal Young's modulus is $Y \equiv (\partial\sigma/\partial\epsilon)_T$. Show that if Y is constant so is $\alpha \equiv (\partial\sigma/\partial T)_\epsilon$. The volumetric specific heat at constant strain is $c_\epsilon \equiv (\partial \mathrm{u}/\partial T)_\epsilon$ where u is the internal energy per unit volume. Derive algebraic equations for the energy and entropy per unit of volume (u and s) for a slightly stretched wire with constant Y and c_ϵ.

8·26 Using the generalized properties charts in Appendix B and the critical-point data of Table B·8, and the ideal-gas data of Table B·13, estimate the molal enthalpy, entropy, internal energy, and the density of the following substances at the indicated states.

(*a*) H_2 at 600°K, 50 atm
(*b*) He at 500°K, 10 atm
(*c*) CO_2 at 200 atm, 200°K

8·27 Derive an expression analogous to Eq. (8·66) for $u - u_{pg}$. Derive an equation for $u - u_{pg}$ using this expression and the Beattie-Bridgeman equation.

8·28 Derive an expression analogous to Eq. (8·67) for $\hat{s} - \hat{s}_{pg}(T, \hat{v})$ using Eq. (8·15). Derive an equation for $\hat{s} - \hat{s}_{pg}(T, \hat{v})$ using this expression and the Beattie-Bridgeman equation.

8·29 Solve Prob. 8·26 using the equations developed in Probs. 8·27 and 8·28.

8·30 The radiation energy flux from the sun is about 400 Btu/hr-ft^2 near the earth. Estimate the radiation pressure and the amount of solar-sail area (ft^2) required for 1 lbf of thrust.

8·31 Consider an idealized liquid for which $P = A(v_0 - v)$, where A and v_0 are constants. Derive algebraic equations for energy, enthalpy, and entropy, assuming c_P is constant. Compare these with the equations for the incompressible liquid.

CHAPTER NINE

CHARACTERISTICS OF SOME THERMODYNAMIC SYSTEMS

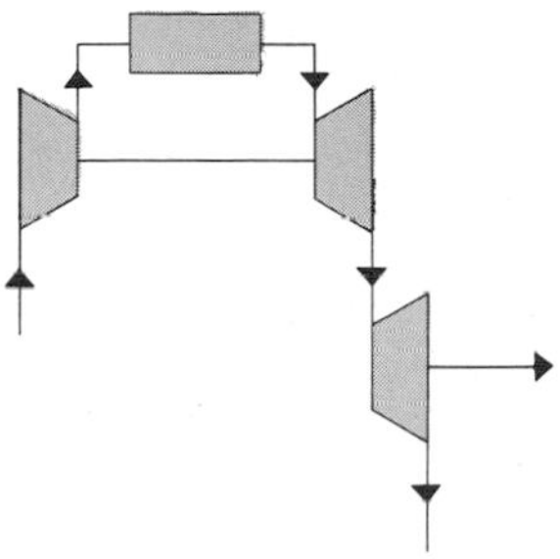

9·1 ANALYSIS OF THERMODYNAMIC SYSTEMS

Thermodynamics is invaluable in the analysis of any system involving energy transfers; the most common and practical uses of thermodynamics in engineering are in analysis of systems containing some sort of working substance, usually in a liquid or gaseous phase, which is flowing or circulating through the device. In this chapter we shall examine the characteristics of a number of thermodynamic systems, mostly of this variety, and in addition, we shall look at the behavior of some more unusual devices which show promise of practical utility in the future. These characteristics may be predicted from a combination of thermodynamic analysis and experience with operating hardware. For the most part we shall consider systems sufficiently idealized that analysis of their performance is within the range of our studies thus far.

The general methodology for energy analysis of a thermodynamic system was presented and illustrated in Chap. Five, and subsequent material should have afforded considerable practice with these important tools. In addition, we now have the many consequences of the second law at our disposal and are in a position to employ these in discussing the performance of thermodynamic systems. The second law places strong limitations on the performance of thermal energy-conversion and thermal transfer systems,† and we shall examine these in the following discussions.

The value of the process representation in the analysis of a thermodynamic system was emphasized in Chap. Five. Especially important is the temperature-entropy plane; when matter undergoes a reversible process, the sequence of states through which it passes traces out a line on the T-s plane (Fig. 9·1). Since the process is reversible, the energy transferred as heat *to* a unit of mass of

† Refrigerators, heat pumps, etc.

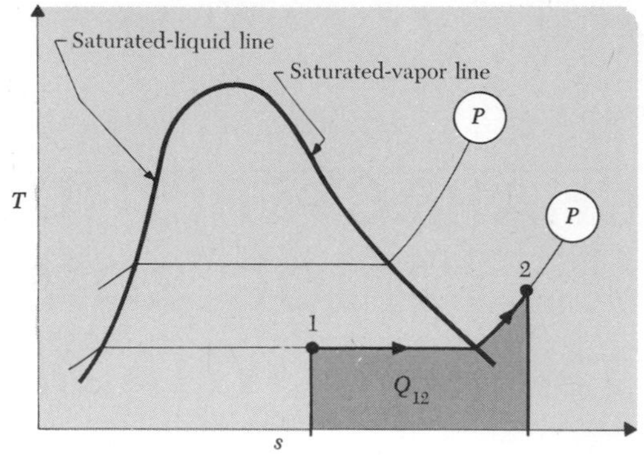

FIG. 9·1 *The T-s plane is particularly useful in showing amounts of energy transfer as heat*

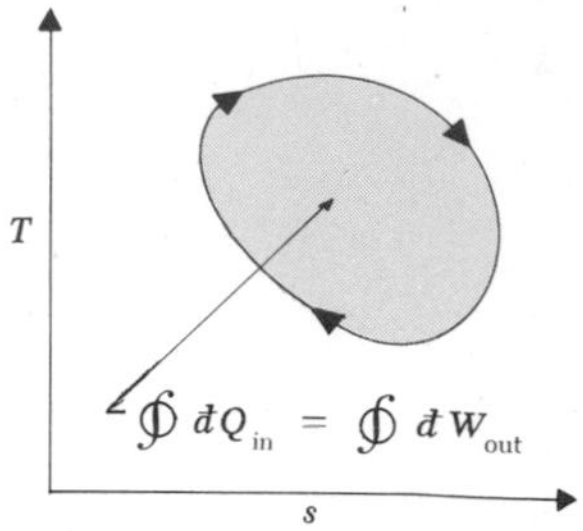

FIG. 9·2 *The cyclic integral of T ds represents the net energy transfer as heat to the substance*

the substance is represented by the area under the curve on the T-s plane. If the substance undergoes a cyclic process, there will be no net change in its internal energy over a cycle, and consequently the net energy transferred to a unit mass of the substance as heat during the cycle must equal the net energy transfer as work from the substance (work done), and both equal the area enclosed by the reversible path on the T-s plane (Fig. 9·2). The T-s process representation can therefore be a very graphic aid in comparing and evaluating thermodynamic systems, and we shall make extensive use of it in this chapter. Other thermodynamic planes are also quite descriptive, as will be seen.

9·2 THE CARNOT CYCLE

The *Carnot cycle* is the reversible cycle defined by two isothermal processes and two isentropic processes (Fig. 9·3). Since a reversible isentropic process is adiabatic, the only energy transfer as heat to a piece of substance undergoing a Carnot cycle occurs during the isothermal processes. The Carnot cycle constitutes a reversible $2T$ engine,† and consequently the ratios of the energy transfers as heat defined in Fig. 9·3 are given by‡

$$\blacktriangleright \qquad \frac{Q_H}{Q_C} = \frac{T_H}{T_C}$$

† See Sec. 9·7 for a discussion of a particular Carnot-cycle engine.
‡ This relation can easily be derived at will from $đQ_{rev} = T\,dS$, since

$$\frac{Q_H}{Q_C} = \frac{T_H(S_3 - S_2)}{T_C(S_4 - S_1)} = \frac{T_H}{T_C}$$

Its energy-conversion efficiency is therefore

$$\eta = \frac{W}{Q_H} = \frac{Q_H - Q_C}{Q_H} = 1 - \frac{T_C}{T_H} \tag{9·1}$$

Highest efficiencies will be obtained when the ratio T_C/T_H is as small as possible. One would like to add the energy as heat at as high a temperature as possible and reject energy as heat at the lowest possible temperature; the practical limitations on T_H and T_C were discussed in Chap. Seven.

The Carnot cycle operates as a refrigerator when reversed (Fig. 9·4). The area enclosed by its *T-s* process path would represent the work required per cycle of operation, and we should like this to be as small as possible. This suggests that having T_H as close as possible to T_C is most desirable. A refrigeration cycle is rated in terms of its *coefficient of performance* (cop):

$$\text{cop}_{\text{refrig}} = \frac{Q_C}{W} \tag{9·2}$$

For the Carnot refrigerator,

$$\text{cop} = \frac{Q_C}{Q_H - Q_C} = \frac{T_C}{T_H - T_C} \tag{9·3}$$

Unlike the efficiency, the cop can range from zero to infinity. For a Carnot refrigerator extracting energy as heat from a cold space at 0°F and transferring

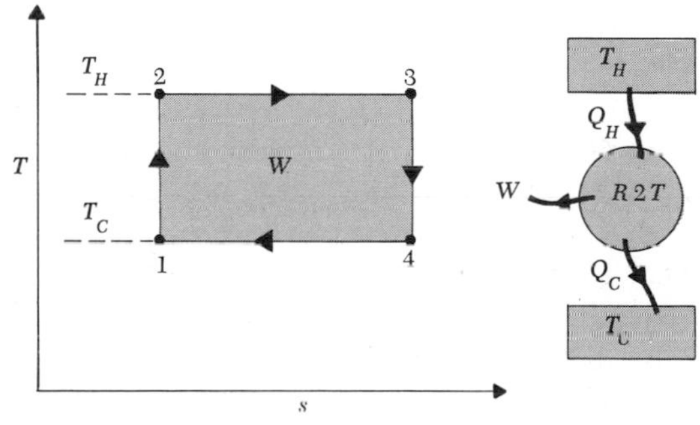

FIG. 9·3 *The Carnot engine*

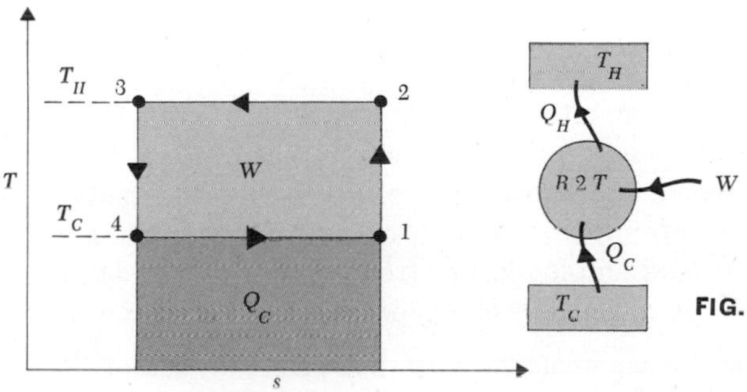

FIG. 9·4 *The Carnot refrigerator*

energy as heat to an environment at 60°F,

$$\text{cop} = \frac{460}{520 - 460} = 7.7$$

Real refrigeration systems operating between the same two temperatures would have coefficients of performance of the order of 2 to 3.

An interesting use of the refrigerator is as a *heat pump*. Here the objective is not to keep a region cool but instead to keep a region (such as a house) warm. The energy transfer to the hot space is then of prime interest, and it is customary to define the cop as

$$\blacktriangleright \qquad \text{cop}_{\text{heat pump}} = \frac{Q_H}{W} \tag{9·4}$$

Then, for a Carnot heat pump,

$$\blacktriangleright \qquad \text{cop} = \frac{Q_H}{Q_H - Q_C} = \frac{T_H}{T_H - T_C} \tag{9·5}$$

For example, a Carnot heat pump taking energy from the outdoors at 10°F and transferring energy into a home at 70°F would have a cop of

$$\text{cop} = \frac{530}{530 - 470} = 8.8$$

This means that the homeowner would be getting energy into the house equal to almost nine times the electrical energy showing up on his utility bill. A practical heat pump might have a cop of 3 to 4, but even this makes a heat pump far superior to direct electric-resistance heating from the point of view of utility costs.†

The Carnot cycle is very useful in estimating limits of efficiency for given operating temperatures; no real system limited by the same temperatures could exceed the performance of a Carnot cycle, since the efficiency of any irreversible $2T$ engine is less than Carnot-cycle efficiency. Unfortunately, it is very difficult to build a real device to operate on the Carnot cycle, and its chief value is as a standard of comparison for real energy-conversion and refrigeration systems.

9·3 PATTERN PROCESSES

In thermodynamic analysis one often knows the initial state of a substance and can compute the work done or the energy transferred as heat only if something is known about the process undergone by the substance. The analyst frequently has to make appropriate idealizations in order to render the analysis tractable; the idealized processes employed are frequently referred to as *pattern processes*. For example, if a gas is being compressed very slowly in a

† The capital cost of the heat pump would, however, be significantly greater.

massive container, there would be plenty of time for energy to be transferred as heat, and a good idealization might be that the gas is always at the container temperature, that is, that the process is isothermal. In this case the isothermal process would be called the pattern process, and it represents a simplified model of what actually might occur.

When a substance undergoes a process very rapidly there will be little time for energy transfer as heat to occur, and we might make the idealization that the process is adiabatic. If, in addition, the irreversibilities discussed in Chap. Seven are not too important, it might also be appropriate to idealize that the process is reversible. The second law tells us that the entropy of matter undergoing a process which is both reversible and adiabatic will not change. Such an *isentropic process* is the pattern process normally employed for

Restrained adiabatic compression or expansion of a gas in a piston-cylinder system
Compression or expansion of a fluid in a steady-flow adiabatic compressor, turbine, or pump
Frictionless adiabatic flow of a substance through a duct
Adiabatic magnetization or demagnetization
Adiabatic polarization or depolarization

The actual process may not be very close to the pattern process, and in such cases the analyst often introduces some sort of *performance parameter* to account quantitatively for the departures from the idealized behavior. For example, in analysis of *turbines* we would introduce the *isentropic efficiency*, defined as

$$\blacktriangleright \qquad \eta_s \equiv \frac{W}{W_s} \tag{9·6}$$

Here W represents the work output that would be measured from an actual adiabatic turbine, and W_s is the theoretical work output of an isentropic-process turbine operating with the same inlet state and discharge pressure. The isentropic efficiency is not an energy-conversion efficiency, but rather a parameter that compares an actual device to an ideal (pattern) device. Second-law analysis indicates that $\eta_s \leq 1$. The value of η_s depends upon the design of the turbine blades, nozzle, and diffuser, and prediction of efficiencies requires some fairly sophisticated fluid-mechanical analysis. Small turbines have isentropic efficiencies of the order of 60 to 80 percent; large steam and gas turbines with isentropic efficiencies of the order of 90 percent have been built in recent years.

The isentropic efficiency of an adiabatic *compressor*, or pump, is instead defined as

$$\blacktriangleright \qquad \eta_s \equiv \frac{W_s}{W} \tag{9·7}$$

Since the work required to produce a given pressure rise in an actual adiabatic compressor is greater than that for an isentropic compressor, η_s is always† less than 1, as we showed from the second law in Sec. 7·17. The ideal and actual devices are considered to have the same inlet state and the same discharge pressure. Small centrifugal hydraulic pumps have efficiencies of the order of 40–60 percent; the axial and centrifugal compressors employed in gas-turbine power plants and in jet engines have isentropic efficiencies in the range of 75–85 percent. The fact that small gas-turbine power systems have become practical realities in recent years is largely a result of advances in technology that have produced these levels of compressor efficiencies.

Isentropic efficiencies of *nozzles* are defined in terms of the discharge kinetic energy of the actual device compared to that for an ideal isentropic nozzle,

$$\blacktriangleright \quad \eta_s \equiv \frac{(V^2/2g_c)}{(V^2/2g_c)_s} \tag{9·8}$$

The ideal and actual nozzles are considered to have the same inlet state and the same discharge pressure. Nozzle efficiencies are typically quite high (of the order of 90–95 percent); the main irreversibility is due to friction on the walls, and this is usually of minor importance, especially in very large nozzles.

Fluid flowing through a heat exchanger, nuclear reactor, or combustion chamber is retarded by friction. However, in well-designed systems the resulting pressure drop can be made quite small, and consequently the pressure is very nearly equal at every point in the flow.‡ The pattern process for fluid being heated in steady flow is therefore one of *constant pressure*. The analyst will often assume some pressure drop, based on experience or other calculations, in order to make a slightly better calculation. However, the constant-pressure pattern process is usually quite satisfactory for preliminary system studies.

The use of pattern processes and component efficiencies allows us to make thermodynamic calculations of system performance without knowledge of the details of the hardware construction. We can learn a great deal about a proposed system from the process representation for fluid that circulates through the device. Temperature-entropy diagrams are particularly useful for reasons already mentioned. The *Mollier diagram* (*h-s* plane) is also very useful; vertical distances on this diagram are proportional to the energy transfer as work per lbm for an adiabatic compressor or turbine and to the energy transfer as heat for a steady-flow heater. Furthermore, the isentropic process conveniently appears as a vertical line, allowing the end state for an idealized adiabatic process to be found easily. In approaching a new system it is generally a good idea first to make a simple schematic flow diagram and then to

† If energy is transferred as heat from the actual compressor, η_s can exceed unity. Reversible adiabatic compression requires less work than irreversible adiabatic compression, but reversible isothermal compression requires even less work for a given pressure increase.

‡ For a constant-area duct.

sketch the process representation on an appropriate thermodynamic plane. Working out the process representation provides an understanding of how the system works and of any limitations imposed by the second law and orients thinking as to how to proceed with first-law analysis. We shall illustrate these ideas in the sections to follow.

9·4 A PARTICULAR THERMAL POWER SYSTEM

Thermodynamics developed as a result of nineteenth-century work with reciprocating steam engines. Present-day applications of thermodynamics go well beyond this single area, but vapor power systems remain a major source of electrical power and continue to grow in importance with the perfection of nuclear-reactor boilers.

Modern vapor power systems employ rotating rather than reciprocating machinery, for numerous practical reasons. The flow diagram and process representation for a simple *Rankine cycle* are shown in Fig. 9·5. We treat a somewhat idealized system for simplicity. Liquid is compressed by the pump and fed to the boiler. The boiler evaporates the fluid and delivers high-pressure vapor to the power producing turbine. In the system shown, the turbine discharges to the atmosphere, and the only fluid which we might possibly afford to throw away in this manner is water.

To get some feeling for vapor power systems and to illustrate the general

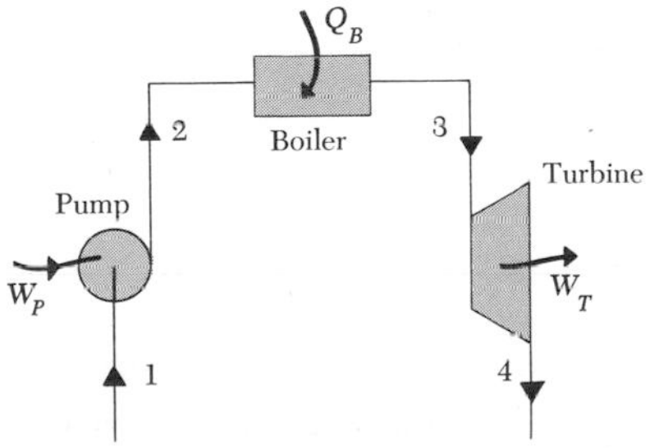

FIG. 9·5 *A simple Rankine vapor power system*

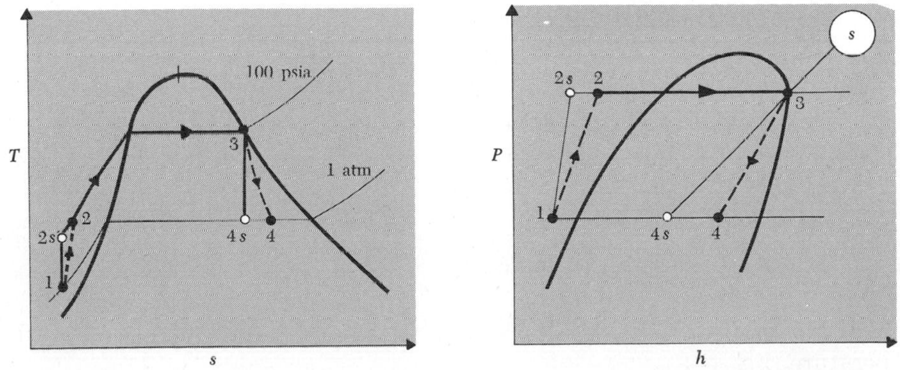

method of system analysis, we shall now analyze this system. Let us assume the following

Working fluid, water
State 1, liquid at 80°F and 1 atm
State 2, 100 psia
State 3, saturated vapor at 100 psia
State 4, 1 atm pressure
$\eta_s = 0.60$ for pump, $\eta_s = 0.80$ for turbine
Kinetic and potential energies negligible at states 1, 2, 3, and 4; pump and turbine adiabatic
Steady flow steady state, water in thermodynamic equilibrium at 1, 2, 3, and 4

An energy balance on the pump yields

$$W_P = h_2 - h_1$$

where W_P is the shaft-work input for each unit of mass handled by the pump. Having no tabular or graphical equation-of-state information for subcooled liquid water, we shall treat it as an incompressible liquid. Using Eq. (8·74), the W_P for an ideal adiabatic pump would be (isentropic process)

$$W_{Ps} = v(P_{2s} - P_1)$$

From Table B·1, $v = 0.0161$ ft³/lbm. Then,

$$W_{Ps} = 0.0161 \times (100 - 14.7) \times 144/778 = 0.253 \text{ Btu/lbm}$$

The actual device then requires

$$W_P = \frac{W_s}{\eta_s} = \frac{0.253}{0.6} = 0.42 \text{ Btu/lbm}$$

The value of h_1 may be found using the incompressible-liquid equation of state in conjunction with the tabulated thermodynamic properties. This particular case was worked as an example in Sec. 8·9, where we found $h_1 = 48.06$ Btu/lbm. We therefore determine h_2 as

$$h_2 = h_1 + W_P = 48.06 + 0.42 = 48.48 \text{ Btu/lbm}$$

T_2 may be found from Eq. (8·74),

$$T_2 = T_1 + \frac{(h_2 - h_1) - v(P_2 - P_1)}{c}$$

$$= 80 + \frac{0.42 - 0.25}{1.0} = 80.2\text{°F}$$

Note the very small work requirement of the pump and the very slight temperature rise.

From Table B·1*b* we find $h_3 = 1187.2$ Btu/lbm. An energy balance on the boiler then gives

$$Q_B = h_3 - h_2 = 1187.2 - 48.48 = 1138.7 \text{ Btu/lbm}$$

where Q_B is the energy transfer as heat to the boiler per lbm of water.

An energy balance on the turbine yields

$$W_T = h_3 - h_4$$

where W_T is the shaft-work output per lbm of fluid. To determine state 4 we must first fix state 4*s*. From Table B·1*b* we read

$$s_3 = 1.6026 \text{ Btu/lbm-°R}$$
$$s_{f4} = 0.3120 \text{ Btu/lbm-°R} \qquad s_{g4} = 1.7566 \text{ Btu/lbm-°R} \qquad \text{(at 1 atm)}$$
$$s_{fg4} = s_{g4} - s_{f4} = 1.4446 \text{ Btu/lbm-°R} \qquad \text{(at 1 atm)}$$

Since $s_{4s} = s_3$,

$$s_{4s} = (1 - x_{4s})s_{f4} + x_{4s}s_{g4} = s_{f4} + x_{4s}s_{fg4}$$
$$x_{4s} = \frac{1.6026 - 0.3120}{1.4446} = 0.893$$

Again in Table B·1*b* we find

$$h_{f4} = 180.07 \text{ Btu/lbm}$$
$$h_{fg4} = 970.3 \text{ Btu/lbm} \qquad \text{(at 1 atm)}$$

Thus

$$h_{4s} = h_{f4} + x_{4s}h_{fg4} = 180 + 0.893 \times 970.3 = 1046 \text{ Btu/lbm}$$

Consequently,

$$W_{Ts} = h_3 - h_{4s} = 1187 - 1046 = 141 \text{ Btu/lbm}$$

Then

$$W_T = W_{Ts}\eta_s = 141 \times 0.8 = 112 \text{ Btu/lbm}$$
$$h_4 = h_3 - W_T = 1187 - 112 = 1075 \text{ Btu/lbm}$$

The discharge quality is then

$$x_4 = \frac{h_4 - h_{f4}}{h_{fg4}} = \frac{1075 - 180}{970} = 0.922$$

Note that the turbine-discharge temperature is 212°F, so that the steam whic is thrown away is quite energetic.

To summarize, we have found

$$W_T = 112 \text{ Btu/lbm}$$
$$W_P = 0.4 \text{ Btu/lbm}$$
$$Q_B - 1130 \text{ Btu/lbm}$$

Part of the turbine work is required to drive the pump. One of the attractive features of vapor power plants is that this is a small fraction of the turbine-work output. In this particular case the *back-work ratio* is

$$\text{bwr} = \frac{W_P}{W_T} = \frac{0.4}{112} \approx 0.004$$

The energy-conversion efficiency of this plant is then

$$\eta = \frac{W_{\text{net}}}{Q_B} = \frac{112 - 0.4}{1139} = 0.099$$

Since $P_1 = P_4$ in this example, we could close the cycle with the addition of a condenser. Keeping states 1 and 2 fixed, this additional device would not influence the efficiency of the system. The energy that would be transferred as heat from the condenser can be determined by an overall energy balance, which yields

$$Q_C = Q_B - W_{\text{net}} = 1139 - 111.6 = 1027 \text{ Btu/lbm}$$

Most of the energy fed into the boiler as heat would be thrown away in the condenser; only 9.9 percent is converted to useful shaft work.

It is instructive to compare the energy-conversion efficiency of this system to that of a Carnot cycle operating between the same temperatures ($T_3 = 327.81°F$ and $T_1 = 80°F$). For the Carnot cycle

$$\eta = 1 - \frac{460 + 80}{460 + 328} = 0.315$$

Some of the difference can be attributed to irreversibilities in the turbine, but the major difference is due to the fact that the temperatures at which energy is transferred as heat to and from the working fluid are more widely separated for the Carnot cycle (see Fig. 9·6). Note that the area enclosed by the vapor-cycle process path is not equal to the net work output per lbm of fluid, since

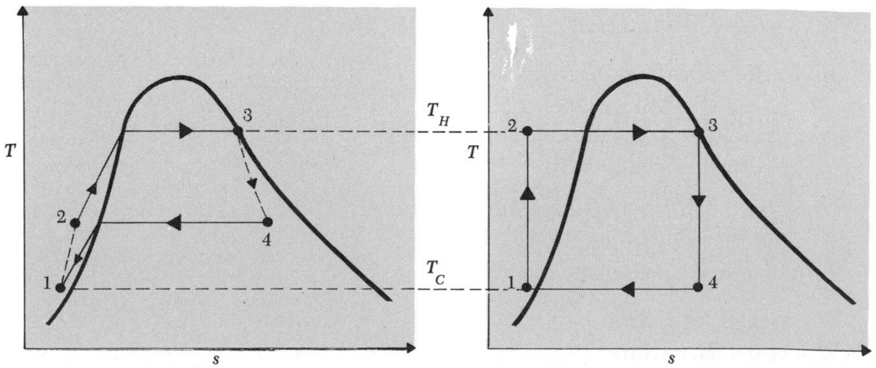

FIG. 9·6 *Comparison with a Carnot cycle*

the processes that we treated were not all reversible. The performance of this plant is dismally poor by modern standards. In the next section we shall examine some ways of obtaining better performance, making considerable use of process representations to show why improvements are obtained.

9·5 VAPOR POWER SYSTEMS

Suppose we are given the job of doubling the efficiency of the Rankine vapor power system just analyzed. How should we approach the problem? One good way would be to first take a qualitative look at the sorts of modifications that are reasonable to make and then make appropriate thermodynamic analyses to evaluate those schemes that seem most promising. From our knowledge about the desirability of adding energy as heat at high temperature and removing it at low temperature, we should look for ways to make the T-s diagram taller. The condensing system of Fig. 9·6 rejects heat at 212°F. If we could operate the condenser at a reduced pressure, condensation would occur at a lower temperature, and we could conceivably go as low as the temperature of the surrounding atmosphere. This change would not affect the energy addition in the boiler but would mean that we could obtain a larger enthalpy change in the turbine, as can be seen by inspection of the h-s diagram of Fig. B·2. In fact, condensation at 100°F would allow us to double the turbine output, thereby accomplishing the assigned task.†

A second easy modification which is less rewarding would be the addition of *superheating*. This extra energy input would permit us to operate with a higher turbine-inlet enthalpy, and since the lines of constant pressure diverge on the h-s plane, we could get more power from the turbine. However, additional energy would have to be added as heat, which would tend to offset the power gain. A Rankine cycle with superheat is shown in Fig. 9·7.

The lifetime of a turbine is a function of the quality of the vapor impinging on the blades. If the moisture content is high, erosion can be quite severe, and consequently most vapor turbines operate with exhaust qualities of 0.90 or

† Contrary to popular belief, James Watt did not invent the steam engine. He merely added a low-pressure condenser.

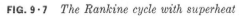

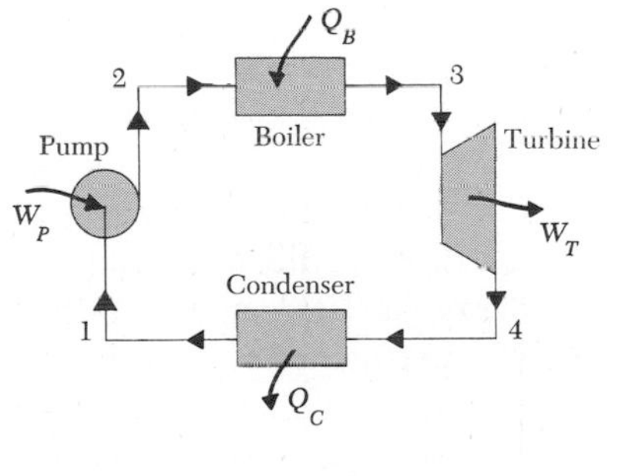

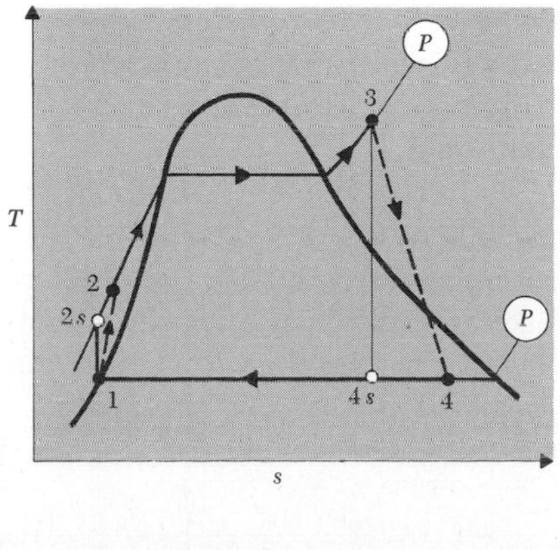

FIG. 9·7 *The Rankine cycle with superheat*

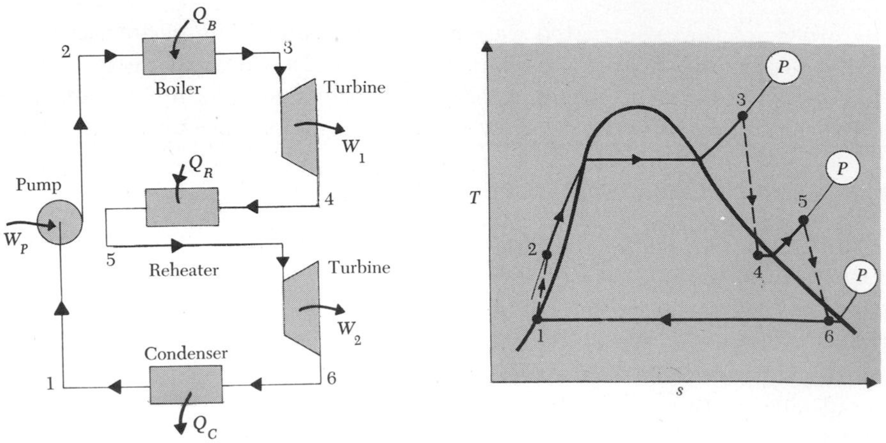

FIG. 9·8 *A Rankine cycle with one reheat stage*

more. It is evident from the T-s diagram that high pressures are necessary to increase the cycle efficiency, and for a given maximum temperature an increase in boiler pressure will generally mean a reduction in the quality of the flow in the turbine. For this reason *multiple staging with reheat* is often employed in a modification of the Rankine cycle. The system schematic and process representation are shown in Fig. 9·8. Reheat may or may not improve the efficiency, depending on operating conditions and characteristics of the working fluid.

The reheat cycle has the practical disadvantage that the same amount of flow is circulating through the entire system. The low-pressure turbine stage is therefore considerably larger than the high-pressure stage, disproportionately so in regard to its power output per unit of cost. A second disadvantage is that the liquid must be preheated before it can be evaporated. A modification of the Rankine cycle often employed in large systems is *extraction and regeneration*, shown schematically in Fig. 9·9. For purposes of clarity we show the pump and turbine processes as isentropic, though in reality they would be irreversible. Part of the flow emerging from the first-stage turbine is bled off and condensed in a high-pressure condenser. The energy transferred from this fluid is added as heat to the low-temperature liquid emerging from the main pump. The only energy which must be added as heat is that required to take the total stream from state 5 to state 6, and a considerable improvement in efficiency can be obtained.

In theory, if an infinite number of extraction and regeneration stages could be employed, the external addition of energy as heat would take place at one temperature, and the external removal of energy as heat would take place isothermally in the low-pressure condenser. The performance of this limiting system is then that of a reversible $2T$ engine, that is, of a Carnot cycle. This is very interesting, for the process representation does not look much like that of the Carnot cycle (see Fig. 9·10). In large central power stations employ-

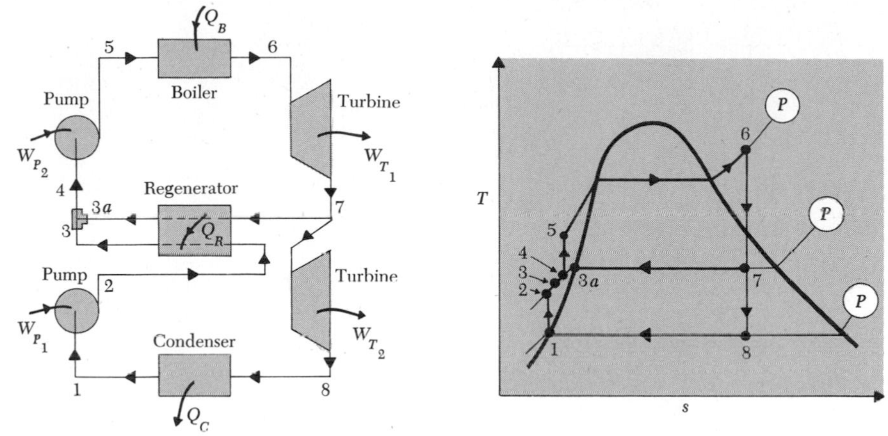

FIG. 9·9 *Idealized Rankine cycle with one stage of regeneration*

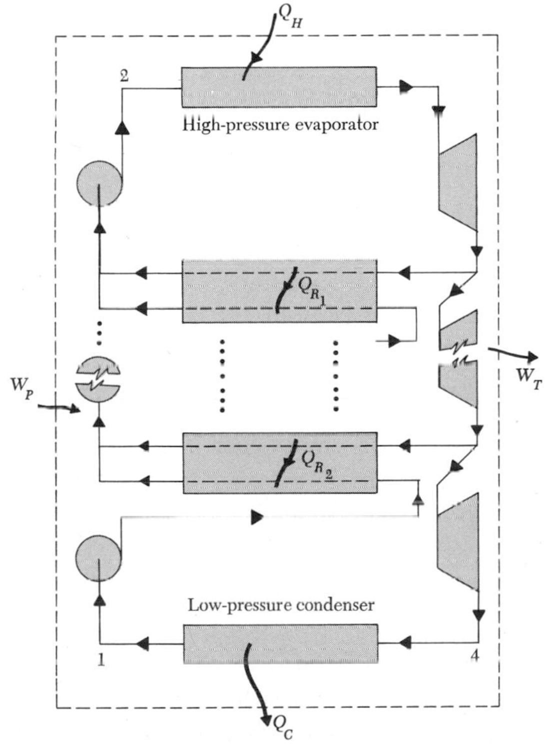

FIG. 9·10 *Idealized vapor cycle with an infinite number of reheat and regeneration stages*

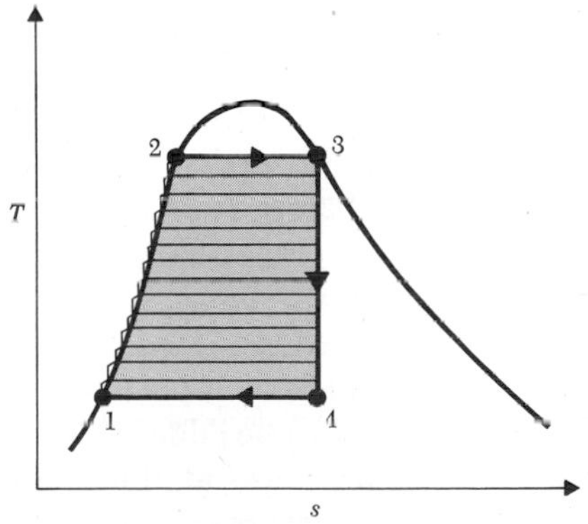

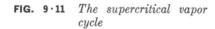

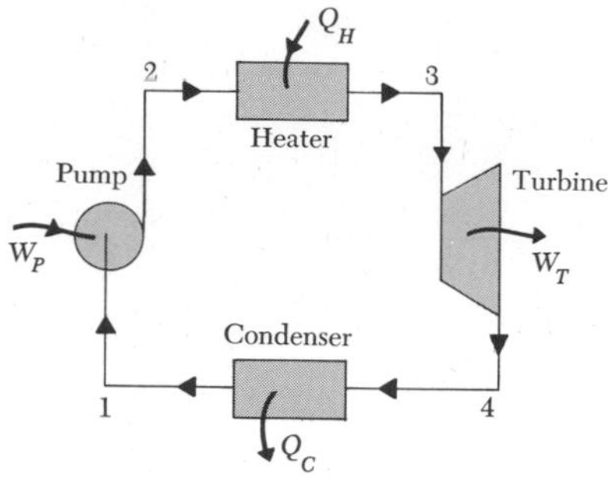

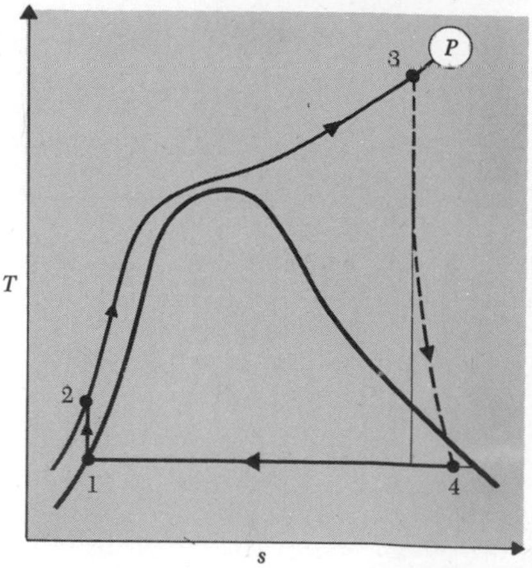

FIG. 9·11 *The supercritical vapor cycle*

ing reheat, regeneration, and extraction, efficiencies of the order of 30–35 percent have been obtained.

Another means for going to higher temperatures is the *supercritical cycle* (Fig. 9·11), in which the change from liquid to gas takes place continuously at a pressure greater than the critical pressure. A number of supercritical steam power stations have been built, and there is currently quite a bit of interest in this type of plant.

The *binary vapor cycle,* employing two fluids, is another means of devising higher-performance thermal power systems. The high-pressure fluid is selected to have a reasonable vapor pressure at its operating conditions, as is the lower-pressure fluid. The hardware and process representations for such a system are shown in Fig. 9·12. The energy transferred as heat from the "topping cycle" is used to evaporate the fluid in the main cycle. The effect is to increase the temperatures at which energy is added externally, increasing the energy-conversion efficiency. Mercury-steam binary plants have been designed with efficiencies approaching 50 percent, and at least one with an efficiency of the order of 40 percent has been built. Sulfur-steam binary systems powered by nuclear-heat sources have been studied, and it appears that the binary cycle may be one way to overcome the present high costs of nuclear electric power.

Steam has been used as the working fluid in most Rankine cycles; water is easily available at low cost and has a high latent heat of evaporation, so that a lot of energy can be added per lbm in the boiler. It also has entirely reasonable saturation pressures at the temperatures desired for operation. However, the critical temperature of water is 705.6°F, and consequently a Rankine cycle using steam is restricted to boiler temperatures lower than 700°F. Other fluids can be used to allow higher boiler temperatures to be reached, and there has been considerable interest in using mercury, particularly in high-temperature Rankine cycles for use in space vehicles. Unfortunately, the fluids that have reasonable vapor pressures at high temperatures have very low vapor pressures at low temperatures, and consequently the piping on the low-pressure side of the cycle has to be large to accommodate the volume of flow. Furthermore, air leakage can be a problem if the internal pressure is less than 1 atm. It should be evident that there are many practical and economic considerations which must be taken into account in selecting the working fluid for any thermal power system.

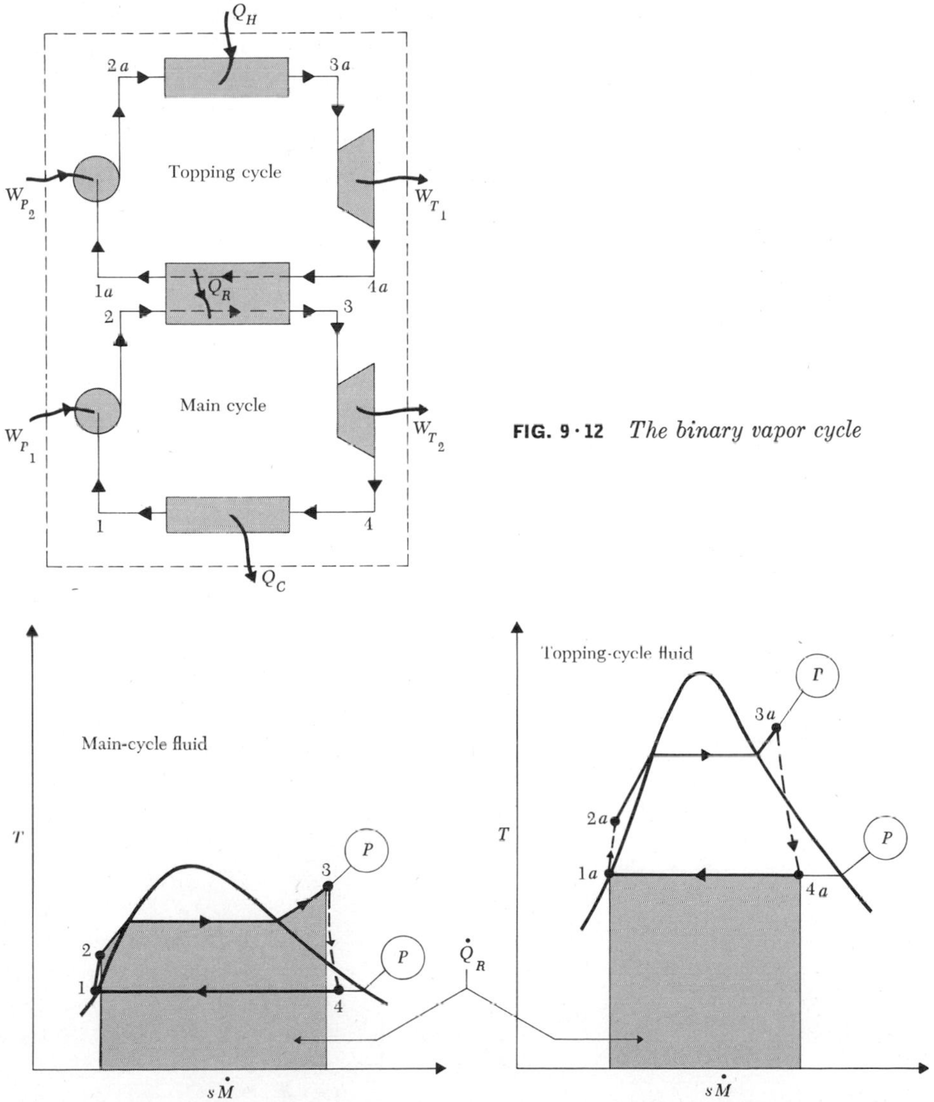

FIG. 9·12 *The binary vapor cycle*

9·6 A PARTICULAR GAS POWER SYSTEM

A gas power system is one which employs only the gaseous form of the working fluid. The internal-combustion engine was developed before gas-turbine power systems, primarily because the technology of the time could achieve much more efficient compression and expansion in reciprocating rather than rotating devices. Also, the intermittent cooling of the cylinder by the fresh fuel-air mixture permits a reciprocating engine to operate at higher gas temperatures than can be used in steady-flow systems. Metallurgical advances in recent years now make the gas-turbine system seem very attractive for power production in the range of a few hundred horsepower to a few megawatts, particularly where mobility is a prime requirement. At one time it appeared that vapor cycles would be the standard auxiliary power source in large space vehicles, but gas-turbine systems have since gained much favor, primarily because of the higher degree of reliability possible with use of an inert fluid.

In order to gain some appreciation for the problems of gas-turbine power production, let us analyze a very simple open-cycle system, shown in Fig. 9·13. We make the following idealizations:

Working fluid, air, treated as a perfect gas
State 1, 60°F and 1 atm
State 2, 4 atm
State 3, 1000°F and 4 atm
State 4, 1 atm
$\eta_s = 0.65$ for compressor, $\eta_s = 0.87$ for turbine
Kinetic and potential energies negligible at states 1, 2, 3, 4; compressor and turbine adiabatic; steady flow steady state; equilibrium states at 1, 2, 3, and 4

The analysis consists of determining the various states and computing the energy transfers as heat and work per unit of mass of air. Energy balances on

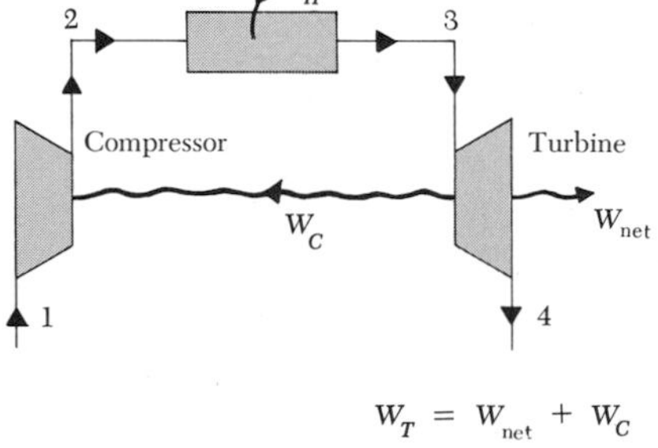

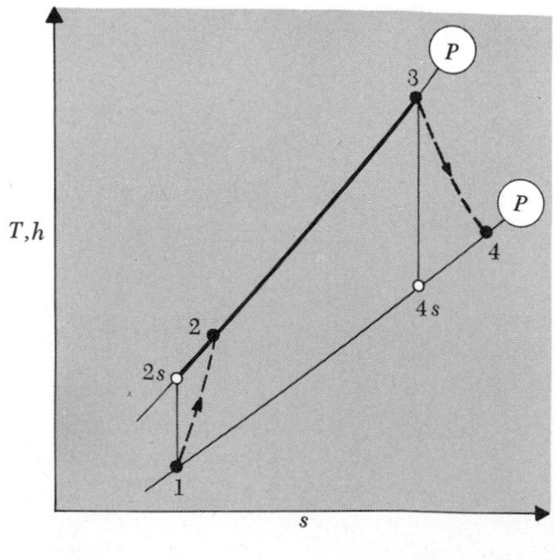

FIG. 9·13 *A simple gas-turbine power system*

the three components yield

$$W_C = h_2 - h_1 \qquad W_T = h_3 - h_4 \qquad Q_H = h_3 - h_2$$

Noting that

$$\frac{R}{c_P} = \frac{c_P - c_v}{c_P} = \frac{k-1}{k}$$

we find from Eq. (8·46*b*) that

$$\frac{T_{2s}}{T_1} = \left(\frac{P_{2s}}{P_1}\right)^{(k-1)/k} \qquad \frac{T_3}{T_{4s}} = \left(\frac{P_3}{P_{4s}}\right)^{(k-1)/k}$$

Thus, since $(k - 1)/k = 0.286$,

$$T_{2s} = T_1 \times 4^{0.286} = 520 \times 1.486 = 774°\text{R}$$

Using Eq. (8·45) to determine enthalpy changes, the calculations give

$$W_{Cs} = h_{2s} - h_1 = c_P(T_{2s} - T_1) = 0.24 \times (774 - 520) = 61.0 \text{ Btu/lbm}$$

$$W_C = \frac{W_{Cs}}{\eta_s} = \frac{61.0}{0.65} = 93.9 \text{ Btu/lbm}$$

$$W_C = h_2 - h_1 = c_P(T_2 - T_1)$$

$$T_2 = T_1 + \frac{W_C}{c_P} = 520 + \frac{93.9}{0.24} = 911°\text{R}$$

$$Q_H = h_3 - h_2 = c_P(T_3 - T_2) = 0.24 \times (1460 - 911) = 131.5 \text{ Btu/lbm}$$

$$T_{4s} = T_3 \times 4^{-0.286} = \frac{1460}{1.486} = 983°\text{R}$$

$$W_{Ts} = h_3 - h_{4s} = c_P(T_3 - T_{4s}) = 0.24 \times (1460 - 983) = 114.2 \text{ Btu/lbm}$$
$$W_T = W_{Ts}\eta_s = 0.87 \times 114.2 = 99.4 \text{ Btu/lbm}$$
$$W_T = h_3 - h_4 = c_P(T_3 - T_4)$$

$$T_4 = T_3 - \frac{W_T}{c_P} = 1460 - \frac{99.4}{0.24} = 1047°\text{R}$$

The back-work ratio is then

$$\text{bwr} = \frac{W_C}{W_T} = \frac{93.9}{99.4} = 0.945$$

The net work output is

$$W_{\text{net}} = W_T - W_C = 99.4 - 93.9 = 5.5 \text{ Btu/lbm}$$

and the system energy-conversion efficiency is

$$\eta = \frac{W_{\text{net}}}{Q_H} = \frac{5.5}{131.5} = 0.042$$

We see that compression of a gas takes quite a bit more work than compression of a liquid. Consequently, the back-work ratio for gas power cycles will always be much larger than that for a Rankine cycle. Whereas we can tolerate poor isentropic pump efficiencies in a vapor power system, we must achieve high compressor isentropic efficiency in order to make gas-turbine cycles practicable. The compressor efficiency selected in this example was purposely low in order to emphasize this point. A rather substantial research-and-development effort on axial-flow compressors, beginning in the 1940s, has brought us to the level of about 85 percent for larger machines. With this value in our example,

$$W_C = \frac{61.0}{0.85} = 71.8 \text{ Btu/lbm}$$

$$T_2 = 520 + \frac{71.8}{0.24} = 820°\text{R}$$

$$Q_H = 0.24 \times (1460 - 820) = 153.6 \text{ Btu/lbm}$$

$$\text{bwr} = \frac{71.8}{99.4} = 0.723$$

$$W_{\text{net}} = 99.4 - 71.8 = 27.6 \text{ Btu/lbm}$$

$$\eta = \frac{27.6}{153.6} = 0.180$$

Note that this 20 percent gain in compressor efficiency would reduce the fuel consumption by a factor of more than 4. The importance of good turbomachinery design should now be apparent.

The high level of the turbine outlet temperature (1047°R) may come as a surprise, and it may seem that there should be some way to use this energy. We have to live within the restrictions of the second law, but it is possible to make some gains. We shall discuss these in the next section.

9·7 GAS POWER CYCLES

The pattern cycle for the gas-turbine power system studied in the previous section is known as the *Brayton cycle.* The hardware schematic and process representation for a closed Brayton-cycle system is shown in Fig. 9·14. In the idealized Brayton cycle the compressor and turbine processes are isentropic, and pressure drop across the heat exchangers is neglected. If the working fluid is treated as a perfect gas with constant specific heats, a simple expression for

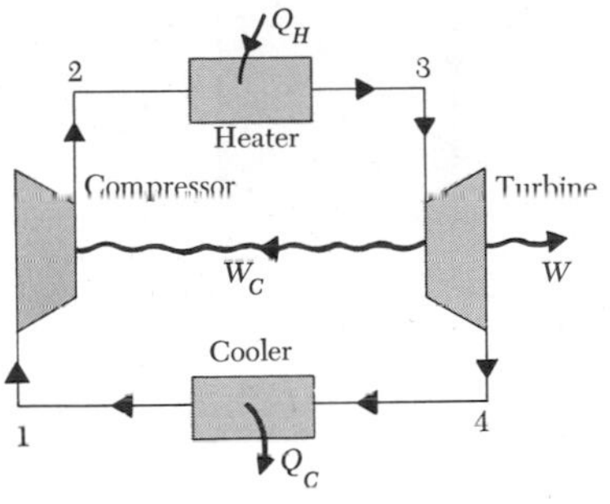

FIG. 9·14 *The Brayton cycle*

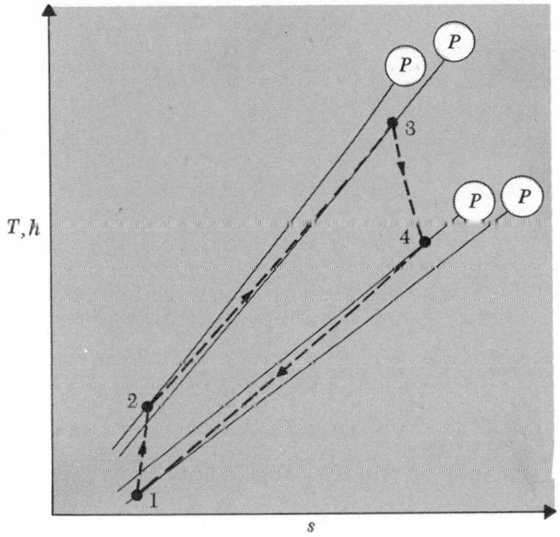

the energy-conversion efficiency may be obtained† in terms of the pressure ratio

$$\eta = 1 - \left(\frac{1}{P^*}\right)^{(k-1)/k} \tag{9·9}$$

where

$$P^* = \frac{P_2}{P_1} = \frac{P_3}{P_4}$$

This relationship for $k = 1.4$ is shown in Fig. 9·15. In particular, for the

† The development is as follows.

Energy balances: $W_T = c_P(T_3 - T_4)$, $W_C = c_P(T_2 - T_1)$, $Q_H = c_P(T_3 - T_2)$
Isentropic processes: $T_2/T_1 = T_3/T_4 = (P^*)^{(k-1)/k} = A$
Conversion efficiency:
$\eta = [(T_3 - T_4) - (T_2 - T_1)]/(T_3 - T_2) = (T_4A - T_4 - T_1A + T_1)/(T_4A - T_1A)$
$\eta = (T_4 - T_1)(A - 1)/[(T_4 - T_1)A] = 1 - 1/A$

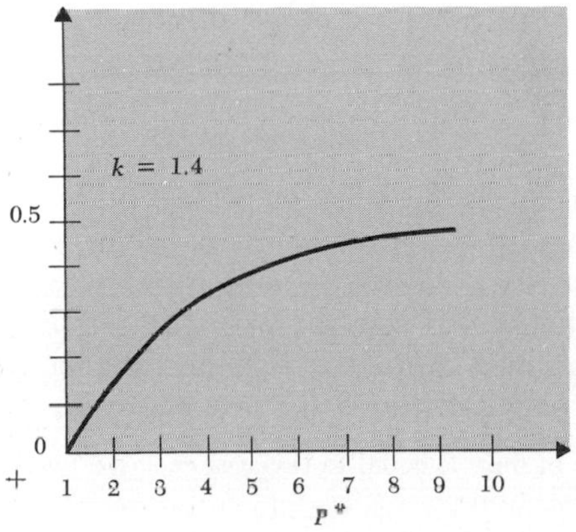

FIG. 9·15 *Idealized Brayton-cycle efficiency*

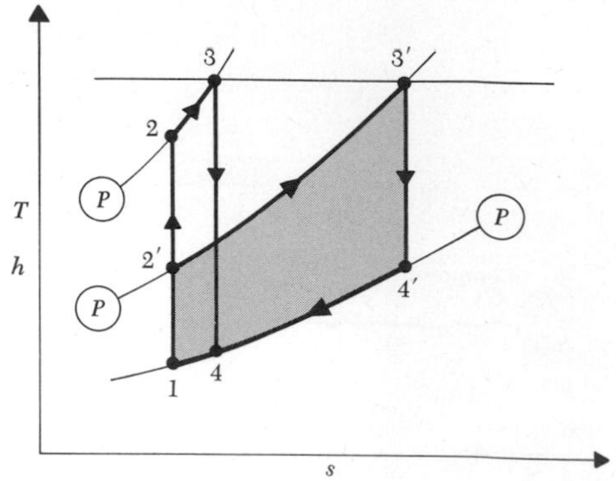

FIG. 9·16 *Two idealized Brayton cycles; the shaded cycle has a greater work output but a lower efficiency*

example of the last section, $P^* = 4$ and $\eta_{\text{ideal}} = 32.7$ percent, about twice what we obtained with the improved compressor. Note that high pressure ratios make the idealized Brayton cycle more efficient. However, compressor efficiency tends to drop off with increased pressure ratio, and this has a compensating effect in a real Brayton cycle. Pressure ratios in the range of 4 to 6 are typical of simple Brayton systems.

In gas-turbine systems intended for prime-mover use, it is usually important to keep engine weight small, which normally means maximizing the work output per lbm of fluid. Metallurgical considerations limit the turbine inlet temperature, and current systems operate at about 1600°F. Within this limitation there will be some pressure ratio which yields a maximum efficiency and another which yields the most work output per unit of mass of fluid, and these two ratios will not generally be the same. Figure 9·16 illustrates this in terms of the T-s process representation.† The primed cycle has a greater work output per unit of mass than does the high-pressure cycle, but a lower conversion efficiency. It may be shown that the pressure ratio yielding the most work per unit of mass for the idealized Brayton cycle of Fig. 9·16 is

$$P^*_{\text{opt}} = \left(\frac{T_3}{T_1}\right)^{k/[2(k-1)]} \tag{9·10}$$

Where a low power-weight ratio is desirable it will be necessary to operate away from the maximum efficiency point. Compromises of this sort continually arise in engineering.

The turbine exhaust temperature of a simple Brayton cycle is quite high; if it exceeds the compressor outlet temperature *regeneration* is possible, as shown in Fig. 9·17 (the ideal cycle is shown there). With a counterflow regenerator it is theoretically possible to heat the gas from state 2 to the temperature of state 5 with energy transferred as heat from the turbine exhaust gases. This would result in cooling of the exhaust gases to the compressor outlet

† Recall that the work output per lbm of fluid is equal to the area enclosed by the T-s process path for a *reversible* process.

temperature (state 2). Systems have been built in which more than 90 percent of the possible regenerative effect has been obtained. The amount of possible regeneration is the largest at low pressure ratios, and in contrast to the simple Brayton cycle, the regenerative cycle yields the highest efficiencies at low pressure ratios. It is much easier to build high-performance compressors and turbines for low pressure differences, and this fact makes the regenerative system even more attractive. Nuclear-powered gas-turbine systems employing regeneration have been built in the power range of 100–300 mw, and automotive and shipboard gas turbines that produce 300–3000 hp are now in use. Efficiencies in the range of 25–30 percent are typical with regeneration.

To illustrate the effect of regeneration, let us put a regenerator into the improved Brayton-cycle example of the previous section. We could conceivably warm the fluid leaving the compressor at 820°R to the turbine outlet temperature (1047°R), but this would require an immense heat exchanger. However, 85 percent of this maximum possible temperature rise could be obtained with a heat exchanger of reasonable size. We therefore assume that the high-pressure gas leaves the regenerator at $820 + 0.85 \times (1047 - 820) = 1013$°R. The heater power would then be reduced to

$$Q_H = 0.24 \times (1460 - 1013) = 107 \text{ Btu/lbm}$$

which would give an energy-conversion efficiency of $\eta = 27.6/107 = 0.26$, a 50 percent improvement over the nonregenerative system. Thus the regenerator would cut fuel costs by about 50 percent, and it is the development of compact and efficient regenerators which is allowing the gas-turbine engine to move into the competitive automotive market.

In larger gas-turbine power stations it is sometimes economical to employ *intercooling and reheat*. An idealized system with one intercooling stage and two stages of reheat is shown in Fig. 9·18. It may be shown from thermodynamic analysis that the total work of compression is less than for a single stage of compression for a given pressure ratio.† Intercooling between com-

† This may be seen graphically from the process representation of Fig. 9·18, since enthalpy changes are related to work input to an adiabatic compressor.

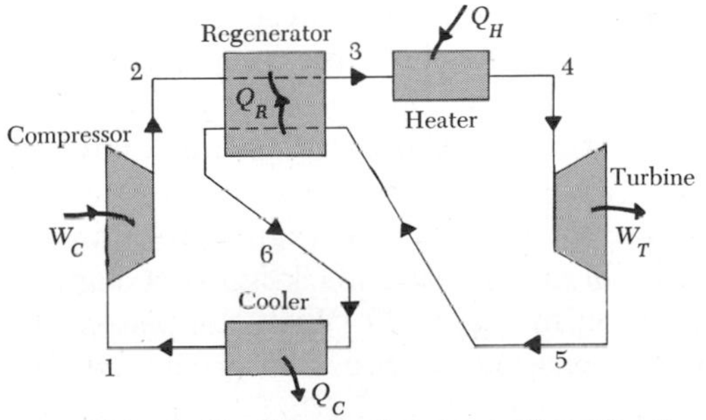

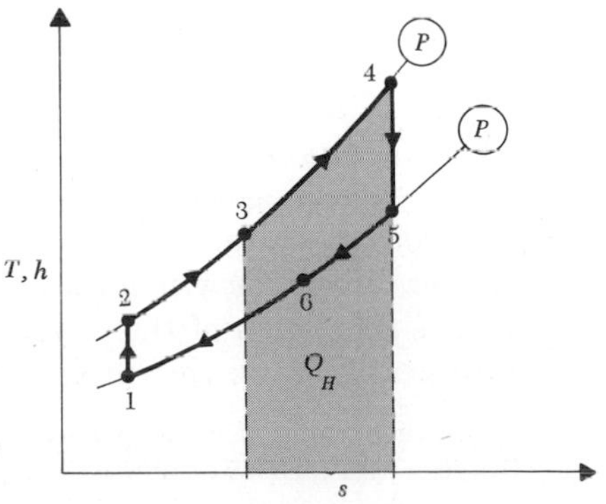

FIG. 9·17 *Idealized regenerative Brayton cycle*

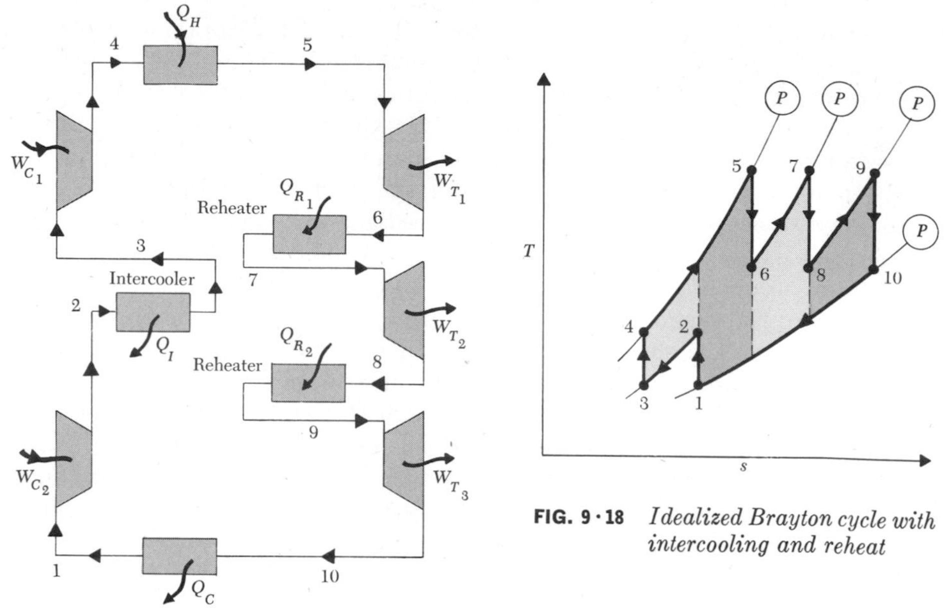

FIG. 9·18 *Idealized Brayton cycle with intercooling and reheat*

pressor stages therefore reduces the compressor work requirement. Similarly, reheat between the turbine stages increases the work output per unit of mass for a given pressure ratio and turbine inlet temperature. The net work output per unit of mass therefore is increased by intercooling and/or reheat. However, the efficiency of a Brayton cycle with intercooling and/or reheat is lower than the simple Brayton-cycle efficiency, for more energy must be added as heat.† Intercooling and reheat do serve to increase the potential for regeneration by increasing the final turbine outlet temperature and at the same time reducing the compressor outlet temperature. Intercooling and reheat are therefore usually used in conjunction with regeneration. In theory, if an infinite number of reheat and intercooling stages are employed, and regeneration is also used, all the energy added externally occurs in the reheat exchangers when the fluid is at its maximum temperature, and all the energy rejection as heat takes place in the intercoolers, where the gas is at its lowest temperature. Thus the limiting case is a $2T$ engine (ideally reversible) having an efficiency given by the Carnot-cycle efficiency (see Fig. 9·19). This is very interesting, for the process representation is quite unlike that of a Carnot cycle. The limiting cycle is also known as the *Ericsson cycle.*

The *Otto cycle* is the pattern cycle for reciprocating spark-ignition engines. The pressure of the gas within the cylinder of an idealized spark-ignition engine is shown as a function of the piston position in Fig. 9·20. With the piston at top dead center (tdc), the intake valve opens and a fresh charge of fuel-air

† Thinking graphically, the portions of the cycle that are "patched on" to the simple Brayton cycle are lower pressure-ratio cycles, and therefore are less efficient.

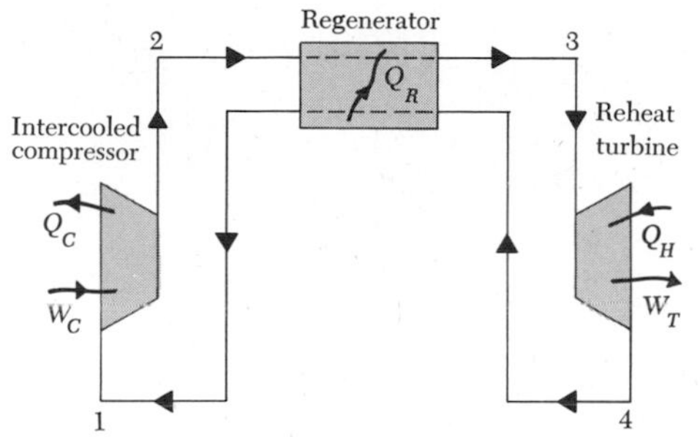

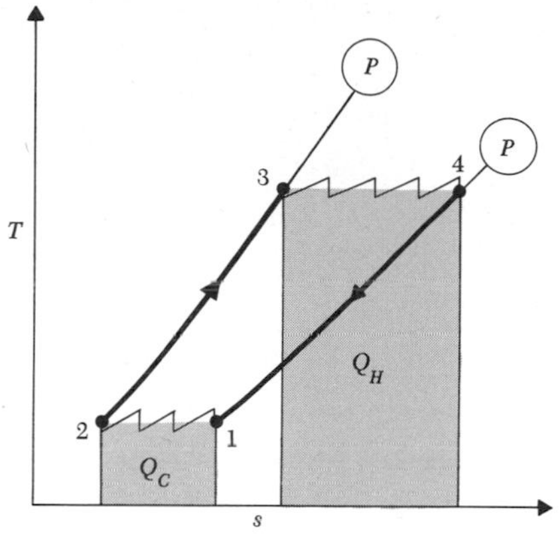

FIG. 9·19 *Idealized Brayton cycle with regeneration and infinite reheat and intercooling stages*

mixture is sucked in. At bottom dead center (bdc) the intake valve closes, and the return stroke causes the gas to be compressed. In the idealized system ignition occurs instantaneously at tdc, causing a rapid rise in temperature and pressure. The gas is then expanded on the outstroke, until at bdc the exhaust valve opens, and the gas "blows down" through the exhaust port. With a fourth stroke the gases are purged out. In the idealized Otto cycle the compression and expansion processes are considered reversible and adiabatic, that is, isentropic, and it is assumed that the pressure within the cylinder during the intake and exhaust strokes is equal to the atmospheric pressure. The work done by the piston on the gas inside the cylinder during the exhaust stroke is exactly equal to the work done on the piston by the gas during the intake stroke, so that useful work output results only from the excess of the work done by the

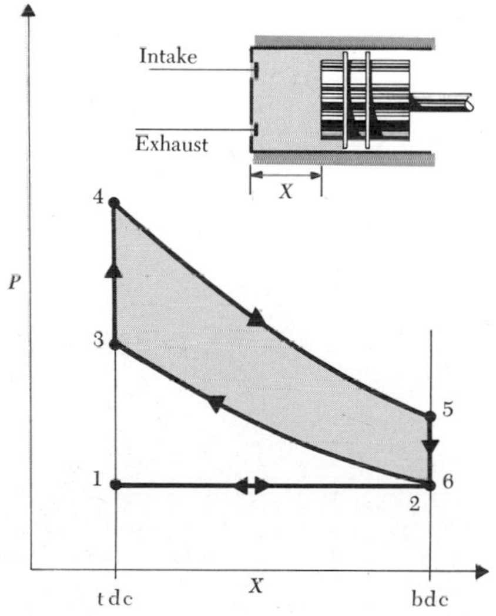

FIG. 9·20 *Pressures in an idealized spark-ignition engine*

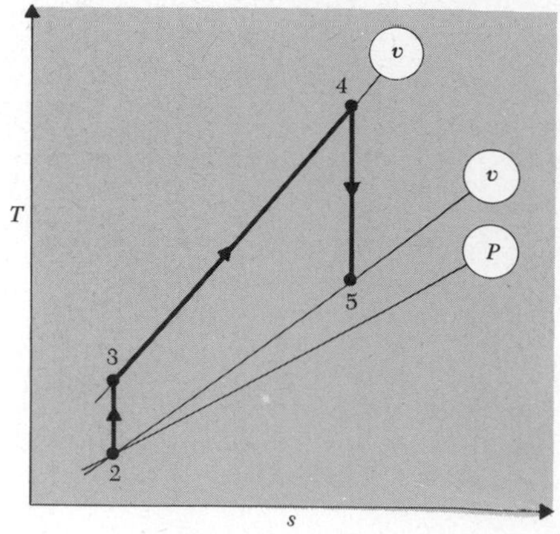

FIG. 9·21 *Idealized Otto-cycle process representation*

gas during the expansion stroke over that done on the gas during the compression stroke.

The process representation for the fluid during the compression, ignition, and expansion parts of the cycle is shown in Fig. 9·21. The combustion process is idealized in terms of a simple energy addition (as heat), and the changes in the chemical composition of the mixture are neglected. If it is further idealized that the gas is a perfect gas with constant specific heats, appropriate thermodynamic analysis leads to a simple algebraic expression for the efficiency of the Otto cycle in terms of the *compression ratio*,

$$\eta = \frac{W_{\text{net}}}{Q_{34}} = 1 - \frac{1}{r^{k-1}} \tag{9·11}$$

where the compression ratio r is

$$r = \frac{v_2}{v_3} = \frac{v_5}{v_4}$$

This relationship for $k = 1.4$ is shown in Fig. 9·22.

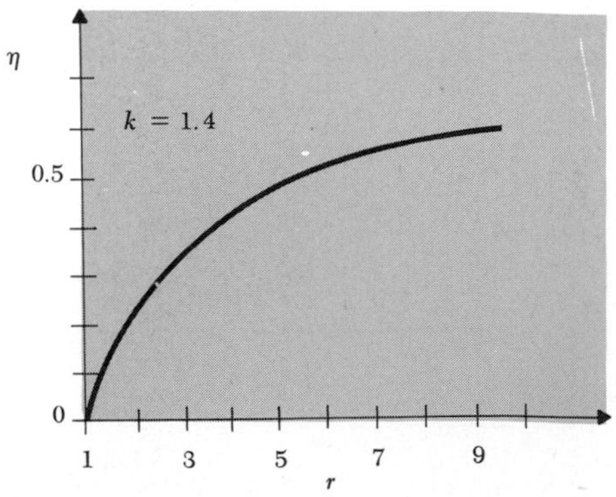

FIG. 9·22 *Otto-cycle efficiency*

A real spark-ignition engine will not meet the performance of the highly idealized Otto cycle. Combustion takes time, and for this reason it is initiated before tdc by "advancing the spark." Furthermore, there will be a pressure drop across the valve during intake and exhaust; the piston must do work on the air to get it out, and this is more than the work done on the piston by the cylinder gases during the intake stroke. Heat transfer is involved, so the compression and expansion processes are not isentropic. The pressure-displacement diagram of a realistic spark-ignition engine is shown in Fig. 9·23.

The *diesel cycle* is the pattern cycle for reciprocating compression-ignition engines. In the idealized system air is compressed to tdc, at which time fuel is injected, and it is idealized that the combustion process takes place at constant pressure for part of the expansion stroke. The remainder of the expansion stroke and the compression stroke are idealized as isentropic. The pressures within the cylinder of an idealized diesel engine are shown in Fig. 9·24. The process representation is shown in Fig. 9·25.

The efficiency of a diesel cycle may be worked out by thermodynamic analysis. If it is assumed that the gas is a perfect gas with constant specific heats, an algebraic expression for the efficiency is obtained in terms of the compression and cutoff ratios,

$$\eta = 1 - \frac{1}{r^{k-1}} \frac{r_c^k - 1}{k(r_c - 1)} \qquad (9 \cdot 12)$$

$$r = \frac{v_2}{v_3} \qquad \textit{compression ratio}$$

$$r_c = \frac{v_4}{v_3} \qquad \textit{cutoff ratio}$$

The idealized diesel-cycle efficiency is shown as a function of the compression and cutoff ratios in Fig. 9·26. Note that the efficiency for $r_c = 1$ is the same as for the Otto cycle, and that in general the diesel cycle has a lower efficiency than the Otto cycle operating at the same compression ratio.

Compression ratios of practical engines are limited by the pressures and temperatures that can be tolerated within the cylinders. In the spark-ignition engine combustion occurs as the gas is being compressed, while in the injection engines (compression-ignition) combustion begins as the gas is being expanded. As a result, diesel engines can operate at higher compression ratios (of the order of 15:1) than can spark-ignition engines (of the order of 8:1), and consequently can obtain comparable and even superior efficiencies.

A common modification on spark-ignition engines for aircraft operation is the *supercharger*, a steady-flow compressor used to compress the air before it enters the reciprocating engine. Supercharging an Otto engine will not improve its efficiency, which is only a function of its compression ratio. In fact, work must be provided to run the supercharger. However, the increase in density of the working fluid produced by the supercharger can result in greater

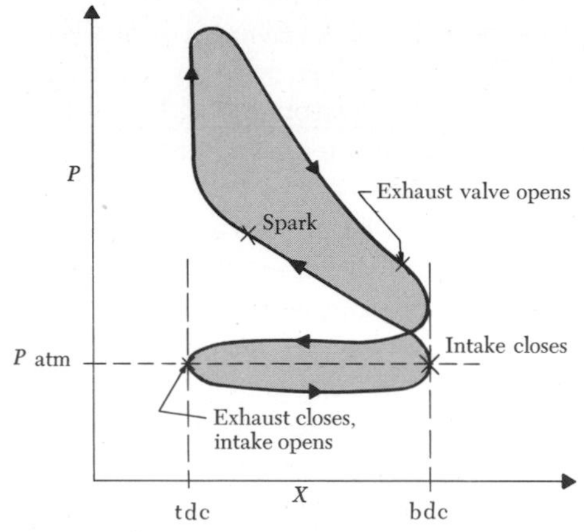

FIG. 9·23 *Pressures in a real spark-ignition engine*

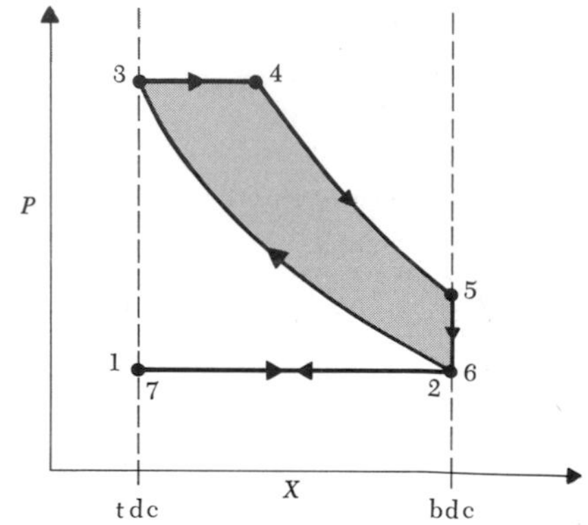

FIG. 9·24 *Pressures in an idealized diesel engine*

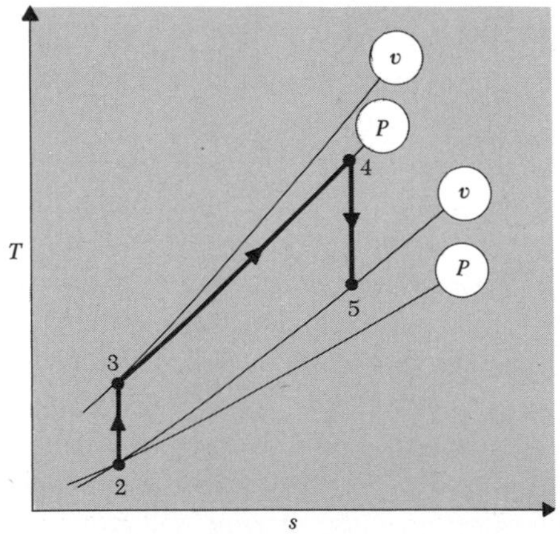

FIG. 9·25 *Idealized diesel-cycle process representation*

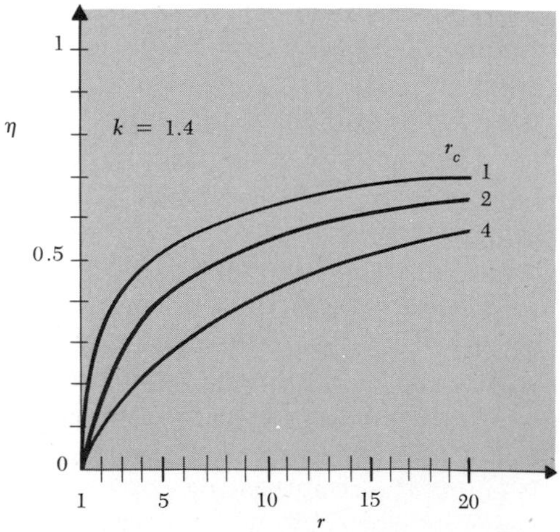

FIG. 9·26 *Idealized diesel-cycle efficiency*

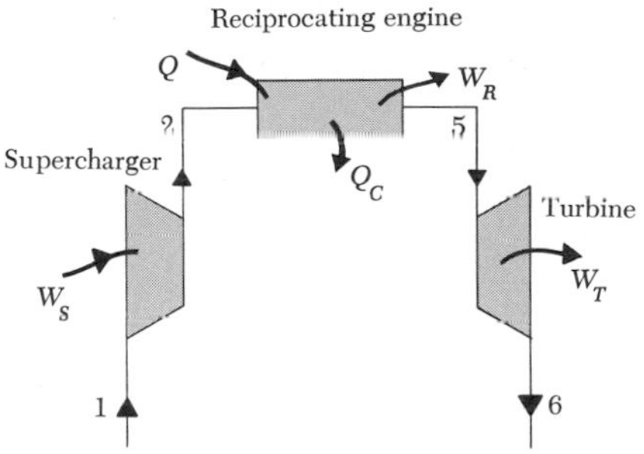

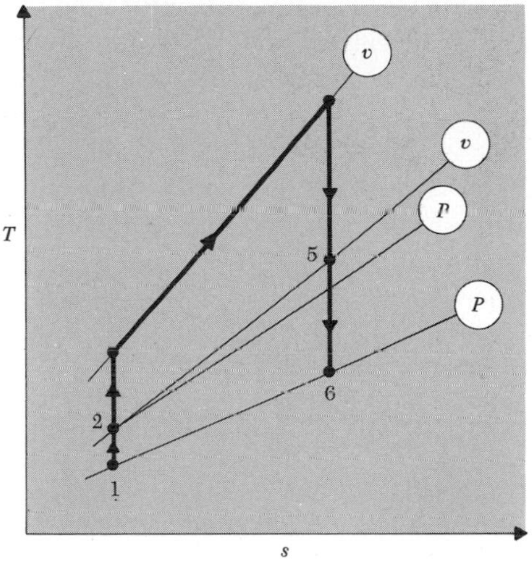

FIG. 9·27 *An idealized compound engine system*

power, since more fluid mass is circulated through the engine. The power-weight ratio is thereby increased. A second modification is the *exhaust turbine*. The pressure in the cylinder of an Otto-cycle engine at bdc is greater than atmospheric pressure, and consequently work can be obtained by passing the gases through a steady-flow turbine. The result is (ideally) an increase in efficiency, since the work obtained from the turbine is greater than that required to drive the compressor.† A flow diagram and a process representation for the idealized turbo-compound engine is shown in Fig. 9·27. Recently there has been considerable interest in turbosupercharging of diesel and spark-ignition engines.

† This may be seen easily by examining the *h-s* process representation for the turbo-supercharged cycle (Fig. 9·27), since the enthalpy changes are related to work for steady-flow adiabatic devices.

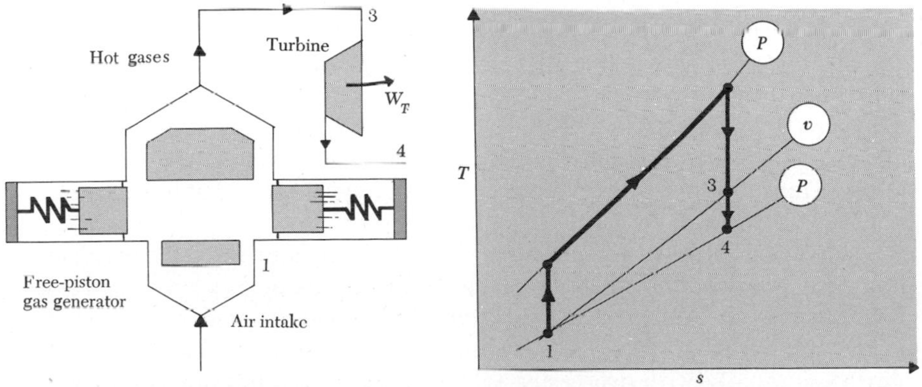

FIG. 9·28 *Idealized free-piston compound engine system*

Here a free-running turbine is used to drive the supercharger directly, and useful power is extracted solely from the reciprocating engine.

An interesting hybrid employs the *free-piston gas generator*. This device consists of a pair of free-floating pistons synchronized to move in opposition. Air is compressed between them as they move together, diesel fuel is injected and ignites spontaneously, and the hot high-pressure gases are exhausted through a power-producing turbine. The system schematic and process representation (idealized) are shown in Fig. 9·28. High isentropic efficiencies are more easily obtained with reciprocating (rather than steady-flow) compressors, and this is a practical advantage of the free-piston system.

9·8 DIRECT-ENERGY-CONVERSION SYSTEMS

The systems discussed in the previous sections may be used for generation of electrical power simply by coupling them to a generator. There is now considerable interest in direct-energy-conversion systems, which avoid the sequence of energy transfer from a heat source to a fluid to turbomachinery to a generator and finally to a load. Many schemes have been suggested, and some have been used for special types of application. As yet no large continuously operating direct-energy-conversion system is in service, though it does appear that this may not be too far in the future. Analyses of these newer systems requires competence in several areas, including thermodynamics, electromagnetics, fluid mechanics, and solid-state physics, and with a few exceptions they are beyond the scope of this text. However, we shall now discuss some of these schemes in a qualitative way, because they have definite importance in engineering.

If a fluid which is a good electrical conductor flows through a magnetic field, an electric field is induced in the fluid, and power can be obtained. Such a device is called a *magnetohydrodynamic* (mhd) *generator*. While liquid metals such as mercury could be used, ionized gases (plasmas) are much more practical for the job of converting internal energy to electricity. The mhd generators now in existence use the products of combustion of fossil fuels, seeded with easily ionized elements, such as cesium, to form the plasma. In the future we can expect to see much more energetic plasmas produced as a result of controlled-fusion reactions. The gas is pressurized, heated, and passed through a nozzle (this looks quite a bit like the Brayton cycle). The high-velocity gases are ducted through a magnetic field, and an electric field perpendicular to the applied magnetic field is developed. A closed-cycle mhd system powered by a nuclear reactor is shown in Fig. 9·29.

Irreversibilities due to friction, ohmic losses, and heat transfer severely limit the practicability of small mhd generators; the most promising use therefore appears to be in conjunction with large central power stations; plants in the 100-mw range have been studied. The electrical conductivity of the gas decreases rapidly with decreasing temperature, which imposes a major limitation on the minimum-operating-temperature range. If the temperature falls

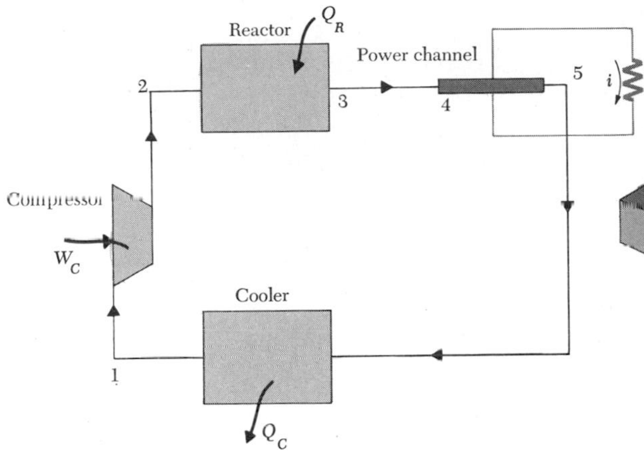

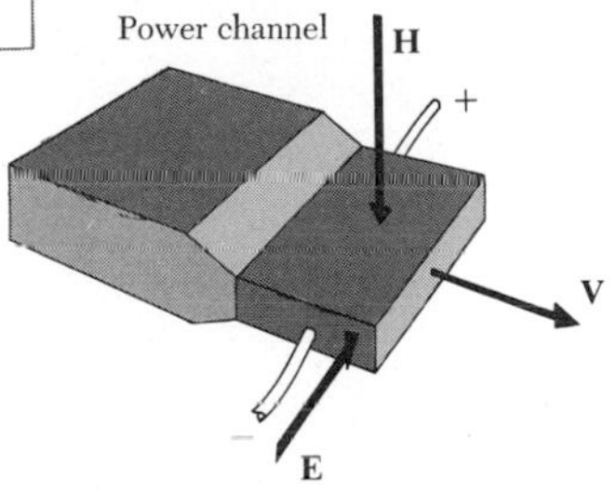

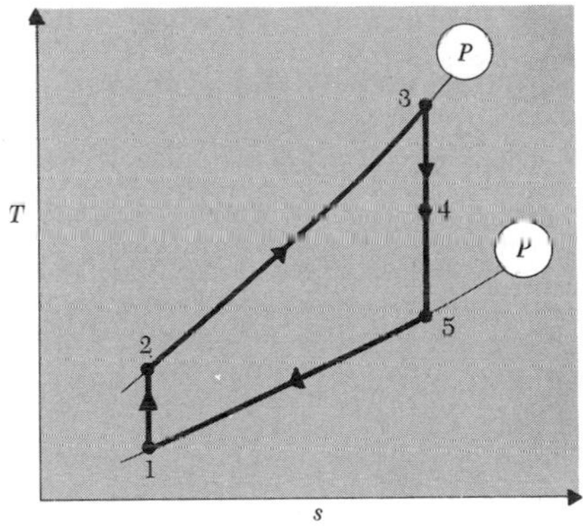

FIG. 9 · 29 *Idealized mhd power generator*

too low the gas will deionize, and the device will open-circuit. The mhd system is therefore best suited to high-temperature operation and looks very attractive as a potential topping system for a binary power plant.

Thermionic converters have recently come into use, particularly for space systems. The converter is essentially a diode, either evacuated or gas-filled. Energy transferred as heat to the cathode causes electrons to stream toward the colder anode, resulting in a flow of current. Energy must be transferred

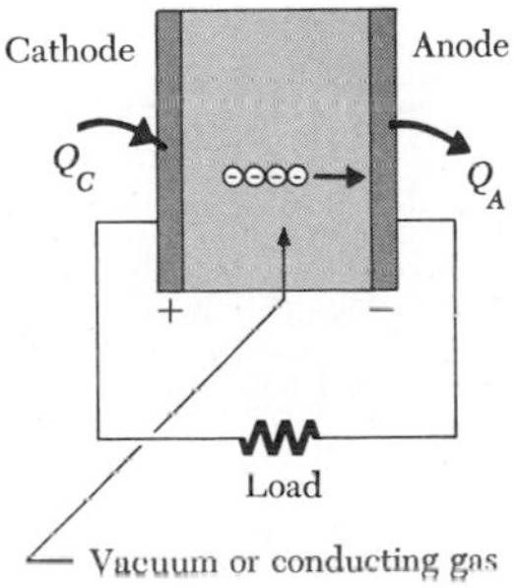

FIG. 9 · 30 *A thermionic generator*

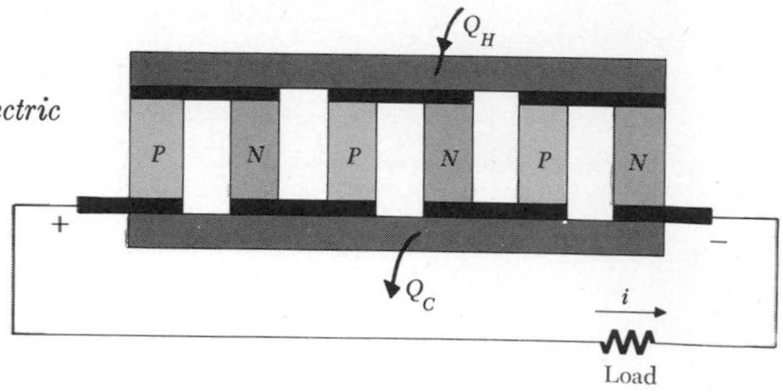

FIG. 9·31 *A thermoelectric converter*

as heat from the anode to maintain it at a suitably lower temperature. A thermionic converter is essentially a heat engine using electrons as the working fluid.

Vacuum diodes must have very close spacings (of the order of 0.02 mm), for otherwise the retarding potential arising from the distribution of electrons in the gap becomes too great for satisfactory operation. Diodes of this type have been operated with cathode temperatures of the order of 1500°K and with the anode at approximately 900°K, yielding power densities of the order of 2–10 watts/cm². The energy-conversion efficiency of these systems is of the order of 3–12 percent. The small spacings are difficult to maintain, especially with large cathode-anode temperature differences, and short-outs are frequent. The gas (plasma) diodes employ easily ionizable elements, such as cesium, whose positively charged ions tend to neutralize the retarding effects of the space charge, allowing larger spacings to be employed (1 mm). Efficiencies of the order of 15 percent have been obtained with this type of plasma diode operated at cathode temperatures of about 2500°K.

The thermionic converter is well suited for the production of electrical power in space from a nuclear-heat source. Since the energy which must be rejected as heat must be radiated to space, and high temperatures are required for low-weight radiators, space-systems designers can accept low efficiency in the interests of lightweight nonmechanical power-conversion equipment. The thermionic converter will probably also find application as a topping device for Rankine power systems.

An interesting type of direct-energy-conversion system already in use in space is the *thermoelectric converter*. A voltage difference will appear across the electrical loop formed by two dissimilar metals or semiconductors if the two junctions between them are kept at different temperatures, and power may then be obtained. Semiconductors are best suited for thermoelectric converters, and systems producing a few watts of power at efficiencies of 6–10 percent are reliable realities today.†

The *fuel cell* is a device in which a chemical reaction is harnessed directly to produce electrical power. Unlike a chemical battery, in which an electrolyte

† Thermoelectric converters powered by kerosene lamps are in wide use in the Soviet Union, chiefly as a power source for radio receivers.

is decomposed into its basic components, a fuel cell utilizes a controlled reaction between components such as hydrogen and oxygen. A schematic of a fuel cell is shown in Fig. 9·32. Gaseous hydrogen and oxygen at pressures of the order of 40 atm enter the cell and are brought into contact with porous electrodes. Between the electrodes is a liquid electrolyte, which serves to limit the reaction rate. Hydrogen diffuses through the porous anode, is absorbed on the surface, and then reacts with the OH^- ions in the electrolyte, forming water and yielding free electrons. Oxygen diffuses through the cathode, is absorbed by the surface, and reacts with the water to form OH^- ions. Thus water is continually being formed at the anode and decomposed at the cathode. The reaction rate is controlled by the rate of migration of OH^- ions through the electrolyte. Electrons flow out of the cell through a load and are returned to the cathode. The maximum cell emf is of the order of 1 volt and depends to a certain extent on the choice of reactants employed.

Fuel cells have been developed for operation in space vehicles and have many other possible applications. A major difficulty of present cells is the relatively short life span of the electrodes, especially when operated with relatively low-grade fuels. Their lifetime can be markedly increased by use of purified hydrogen, but the costs of the purifying operation are presently prohibitive from the standpoint of consumer use. The technology problems of fuel cells appear near resolution, however, and it now seems very likely that electric cars of the future will be powered by fuel cells.

The fuel cell is not a heat engine, and consequently the Carnot efficiency is an irrelevant maximum for fuel-cell performance. However, given a supply of hydrogen and oxygen, more useful power can be obtained with a fuel cell than if the gases were allowed to react spontaneously and a Carnot cycle were run

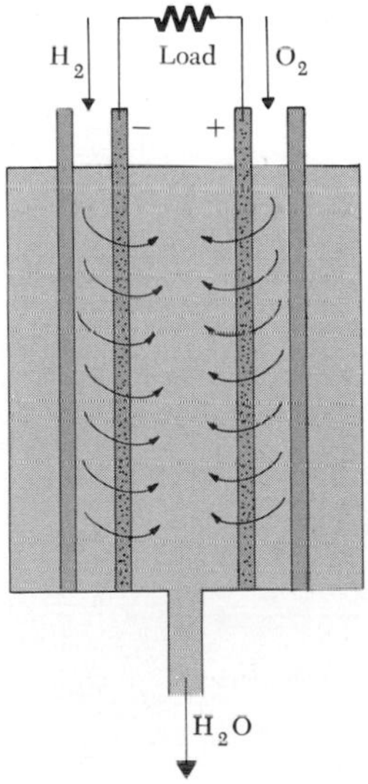

FIG. 9·32 *A fuel cell*

from the high-temperature flame. This is because the voltage of the cell tends to restrain the chemical reaction, much as a piston restrains spontaneous expansion of a gas. A detailed fuel-cell analysis is given in Chap. Eleven.

9·9 THERMAL TRANSFER CYCLES

The Carnot refrigerator and heat pump are two examples of *thermal transfer cycles;* they can (in principle) be used to remove energy as heat from a low-temperature region and transfer a larger amount of energy as heat to a higher temperature region. The Carnot refrigerator provides a useful theoretical limit, but it is not a pattern cycle for any practical refrigeration systems.†

The *vapor-compression refrigeration cycle* is the pattern cycle for the great majority of commercially available refrigeration systems. Its hardware schematic and process representations are shown in Fig. 9·33. The fluid must be evaporated at a temperature lower than that of the cold space and condensed at a temperature higher than that of the warm space. The cycle is almost the reverse of the Rankine power cycle; the difference is that a valve is used to produce the pressure drop, and no attempt is made to extract useful work from

† The magnetic refrigerator does have the Carnot cycle as its pattern cycle, but at present this is more a laboratory tool than a practical device.

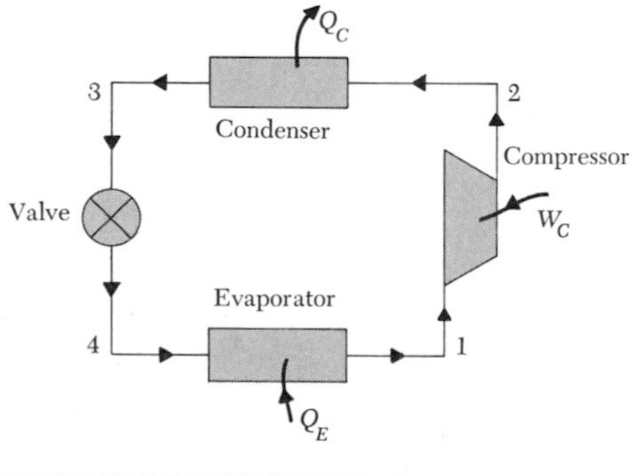

FIG. 9·33 *Vapor-compression refrigeration system*

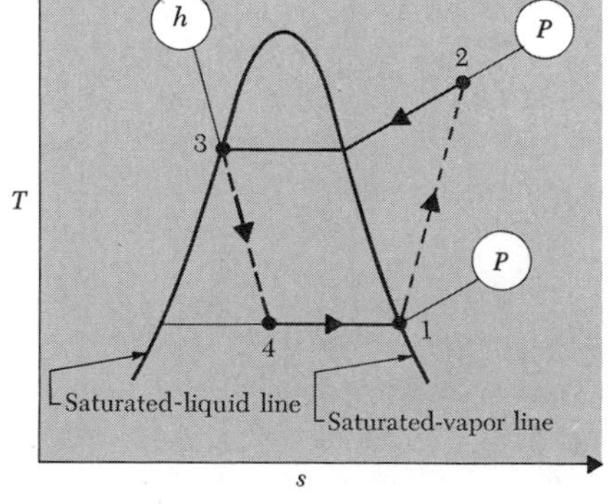

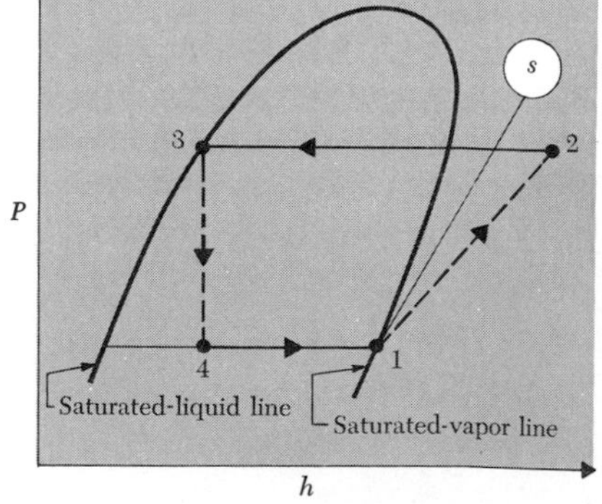

this expansion. The amount of work that could be obtained were the valve replaced by an isentropic turbine would be small in comparison with the compressor work requirement, since the volume changes are quite different. Furthermore, the quality of the mixture at state 4 is normally very low, and it is difficult to make a turbine operate for very long in this range. With the valve, the cycle can never be reversible, since the throttling process is inherently irreversible.

The coefficients of performance of refrigerators and heat pumps are strongly dependent on "lift" (temperature difference between the hot and cold spaces). Household refrigerators have cop values of the order of 4. Devices with higher lift will tend to have lower cop's.

Industrial refrigeration systems employ many variations of the simple cycle of Fig. 9·33. Particularly common is the multiple-evaporator system (Fig. 9·34). It is used in situations where simultaneous refrigeration at two or more temperature levels is desired.

An interesting application of vapor-compression refrigeration is in the production of liquid oxygen. The simplified system diagram and process representation for one type of lox plant are shown in Fig. 9·35.

The *vacuum refrigeration system* can be employed when refrigeration at temperatures slightly above 32°F is desired. In this system a steam ejector replaces the compressor, and the only moving parts are the pump impellers. The ejector maintains the flash chamber at a low pressure, where the saturation temperature is at the desired low level. The system schematic and process representation (idealized) are shown in Fig. 9·36.

The reverse of the Brayton cycle can be used as a refrigeration cycle, and

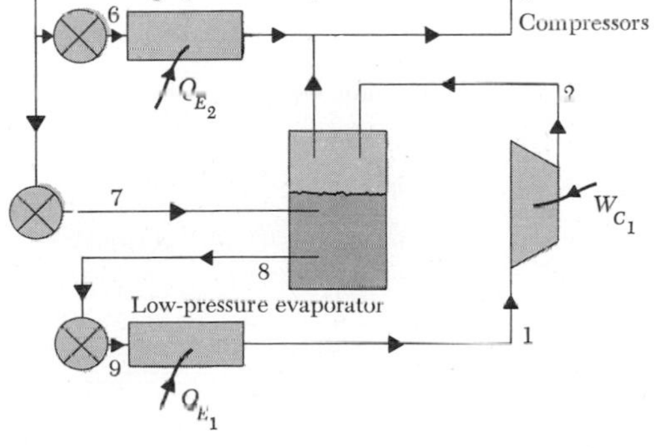

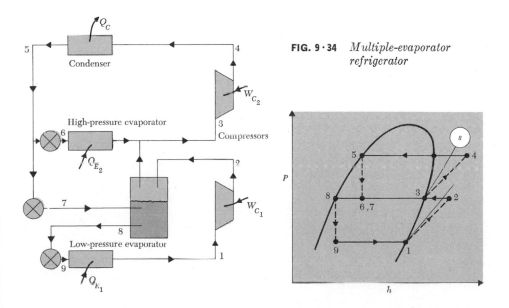

FIG. 9·34 *Multiple-evaporator refrigerator*

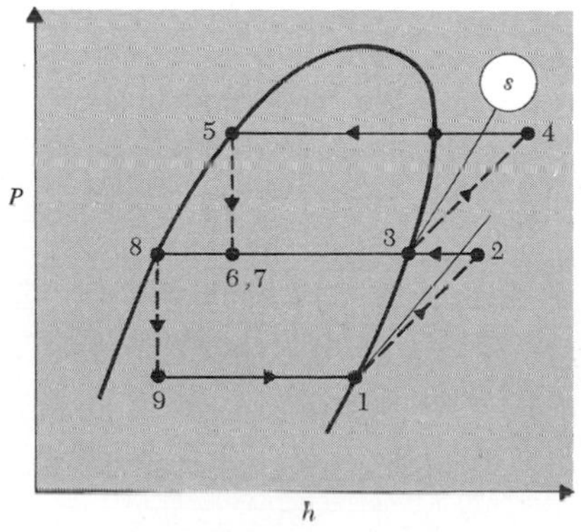

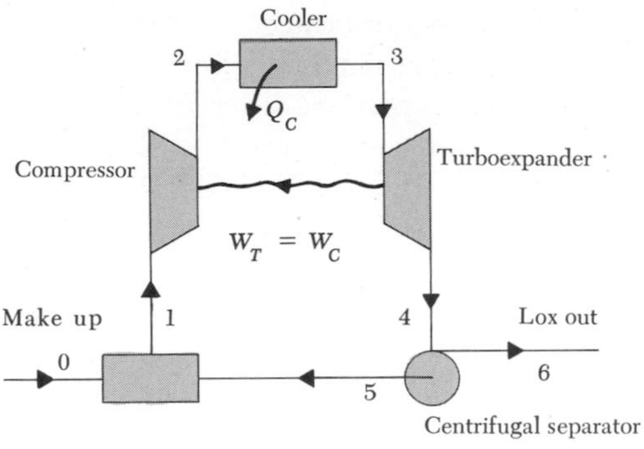

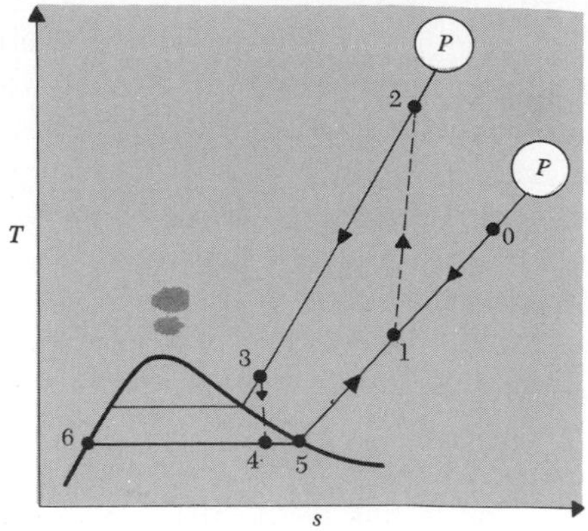

FIG. 9·35 *Oxygen liquefaction*

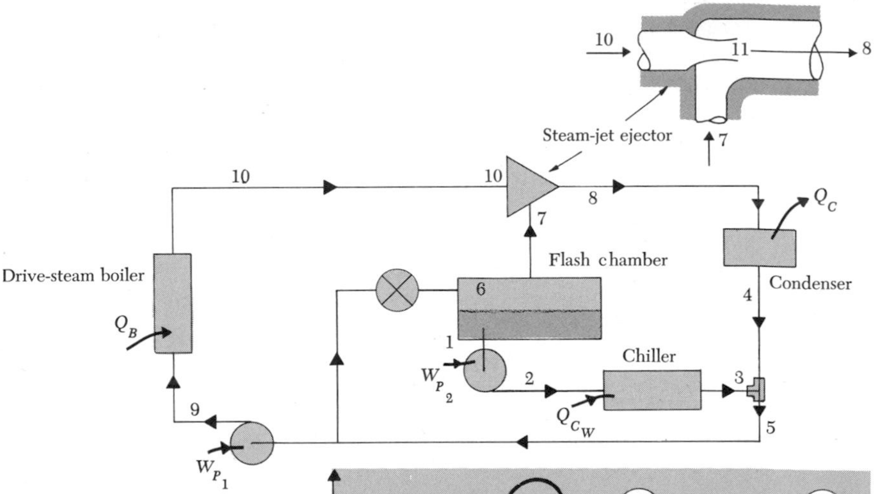

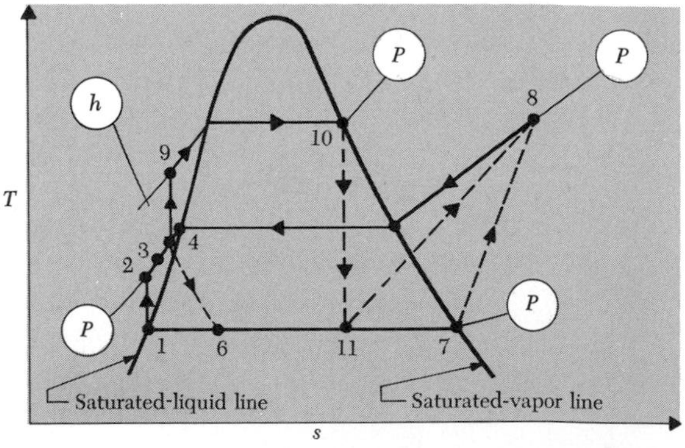

FIG. 9·36 *A vacuum refrigeration system*

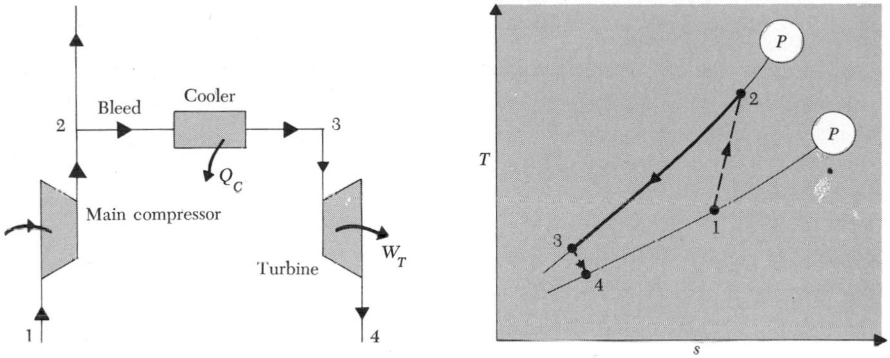

FIG. 9 · 37 *Air-cycle refrigeration*

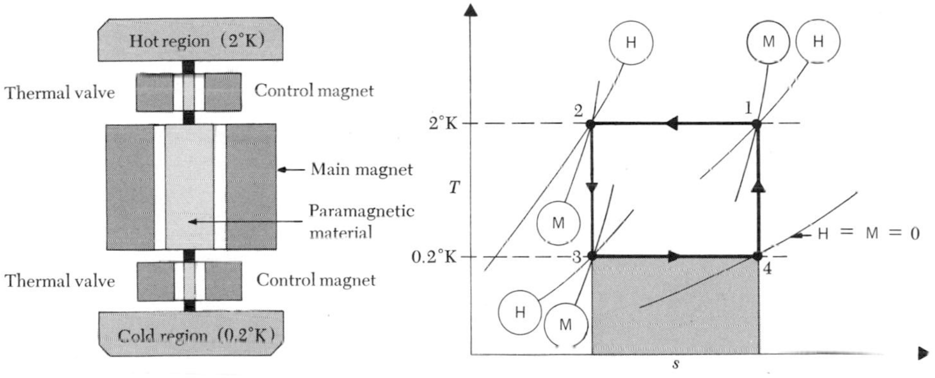

FIG. 9 · 38 *Low-temperature magnetic refrigeration*

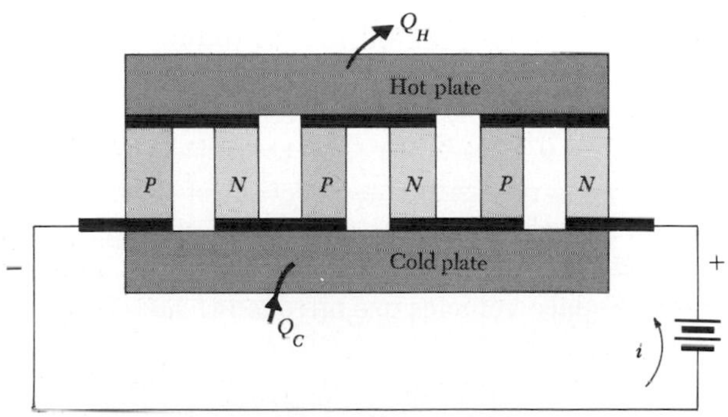

FIG. 9 · 39 *A thermoelectric refrigerator*

such systems are in common use aboard jet aircraft. Air is bled from the discharge of the main-engine compressor and expanded through a small turbine. The shaft power from the turbine is usually used to drive the fans circulating air through the cabin. The flow schematic and process representation (idealized) for this *air-cycle refrigeration system* are shown in Fig. 9·37.

Magnetic refrigerators taking advantage of the magnetic and superconducting properties of materials at low temperatures have been built for laboratory use.† A sample of material is magnetized slowly while in contact with the "high-temperature" region, then suddenly (adiabatically) demagnetized, then demagnetized slowly while in contact with the low-temperature region, and finally magnetized adiabatically, returning to the initial state. Contact with the low- and high-temperature regions is made through superconductors. Lead is an electrical superconductor at low temperatures and a very poor thermal conductor. If a small field (only a few hundred gauss) is applied to the lead, it undergoes a transition to a normal electrical conduction state, in which it is a good thermal conductor. A "thermal valve" can thereby be made. The schematic diagram and process representation for this type of magnetic refrigerator are shown in Fig. 9·38. The processes undergone by the magnetic substance are in the limit reversible, so that the limiting behavior is that of a Carnot cycle.

Another type of nonmechanical refrigeration system is the *thermoelectric refrigerator* (see Fig. 9·39). Application of an electric potential to a current loop formed from two dissimilar metals (or semiconductors) gives rise to a temperature difference between the two junctions. Energy may be transferred as heat to the loop at one junction and from the loop at the other, giving rise to a refrigeration effect. Recently a patent‡ was issued for an electric blanket employing thermoelectric elements which can, in principle, be used either for heating or cooling. Unfortunately, rather high amperage direct currents are presently required, and it is questionable just when such a blanket might become a consumer good.

9·10 A SIMPLE THRUSTING SYSTEM

Thermodynamics plays an important role in the analysis of propulsion systems. Let us consider one of the simpler types of thrust producers, shown in Fig. 9·40. Gas at high pressure is bled from a storage bottle to a plenum chamber, from which it is exhausted through a nozzle. The pressure forces acting on the chamber walls are shown in Fig. 9·40*b*. Note that there is a net force which would tend to accelerate the walls opposite the direction of flow. This type of *blowdown thruster* is used in low-thrust situations where simplicity and reliability are key factors and where propellant weight is not vital. The attitude-control systems of our current space vehicles use nitrogen thrusters in the range 1–100 lbf.

† C. V. Heer, et al., *Rev. Sci. Instr.*, vol. 25, no. 11, p. 1088.
‡ Patent no. 3080723.

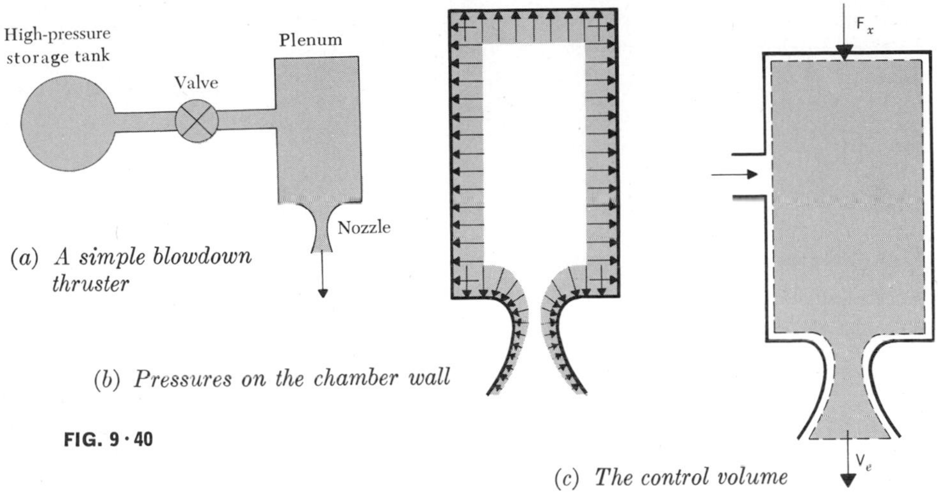

(a) *A simple blowdown thruster*

(b) *Pressures on the chamber wall*

(c) *The control volume*

FIG. 9·40

The thrust of a propulsion system is the force which the fluids exert on the container as a result of nonuniformities in pressure distribution. Examination of Fig. 9·40*b* would indicate that this force is roughly P_0A_t, where P_0 is the chamber, or *stagnation*, pressure, and A_t is the throat area of the nozzle. An exact calculation of thrust requires application of the *momentum principle* to a control volume surrounding the gas and cutting across the exit plane of the nozzle. The momentum principle is a generalization of Newton's law arising from a control-volume transformation. We shall omit the development and merely give the result of this transformation in Table 9·1. Here $\dot{\mathcal{P}}_M$ denotes the *rate of production of momentum*, as defined in the table.

Let us now apply the momentum principle to the control volume of Fig. 9·40*c*, assuming that the system is steady flow steady state, one-dimensional at

TABLE 9·1 THE MOMENTUM PRINCIPLE

System	*Momentum equation*
Isolated system	$\dot{\mathcal{P}}_M = \dfrac{d(\mathbf{Mom})}{dt} = 0$
Control mass	$\dot{\mathcal{P}}_M = \dfrac{d(\mathbf{Mom})}{dt} = g_c\mathbf{F}$
Control volume	$\dot{\mathcal{P}}_M = \dfrac{d(\mathbf{Mom})}{dt} + \sum_{\text{out}} \dot{M}\mathbf{V} - \sum_{\text{in}} \dot{M}\mathbf{V} = g_c\mathbf{F}$

Mom is total momentum of matter within the system. **V** is the momentum of a unit mass of matter crossing the boundaries. **F** is the total force exerted on the control volume.

the inlet and exit planes, and fixed in space. We write the momentum equation for the x direction, since this is the component of force we seek. The entering fluid has no momentum in this direction, and the rate of storage of momentum $d(\mathbf{Mom})/dt$ is zero by the steady-flow steady-state and no-acceleration idealizations. The only terms remaining are

$$\dot{M}\mathsf{V}_e = g_c(\mathsf{F}_x - P_e A_e)$$

Here F_x is the force exerted by the walls on the fluid, and $P_e A_e$ is the force acting across the exit plane. Often the exit pressure force is negligible, and

$$\mathsf{F}_x \approx \frac{\dot{M}\mathsf{V}_e}{g_c} \tag{9·13}$$

Thermodynamics becomes involved when we want to calculate the discharge velocity in order to determine the thrust. Consider the control volume of Fig. 9·41. We assume that the flow is steady, one-dimensional, and adiabatic, and that the kinetic energy of the fluid in the plenum chamber is negligible. An energy balance then gives

$$h_0 = h + \frac{\mathsf{V}^2}{2g_c} \tag{9·14}$$

Let us further assume that the fluid is a perfect gas with constant specific heats. Then, using Eq. (8·45), we can relate the chamber (stagnation) temperature T_0 to the temperature and velocity at any flow section and express the result as

$$\frac{T}{T_0} = 1 - \frac{\mathsf{V}^2}{2g_c c_P T_0} \tag{9·15}$$

If we further idealize that the process undergone by the fluid is isentropic, then from Eq. (8·46b) we have

$$\frac{P}{P_0} = \left(\frac{T}{T_0}\right)^{k/(k-1)} = \left(1 - \frac{\mathsf{V}^2}{2g_c c_P T_0}\right)^{k/(k-1)} \tag{9·16}$$

The process representation is shown in Fig. 9·41.

The dynamics and thermodynamics, plus conservation of mass, allow complete analysis of this thrusting system. Equations (9·14) and (9·15) hold at any section of the flow (provided our idealizations are reasonable), and in particular at the exit plane. They tell us that the more the gas is expanded in the nozzle, the higher will be the exit velocity, and consequently the greater will be the thrust.

As an example, suppose we consider a system with $P_e/P_0 = 0.1$ and a stagnation temperature of 80°F. For nitrogen $k = 1.4$ and $c_P = 0.24$ Btu/lbm-°F,

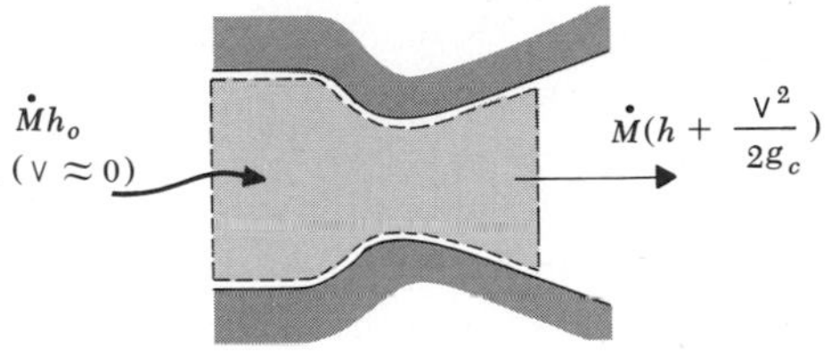

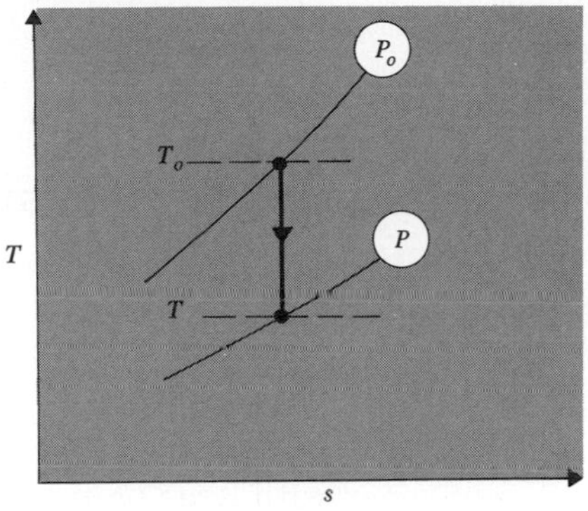

FIG. 9·41 *The thermodynamic analyses*

so the temperature at the exit plane would be†

$$T = T_0\left(\frac{P}{P_0}\right)^{(k-1)/k} = 540 \times 0.1^{0.286} = 279°\text{R}$$

The exit velocity may now be calculated from Eq. (9·15),

$$\mathsf{V} = \sqrt{2 \times 32.2 \times 0.24 \times 540 \times (1 - {}^{279}\!/_{540}) \times 778} = 1770 \text{ ft/sec}$$

The thrust calculation would require knowledge of the mass-flow rate. A useful measure of the performance of a propulsion system is the *specific impulse,* or thrust force per unit of mass-flow rate. For our system

$$SI = \frac{\mathsf{F}_x}{\dot{M}} \approx \frac{\mathsf{V}_e}{g_c}$$

so

$$SI = \frac{1770}{32.2} = 55 \text{ lbf/(lbm/sec)}$$

Hence, a 25-lbf nozzle will require about 0.5 lbm of nitrogen per thrusting second.

Inspection of Eq. (9·16) indicates that there is a limit on the velocity which can be obtained by isentropic expansion of a gas. Since the pressure cannot fall below zero,

$$\mathsf{V}_{\max} = \sqrt{2g_c c_P T_0}$$

which for our case amounts to 2540 ft/sec. Thus the best specific impluse we could hope to obtain with the blowdown thruster is of the order of 80 lbf/(lbm/sec). We see that higher specific impulse with a gaseous flow requires higher stagnation temperatures. In the next section we shall examine the per-

† This extreme cold would tend to freeze any water vapor in the gas, and such little ice crystals are believed to be the cause of the "fireflies" seen by astronauts.

formance of some more powerful propulsion systems, indicating the sorts of specific impulses that they attain.

9·11 THERMAL THRUSTING SYSTEMS

The earliest thrusting systems for aircraft propulsion were merely propellers driven by internal-combustion engines. The turboprop engine, used aboard commercial cargo aircraft, is an open-cycle gas-turbine engine in which the turbine drives the propeller.

The attainment of higher speed flight requires higher jet velocities than can be obtained with large propellers, and the turbojet engine has become the workhorse of larger commercial and military aircraft. It is essentially a gas-turbine plant in which the turbine-power output is just sufficient to drive the compressor. The turbine exhaust is fed to a nozzle from which the flow is discharged at high velocity. A system schematic and idealized process representation are shown in Fig. 9·42. Military aircraft employ an afterburner, which is essentially a reheat device (Fig. 9·43). The afterburner provides greater nozzle-exhaust velocities and substantially increases the engine thrust. Specific impulses of the order of 60 lbf/(lbm/sec) are typical for modern jet engines. The afterburner increases this somewhat but greatly increases fuel consumption, and consequently, afterburners are "cut in" only for short periods of high thrust.

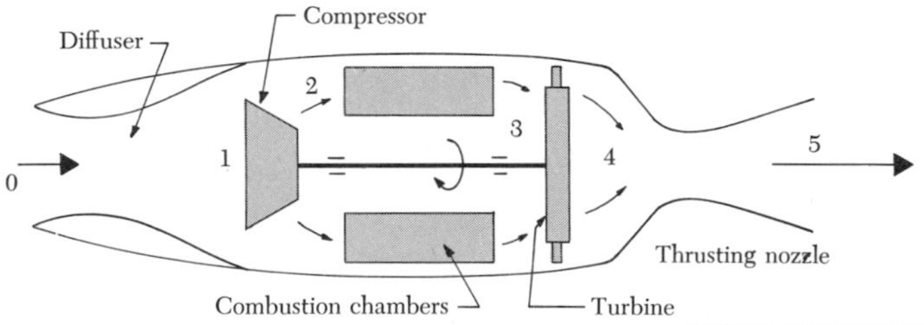

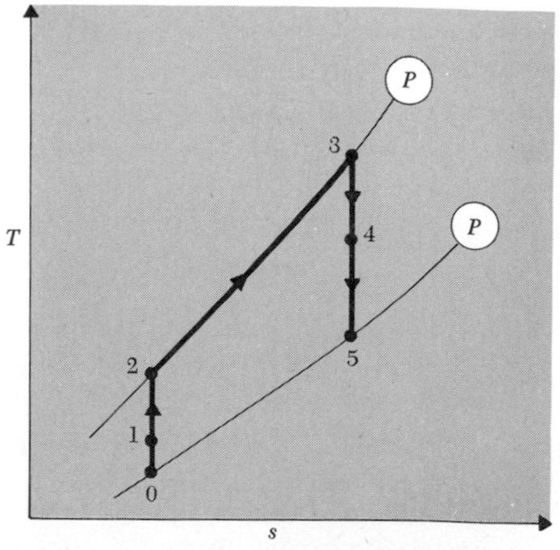

FIG. 9·42 *An idealized turbojet engine*

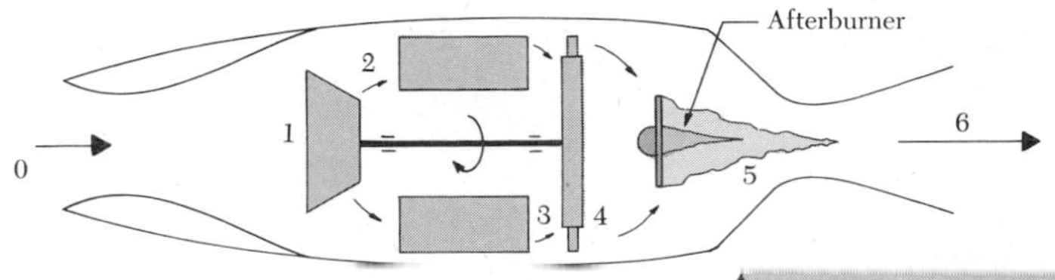

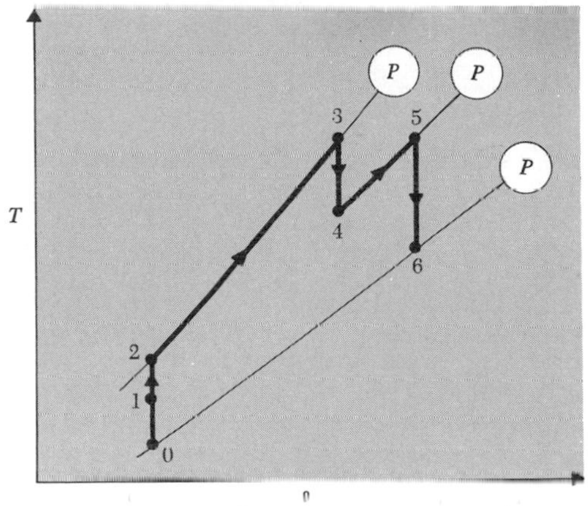

FIG. 9 · 43 *Idealized turbojet engine with afterburner*

The choice of a propulsion system for aircraft involves many factors. Propeller systems are best suited to low-speed flight (300 mph); these engines derive their thrust by accelerating relatively large amounts of air to a modest velocity. In contrast, high-speed aircraft are best powered by jet engines, which provide thrust by accelerating smaller amounts of air to much higher velocities. In the high subsonic range (600 mph) the hybred *turbofan engine* has proven the best choice where fuel economy is a prime factor. The turbofan is a jet engine which derives additional thrust from a *ducted propeller*, or *bypass fan*, which is driven off the main turbine shaft. The amount of thrust contributed by the two streams can be adjusted by varying the ratio of the bypass air-flow rate to the engine air-flow rate, and an optimum design thereby

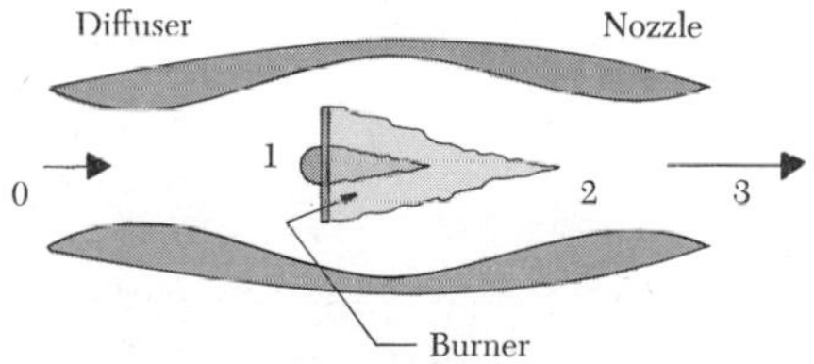

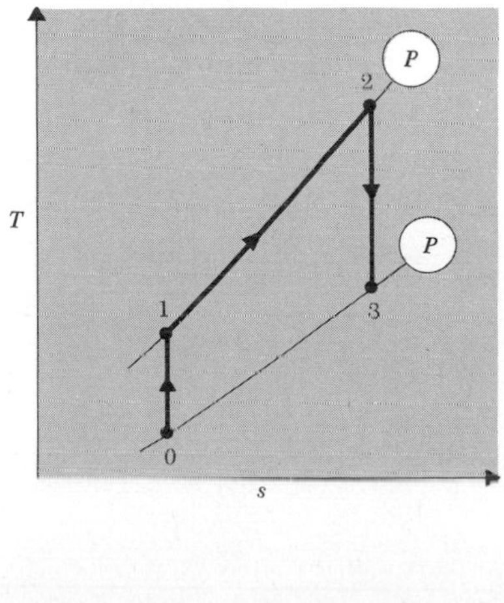

FIG. 9 · 44 *An idealized ramjet engine*

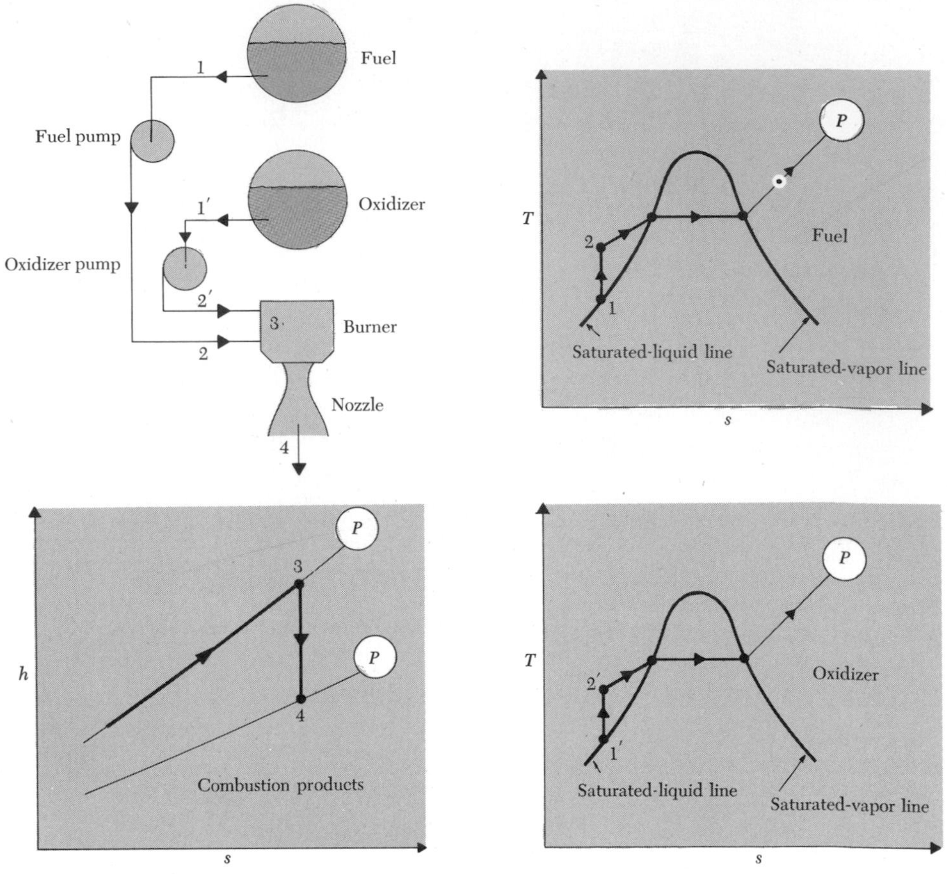

FIG. 9·45 *A chemical-rocket engine*

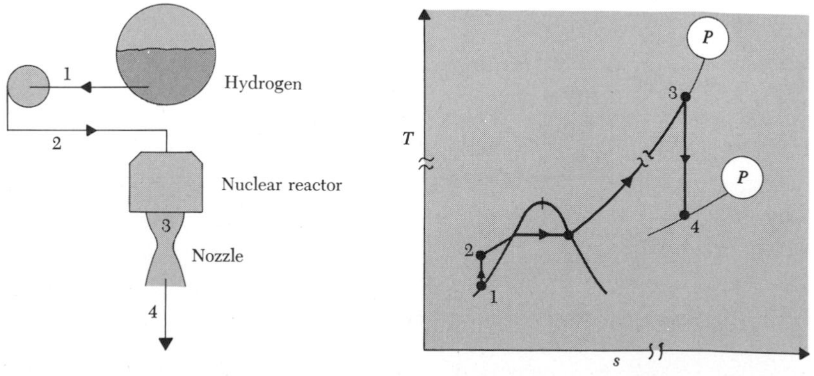

FIG. 9·46 *The hydrogen-rocket engine*

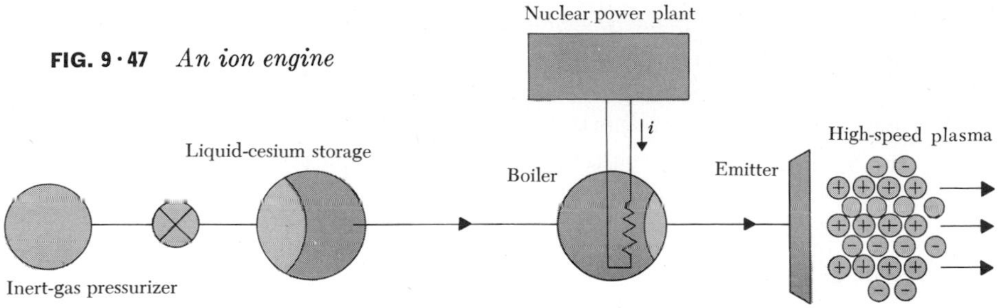

FIG. 9·47 *An ion engine*

obtained for any particular type of mission. Bypass ratios in the range 0.5–2.5 are typical of current systems.

The *ramjet* is a carefully designed flow passage that uses the momentum of the onrushing air for compression, thereby entirely eliminating any moving parts. The aircraft must already be flying at a considerable speed before the ramjet engine can be started. Commercial supersonic transport craft may eventually employ turbojet engines for takeoff, ascent, descent, and landing and switch to ramjets for high-altitude supersonic cruising. A system schematic and process representation are shown in Fig. 9·44. Ideally the diffuser process is isentropic, but boundary-layer separation on the diffuser walls makes it difficult to achieve high isentropic efficiency in real supersonic diffusers.

Chemical-rocket engines are essentially open Rankine cycles in which the turbine is replaced by a rocket nozzle. Since a chemical rocket carries its own oxidizer, it is especially well suited for operation in space. Chemical rockets have specific impulses in the range of 180–250 lbf/(lbm/sec). A system schematic and highly idealized process representation are shown in Fig. 9·45.

It may be shown that the highest specific impulse is obtained for the lightest possible particles. Hydrogen has therefore been studied in conjunction with a nuclear-reactor energy source, and it appears that specific impulses of the order of 900 lbf/(lbm/sec) can be obtained. The nuclear hydrogen rocket will probably become an important engine for future space flights.

Ion engines offer the possibility of high specific impulses and will probably be used on long-term space voyages. An easily ionized element, such as cesium, is evaporated and then brought into contact with a suitable high-temperature surface. Electrons are removed at the surface, and the cesium ions and electrons are accelerated by appropriate electric fields and then mixed to form a neutral beam which is shot from the end of the engine. Specific impulses of the order of 10,000 lbf/(lbm/sec) are possible. A schematic of a proposed ion engine is shown in Fig. 9·47.

SELECTED READING

Lee, J., and F. Sears, *Thermodynamics*, 2d ed., chaps. 11–13, Addison-Wesley Publishing Co., Inc., Reading, Mass., 1962.

Obert, E., and R. Gaggioli, *Thermodynamics*, 2d ed., chaps. 15, 17, and 18, McGraw-Hill Book Company, New York, 1963.

Van Wylen, G., and R. Sonntag, *Fundamentals of Classical Thermodynamics*, chap. 9, John Wiley & Sons, Inc., New York, 1965.

Wark, K., *Thermodynamics*, chaps. 16 and 17, McGraw-Hill Book Company, New York, 1966.

QUESTIONS

9·1 What is the significance of the area under a line on a T-s plane?

9·2 Derive the Carnot-cycle efficiency from things which you remember.

9·3 What is an isentropic process? What processes might reasonably be idealized as isentropic?

9·4 What is an isentropic efficiency?

9·5 Give an argument for idealizing a steady-flow heating process as isobaric.

9·6 To what matter does the process representation of Fig. 9·3 pertain?

9·7 What is the reason for using reheat in a Rankine cycle?

9·8 How do the back-work ratios (work input-work output) of the Rankine and Brayton cycles compare?

9·9 What is the reason for using a topping cycle?

9·10 What is the reason for supercharging an engine?

9·11 Why do intercooling and reheat lower the efficiency of a nonregenerative gas-turbine power system?

9·12 Explain with the aid of process representations why nonregenerative gas-turbine systems operate at higher pressure ratios than regenerative systems.

9·13 Is the thermoelectric converter a thermodynamic system?

9·14 What is the function of the valve in a vapor refrigeration system?

9·15 Can the cop of a heat pump ever exceed unity?

9·16 What is an afterburner?

9·17 Why does a ramjet not have a turbine?

9·18 What is a turboprop engine?

9·19 Why do jet engines have diffusers at the inlet?

9·20 Is a high or a low pressure ratio most desirable for a jet engine?

9·21 Can regeneration be used in jet engines?

9·22 Why does the hydrogen engine have a higher specific impulse than a chemical rocket?

9·23 Why is the ion engine not being considered for launchings, but being planned for long-term inflight propulsion?

PROBLEMS

9·1 Determine the isentropic efficiency of the turbine example of Sec. 5·4.

9·2 Determine the isentropic efficiency of the compressor in the heat-pump example of Sec. 5·4.

9·3 Air is to be compressed from atmospheric pressure at 60°F to 100 psia in a centrifugal compressor (isentropic efficiency about 0.70). The flow rate will be 500 lbm/min. Specify the hp requirement for the driving motor.

9·4 Air enters an adiabatic nozzle at 1000°F and 20 psia and emerges at 1 psia. The isentropic efficiency of the nozzle is known to be 0.96. Determine the discharge velocity.

9·5 Oxygen flows through a flow-metering nozzle located in a 1-in.-diameter pipe. The nozzle throat diameter is ¼ in. The upstream pressure and temperature are 40 psia and 100°F, and the pressure at the nozzle throat is 10 in. of water lower than the upstream pressure. Determine the oxygen-flow rate, assuming $\eta_s = 0.94$.

9·6 What is the value of the efficiency of the adjacent reversible cycle?

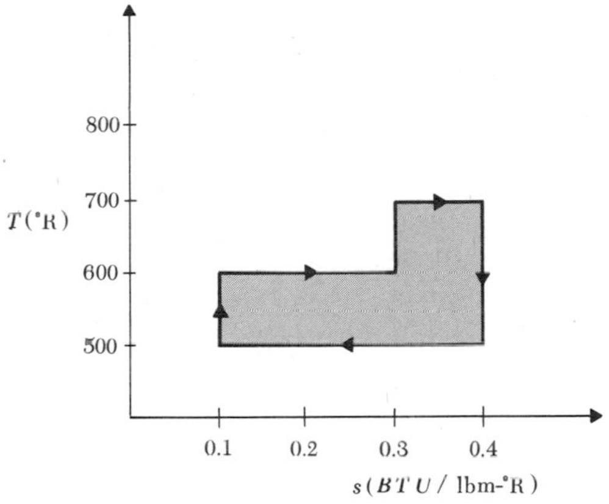

9·7 Determine the energy-conversion efficiency that could be obtained in the example of Sec. 9·4 if the saturated liquid emerging at 212°F from the condenser is fed directly to the pump. Specify the flow rate and boiler-heat input for 1 Mw of output power.

9·8 Determine the energy-conversion efficiency that could be obtained from the system of Sec. 9·5 by addition of a superheater giving 200°F of superheat. Use the same turbine efficiency and condensing pressure (0.949 psia). Specify the flow rate and boiler-heat input for 1 Mw of output power.

9·9 Calculate the energy-conversion efficiency that could be obtained with the zero superheat system of Sec. 9·5 by operating the boiler at 400 psia, retaining the condensing temperature of 100°F. What other problems might result in the operation of this system? Specify the flow rate and boiler-heat input required for 1 Mw of output power.

9·10 Determine the energy-conversion efficiency for a supercritical steam power plant where condensation occurs at 100°F and the high-pressure side is at 4000 psia. Assume that the maximum system temperature is 1000°F and that the overall isentropic efficiency of the turbines (several used in series) is 0.90. The pump efficiency is 0.60. Specify the heating rate and steam-flow rate for 100 Mw of power output.

9·11 A supercritical CO_2 power plant powered by a low-temperature nuclear source has been proposed for operation in the Arctic. The high-pressure side is at 1100 psia, and condensation occurs at −40°F. Assuming pump and turbine efficiencies of 0.50 and 0.85 and a peak cycle temperature of 200°F, determine the system energy-conversion efficiency and the required reactor power and CO_2-flow rate for 2 kw net output.

9·12 A mercury-vapor power cycle for use in space operates on the Rankine cycle, except that a valve is added between the boiler and the turbine. Condensation occurs at 10 psia, and saturated liquid at this pressure enters the electromagnetic pump, which has an isentropic efficiency of 0.12. The boiler operates at 180 psia and delivers 0.98-quality vapor at this pressure. The valve drops the pressure to 100 psia before the fluid enters the turbine, which has an isentropic efficiency of 0.60. Make a thermodynamic analysis of this system and determine the energy-conversion efficiency, mercury-flow rate, reactor thermal power, and condenser heat-rejection rate for 10 kw of power output. What happens to the energy transferred as heat from the condenser?

9·13 Determine the performance of the system of Prob. 9·12 when the valve is wide open (no pressure drop).

9·14 The valve in Prob. 9·12 is necessary to reduce the moisture content of the vapor in the turbine. Suppose an effective zero-g boiler-superheater could be designed such that the valve could be eliminated and the boiler pressure reduced to 100 psia, keeping the turbine inlet state the same as in Prob. 9·12. Determine the performance of this system.

9·15 A cesium-vapor power plant for use in space operates with a boiler pressure of 50 psia and a condensing temperature of 1000°F. The maximum vapor temperature is 2200°F. The isentropic efficiencies of the pump and turbine are 0.65 and 0.70, respectively, and the system operates on the Rankine cycle. Determine the system performance. Compute the conversion efficiency, reactor heat-transfer rate, flow rate, condenser heat-rejection rate, and turbine hp for 10 Mw of power.

9·16 Suppose the cesium-vapor cycle of Prob. 9·15 is used as a topping cycle for the steam power cycle of Prob. 9·10. The flow rates of the two systems will not be the same as in these problems. Determine the efficiency of the combined plant, and specify the heat-transfer rates for the cesium boiler, the cesium-steam heat exchanger, and the steam condenser, and the pump and turbine hp for 300 Mw of total power, using the same component efficiencies.

9·17 Suppose the mercury-vapor cycle of Prob. 9·12 is used as a topping cycle for a Rankine steam power plant in which the evaporation occurs at 550°F and condensing occurs at 70°F. The steam-turbine inlet state has 75 F° of superheat. The isentropic efficiencies of the pump and turbine are 0.65 and 0.90 in the steam system. Determine the system efficiency, mercury and steam flow rates, the heat-transfer rates for the mercury and steam boilers and the condenser, and the pump and turbine hp for 300 Mw of total power output.

9·18 Air is to be compressed from 1 atm to 300 psia. Determine the work required for an isentropic compressor and for a highly cooled compressor in which the air undergoes an isothermal process. What is the isentropic efficiency of the isothermal compressor? What is the *isothermal efficiency* of the isentropic compressor ($\eta_T \equiv W_T/W$)? The inlet temperature is 60°F.

9·19 Determine the compressor efficiency for the example of Sec. 9·6 below which the plant would not be self-sustaining, all other things being equal.

9·20 Using the 0.85-efficient compressor, determine the efficiency of the system of Sec. 9·6 as a function of pressure ratio, keeping the turbine inlet temperature fixed. What pressure ratio must be achieved before the system can be started? Specify the flow rate, heating and cooling rates, compressor and turbine power, and pressure ratio (*a*) at the maximum efficiency point and (*b*) at the minimum flow-rate point for 300 hp of net shaft power.

9·21 Work Prob. 9·20, adding a regenerator and raising the turbine inlet temperature to 1400°F. Assume the regenerator effectiveness is 85 percent.

9·22 Derive Eq. (9·10).

9·23 Derive Eq. (9·11).

9·24 Derive Eq. (9·12).

9·25 A closed-cycle gas-turbine power plant, such as might be used to provide power for a remote experimental station, is shown below. Typical component performance factors might be compressor isentropic efficiency 0.80, turbine isentropic efficiency 0.82, and *regenerator effectiveness* $(T_3 - T_2)/(T_5 - T_2) = 0.85$.

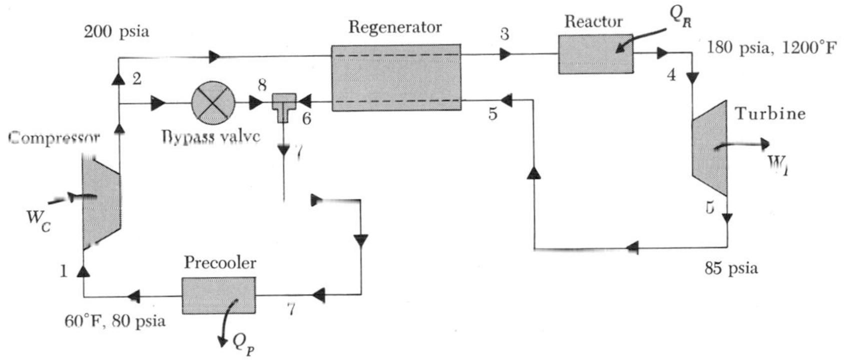

The objective here is to analyze this system for two cases: (*a*) bypass valve closed, that is, maximum output power, and (*b*) bypass valve opened such that the system is self-sustaining, but no net output power. The assumed compressor pressure ratio of 2.5:1 is typical for a regenerative gas-turbine power system. The function of the bypass valve is load control. Making suitable idealizations, determine the state points for the two operating conditions. Note that states 1 and 4 are fixed, and you can start from these. The working fluid in the system is nitrogen, which may be assumed to be a perfect gas with constant specific heats.

Calculate the overall energy-conversion efficiency, the reactor heat-transfer rate (kw), the compressor and turbine powers (hp), the precooler load (Btu/hr), and the flow rates (lbm/hr) for the case of (*a*) no bypass flow, net output power of 500 kw, and (*b*) same compressor flow, no net power (zero load, self-sustaining). What would be the efficiency for no bypass flow if the regenerator were eliminated (bigger reactor and precooler)?

9·26 A gas-turbine power plant for vehicular use consists of the components shown. Air enters at state 1 and is compressed, heated, and expanded in a two-stage turbine system. The first turbine is used to drive the compressor and the second to power the vehicle. A valve for load control is located between the two turbines.

The objective is to make a preliminary study of the feasibility of such a system. You may make the following idealizations:

All turbomachinery adiabatic (isentropic efficiencies as given)
Mass of fuel added in combustion negligible; to be treated simply as a device in which energy is added as heat to the air
Kinetic and potential energies negligible at the numbered state points
Air a perfect gas
Process in combustor isobaric ($P_2 = P_3$)
Maximum permissible air temperature 1600°F (metallurgical limit)

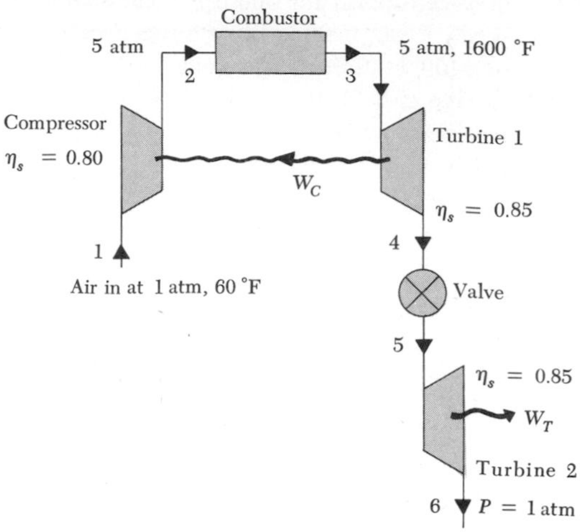

Determine states 5 and 6 for the two cases of (*a*) full power, valve wide open (state 4 = state 5), and (*b*) no power, no work from turbine 2 (state 5 = state 6). Show these on your scale *T-s* diagram and add them to your table. Determine the compressor work requirement, the work delivered by turbines 1 and 2 for these two cases, and the heat input required, all per lbm of air. Compute the full-load system efficiency, W_{shaft}/Q. For the case where the system is running at full power, delivering 300 hp, what air flow rate is required? If the energy transfer as heat to the air in the combustor is equivalent to 19,000 Btu/lbm of fuel, what fuel flow rate is required, what is the air-fuel ratio for this engine, and what is the full-load specific fuel consumption (lbm of fuel per hp-hr)?

9·27 A small turbojet engine for use in takeoff assist is to be designed to the following specifications:

Static sea-level thrust, 1000 lbf
Fuel, gasoline
Size, maximum diameter not to exceed 18 in.

Since the engine is to be used for takeoff assist, it will be operated at sea level, and you may therefore assume that the temperature and pressure at the compressor inlet are 1 atm and 60°F. For a small engine of this type a compressor can probably be built to raise the pressure to 6.5 atm with an isentropic efficiency of 80 percent, so use these values there. A small turbine is needed to deliver the work required by the compressor, and one with an 80 percent isentropic efficiency can probably be made. However, the turbine inlet temperature should probably not exceed 2000°F, so take this as T_3 (see Fig. 9·42). If the supersonic nozzle is properly designed, it will exhaust the gas at a pressure of 1 atm, so assume this to be the case. The energy added as heat to the air in the combustor is 20,000 Btu/lbm of fuel.

The objective is to make a preliminary analysis of such an engine. Using the assumed values, calculate the compressor work requirement (Btu/lbm), the air-fuel ratio (lbm of air/lbm of fuel), and the state of the air entering the nozzle (P and T). You may neglect the mass of fuel added to the air. If the nozzle is adiabatic and frictionless and no shock waves occur, the flow in the nozzle may be idealized as being isentropic. Calculate the state of the gas leaving the nozzle and determine the exit velocity.

The Mach number in compressible flow is the ratio of the velocity at any point to the velocity of sound at that point,

$$M = \frac{V}{a}$$

For a perfect gas, it may be shown that the speed of sound a† is

$$a = \sqrt{g_c kRT}$$

Calculate the speed of sound and the Mach number at the nozzle exit. At the throat the Mach number is 1. Calculate the velocity, temperature, pressure, and density of the air at the throat.

The specific impulse for this engine may be shown to be

$$\mathcal{SI} = \frac{1}{g_c} (V_5 - V_1)$$

The velocity at the compressor inlet would be of the order of 200 ft/sec; assuming this value, calculate the specific impulse. Calculate the air-flow rate required to produce the specified 1000-lbf thrust. Calculate the density at the nozzle discharge and determine the flow area and nozzle diameter at this point. In a similar manner, calculate the throat area and diameter. Assuming that the free-flow area at point 1 is 80 percent of the frontal area and that the outside of the engine has the maximum diameter of 18 in., calculate the velocity and Mach number at the engine inlet. Calculate the fuel required to run this engine at full load for a 1-min takeoff-assist period.

9·28 An aerospace plane uses turbojet engines for takeoff and ramjet engines for upper-atmosphere flight. Assuming that the vehicle is flying at 5000 mph through the air at −40°F, determine the temperature of the air entering the combustion chamber of the ramjet engine.

9·29 Estimate the maximum specific impulses for the following thrusting systems:
(*a*) $T_0 = 3000$°F, $k = 1.3$, $c_P = 0.27$ Btu/lbm-°F
(*b*) $T_0 = 6000$°F, hydrogen
(*c*) Ion engine, cesium plasma ejected at 1 percent of the speed of light

9·30 Consider a blowdown thrusting system which will use hydrogen as the working fluid. The hydrogen will be stored in a high-pressure tank at 3000 psia, from which it will be bled to a chamber having a regulated pressure of 200 psia. The system temperature will be approximately 80°F. The thrusting nozzles will operate with an exit pressure of 10 psia. Determine the specific impulse. What flow rate is required for 40 lbf thrust? How large must the storage vessel be if the total thrusting requirement is 1000 lbf-sec?

† Do not confuse a here with the Helmholtz function.

9·31 Estimate the power requirements of a cesium-ion engine which produces 1 lbf of thrust. The ions are ejected at 5 percent of the speed of light. How much power is used for vaporization and how much for acceleration? What is the specific impulse of this engine? How might the required power be generated?

9·32 It has been proposed that a small rocket system for orientation of a space satellite could be built schematically as shown below. A two-phase substance would be stored in the tank. The vapor would be bled off to be ejected through the nozzle. Energy would be added as heat so that the temperature of the fluid in the tank remained constant. The valve would provide throttling as necessary prior to the passing of flow through the supersonic nozzle.

The purpose of this problem is the study of this system. Assume the following:

Substance, freon-12
Design restrictions: minimum temperature in system 30°F, minimum permissible quality in nozzle 0.98
Flow treated as steady between 1 and 4, state of vapor inside the tank constant (saturated vapor at tank temperature, 100°F)
Nozzle exhausts to free space, so $P_{amb} = 0$ (note that $P_4 > 0$)
Nozzle flow isentropic, V_2 negligible, valve adiabatic

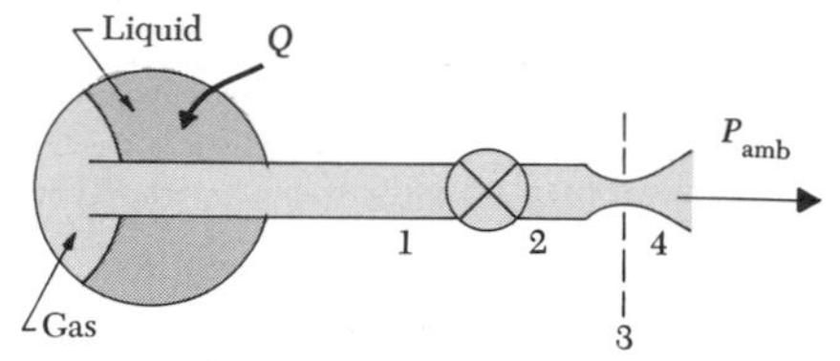

Sketch the process representation in the tank, starting from a completely liquid-filled tank and ending up with only saturated vapor. Sketch the representation of the processes between 1 and 4 on an *h-s* plane for the following three cases:

(*a*) No valve ΔP, state 4 at minimum quality
(*b*) State 4 at minimum temperature, minimum quality
(*c*) Intermediate case between (*a*) and (*b*)

Making suitable idealizations, compute the nozzle exit area A_4 and the flow rate required per lbm of thrust force for each of the three cases. Plot these quantities against the nozzle stagnation pressure P_2. The design requiring the least flow will be the lightest. Perhaps you will have to look at a couple of additional cases to pinpoint this optimum.

9·33 It has been suggested that a used household refrigerator might be modified to serve as a heat pump for heating a swimming pool. The purpose of this problem is the evaluation of this suggestion. First estimate the performance of the refrigerator operating as a refrigerator. Assume the following:

Working substance, freon-12
Motor 1 hp, 1750 rpm
η_M = mechanical efficiency of motor = 0.95
η_s = compressor isentropic efficiency = 0.85
Compressor driven at motor speed
η_{vol} = compressor volumetric efficiency† = 0.70

† η_{vol} = (volume-flow rate based on inlet density)/(compressor-displacement rate).

Condensing temperature 120°F
Evaporating temperature 0°F
Compressor inlet 10 F° superheat†
Condenser discharge, saturated liquid

Making suitable idealizations and employing proper analysis methodology, determine the cycle state points, flow rate when the motor draws 1 hp of electrical power, volume flow rate (based on compressor inlet state), compressor-displacement rate, rate of heat transfer from cold space and to kitchen, heat-pump cop, and refrigerator cop.

Now, if this device is used as a swimming-pool heat pump, the evaporator temperature will be much higher, since the environment temperature will be higher than the refrigerator cold space. Also, the condenser temperature can be lower, owing to improved heat-transfer characteristics when water rather than kitchen air is on the outside of the condenser coils. However, the flow rate will be altered because of the different compressor inlet density. Analyze the heat-pump operation, assuming the following conditions†

$\eta_{vol} = 0.70$
Motor speed 1750 rpm
Condensing temperature 90°F
Evaporating temperature 20°F
Compressor inlet 10°F superheat
Condenser discharge, saturated liquid

Determine the cycle state points, flow rate, required motor power, heat-transfer rate to pool, and heat-pump cop. The swimming-pool heating requirement will be of the order of 25,000 to 50,000 Btu/hr. What is your evaluation of this suggestion?

9·34 A paramagnetic refrigeration system uses iron-ammonium alum in a cyclic process. The refrigeration cycle begins with a slow isothermal magnetization at 2°K, brought about by slowly increasing the external field H to 20,000 gauss. This is followed by a sudden reduction of the external field to 1000 gauss, which suddenly drops the temperature of the alum. The alum is then put into thermal contact with the region to be maintained at low temperature, and the external field is slowly reduced to zero. The external field is then suddenly increased, causing the temperature to rise to 2°K and completing the cycle. The sudden processes may be idealized as adiabatic and the other processes as isothermal. Using the equation of state of Fig. B·12, calculate the amount of energy pumped per cycle from the cold space by 15 g of the alum, and the cold-space temperature. What net energy input must the external field supply to the alum (as work per cycle)?

9·35 Suppose geothermal steam is available at 75 psia, saturated vapor, at the rate of 100 lbm/hr. Design a power system to utilize as much of the energy of this steam as you can, assuming that the environmental temperature is 60°F. Specify the required component efficiencies, energy-transfer rates, intermediate states, and so on.

† 10 F° above saturated vapor at same pressure.

9·36 A stream of CO_2 at 20°F, 50 psia, 1200 ft/sec is needed for a chemical processing plant. The required flow rate is 2 lbm/sec. Design a system to obtain this flow. Bottled liquid CO_2 is available at room temperature (60°F).

9·37 A very low level thruster is required for a deep space probe. It has been suggested that subliming CO_2 be used. The CO_2 will be maintained at −60°F, and the required thrust is 0.01 lbf. Design a system to utilize the CO_2 vapor, which should not go below −140°F. Specify the nozzle exit area, the flow rate, intermediate states, other apparatus, and so on.

9·38 A refrigeration system capable of removing 10,000 watts is required for cooling a computer. The cold space will be maintained at 45°F, and the ambient temperature is 75°F. Allowing 10°F temperature difference on either side of the system for heat transfer, design a refrigeration system for this task. Specify component efficiencies, intermediate states, energy-transfer rates, and so on.

9·39 Design a desert power plant that uses solar energy as the energy source. The boiler temperature can be as high as 200°F, and the condenser temperature will be 100°F. The pressure within the system should be greater than atmospheric to avoid contamination by air. The total power requirement is 10 kw.

9·40 Design an Arctic power plant that uses solar energy as the power source. The boiler temperature can be as high as 100°F and the condenser temperature as low as −60°F. The internal pressure must exceed atmospheric to avoid contamination by air. The total power requirement is 5 kw.

9·41 A wind tunnel experiment requires air at 500°F, 0.01 atm, moving at 2200 ft/sec through a 0.2 ft^2 test section. Design a system to produce the desired flow from atmospheric air. Specify the hardware required, energy-transfer rates, flow rates, etc.

9·42 Oxygen is available at room temperature and 0.2 atm. Design a system in which the oxygen can be liquified at a rate of 10 lbm/min. The environmental temperature is 60°F, and the liquid oxygen can be stored at 10 atm.

9·43 A mercury vapor jet at 400 ft/sec, 1 atm, 1400°F is required for a commercial process. Design a system to obtain this jet from liquid mercury at room temperature; the required mass flow rate is 100 lbm/hr.

9·44 In a certain power system cesium vapor is available at 50 psia and 1400°R. Vapor is to be bled from this point at 0.2 lbm/min, and fed to an auxiliary apparatus at 2200°F, 0.3 psia. Design a system for this job.

9·45 It is proposed that warm water from the gulf stream (75°F) be used as an energy source for a power system for an oceanic research station. Cold water from 2000 ft below the surface will be used as the energy sink (35°F). Design a vapor power system using freon-12 for this operation, assuming a power requirement of 10 kw. Specify the freon flow rate, heat exchanger energy-transfer rates, compressor and pump power requirements. Assuming that the cold water leaves the condenser 10°F below the condensing temperature, and is discharged at the water surface, estimate the cold-water pumping power required. How might this pumping power be reduced?

9·46 A liquid having $c_P = c_v = 0.4$ Btu/lbm-°F is to be cooled in a parallel flow heat exchanger from 60°F to 30°F for a particular laboratory experiment. The liquid flow rate will be 100 lbm/hr. The cooling is to be accomplished using one of the following bottled gases:

(*a*) Air at 100 psia, 60°F

(*b*) Freon-12 at 72.4 psia, 60°F
(*c*) CO_2 at 500 psia, 60°F
(*d*) H_2O vapor at 20°F
The gas can be bled through the heat exchanger, and will be discharged to the atmosphere. No auxiliary hardware (other than a valve) can be used.

Only one of these gases will work for this purpose. Explain why each of the others is not satisfactory, using appropriate process sketches to make your points. For the gas that will work, specify the system configuration, gas flow rate, and so on. Use as little of the gas as possible with your system.

9·47 A dentist's drill of new design requires 0.01 hp. It will be driven by a small air turbine in the drill tip, with the discharged air used to blow chips away. The air must emerge from the drill at low velocity, atmospheric pressure, 75°F. Compressed air at 100 psia, 70°F is available to run the device.

Design a simple system which will work in the manner indicated. Sketch the *h-s* process representation for your system, and explain the concept of your design briefly, using this diagram. Then calculate the required air flow, power input to any heaters, pressure drop across any valves, and so on. Use the perfect-gas approximations and the following turbine operating conditions:

$P_{\text{inlet}}/P_{\text{outlet}} = 3$ isentropic efficiency 60%

9·48 It has been proposed that power for an artificial heart be generated by a small reciprocating gas engine implanted in the chest. The body would act as the energy source (99°F) and energy would be rejected as heat to inhaled air (85°F). Investigate the feasibility of this proposal, presuming that 0.02 hp are required and that the cycle rate must be about 80 cycles/min.

9·49 A proposed scheme for powering an artificial heart imagines that breathed air will be expelled from the lungs through a simple mechanical engine. The body itself then powers the heart directly. Making suitable estimates and design calculations, investigate this proposal. The heart requires about 0.02 hp.

CHAPTER TEN

THERMODYNAMICS OF NONREACTING MIXTURES

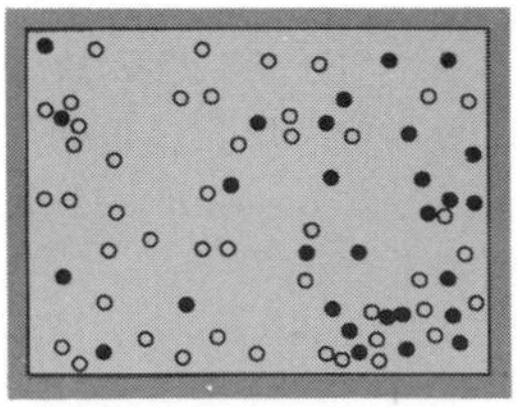

10·1 DESCRIPTIONS OF MIXTURES

A *mixture* is any collection of molecules, ions, electrons, and so on. Each group of particles, distinguishable from the others by virtue of chemical structure, is called a *constituent* (or *species*) of the mixture. In mixtures where chemical reactions occur the amount of each constituent present cannot necessarily be varied independently. *Components* are those constituents the amounts of which can be independently varied. In this chapter we shall deal exclusively with nonreacting mixtures, in which each and every constituent is also a component.

A quantity of matter that is homogeneous in chemical composition and physical structure is called a *phase.* A phase can contain several components; for example, a mixture of gases would be a phase, and a mixture of the same substances in liquid form would be a different phase. A system having only one phase is called *homogeneous,* and a system with more than one phase is *heterogeneous.* A *pure substance* has the same chemical structure in all states, but may have several distinguishable phases.

The composition of a mixture may be described by specification of either the *mass* or the *number of moles* of each constituent. Two ways of specifying the composition independently of the quantity of the mixture are the *mass fraction,*†

$$\blacktriangleright \qquad \Phi_i \equiv \frac{M_i}{\sum_i M_i} = \frac{M_i}{M} \tag{10·1}$$

and the *mole fraction,*

$$\blacktriangleright \qquad \chi_i \equiv \frac{\mathfrak{N}_i}{\sum_i \mathfrak{N}_i} = \frac{\mathfrak{N}_i}{\mathfrak{N}} \tag{10·2}$$

† The subscript i refers to any single unspecified constituent.

M and $\mathfrak{N}$ denote the total mass and total number of moles, respectively. The *molal mass* of the mixture is then

$$\hat{M} = \frac{\sum_i M_i}{\sum_i \mathfrak{N}_i} = \frac{\sum_i \hat{M}_i \mathfrak{N}_i}{\mathfrak{N}}$$

or

$$\blacktriangleright \quad \hat{M} = \sum_i x_i \hat{M}_i \tag{10·3}$$

For example, air is a mixture of approximately 3.76 moles of nitrogen for every mole of oxygen. The mole fractions are therefore

$$x_{N_2} = \frac{3.76}{4.76} = 0.79$$

$$x_{O_2} = \frac{1.00}{4.76} = 0.21$$

Then

$$\hat{M}_{air} = 0.79 \times 28.02 + 0.21 \times 32.00 = 28.97 \text{ lbm/lbmole}$$
$$= 28.97 \text{ g/gmole} = 28.97 \text{ kg/kgmole}$$

In this chapter we shall restrict ourselves to *simple compressible mixtures*, for which the only significant reversible work mode is volume change. According to the state postulate, the extensive thermodynamic state of any simple compressible mixture will be specified solely by its composition, energy, and volume. Its composition is specified by the set of mole numbers $\mathfrak{N}_1, \ldots, \mathfrak{N}_n$ of the n components. Thus the total entropy could be viewed functionally as

$$S = S(U, V, \mathfrak{N}_1, \mathfrak{N}_2, \ldots, \mathfrak{N}_n)$$

The derivatives of this function define the temperature, pressure, and electrochemical potentials. For temperature T

$$\blacktriangleright \quad \frac{1}{T} \equiv \left(\frac{\partial S}{\partial U}\right)_{V,\mathfrak{N}_1,\ldots,\mathfrak{N}_n} \tag{10·4}$$

For pressure P

$$\blacktriangleright \quad \frac{P}{T} \equiv \left(\frac{\partial S}{\partial V}\right)_{U,\mathfrak{N}_1,\ldots,\mathfrak{N}_n} \tag{10·5}$$

For the molal *electrochemical potential* $\hat{\mu}_i$ of the ith component,

$$\blacktriangleright \quad -\frac{\hat{\mu}_i}{T} \equiv \left(\frac{\partial S}{\partial \mathfrak{N}_i}\right)_{U,V,\mathfrak{N}_1,\ldots,\mathfrak{N}_{i-1},\mathfrak{N}_{i+1},\ldots,\mathfrak{N}_n} \tag{10·6}$$

The definitions of temperature and pressure are equivalent to those introduced in Chap. Seven. The significance of the electrochemical potential will be explained shortly.

The Gibbs equation for a mixture is obtained by differentiation of the entropy,

$$\blacktriangleright \quad dS = \frac{1}{T}\,dU + \frac{P}{T}\,dV - \sum_i \frac{\hat{\mu}_i}{T}\,d\mathfrak{N}_i \tag{10·7}$$

We shall use this important equation later in the chapter. Note that if the composition does not change then each of the $d\mathfrak{N}_i$ are zero, and Eq. (10·7) reduces to Eq. (8·1), the Gibbs equation for a single substance.

10·2 MIXTURES OF INDEPENDENT SUBSTANCES

If we can idealize that the allowed quantum states of a given constituent are not influenced by the presence of the other constituents, the properties of the mixture may be determined from the "private" properties of its constituents. We call this a *mixture of independent substances.* Gas mixtures that are not too dense and some liquid and solid solutions (*ideal solutions*) may be treated in this manner.

In a mixture of independent substances each species has a "private" energy, and hence the total energy is

$$U = \sum_i U_i$$

Here U_i is the internal energy of the ith constituent.

Since the allowed quantum states of the constituents are independent, the mixture quantum states are determined from all possible combinations of constituent quantum states. As we saw in Chap. Six, the entropy of such a system is the sum of the entropies of its independent subsystems (the constituents). Hence,

The entropy of a mixture of independent substances is the sum of the entropies of the constituents,

$$S = \sum_i S_i$$

This fact is known as the *Gibbs rule.*

Let us consider a mixture of two independent substances A and B, each filling the total volume V. The entropy of the mixture can be expressed functionally as (for given amounts of A and B)

$$S = S_A(U_A, V) + S_B(U_B, V)$$

This will be true as long as each constituent is in a thermodynamic equilibrium state, even though the two constituents may not be in equilibrium with one another. We can find the condition of equilibrium between the constituents by isolating the mixture and finding the configuration of maximum entropy. The total internal energy, $U = U_A + U_B$, must remain fixed during this maximization. Differentiating the entropy with respect to U_A and keeping the volume and total internal energy fixed, we find

$$\frac{\partial S}{\partial U_A} = \left(\frac{\partial S_A}{\partial U_A}\right)_V + \left(\frac{\partial S_B}{\partial U_B}\right)_V \frac{dU_B}{dU_A} = \left(\frac{\partial S_A}{\partial U_A}\right)_V - \left(\frac{\partial S_B}{\partial U_B}\right) = 0$$

Hence, for maximum entropy,

$$T_A = T_B$$

We see that the equilibrium state will be one in which the temperatures of the two constituents are equal. This demonstration may be extended to mixtures of more than one constituent by the method of undetermined multipliers.

The pressure of the mixture is given by Eq. (10·5) as

$$P = \sum_i \left[T\left(\frac{\partial S}{\partial V}\right)_U\right]_i = \sum_i P_i$$

Here P_i is the pressure which the ith constituent would have if it occupied the *same volume* as the mixture at the mixture temperature; P_i is called the *partial pressure* of the ith constituent. The fact that the total pressure is equal to the sum of the partial pressures for a mixture of independent substances is known as the *Dalton rule*.

A microscopic interpretation of the Dalton rule is helpful. The partial pressures represent the contribution to the average normal force per unit of area acting on the boundaries, resulting from impacts of the various constituents. The fact that the constituents are independent means that the average normal velocity of impacting particles of a constituent is not influenced by the presence of the other species.

To summarize, a mixture of independent substances in equilibrium has the following properties:

▶ $$U = \sum_i U_i \tag{10·8}$$

▶ $$S = \sum_i S_i \tag{10·9}$$

▶ $$T_1 = T_2 = \cdots = T \tag{10·10}$$

▶ $$P = \sum_i P_i \tag{10·11}$$

When the mixture has only one phase, it is convenient to work with the specific, or intensified properties. The specific internal energy of the mixture is

$$u = \frac{U}{M} = \sum_i \frac{M_i}{M} u_i = \sum_i \Phi_i u_i$$

or, on a molal basis,

$$\hat{u} = \sum_i \chi_i \hat{u}_i$$

The molal enthalpy of the mixture is

$$\hat{h} = \hat{u} + P\hat{v} = \sum_i \chi_i \hat{u}_i + \left(\sum_i P_i\right) \hat{v}$$

The molal enthalpy of the ith constituent may be written as

$$\hat{h}_i = \hat{u}_i + P_i \hat{v}_i = \hat{u}_i + P_i \frac{V}{\mathfrak{N}_i}$$

Since the molal specific volume of the mixture is

$$\hat{v} = \frac{V}{\sum_i \mathfrak{N}_i} = \frac{V}{\mathfrak{N}}$$

we can write

$$\hat{h} = \sum_i \chi_i \hat{u}_i + \sum_i \left(\frac{\mathfrak{N}_i}{\mathfrak{N}} P_i \frac{V}{\mathfrak{N}_i}\right) = \sum_i \chi_i \hat{h}_i$$

Similarly, it follows from Eq. (10·9) that

$$\hat{s} = \sum_i \chi_i \hat{s}_i$$

The molal specific heats of a mixture are defined as

$$\hat{c}_v \equiv \left(\frac{\partial \hat{u}}{\partial T}\right)_{\hat{v},\chi_1,\chi_2,\ldots,\chi_n}$$

$$\hat{c}_P \equiv \left(\frac{\partial \hat{h}}{\partial T}\right)_{P,\chi_1,\chi_2,\ldots,\chi_n}$$

Thus

$$\hat{c}_v = \sum_i \chi_i \left(\frac{\partial \hat{u}_i}{\partial T}\right)_{\hat{v}} = \sum_i \chi_i \hat{c}_{v_i}$$

$$\hat{c}_P = \sum_i \chi_i \left(\frac{\partial \hat{h}_i}{\partial T}\right)_P = \sum_i \chi_i \hat{c}_{P_i}$$

We see that the molal internal energy, enthalpy, entropy, and specific heats for a mixture of independent substances are merely the sums of the contributions of each constituent evaluated at the mixture volume and temperature† and weighted by their respective mole fractions.

† Equivalently, evaluated at the mixture temperature and their respective partial pressures.

Summarizing,

$$\blacktriangleright \quad \hat{u} = \sum_i \chi_i \hat{u}_i(T, P_i) \tag{10·12}$$

$$\blacktriangleright \quad \hat{h} = \sum_i \chi_i \hat{h}_i(T, P_i) \tag{10·13}$$

$$\blacktriangleright \quad \hat{s} = \sum_i \chi_i \hat{s}_i(T, P_i) \tag{10·14}$$

$$\blacktriangleright \quad \hat{c}_v = \sum_i \chi_i \hat{c}_{v_i}(T, P_i) \tag{10·15}$$

$$\blacktriangleright \quad \hat{c}_P = \sum_i \chi_i \hat{c}_{P_i}(T, P_i) \tag{10·16}$$

Since each of the constituents occupies the same volume, the ratio of the specific volumes of any two, based on their partial pressures and the mixture temperature, is inversely proportional to the ratio of their two masses,

$$\frac{v_i(T, P_i)}{v_j(T, P_j)} = \frac{V/M_i}{V/M_j} = \frac{M_j}{M_i} \tag{10·17}$$

We shall now apply these results to the special case of perfect-gas mixtures.

10·3 MIXTURES OF PERFECT GASES

Consider a mixture of perfect gases, each obeying the equation

$$PV = \mathfrak{N}\mathfrak{R}T \tag{10·18}$$

We idealize that this is a mixture of independent substances, so that the results of the preceding section may be applied directly. In particular, the partial pressure of the ith constituent is

$$P_i = \frac{\mathfrak{N}_i}{V}\mathfrak{R}T$$

The total pressure is then

$$P = \sum_i P_i = \left(\sum_i \mathfrak{N}_i\right)\frac{\mathfrak{R}T}{V} = \frac{\mathfrak{N}\mathfrak{R}T}{V}$$

The ratio of the partial pressure of any constituent to the total pressure is therefore equal simply to its mole fraction,

$$\blacktriangleright \quad \frac{P_i}{P} = \frac{\mathfrak{N}_i\mathfrak{R}T/V}{\mathfrak{N}\mathfrak{R}T/V} = \frac{\mathfrak{N}_i}{\mathfrak{N}} = \chi_i \tag{10·19}$$

The *partial volume*† of the *i*th constituent is

$$V_i = \frac{\mathfrak{N}_i \mathfrak{R} T}{P} = \frac{\mathfrak{N}_i}{\mathfrak{N}} V = \chi_i V$$

The *volume fraction* of the *i*th constituent is defined as

$$\blacktriangleright \qquad \Psi_i \equiv \frac{V_i}{V} = \chi_i \tag{10·20}$$

The mole fraction is seen to be equal to both the pressure fraction and the volume fraction. This fact is extremely useful in laboratory analysis of gas composition.

Consider a mixture system in an initial state where the constituents are separated, each at the same temperature and pressure, each at its partial volume. The gases are allowed to mix within the isolated system. The mixture will eventually reach an equilibrium state in which the partial-pressure fractions will be equal to the initial volume fractions. Denoting the final state by 2 and the initial state by 1 and using the fact that the energy of a perfect gas is a function of its temperature only, it follows that

$$\hat{u}_1 = \hat{u}_2 = \sum_i \chi_i \hat{u}_i(T_1) = \sum_i \chi_i \hat{u}_i(T_2)$$

Each of the internal energies is monotone in T. Therefore, since the mole fractions are fixed, any temperature change would result in a change in the total internal energy. Since this internal energy is fixed, the temperature will not change when the ideal gases are allowed to mix. The pressures initially and finally are therefore related by

$$\frac{P_{i2} V_{i2}}{P_{i1} V_{i1}} = \frac{\mathfrak{N}_i \mathfrak{R} T}{\mathfrak{N}_i \mathfrak{R} T}$$

or

$$\frac{P_{i2}}{P_1} \frac{V}{V_{i1}} = 1$$

so that

$$\blacktriangleright \qquad \frac{P_{i2}}{P_1} = \frac{V_{i1}}{V} = \chi_i$$

Thus the ratio of the final partial pressure to the initial pressure will be equal to the mole fraction. This indicates that the initial common pressure is the same as the final total pressure, so that *the pressure will not change when perfect gases are allowed to mix.* The entropy change of the *i*th constituent will

† Volume which would be occupied by *i*th constituent at the mixture temperature and pressure.

then be [see Eq. (8·38)]

$$s_{i2} - s_{i1} = [\phi_i(T) - R_i \ln P_{i2}] - [\phi_i(T) - R_i \ln P_1]$$
$$= -R_i \ln \frac{P_i}{P} = -R_i \ln \chi_i$$

The change in the molal entropy of the ith constituent is then

$$\hat{s}_{i2} - \hat{s}_{i1} = -\mathcal{R} \ln \chi_i$$

The total change in entropy occurring when *different* gases are allowed to mix in an isolated system at constant temperature and pressure is therefore

$$S_2 - S_1 = -\mathcal{R} \sum_i \mathfrak{N}_i \ln \chi_i = \mathcal{R} \sum_i \mathfrak{N}_i \ln \frac{1}{\chi_i} \tag{10·21}$$

The mole fractions are all less than unity, and therefore the entropy change within the isolated system is seen to be positive. It should be noted that two samples of the same gas cannot be treated as independent substances, and therefore the above result applies only to mixtures of different gases.

10·4 APPLICATION TO AIR–WATER-VAPOR MIXTURES

Water vapor at pressures below 1 atm may be idealized as a perfect gas,† and consequently, the theory developed in the previous sections has important application in the study of air–water-vapor mixtures. If the partial pressure of the water vapor corresponds to the saturation pressure of water at the mixture temperature, the mixture is said to be *saturated.*‡ A closed volume of air in contact with water will, given sufficient time, become fully saturated, and then the partial pressure of the water vapor in the air will be given by the saturation pressure of water at the air temperature, as given by Table B·1. Air that has not been in contact with water for a sufficiently long period of time may not be saturated. The water in such a mixture would then be *superheated.*

If an air–water-vapor mixture that is not saturated is cooled at constant pressure, the mixture will eventually reach the saturation temperature corresponding to the partial pressure of the water vapor. This is called the *dew-point temperature* because it is associated with the formation of liquid droplets (dew). The constant-pressure cooling process and the dew point are shown in Fig. 10·1.

The composition of an air–water-vapor mixture is often indicated by the *specific humidity,* defined as the ratio of the mass of water vapor to the mass

† See the examples in Sec. 4·8.

‡ Actually the presence of air alters the saturation pressure by a very small amount. We shall neglect this effect here; its magnitude is calculated in Sec. 10·9.

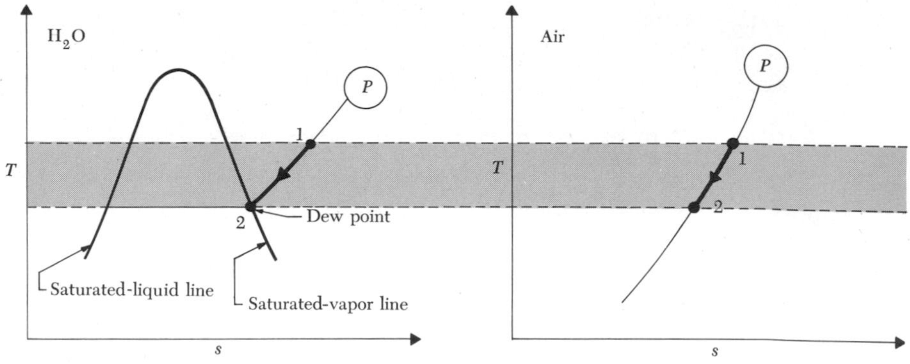

FIG. 10·1 *The dew point*

of air in the mixture,

$$\blacktriangleright \qquad \gamma \equiv \frac{M_w}{M_a} \tag{10·22}$$

An alternate specification is the *relative humidity*, which is defined as the ratio of the partial pressure of the water vapor to the saturation pressure at the mixture temperature† (see Fig. 10·2),

$$\blacktriangleright \qquad \phi \equiv \frac{P_w}{P_g} \tag{10·23}$$

Since the mass ratios are inversely proportional to the specific-volume ratios [Eq. (10·17)],

$$\gamma = \frac{M_w}{M_a} = \frac{v_a(T, P_a)}{v_w(T, P_w)} \tag{10·24}$$

† In this section ϕ denotes only the relative humidity and should not be confused with the function $\phi(T)$ in the entropy expression for a perfect gas.

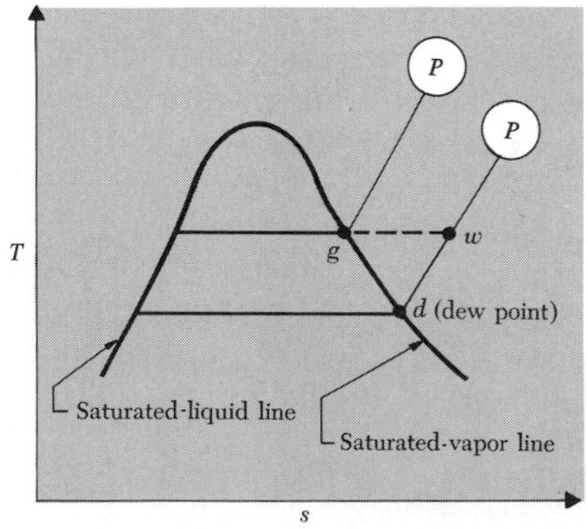

FIG. 10·2 *Saturation and partial pressure*

We have idealized the vapor as a perfect gas; then, since $T_g = T_w$,

$$\phi = \frac{P_w}{P_g} = \frac{v_g(T, P_g)}{v_w(T, P_w)} \tag{10·25}$$

$$\gamma = \phi \frac{v_a(T, P_a)}{v_g(T, P_g)} \tag{10·26}$$

Using the perfect-gas equation of state,

$$\gamma = \frac{R_a T/P_a}{R_w T/P_w} = 0.622 \frac{P_w}{P_a} \tag{10·27}$$

Then, combining with Eq. (10·25),

► $$\phi = \frac{\gamma P_a}{0.622 P_g} \tag{10·28}$$

Finally, the total pressure is given by Dalton's rule as the sum of the air and water pressures,

► $$P = P_a + P_w \tag{10·29}$$

The humidity can in principle be measured with an *adiabatic saturator*. This is a device into which flows the air–water-vapor mixture of unknown humidity, out of which flows a saturated air–water-vapor mixture at some lower adiabatic-saturation temperature, and to which water is added continuously. Schematic and process representations for an adiabatic saturator are shown in Fig. 10·3. The device is sufficiently long that equilibrium between the air–water-vapor mixture is obtained by the time the mixture reaches the exit. Thus the temperature of the mixture at state 3 will be the same as that of water at state 3, and we assume the water temperature is uniform, so that $T_2 = T_3$. Using the properties of perfect-gas mixtures and idealizing the device as adiabatic, energy and mass balances allow us to develop the expression

$$h_{a1} + \gamma_1 h_{w1} + (\gamma_3 - \gamma_1) h_{w2} = h_{a3} + \gamma_3 h_{w3} \tag{10·30}$$

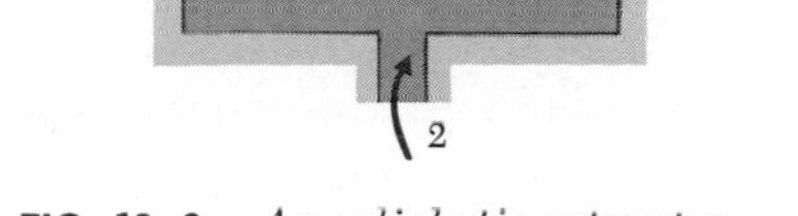

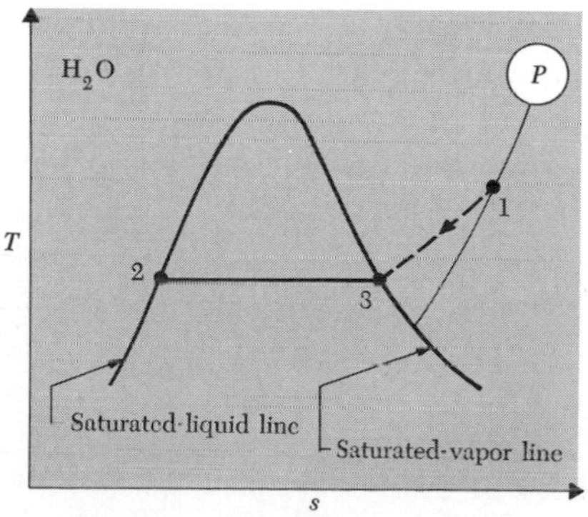

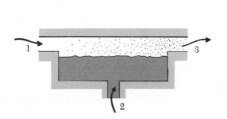

FIG. 10·3 *An adiabatic saturator*

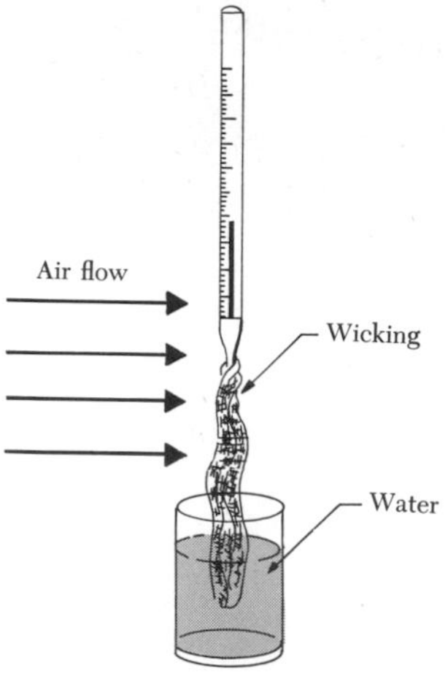

FIG. 10·4 *A wet-bulb thermometer*

Measurements of the pressure and temperatures allow determination of all the enthalpies and the specific humidity at state 3 from the equations of state of air and H_2O. The one remaining unknown in Eq. (10·30) is the specific humidity at state 1, which may then be calculated from the equation.

A more convenient means for measuring humidity is the *wet-bulb thermometer* (Fig. 10·4). Water brought up the wick by capillary action is evaporated to the air flowing around the bulb, so that the air inside the wick becomes saturated at the temperature of the water in the wick. This temperature will be influenced by the rates of heat and mass transfer from the water to the air, which in turn depend on the configuration of the bulb, air velocity, and other factors. The wet-bulb temperature is therefore not a property of the gas mixture, since it depends upon the nature of the measuring instrument. However, it has been found experimentally that the wet-bulb temperature is very close to the adiabatic-saturation temperature for air–water-vapor mixtures, and thus it provides a satisfactory estimate for this property of the mixture.

The solution of Eq. (10·30) can be represented in a convenient graphical form, the *psychrometric chart* (Fig. B·13). This chart is based on an adiabatic-saturation process at 1 atm. More complete charts available in handbooks include correction factors for pressure; the values of specific humidity obtained from the chart of Fig. B·13 will be correct to within a few percent at pressures within 1 in. of mercury of atmospheric pressure. At lower or higher pressures the errors in using this chart become significant, and a more complete psychrometric chart should be consulted.† Note that the dew point and adiabatic-saturation temperature (wet-bulb temperature) are identical for a saturated mixture. The dry-bulb temperature is simply the mixture temperature.

As an example, suppose that wet- and dry-bulb temperatures measured in moist air at 1 atm of pressure are 70 and 90°F, respectively. We shall now

† On some charts enthalpies are given; however, the datum state is generally not the same as employed in the steam tables, and the user must be careful not to mix the two.

find the specific and relative humidities and the thermodynamic properties of the mixture. From Fig. B·13 we read, for $T_{DB} = 90°\text{F}$ and $T_{WB} = 70°\text{F}$,

$$\begin{aligned} \gamma &= 78 \text{ grains of vapor per lbm of dry air} \\ P_w &= 0.25 \text{ psia} \\ \phi &= 0.37 \\ T_{DP} &= 60°\text{F} \end{aligned}$$

The partial pressure of the air is therefore

$$14.70 - 0.25 = 14.45 \text{ psia}$$

The mole fractions of air and water vapor are then

$$\chi_a = \frac{14.45}{14.70} = 0.983$$

$$\chi_w = \frac{0.25}{14.70} = 0.017$$

The mixture molal mass is then (see Table B·6)

$$\begin{aligned} \hat{\mathcal{M}} &= 28.97 \times 0.983 + 18.016 \times 0.017 \\ &= 28.8 \text{ lbm/lbmole} = 28.8 \text{ g/gmole} \end{aligned}$$

Note that the presence of water vapor will always decrease the molal mass of the mixture from that for dry air. The mixture density is then

$$\rho = \frac{P}{(\mathcal{R}/\hat{\mathcal{M}})T} = \frac{14.70 \times 144}{(1545/28.8) \times 550} = 0.0718 \text{ lbm/ft}^3$$

Since the enthalpy of a perfect gas depends only on temperature, we may read the enthalpy of the water vapor from Table B·1*a*, even though it is not in a saturation state. Thus

$$h_w(90°\text{F}) = h_g(90°\text{F}) = 1100.9 \text{ Btu/lbm}$$

or

$$\hat{h}_w = 1100.9 \times 18.016 = 19{,}850 \text{ Btu/lbmole}$$

The enthalpy of the air may be obtained from the air tables (Table B·9), which assume perfect-gas behavior, as

$$\begin{aligned} h_a &= 131.5 \text{ Btu/lbm} \\ \hat{h}_a &= 131.5 \times 28.97 = 3810 \text{ Btu/lbmole} \end{aligned}$$

The molal enthalpy of the mixture, relative to the datum states used in the steam and air tables, is then

$$\hat{h} = 0.983 \times 3810 + 0.017 \times 19{,}850 = 4080 \text{ Btu/lbmole}$$

so

$$h = \frac{4080}{28.8} = 141.5 \text{ Btu/lbm}$$

The molal entropy of the water vapor could be obtained from superheat tables, but they do not extend down to 90°F. Instead we extrapolate from the saturation tables, treating the vapor as a perfect gas. Using Eq. (8·38), we find

$$\hat{s}(T, P) - \hat{s}_g(T) = -\mathcal{R} \ln \frac{P}{P_g(T)}$$

Then, with the help of Table B·1a,

$$\hat{s}_w = 2.0087 \times 18.016 - 1.986 \ln \frac{0.25}{0.6982} = 38.14 \text{ Btu/lbmole-°R}$$

In determining the entropy of the air we must select a datum state. Table B·9 is based on 0°R (extrapolated perfect gas); consequently, we select 1 atm and 0°R for the entropy datum. Then, using Eq. (8·38),

$$s_a(T, P) = \phi(T) - R_a \ln \frac{P}{1 \text{ atm}}$$

From Table B·9,

$$\hat{s}_a = 0.6051 \times 28.97 - 1.986 \ln \frac{14.45}{14.7}$$
$$= 17.55 \text{ Btu/lbmole-°R}$$

Then the mixture entropy, relative to the indicated air and H_2O data, is

$$\hat{s} = 0.983 \times 17.55 + 0.017 \times 38.14 = 17.91 \text{ Btu/lbmole-°R}$$
$$s = \frac{17.91}{28.8} = 0.622 \text{ Btu/lbm-°R}$$

Finally, for c_P (see Table B·6),

$$\hat{c}_P = 0.983 \times 6.95 + 0.017 \times 8.07 = 6.98 \text{ Btu/lbmole-°R}$$
$$c_P = \frac{6.98}{28.8} = 0.242 \text{ Btu/lbm-°R}$$

Constant-pressure heating will not change the specific humidity but will change the relative humidity. Such a process is shown in Fig. 10·5 (see Fig. B·13). Constant-pressure cooling will not change the specific humidity unless the mixture is cooled to the adiabatic-saturation temperature. Further cooling would then result in condensation and a lowering of the specific humidity. Such a process is shown by Fig. 10·6.

Dehumidification may be accomplished by first cooling, allowing some vapor to condense, and then reheating the mixture. The hardware schematic and process representation (on the psychrometric chart) for a system to accomplish this are shown in Fig. 10·7. Some commercial air conditioners employ spray cooling, in which chilled water is injected into the air, lowering its temperature below the original dew point, allowing a net dehumidification when the mixture is reheated. Such a system is shown in Fig. 10·8.

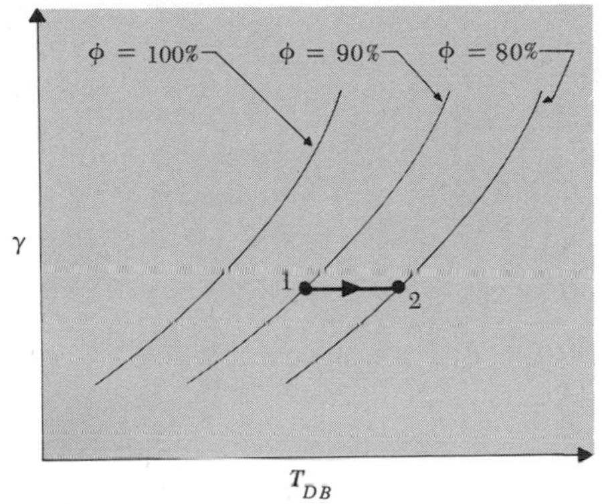

FIG. 10·5 *Heating reduces relative humidity*

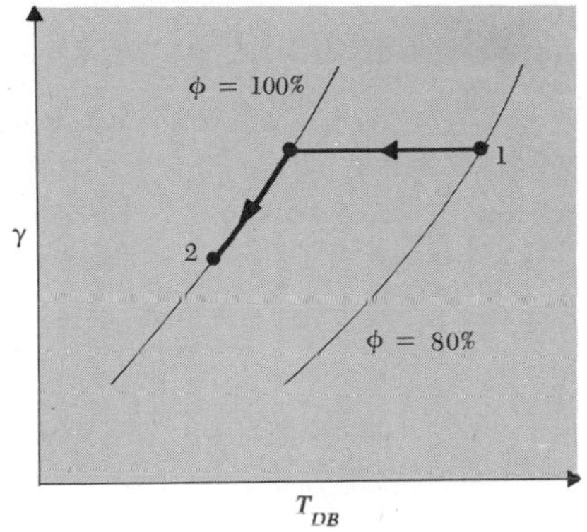

FIG. 10·6 *A cooling and condensation process*

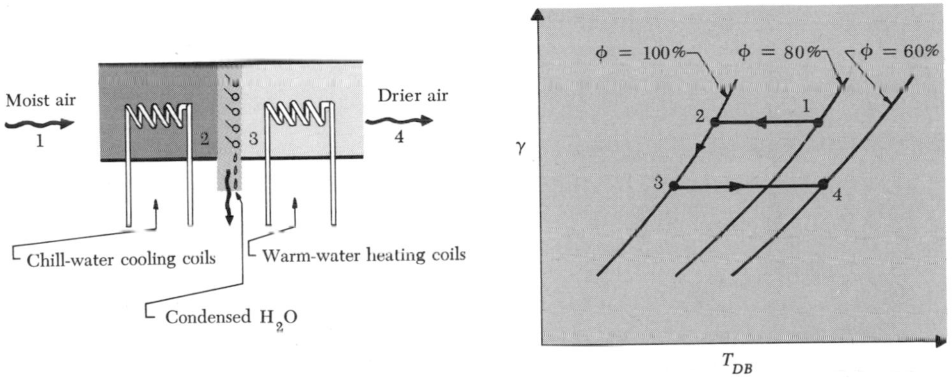

FIG. 10·7 *Dehumidification*

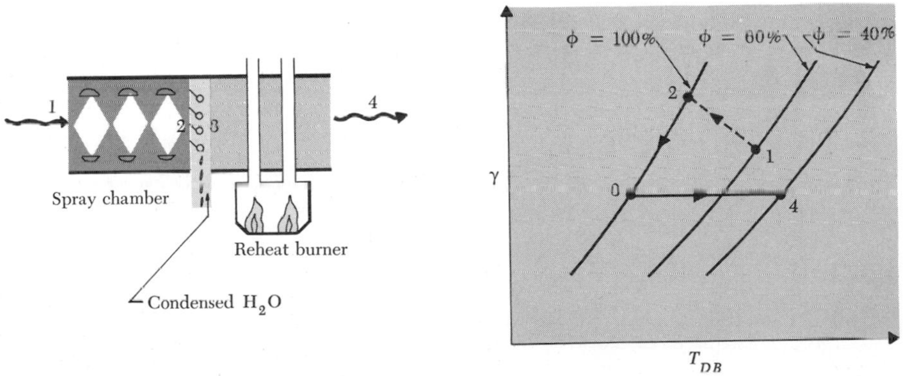

FIG. 10·8 *Spray dehumidification*

10·5 EQUILIBRIUM BETWEEN MIXTURE PHASES

Consider an isolated system consisting of a two-phase mixture, such as a gaseous water-vapor–nitrogen mixture in contact with liquid water containing nitrogen in solution. We seek the conditions of equilibrium between the two phases (see Fig. 10·9). Assuming that the allowed quantum states for the two

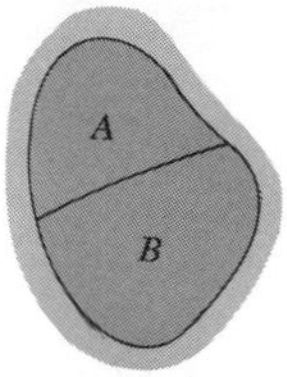

FIG. 10·9 *Equilibrium between mixture phases*

phases are independent, the entropy of the system will be the sum of the entropies of the two phases. We imagine isolating the system; the equilibrium state will be the one of maximum system entropy, selected from all possible states having the same total internal energy, volume, and mass of each component. We denote the entropy of the combined system by S_C and have

$$S_C = S_A(U_A, V_A, \mathfrak{M}_{1A}, \ldots, \mathfrak{M}_{nA}) + S_B(U_B, V_B, \mathfrak{M}_{1B}, \ldots, \mathfrak{M}_{nB})$$

The isolation constraints require

$$U_A + U_B = \text{constant}$$
$$V_A + V_B = \text{constant}$$
$$\mathfrak{M}_{iA} + \mathfrak{M}_{iB} = \text{constant}$$

Thus we are free to vary only $U_A, V_A, \mathfrak{M}_{1A}, \ldots, \mathfrak{M}_{nA}$ in seeking the maximum of S_C. The condition

$$\left(\frac{\partial S_C}{\partial U_A}\right)_{V_A,\mathfrak{M}_{1A},\ldots,\mathfrak{M}_{nA}} = 0$$

leads directly to

$$\blacktriangleright \qquad \frac{1}{T_A} = \frac{1}{T_B} \qquad T_A = T_B \tag{10·31}$$

The condition

$$\left(\frac{\partial S_C}{\partial V_A}\right)_{U_A,\mathfrak{M}_{1A},\ldots,\mathfrak{M}_{nA}} = 0$$

requires that

$$\frac{P_A}{T_A} = \frac{P_B}{T_B}$$

and since the temperatures are equal,

$$\blacktriangleright \quad P_A = P_B \tag{10·32}$$

The condition

$$\left(\frac{\partial S_C}{\partial \mathfrak{N}_{iA}}\right)_{U_A, V_A, \mathfrak{N}_{1A}, \ldots, \mathfrak{N}_{(i-1)A}, \mathfrak{N}_{(i+1)A}, \ldots, \mathfrak{N}_{nA}} = 0$$

indicates that

$$\left(\frac{\hat{\mu}_i}{T}\right)_A = \left(\frac{\hat{\mu}_i}{T}\right)_B \qquad i = 1,2, \ldots, n$$

But since the temperatures must also be equal, a necessary condition for equilibrium between the phases is

$$\blacktriangleright \quad \hat{\mu}_{iA} = \hat{\mu}_{iB} \tag{10·33}$$

These results may be extended to mixtures with more than two phases; necessary conditions for equilibrium are

The temperature of every phase must be the same.
The pressure of every phase must be the same.
The electrochemical potential of each component must have the same value in every phase.

Consider again the system of Fig. 10·9. Suppose that the two phases are in thermal and mechanical equilibrium, and that the electrochemical potentials of all but constituent i are equal in both phases. The entropy change of the combined system associated with any interaction will then be simply

$$dS_C = dS_A + dS_B = \left(\frac{\hat{\mu}_{iB}}{T} - \frac{\hat{\mu}_{iA}}{T}\right) d\mathfrak{N}_{iA}$$

where $d\mathfrak{N}_{iA}$ represents an infinitesimal number of moles of constituent i transferred from B to A. Since the combined system is isolated, the second law requires that $dS_C \geq 0$, and

$$(\hat{\mu}_{iB} - \hat{\mu}_{iA})\, d\mathfrak{N}_{iA} \geq 0$$

The equality is associated with reversible transfer between the two phases, which can occur only if $\hat{\mu}_{iA} = \hat{\mu}_{iB}$. For the inequality to hold,

$$\begin{aligned} \text{if } \hat{\mu}_{iB} > \hat{\mu}_{iA} \quad & \text{then} \quad d\mathfrak{N}_{iA} > 0 \\ \hat{\mu}_{iB} < \hat{\mu}_{iA} \quad & \text{then} \quad d\mathfrak{N}_{iA} < 0 \end{aligned}$$

We conclude that the electrochemical potential acts as a driving force for mass transfer. Any species will try to move from the phase having the higher electrochemical potential for that species to the phase having lower electrochemical potential. This fact forms the basis for predictions and analysis of the solubility or insolubility of one species in another. It is also useful in studying the distribution of free electrons between dissimilar metals in contact.

10·6 EVALUATION OF THE ELECTROCHEMICAL POTENTIAL

Consider a single phase. Increasing the mass of the phase and keeping the temperature, pressure, and component proportions unchanged will not change the energy, volume, or entropy per unit of mass of the phase. In other words, because a phase is homogeneous any sample taken from it will have the same intensive state. This condition may be expressed by

$$U(T, P, \lambda\mathfrak{M}_1, \ldots, \lambda\mathfrak{M}_n) = \lambda U(T, P, \mathfrak{M}_1, \ldots, \mathfrak{M}_n)$$
$$V(T, P, \lambda\mathfrak{M}_1, \ldots, \lambda\mathfrak{M}_n) = \lambda V(T, P, \mathfrak{M}_1, \ldots, \mathfrak{M}_n)$$
$$S(T, P, \lambda\mathfrak{M}_1, \ldots, \lambda\mathfrak{M}_n) = \lambda S(T, P, \mathfrak{M}_1, \ldots, \mathfrak{M}_n)$$

Here λ is any factor. Of particular interest in mixture thermodynamics is the Gibbs function,

$$\blacktriangleright \quad G \equiv U + PV - TS \tag{10·34}$$

Because of the relations above, it also follows that the Gibbs function of a phase is such that

$$G(T, P, \lambda\mathfrak{M}_1, \ldots, \lambda\mathfrak{M}_n) = \lambda G(T, P, \mathfrak{M}_1, \ldots, \mathfrak{M}_n)$$

Differentiating with respect to λ,

$$\sum_i \frac{\partial G(T, P, \lambda\mathfrak{M}_1, \ldots)}{\partial(\lambda\mathfrak{M}_i)} \mathfrak{M}_i = G(T, P, \mathfrak{M}_1, \ldots, \mathfrak{M}_n)$$

This must hold for all values of λ; setting λ equal to unity,

$$\sum_i \mathfrak{M}_i \frac{\partial G(T, P, \mathfrak{M}_1, \ldots, \mathfrak{M}_n)}{\partial\mathfrak{M}_i} = G(T, P, \mathfrak{M}_1, \ldots, \mathfrak{M}_n) \tag{10·35}$$

We shall return to this result in a moment.

Taking the differential of the Gibbs function,

$$dG = dU + P\,dV + V\,dP - T\,dS - S\,dT$$

Upon combination with the Gibbs equation (10·7) we find

$$dG = V\,dP - S\,dT + \sum_i \hat{\mu}_i\,d\mathfrak{M}_i \tag{10·36}$$

We therefore recognize the electrochemical potentials as

$$\blacktriangleright \quad \hat{\mu}_i = \left(\frac{\partial G}{\partial\mathfrak{M}_i}\right)_{P,T,\mathfrak{M}_1,\ldots,\mathfrak{M}_{i-1},\mathfrak{M}_{i+1},\ldots,\mathfrak{M}_n} \tag{10·37}$$

Equation (10·35) then simplifies to

$$\blacktriangleright \quad G = \sum_i \hat{\mu}_i \mathfrak{N}_i \tag{10·38}$$

A particularly important case is that of the *pure phase,* containing only one constituent. The above equation then yields

$$\blacktriangleright \quad \hat{\mu} = \frac{G}{\mathfrak{N}} = \hat{g} \tag{10·39}$$

Hence, *the electrochemical potential for a pure phase is simply the Gibbs function of the phase.*

We now introduce a special conceptual system analogous to the TER and MER used in Chap. Seven. A *constituent reservoir* (CR) is conceived as a large region of constant volume which can be connected to a system under study by a rigid, semipermeable, diathermal membrane (Fig. 10·10). The membrane is

FIG. 10·10 *Evaluating the electrochemical potential with the help of a constituent reservoir*

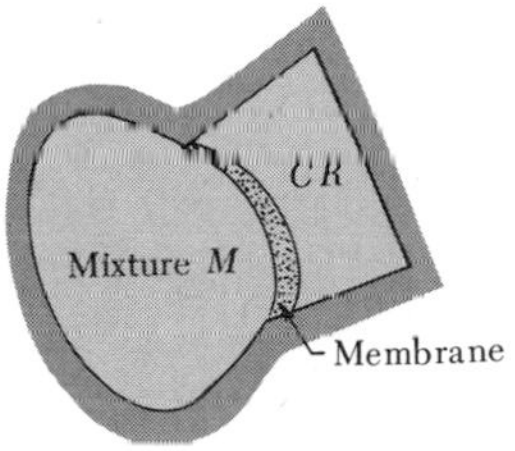

conceived to be permeable only to one constituent, and hence the CR becomes a warehouse for a pure phase of that constituent. Energy transfer as heat across the membrane permits the CR to reach thermal equilibrium with a system. The CR is assumed to have no internal irreversibility, and to possess a uniform internal state. Since its volume is fixed, any entropy changes will be given by [see Eq. (10·7)]

$$dS_{\mathrm{CR}} = \frac{dU_{\mathrm{CR}}}{T} - \frac{\hat{\mu}_i}{T} d\mathfrak{N}_i \tag{10·40}$$

Consider now a single-phase mixture in contact with a CR containing a pure phase of component 1. The combined system is isolated (Fig. 10·10), and its equilibrium state will be that which maximizes its entropy, subject to the constraints that

$$\begin{aligned} U_M + U_{\mathrm{CR}} &= \text{constant} \\ V_M &= \text{constant} \\ V_{\mathrm{CR}} &= \text{constant} \\ \mathfrak{N}_{iM} &= \text{constant} \qquad i = 2,3, \ldots ,n \\ \mathfrak{N}_{1M} + \mathfrak{N}_{1\mathrm{CR}} &= \text{constant} \end{aligned}$$

Here the subscript M denotes the mixture and CR denotes the reservoir. Because of the constraints, only U_M and $\mathfrak{N}_{1M}$ can be varied in seeking the maximum of S_C, the entropy of the combined system. Necessary conditions for equilibrium are therefore

$$\left(\frac{\partial S_C}{\partial U_M}\right)_{\mathfrak{N}_{1M}} = 0$$

$$\left(\frac{\partial S_C}{\partial \mathfrak{N}_{1M}}\right)_{U_M} = 0$$

The first of these leads to

$$\left[\left(\frac{\partial S}{\partial U}\right)_{V,\mathfrak{N}_1,\ldots,\mathfrak{N}_n}\right]_M = \left[\left(\frac{\partial S}{\partial U}\right)_{V,\mathfrak{N}}\right]_{CR}$$

which means that

$$T_M = T_{CR}$$

The second condition gives

$$\left[\left(\frac{\partial S}{\partial \mathfrak{N}_1}\right)_{U,V,\mathfrak{N}_2,\ldots,\mathfrak{N}_n}\right]_M = \left[\left(\frac{\partial S}{\partial \mathfrak{N}}\right)_{U,V}\right]_{CR}$$

Since $T_M = T_{CR}$, this requires

$$\hat{\mu}_{1M} = \hat{\mu}_{CR}$$

But the reservoir is a pure phase, so that $\hat{\mu}_{CR} = \hat{g}_{CR}$. This result may be shown to hold in general, and thus

$$\blacktriangleright \quad \hat{\mu}_i = \hat{g}_i(T, P^*) \tag{10·41}$$

where P^* is the pressure that would exist in a pure phase of the ith component in contact with the mixture through a rigid diathermal membrane permeable only to the ith component. In principle this provides a means for measuring the electrochemical potential of every component in a mixture.

10·7 ELECTROCHEMICAL POTENTIALS IN A MIXTURE OF PERFECT GASES

We can obtain a simple expression for the electrochemical potential of a constituent in a mixture of perfect gases. The Gibbs function for the mixture is

$$\begin{aligned} G &\equiv U + PV - TS \\ &= \sum_i \mathfrak{N}_i \hat{u}_i + V \sum_i P_i - T \sum_i \mathfrak{N}_i \hat{s}_i = \sum_i \mathfrak{N}_i \hat{g}_i(T, P_i) \end{aligned} \tag{10·42}$$

In particular, for a two-constituent mixture,

$$G = \mathfrak{N}_1 \hat{g}_1(T, P_1) + \mathfrak{N}_2 \hat{g}_2(T, P_2)$$

Then, using Eq. (10·37),

$$\hat{\mu}_1 = \left(\frac{\partial G}{\partial \mathfrak{N}_1}\right)_{T,P,\mathfrak{N}_2}$$

$$= \hat{g}_1(T, P_1) + \left[\mathfrak{N}_1 \left(\frac{\partial \hat{g}_1}{\partial P_1}\right)_T \left(\frac{\partial P_1}{\partial \mathfrak{N}_1}\right)_{\mathfrak{N}_2,P,T} + \mathfrak{N}_2 \left(\frac{\partial \hat{g}_2}{\partial P_2}\right)_T \left(\frac{\partial P_2}{\partial \mathfrak{N}_1}\right)_{\mathfrak{N}_2,P,T}\right] \tag{10·43}$$

The partial pressures are related to the mole fractions by Eq. (10·19)

$$P_1 = P\frac{\mathfrak{N}_1}{\mathfrak{N}_1 + \mathfrak{N}_2} \qquad P_2 = P\frac{\mathfrak{N}_2}{\mathfrak{N}_1 + \mathfrak{N}_2}$$

Hence

$$\left(\frac{\partial P_1}{\partial \mathfrak{N}_1}\right)_{\mathfrak{N}_2,P} = \frac{P}{\mathfrak{N}_1 + \mathfrak{N}_2} - \frac{P\mathfrak{N}_1}{(\mathfrak{N}_1 + \mathfrak{N}_2)^2} = \frac{\mathfrak{N}_2 P}{(\mathfrak{N}_1 + \mathfrak{N}_2)^2}$$

$$\left(\frac{\partial P_2}{\partial \mathfrak{N}_1}\right)_{\mathfrak{N}_2,P} = -\frac{P\mathfrak{N}_2}{(\mathfrak{N}_1 + \mathfrak{N}_2)^2}$$

From Eqs. (8·9*a*) and (8·23) it follows that

$$\left(\frac{\partial \hat{g}_1}{\partial P_1}\right)_T = \frac{\mathfrak{R}T}{P_1} \qquad \left(\frac{\partial \hat{g}_2}{\partial P_2}\right)_T = \frac{\mathfrak{R}T}{P_2}$$

Thus the term within brackets in Eq. (10·43) is

$$\mathfrak{N}_1 \frac{\mathfrak{R}T}{P_1}\left(\frac{\mathfrak{N}_2 P}{\mathfrak{N}^2}\right) - \mathfrak{N}_2 \frac{\mathfrak{R}T}{P_2}\left(\frac{\mathfrak{N}_2 P}{\mathfrak{N}^2}\right) = \mathfrak{R}T\frac{\mathfrak{N}_2}{\mathfrak{N}}\left(\frac{\mathfrak{N}_1}{\mathfrak{N}}\frac{P}{P_1} - \frac{\mathfrak{N}_2}{\mathfrak{N}}\frac{P}{P_2}\right)$$

and vanishes by Eq. (10·19); hence Eq. (10·43) reduces to

$$\hat{\mu}_1 = \hat{g}_1(T, P_1)$$

Thus, *the molal electrochemical potential of a constituent is equal to its molal Gibbs function, evaluated at the mixture temperature and its partial pressure.* This result may be shown to be true for every constituent in a mixture of perfect gases,

▶ $$\hat{\mu}_i = \hat{g}_i(T, P_i) \tag{10·44}$$

An alternative expression that can be obtained using Eq. (8·38) is

$$\hat{\mu}_i = \hat{g}_i(T, P) + \mathfrak{R}T \ln P_i - \mathfrak{R}T \ln P$$

Thus, for a mixture of perfect gases,

▶ $$\hat{\mu}_i = \hat{g}_i(T, P) + \mathfrak{R}T \ln x_i \tag{10·45}$$

This latter form is particularly convenient in analysis of reacting perfect-gas mixtures, as we shall see in the next chapter.

10·8 THE GIBBS PHASE RULE

Since the molal Gibbs function is an intensive property, the electrochemical potential must also be intensive (this can be seen from the definition). Consequently it depends on the proportions of the mixture but not on the amounts of each component present. Within a given phase the temperature and pressure may be independently varied (by heating and compression), and in addition, the proportions within the phase may be varied by altering the mole fractions. However, the mole fractions must add up to unity, and therefore only $n - 1$ of these are independently variable. Thus, within a given phase we may think of the electrochemical potential as being uniquely determined by specifications of T, P, and all but one of the mole fractions,

$$\hat{\mu}_i = \hat{\mu}_i(T, P, \chi_1, \chi_2, \ldots, \chi_{n-1})$$

With this functional relation, and with the condition that the electrochemical potentials of a component must have the same value in all coexisting phases, we can now establish an important rule governing the number of possible coexisting phases.

Consider a mixture of phases of a single component. The electrochemical potential of each phase is a function of temperature and pressure. We denote these by

$$\hat{\mu}'(T, P), \hat{\mu}''(T, P), \hat{\mu}'''(T, P), \ldots$$

Henceforth the primes refer to phases. Now, suppose we have an equilibrium mixture of two phases of the substance. Then, from the condition of equilibrium,

$$\hat{\mu}'(T, P) = \hat{\mu}''(T, P)$$

This condition provides a relation between T and P which must be satisfied for all equilibrium mixture states that contain two phases. It may be rewritten functionally as

$$T = T(P)$$

showing that the temperature and pressure of a mixture of two phases of a single substance are not independently variable.

Suppose the mixture is in an equilibrium state with three phases of the same substance present. The equilibrium condition is then

$$\hat{\mu}'(T, P) = \hat{\mu}''(T, P) = \hat{\mu}'''(T, P)$$

This amounts to two equations in the variables T and P, which suffice to determine the unique values of T and P at which the three phases can coexist. Thus, while it is possible to have a two-phase mixture of a substance over a range of temperatures, a mixture of three specified phases can exist only at a single temperature and pressure, called the *triple point*. A substance that can exist

150

100

$T(^\circ C)$ Liquid 7

50

6

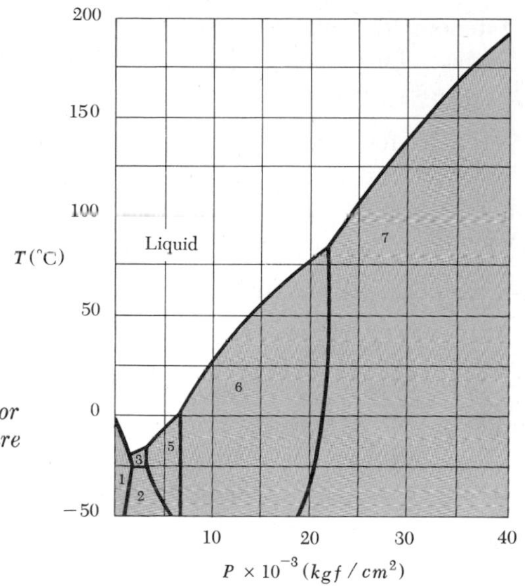

FIG. 10·11 *Phase diagram for* H_2O. *The shaded portions are different solid phases* 0

5

1

2

−50

10 20 30 40

$P \times 10^{-3} (kgf / cm^2)$

in several phases may have several triple points; six are evident in the phase diagram for water of Fig. 10·11.

While a single substance can exist in many phases, only three phases can coexist in equilibrium. Coexistence of four phases would require that three conditions of equilibrium in two variables (P and T) be satisfied, and no solution would be possible in general.

We might restate these observations as follows: given a mixture of a single component, the number of properties from the set (T, P) that may be independently fixed is equal to 3 minus the number of phases. This is a special case of the Gibbs phase rule.

Consider now a mixture of n components in p phases. For each component there will be a total of $p - 1$ equations of equilibrium of the form

$$\hat{\mu}_i'(T, P, \chi_1', \ldots, \chi_{n-1}') = \hat{\mu}_i''(T, P, \chi_1'', \ldots, \chi_{n-1}'')$$

Thus there will be a total of $n(p - 1)$ conditions of equilibrium that must be satisfied. The state of each phase is described by its temperature, pressure, and $n - 1$ mole fractions. The set of possible intensive variables which might conceivably be varied is therefore

▶ $\qquad (T, P, \chi_1', \chi_2', \ldots, \chi_{n-1}', \chi_1'', \ldots, \chi_{n-1}^p)$

and is exactly $p(n - 1) + 2$ in number. But because of the $n(p - 1)$ equilibrium conditions, the number of these which are freely variable is only

$$f = p(n - 1) + 2 - n(p - 1)$$

or

▶ $\qquad f = n - p + 2$ $\qquad\qquad\qquad\qquad\qquad\qquad$ (10·46)

Here f denotes the number of independently variable intensive properties *from the list above*. This result is known as the *Gibbs phase rule*.

For the single-component mixture discussed earlier, we have the following:

$f = 2$ for one phase
$f = 1$ for two phases
$f = 0$ for three phases
No more than three phases permitted

It should be pointed out that the number of independently variable extensive properties from the set

$$(U, V, \mathfrak{N}_1, \ldots, \mathfrak{N}_n)$$

is always $n + 2$. The Gibbs rule does *not* pertain to this set, but rather to the set of *intensive* properties listed above.

To illustrate application of the phase rule, consider a two-component mixture. The largest number of coexisting phases possible is four ($n = 2$, $p = 4$, $f = 0$). This will occur only at particular values of pressure, temperature, and phase composition. At a given pressure three phases may coexist in states for which the following conditions are satisfied:

$$\hat{\mu}_1'(T, P, \chi_1') = \hat{\mu}_1''(T, P, \chi_1'') = \hat{\mu}_1'''(T, P, \chi_1''')$$
$$\hat{\mu}_2'(T, P, \chi_1') = \hat{\mu}_2''(T, P, \chi_1'') = \hat{\mu}_2'''(T, P, \chi_1''')$$

This set of four independent equations contains the five variables T, P, χ_1', χ_1'', χ_1''', and in principle could be reduced to the form

$$T = T(P)$$

Thus at a given pressure three phases could coexist only at one temperature and mixture composition ($n = 2, p = 3, f = 1$). With two phases ($n = 2, p = 2$, $f = 2$) the equilibrium conditions are functionally equivalent to

$$T = T(P, \chi_1')$$

Hence the temperature at which two phases can coexist is to be determined by pressure and the mole fraction of one component in one of the phases. In a single-phase mixture ($n = 2, p = 1, f = 3$) the temperature, pressure, and one mole fraction can be arbitrarily prescribed.

A typical phase diagram for a liquid-vapor binary† mixture is shown in Fig. 10·12. The graph is made on a plane of constant pressure from the three-dimensional T-P-χ_1 space. If a liquid mixture originally at A is heated, evaporation will occur when state B is reached. The first vapor to escape will have the composition of D. A mixture at state C would actually contain liquid at state B and vapor at state D, much as a two-phase single-component mixture contains saturated liquid and saturated vapor.

† Having two components.

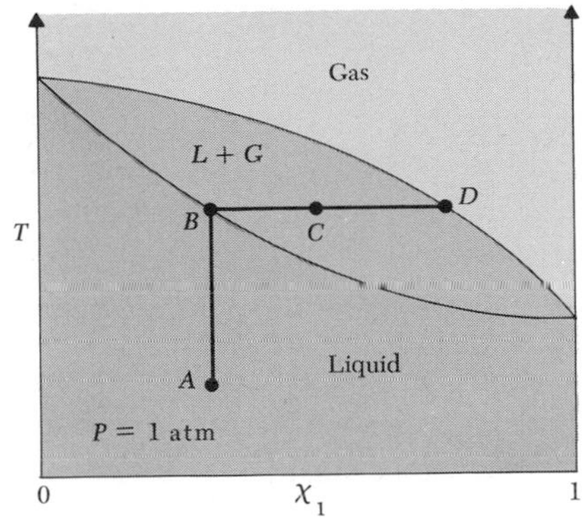

FIG. 10·12 *Typical phase diagram for a liquid-vapor binary mixture*

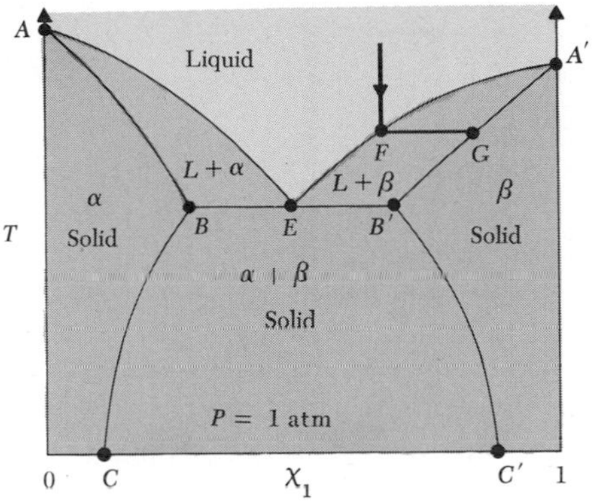

FIG. 10·13 *Typical phase diagram for a solid-liquid binary mixture*

Phase diagrams for solid-liquid binary solutions often appear as shown in Fig. 10·13. Again only a single constant-pressure plane is shown. Two solid phases, labeled α and β, exist. The curves ABC and $A'B'C'$ are called *solidus curves*, and the curve AEA' is the *liquidus* curve. Suppose we start cooling a liquid having the composition of state F. When F is reached, the β-phase solid will start to precipitate with the composition G. The only composition for which the condensed solid would have the identical composition as the liquid is the *eutectic* solution (E).

The line BEB' represents the locus of three phase states. The Gibbs phase rule requires that all such states have a common temperature for a given pressure, and consequently the line is an isotherm.

It is difficult to sketch the three-dimensional T-P-χ_1 phase space. If we could, the eutectic point would trace out a curved line, and at a particular pressure a vapor phase would be encountered. The phase rule tells us that there would be a unique point in the phase space at which this would occur. No more than four coexisting phases could ever be found.

Phase diagrams for solid-liquid systems may be familiar from courses dealing with metallurgy. If so, you may recall that a eutectic solution makes good alloy castings, because it freezes very uniformly. You probably also wondered why certain multiple-phase lines were isotherms, while others were not. Now it can be seen that thermodynamics provides a sound theoretical basis for these things in the phase rule.

10·9 ALTERATION OF THE SATURATED-VAPOR PRESSURE BY AN INERT GAS

As a second application of the thermodynamic theory of nonreacting mixtures, consider a vessel containing a liquid, above which is a mixture of its vapor and an inert gas (see Fig. 10·14). We treat the inert gas and vapor as a mixture

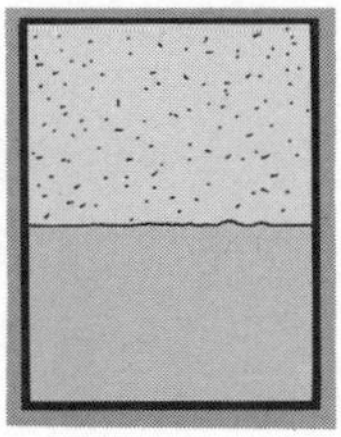

FIG. 10·14 *The system*

of independent substances. Liquid will evaporate until the gas space is saturated; we wish to learn how much the presence of the inert gas alters the saturated-vapor pressure from that which would be obtained without the inert component.

The conditions of equilibrium between phases require that the chemical potential of each component have the same value in all phases. The liquid constitutes one phase and the gas mixture the other. We assume that no inert gas is present in the liquid, so it constitutes a pure phase. The electrochemical potential of the pure liquid phase [see Eq. (10·39)] is

$$\hat{\mu}_f = \hat{g}_f(T, P)$$

where $\hat{g}_f(T, P)$ denotes the Gibbs function of the liquid as a function of the temperature T and total pressure P. Under our perfect-gas idealizations the electrochemical potential of the vapor in the mixture [see Eq. (10·44)] is

$$\hat{u}_g = \hat{g}_g(T, P_g)$$

where $\hat{g}_g(T, P_g)$ denotes the molal Gibbs function of the vapor as a function of T and the vapor pressure P_g. Imagine increasing the amount of the inert gas present, keeping the temperature constant. Since the electrochemical potentials $\hat{\mu}_f$ and $\hat{\mu}_g$ remain equal, they must change in the same amount, and we have

$$\left(\frac{\partial \hat{g}_f}{\partial P}\right)_T dP = \left(\frac{\partial \hat{g}_g}{\partial P_g}\right)_T dP_g$$

In Chap. Eight we showed [Eq. (8·9*a*)] that

$$\left(\frac{\partial g}{\partial P}\right)_T = v(P, T)$$

Therefore the change in the partial pressure of the vapor is related to the change in the total (liquid) pressure by

$$dP_g = \frac{\hat{v}_f(P, T)}{\hat{v}_g(P_g, T)} dP$$

If the molal volume of the vapor is very large compared to that of the liquid, such as is the case with water at room temperatures, the vapor-pressure change will be very small compared to the change in the total pressure, and in many engineering calculations it is satisfactory to neglect alteration of the vapor pressure by the presence of an inert gas.

If we idealize that the specific volume of the liquid is constant and bring in the perfect-gas equation of state to evaluate $\hat{v}_g$, we obtain

$$\mathcal{R}T \frac{dP_g}{P_g} = \hat{v}_f \, dP$$

Integrating between two configurations 1 and 2,

$$\mathcal{R}T \ln \frac{P_{g2}}{P_{g1}} = \hat{v}_f \cdot (P_2 - P_1)$$

or

$$\frac{P_{g2}}{P_{g1}} = \exp \left[\frac{\hat{v}_f(P_2 - P_1)}{\mathcal{R}T} \right]$$

For example, consider starting with a vessel containing nothing but water and water vapor at 60°F. The initial vapor pressure will be equal to the saturation pressure of pure H_2O, which we find from Table B·1*a* as 0.256 psia. The liquid specific volume is 0.016 ft³/lbm, and hence

$$\hat{v}_f = 0.016 \times 18.016 = 0.288 \text{ ft}^3/\text{lbmole}$$

Imagine adding enough inert gas, such as air, to bring the total pressure up to 1 atm, cooling as necessary to keep the temperature constant. The final water-vapor pressure P_{g2} will be given by

$$\frac{P_{g2}}{P_{g1}} = \exp \left[\frac{0.288 \times (14.7 - 0.26) \times 144}{1545 \times 520} \right] = e^{0.00075} = 1.00075$$

Thus the change in saturation pressure produced by the presence of the inert gas is very small for air–water-vapor mixtures at 1 atm and may be neglected in engineering calculations. This will be true whenever $\hat{v}_f/\hat{v}_g \ll 1$. However, if $\hat{v}_f$ is an appreciable fraction of $\hat{v}_g$, the presence of an inert constituent in the gas phase can markedly influence the saturation pressure.

SELECTED READING

Lee, J., and F. Sears, *Thermodynamics*, 2d ed., chap. 10, Addison-Wesley Publishing Co., Inc., Reading, Mass., 1962.

Van Wylen, G., and R. Sonntag, *Fundamentals of Classical Thermodynamics*, chap. 11, John Wiley & Sons, Inc., New York, 1965.

Wark, K., *Thermodynamics*, chaps. 11 and 19, McGraw-Hill Book Company, New York, 1966.

Zemansky, M. W., *Heat and Thermodynamics*, 4th ed., chap. 15, McGraw-Hill Book Company, New York, 1957.

QUESTIONS

10·1 What are mass fractions, volume fractions, and mole fractions, and under what circumstances is one equal to another?
10·2 How many independently variable properties are there for a mixture of two compressible electrically polarized gases?
10·3 What is a phase of a mixture?
10·4 What is a mixture of independent substances?
10·5 Under what circumstances are partial pressures equal to the total pressure times the mole fractions?
10·6 How would you compute the specific heat of a mixture of gases (nonperfect) from the known specific heats of its constituents?
10·7 Why is the datum state for enthalpy of a mixture arbitrary? Why can different datums be used for the different species as long as no chemical changes occur?
10·8 What is the meaning of the term "molal specific heat"?
10·9 Why does the entropy not change when two identical gases are allowed to mix?
10·10 What is a psychrometric chart?
10·11 What is the difference between relative humidity and specific humidity? Which do you think is most related to human comfort?
10·12 How can air be dehumidified?
10·13 A "swamp cooler" is simply a burlap sack dripping with water through which air is blown. What happens to the humidity and temperature of the air passing through it?
10·14 What is the chemical potential?
10·15 What is the phase rule?
10·16 Can two phases of ice plus liquid and vapor H_2O exist in equilibrium in any state?
10·17 Why is a triple point better than a two-phase point as the fixed point on a temperature scale?
10·18 What is the greatest number of coexisting phases for a three-component (tertiary) mixture?
10·19 What happens to the pressure of a vapor above its liquid when an inert nondissolving gas is introduced with the vapor? Does the vapor condense or does more evaporate when the inert gas is added at constant temperature?

PROBLEMS

10·1 Air is roughly 21 percent oxygen and 79 percent nitrogen (by volume). Calculate the specific heat of air from the data in Table B·6 and compare your result with the value given there.
10·2 A gas having a specific-heat ratio k of 1.500 is required for a certain gas-dynamic experiment. Specify a mixture that could be used.
10·3 Oxygen can be separated from air by fractional distillation, which amounts to cooling the air until either nitrogen or oxygen condenses. Which will occur first at 10 atm pressure?
10·4 One ft³ of helium at 1 atm and 80°F is mixed with 2 ft³ of oxygen at 1 atm and 100°F. Specify the partial pressures, mole fractions, mass fractions, and specific

heats of this mixture at 2 atm and 150°F. Determine the difference in the enthalpy and entropy of the mixture between 50 and 100°F at 1 atm.

10·5 A mixture of air and water vapor containing 0.013 lbm of water vapor and 1 lbm of air occupies a tank at 14.7 psia and 90°F. Determine the dew point, relative humidity, and specific humidity.

10·6 How much will the enthalpy of a mixture of 20 percent freon-12 and 80 percent CO_2 (parts by mass) change when the mixture is heated at constant pressure (100 psia) from 140°F to 200°F?

10·7 At what temperature will fractional distillation occur in the mixture of Prob. 10·6 (100 psia), and which component will be first to condense?

10·8 Derive Eq. (10·30).

10·9 For $T_{WB} = 70°F$ and $T_{DB} = 90°F$, determine the relative and specific humidities using the adiabatic-saturator model, and compare your results with those obtained from the psychrometric chart.

10·10 One thousand ft³/min of air at 75°F, 1 atm, and 70 percent relative humidity are to be cooled and dehumidified to 68°F and 55 percent relative humidity by cooling and reheating in a steady-flow air conditioner. Find the temperature to which the air must be cooled and the tonnage of refrigeration required.

10·11 Condensation on cold-water pipes often occurs in warm humid rooms. If the water temperature is 50°F and the room temperature is 75°F, what maximum relative humidity can be tolerated if condensation is to be avoided?

10·12 An air compressor takes in air from the atmosphere at 60°F and 75 percent relative humidity and discharges the air at 100 psia. The compressor isentropic efficiency is 82 percent. What are the relative and specific humidities of the discharged air?

10·13 Develop a psychrometric chart for a mixture of helium and water vapor at 2 atm. Show the 25, 50, 75, and 100 percent relative-humidity lines over the range 40–120°F.

10·14 Develop a psychrometric chart for helium-mercury mixtures at 60 psia for the range 300–500°F. Plot lines of 25, 50, 75, and 100 percent relative humidity.

10·15 A tank contains helium with mercury vapor. Initially the mixture is at 700°F and 2 psia. The mixture is cooled at constant pressure, and at 415°F mercury droplets are observed inside the tank. How much could the pressure of the original mixture have been increased in an isothermal compression before mercury condensation occurred at 700°F? What were the initial relative and specific mercury humidities?

10·16 A mixture of CO_2 and helium is cooled at constant volume from 40°F and 500 psia to −20°F, at which point CO_2 condensation is observed. What was the initial mixture composition?

10·17 A mixture of freon-12 and argon is cooled at constant volume from 200°F and 100 psia to −20°F, at which point freon condensation is observed. What was the initial mixture composition?

10·18 Specify a mixture of freon-12 and CO_2 such that both constituents will condense when the mixture temperature is 0°F. At what mixture pressure will this occur? What will happen when a mixture of this proportion is cooled at 100 psia? At 600 psia?

10·19 Air frequently becomes trapped in refrigeration systems. If the gas in a freon-12 system contains 10 percent air (by mass), how much will the freon-12 saturation pressure be changed when the system temperature is 80°F?

10·20 Air at 85°F and a relative humidity of 80 percent is to be processed in a steady-flow air conditioner, and delivered at 70°F, 50 percent humidity. The air flow rate is 200 ft^3/min. Design a suitable system, specifying any energy-transfer rates, power requirements, temperatures, intermediate states, coolant flow rates, and so on.

10·21 Cooling air for a large computer must be supplied at the rate of 100 ft^3/min. The temperature must be 50 °F, and the humidity less than 0.0005 lbm H_2O/lbm dry air. Suppose the supply air is at 80°F and 50 percent relative humidity. Design a suitable air conditioning system, specifying any energy-transfer rates, coolant flow rates, temperatures, intermediate system states, and so on.

10·22 A simple cooling system using CO_2 sublimation has been proposed for a short-term extravehicular space suit. The CO_2 will be sublimed from a small solid block at 10 psia, and mixed with the breathing gas at 70°F. The breathing rate is nominally 8 ft^3/min, and the mixture must leave the suit at 90°F. The total energy-removal rate is to be 200 Btu/hr. Specify the required CO_2 sublimation rate, the mass requirement for 1 hr of operation, and the mass percent of CO_2 in the inlet mixture.

10·23 CO_2 must be removed from the oxygen in an astronaut life-support system. Suppose the breathing rate is 6 ft^3/min, and that the exhaled mixture contains CO_2 with 10 percent volume fraction. Design a system to continuously remove 95 percent of the CO_2 from the discharged gas, assuming the mixture is delivered at 90°F to the conditioner and to the space suit at 70°F. Specify the volume flow of make-up oxygen required, the processes, power requirements, intermediate states, and so on within the conditioner.

CHAPTER ELEVEN

THERMODYNAMICS OF REACTING MIXTURES

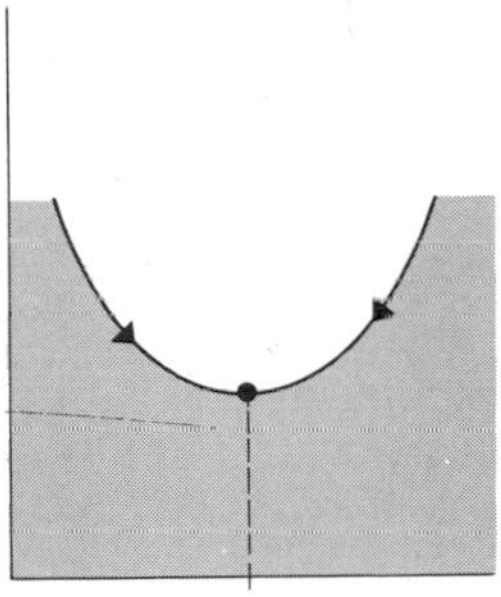

11·1 THE CHEMISTRY OF REACTIONS

In this chapter we shall study the thermodynamics of mixtures which may be undergoing a chemical reaction. The reaction begins with a collection of certain chemical constituents, called the *reactants*, and the chemical reaction causes a rearrangement of the atoms and electrons to form different constituents, called the *products*. Thermodynamic treatments of reaction allow us to determine the equilibrium composition of any mixture of chemical substances. Prediction of reaction rates is beyond the scope of thermodynamics. The topic of chemical kinetics, which deals with reaction rates, will not be discussed in this text.

Associated with every chemical reaction is a chemical equation, derived by applying the conservation of atoms to each of the atomic species involved in some sort of a "unit reaction." For example, the reaction between oxygen and hydrogen to form water can be expressed as

$$2H_2 + O_2 \leftrightarrows 2H_2O \tag{11·1}$$

This expression indicates that two molecules of hydrogen and one molecule of oxygen can combine to form two molecules of water (the reaction may also go in the opposite direction). The coefficients in the chemical equation are called *stoichiometric coefficients* (2, 1, and 2 in this example). The number of hydrogen atoms is conserved, as is the number of oxygen atoms. The chemical equation can also be interpreted as an equation relating the molal masses involved in a reaction; two moles of hydrogen and one mole of oxygen combine to form two moles of water. Note that the number of moles of the products may differ from that of the reactants.

A *stoichiometric mixture* of reactants is one in which the molal proportions of the reactants are exactly as given by the stoichiometric coefficients, so that no excess of any constituent is present. A *stoichiometric combustion* is one in which all the oxygen atoms in the oxidizer react chemically to appear in the products.

The most common oxidizer is air, which for many purposes may be considered as a mixture of 21 percent oxygen and 79 percent nitrogen (mole or volume fractions). The chemical equation for stoichiometric combustion of methane (CH_4) with air is then

$$CH_4 + 2(O_2 + 3.76N_2) \leftrightarrows CO_2 + 2H_2O + 7.52N_2 \tag{11·2}$$

If more air is supplied, not all will be involved in the reaction, and the composition of the products will differ from that of a stoichiometric combustion. The additional air supplied is called *excess air*.

If a reaction occurs in an isolated vessel the internal energy of the products and reactants will be the same, and the entropy of the products will be greater than that of the reactants. Reactions can be made to occur at constant pressure and temperature by allowing the volume to change and transferring energy as heat from the reacting mixture. The internal energy of the products will then be different from that of the reactants. If the products have less internal energy (at constant P and T) the reaction is said to be *exothermic*, and energy must be transferred as heat from the mixture in order to keep the temperature constant. A reaction at constant P and T for which the opposite is true is called *endothermic*. The exothermic reaction is of particular utility in engineering as a means for supplying energy in the form of heat to thermal power systems.

11·2 STANDARDIZED ENERGY AND ENTHALPY

Equations of state for many substances have been worked up from a combination of laboratory data, thermodynamic relations, and quantum-statistical analyses; we are already familiar with the examples given in Appendix B. In the preparation of these equations of state it is customary to select some arbitrary datum state at which the internal energy (or alternatively, the enthalpy) and the entropy are taken to be zero. These equations of state may be used in any thermodynamic analysis involving one substance only (or mixtures of nonreacting substances), since differences in internal energy and entropy between two states are all that ever enter into consideration. However, with chemically reacting systems it is necessary to use a common basis for evaluation of the thermodynamic properties of all substances involved in any particular analysis. For example, suppose we arbitrarily selected some state T_0 and P_0 as the datum for H_2, O_2, and H_2O. Any reaction carried out at this temperature and pressure would result in no change in the internal energy or entropy of the mixture, an obviously incorrect situation. We might pick the datum state for the reactants arbitrarily, but this fixes the datum state for the products.

It might be thought that since energy is a monotonically increasing function of temperature, the energy of all substances at the absolute zero of temperature would be zero. This is certainly not the case, because a considerable amount of energy may be associated with molecular and nuclear binding forces and other energy modes. It does not appear practical to speak of the "absolute energy" of matter. A datum must be selected that will allow us to properly tie together the energy of different substances so that we can make proper energy analyses of chemical reactions.

The procedure we follow is to select some arbitrary datum (temperature and pressure) at which we give zero values to the enthalpy of the basic elements.† It would be nice if this could be absolute zero temperature and, say, 1 atm pressure, but this would require accurate low-temperature data not generally available at the present time. A more practical datum conventionally adopted for chemical thermodynamic tabulations is 25°C (77°F) and 1 atm pressure. This is called the *standard reference state.* By convention, we make the enthalpy of every elemental substance zero at the standard reference state.‡ By elemental substance we mean the substance composed of only one kind of atom in the form in which it exists in equilibrium at the standard reference state. For example, the enthalpy of mercury (Hg, liquid) is zero at the standard reference state, as is the enthalpy of oxygen (O_2, gas) at this temperature and pressure.§

The *enthalpy of formation* of a compound is defined as the difference between the enthalpy of the compound, h^0_{comp}, and the enthalpy of the elemental substances from which it is formed, all evaluated at the standard reference state. It is conventionally denoted by $\Delta h_f{}^0$ and, on a molal basis, is

$$\blacktriangleright \qquad \Delta\hat{h}_f{}^0 \equiv \hat{h}^0_{\text{comp}} - \sum_i \nu_i \hat{h}_i{}^0 \qquad (11\cdot 3)$$

Here $\hat{h}_i{}^0$ is the molal enthalpy of the ith elemental substance involved in the formation reaction, and ν_i is the number of moles of the ith elemental substance involved in forming a single mole of the compound. The enthalpy of formation can be evaluated by appropriate measurements of energy transfers as heat and work and is a frequently tabulated property. Since by convention the elemental substances have zero enthalpy at the standard reference state, the enthalpy of a compound at the standard reference state is merely its enthalpy of formation. The enthalpy at other states may be established using this datum-

† It is customary to give the enthalpy, rather than the internal energy, a zero value at the datum state; this then fixes the value of the energy at the datum state, since absolute values for P and v are measurable.

‡ Recall that different isotopes of an element have the same chemical properties. If no nuclear reactions are involved, the enthalpy of each isotope can be considered zero at this standard state.

§ These may not agree with the graphical and tabular equations of state often presented. The standard reference state is used primarily in chemical thermodynamic literature, as for example, in some places in the *Handbook of Chemistry and Physics.* The user of equation-of-state information should always check the datum, especially if he is analyzing a chemical reaction.

point enthalpy. We call this the *standardized enthalpy*, meaning simply that it is properly related to the enthalpy of other elements and compounds. Values for the standardized enthalpy of several gases are given in Table B·13.

The term "heat of formation" is used sometimes to refer to the enthalpy of formation and sometimes to mean the negative of the enthalpy of formation; the user of any tabulation must be sure which (if either) the tabulator had in mind. The term arises because it may be shown that the energy that must be transferred as heat from the mixture to keep the temperature and pressure constant is equal to the enthalpy of formation.

The complete tie between the states of compounds and elements requires knowledge of the entropy difference between the products and reactants at the standard reference state. We can measure the energy transfer as heat during a constant-temperature reaction, and if it is idealized that the reaction takes place reversibly, the entropy difference can be determined from $dS = (đQ/T)_{\text{rev}}$. However, most reactions occur so rapidly that they can hardly be idealized as reversible. This difficulty may be avoided if we discard the use of arbitrary entropy datums and instead work with absolute entropies. The absolute entropy can be computed using statistical thermodynamics (Chap. Twelve). These calculations are particularly successful for gases, and hence it is not too difficult to calculate the absolute entropy of a substance in some gaseous state. This value can then be used to compute the absolute entropy at other states from entropy tabulations with an arbitrary datum. However, a more common practice is to make use of an additional thermodynamic postulate, the third law of thermodynamics, which we shall now discuss.

11·3 ABSOLUTE ENTROPY AND THE THIRD LAW OF THERMODYNAMICS

Let us first recall the meaning of zero entropy. A state of zero entropy is one for which one single system quantum state is always observed. We would know the microscopic state of a system at zero entropy precisely, with zero uncertainty. Imagine now that we add one quantum of energy to the system, and that this permits it to suddenly take any one of a very large number of quantum states. Assuming each quantum state is equally likely, the entropy change would be

$$\delta S = \mathsf{k} \ln \Omega - 0$$

where Ω is the number of quantum states available to the system with the single quantum of energy. The internal energy change δU would be simply ϵ, the very small amount of energy added. Since Ω is likely to be very large, a tiny increase in energy would give a huge increase in entropy. Recalling the thermodynamic definition of temperature, Eq. (7·9), we are led to suspect that T must be very small when the entropy is zero.

We can illustrate this by a numerical example. Consider 1 cm³ of matter having a mass of the order of 1 g and a molal mass of the order of 20 g/gmole.

This system would contain roughly 3×10^{22} atoms. The quantum of energy added might be possessed by any one of the atoms, so the entropy in the slightly energized state will be approximately

$$S \approx \mathsf{k} \ln N \approx 1.38 \times 10^{-23} \text{ joule/°K} \times \ln (3 \times 10^{22})$$
$$\approx 70 \times 10^{-23} \text{ joule/°K}$$

We imagine adding a quantum of energy by means of a photon having a wavelength equal to 1 cm (this is a reasonable estimate for the least energetic photon that might be captured by 1 cm³ of matter). Its energy is

$$\epsilon = \frac{\mathsf{hc}}{\lambda} = \frac{6.62 \times 10^{-34} \text{ joule-sec} \times 3 \times 10^{8} \text{ m/sec}}{0.01 \text{ m}}$$

$$\epsilon \approx 2 \times 10^{-23} \text{ joule}$$

The temperature is therefore estimated to be

$$T \approx \frac{1}{\delta S/\epsilon} \approx \frac{1}{70 \times 10^{-23}/2 \times 10^{-23}} \approx \frac{1}{35} \text{ °K}$$

This should be interpreted as the "average" temperature over the range $0 < S < 70 \times 10^{-23}$ joule/°K. Since the temperature is a monotonic function of the entropy, the temperature at the zero entropy state may be expected to be even smaller.

On the basis of these considerations we make the following macroscopic postulate:

The temperature of any pure substance in thermodynamic equilibrium approaches zero as the entropy approaches zero.

Conversely, since the temperature is a monotonic function of the entropy,

The entropy of any pure substance in thermodynamic equilibrium approaches zero as the temperature approaches zero.

Expressed mathematically, for a pure substance in equilibrium,

▶ $$\lim_{T \to 0} S = 0 \tag{11·4}$$

This particular form of the postulate is called the *third law of thermodynamics.* The third law was developed in the early 1900s, primarily through the efforts of Nernst, and consequently is often called the *Nernst theorem.*

A considerable body of experimental data supporting the third law now exists. We can calculate the absolute entropy of a substance from the measured thermodynamic properties by integrating the differential equations of state from absolute zero; for gases this requires passage from the solid state through the liquid state and vaporization to get to the gaseous phase. It is also possible to calculate the entropy of gases using statistical thermodynamics. The close agreement of the entropies calculated in these different ways provides some of the strongest evidence in support of the third law.

Some exceptions to the agreement between the macroscopically determined and statistically determined absolute entropies have been claimed, and there is some disagreement as to the validity and generality of the third law, through no one denies its usefulness. According to Fast,† all the exceptions seem to be satisfactorily explained. First of all, the substance must be "pure," since presence of any additional species would immediately give a positional entropy, even at zero temperature. Second, it is necessary to extrapolate to absolute zero, and data down to very low temperatures must be provided. Other apparent exceptions arise from the fact that thermodynamic equilibrium is not maintained as the temperature is reduced. None of these contradicts the third law, which holds only at absolute zero for pure substances in equilibrium states.

The third law permits determination of the absolute entropy of every substance, including elemental substances (Hg, O_2, . . .) and compounds. These entropies are all properly tied to a common base and may therefore be used in analyzing chemical reactions. The absolute entropies of several substances are given in Tables B·12 and B·13.

11·4 AN ILLUSTRATIVE ANALYSIS

Let us consider the combustion of methane in a steady-flow burner. The oxidizer will be air, and we suppose that twice as much air is supplied as is necessary for the combustion (200 percent "theoretical air"). The air will enter at 90°F and 40 psia and the methane at 60°F and 20 psia. The products of combustion emerge at 1 atm. We assume that the burner is adiabatic and the products of combustion contain only CO_2, H_2O, N_2, and O_2 and make the following idealizations:

Oxygen, nitrogen, methane, and CO_2 are perfect gases
The products of combustion constitute a mixture of independent perfect gases‡
Steady flow, steady state
Adiabatic control volume
Equilibrium at inlets and exhaust
Kinetic and potential energies negligible

Our procedure will be to make an energy balance and solve for the enthalpy of the products in terms of the enthalpies of the reactants. The enthalpy, composition, and pressure of the products will then suffice to fix the exhaust temperature.

† J. D. Fast, *Entropy*, p. 85, McGraw-Hill Book Company, New York, 1962.
‡ Since the temperature of the exhaust is expected to be high, we assume that the H_2O will appear as vapor.

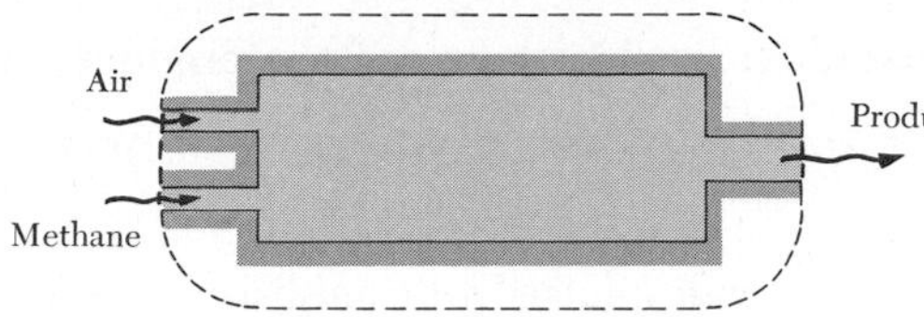

FIG. 11·1 *The control volume*

An energy balance on the control volume of Fig. 11·1, made on a rate basis, gives

$$(\dot{\mathfrak{N}}\hat{h})_{CH_4} + (\dot{\mathfrak{N}}\hat{h})_{O_2} + (\dot{\mathfrak{N}}\hat{h})_{N_2} = (\dot{\mathfrak{N}}\hat{h})_{prod} \tag{11·5}$$

where $\dot{\mathfrak{N}}$ denotes molal mass flow rate. The chemical equation is [compare with Eq. (11·2)]

$$CH_4 + 4(O_2 + 3.76N_2) \leftrightarrows CO_2 + 2H_2O + 2O_2 + 15.04N_2 \tag{11·6}$$

Note that this equation contains the information on conservation of like atoms, and therefore a mass balance would provide redundant information.

We have to evaluate the enthalpies of the reactants before we can calculate the enthalpy of the product mixture. From Table B·12 the standardized enthalpy of methane at the reference state is found as −32,179 Btu/lbmole. From the perfect gas equation of state [Eq. (8·15)] we relate the enthalpy at the inlet state to that at the standard state†

$$\hat{h} - \hat{h}^0 = \hat{c}_P(T - T_0)$$

Using $\hat{c}_P$ from Table B·6, the standardized enthalpy of the inlet CH_4 is therefore

$$\hat{h}_{CH_4} = -32{,}179 + 8.53 \times (60 - 77) = -32{,}325 \text{ Btu/lbmole}$$

The molal enthalpy of the oxygen and nitrogen at 90°F may be evaluated in a similar manner, and we find†

$$\hat{h}_{O_2} = 7.01 \times (90 - 77) + 0 = 91.1 \text{ Btu/lbmole}$$
$$\hat{h}_{N_2} = 6.95 \times (90 - 77) + 0 = 90.3 \text{ Btu/lbmole}$$

Equation (11·5) may be written as

$$\hat{h}_{prod} = \frac{(\dot{\mathfrak{N}}\hat{h})_{CH_4}}{\dot{\mathfrak{N}}_{prod}} + \frac{(\dot{\mathfrak{N}}\hat{h})_{O_2}}{\dot{\mathfrak{N}}_{prod}} + \frac{(\dot{\mathfrak{N}}\hat{h})_{N_2}}{\dot{\mathfrak{N}}_{prod}}$$

From the chemical equation we see that

$$\frac{\dot{\mathfrak{N}}_{CH_4}}{\dot{\mathfrak{N}}_{prod}} = \frac{1}{20.04} = 0.0499$$
$$\frac{\dot{\mathfrak{N}}_{O_2}}{\dot{\mathfrak{N}}_{prod}} = \frac{4}{20.04} = 0.1996$$
$$\frac{\dot{\mathfrak{N}}_{N_2}}{\dot{\mathfrak{N}}_{prod}} = \frac{4 \times 3.76}{20.04} = 0.7505$$

† Recall that the enthalpy of a perfect gas is independent of pressure.

The standardized enthalpy of the product mixture is then

$$\begin{aligned}\hat{h}_{\text{prod}} &= 0.0499 \times (-32{,}325) + 0.1996 \times 91.1 + 0.750 \times 90.3 \\ &= -1527 \text{ Btu/lbmole}\end{aligned}$$

This value will be used to establish the temperature of the exhaust gases.

The mole fractions of the species in the product mixture are, from the chemical equation,

$$\chi_{CO_2} = \frac{1}{20.04} = 0.0499$$

$$\chi_{H_2O} = \frac{2}{20.04} = 0.0998$$

$$\chi_{O_2} = \frac{2}{20.04} = 0.0998$$

$$\chi_{N_2} = \frac{15.04}{20.04} = 0.7505$$

The products of enthalpy may then be written as

$$\hat{h}_{\text{prod}}(T) = \chi_{CO_2}\hat{h}_{CO_2}(T) + \chi_{H_2O}\hat{h}_{H_2O}(T) + \chi_{O_2}\hat{h}_{O_2}(T) + \chi_{N_2}\hat{h}_{N_2}(T)$$

Data for the standardized enthalpies of the constituents in the product mixture may be obtained from Table B·13. Calculation of the product temperature requires iteration, which is summarized in Table 11·1.

TABLE 11·1 PRODUCT ENTHALPY CALCULATION

		2600°R		2700°R	
	χ_i	$\hat{h}_i$	$\chi_i\hat{h}_i$	$\hat{h}_i$	$\chi_i\hat{h}_i$
CO_2	0.0499	−144025	−7187	−142631	−7117
H_2O	0.0998	−84397	−8423	−83279	−8311
O_2	0.0998	+16586	+1655	+17458	+1742
N_2	0.7505	+15686	+11773	+16517	+12396
		$\hat{h}_{\text{prod}}$ =	−2182	$\hat{h}_{\text{prod}}$ =	−1290

Interpolating, we find

$$T_{\text{prod}} = 2600 + \frac{2182 - 1527}{2182 - 1290} \times 100 = 2674°\text{R}$$

This is a typical *adiabatic flame temperature.*†

We presumed (without justification) that the reaction could in fact occur; let us now test this presumption with the aid of the second law. Applying the

† Product temperature obtained in an adiabatic steady-flow combustion process.

second law to the control volume, we find

$$\dot{\mathcal{P}}_s = (\dot{\mathfrak{N}}\hat{s})_{prod} - (\dot{\mathfrak{N}}\hat{s})_{CH_4} - (\dot{\mathfrak{N}}\hat{s})_{O_2} - (\dot{\mathfrak{N}}\hat{s})_{N_2} \geq 0 \tag{11·7}$$

where $\hat{s}$ represents the absolute molal entropy. If the entropy production is positive, the reaction is possible; if it is zero, the reaction is reversible, that is, could go in either direction; if a negative value is calculated, the assumed reaction could not occur.

The absolute molal entropies of the reactant gases will be calculated by extrapolation from the entropies at standard reference state; we treat the gases as perfect, with constant specific heats over the small temperature range of the extrapolation. Equation (8·46*b*) is equivalent to

$$\hat{s} = \hat{s}^0 + \hat{c}_p \ln \frac{T}{T_0} - \mathcal{R} \ln \frac{P}{P_0}$$

where $\hat{s}^0$ is the entropy in the standard reference state (T_0, P_0). The partial pressures of the O_2 and N_2 in the air are proportional to their mole fractions. Thus

$$P_{O_2} = 0.21 \times 40 = 8.4 \text{ psia}$$
$$P_{N_2} = 0.79 \times 40 = 31.6 \text{ psia}$$

The absolute molal entropies of the incoming constituents are then, for CH_4,

$$\hat{s} = 44.47 + 8.53 \times \ln \frac{520}{537} - 1.986 \times \ln \frac{20}{14.7} = 43.58 \text{ Btu/lbmole-°R}$$

for O_2,

$$\hat{s} = 48.986 + 7.01 \times \ln \frac{550}{537} - 1.986 \times \ln \frac{8.4}{14.7} = 50.27 \text{ Btu/lbmole-°R}$$

and for N_2,

$$\hat{s} = 45.755 + 6.95 \times \ln \frac{550}{537} - 1.986 \times \ln \frac{31.6}{14.7} = 44.41 \text{ Btu/lbmole-°R}$$

The molal entropy of the products is computed in Table 11·2, using the data from Table B·13.

TABLE 11·2 PRODUCT ENTROPY CALCULATION

		2600°R		2700°R	
	χ_i	$\hat{s}_i$	$\chi_i\hat{s}_i$	$\hat{s}_i$	$\chi_i\hat{s}_i$
CO_2	0.0499	69.245	3.455	69.771	3.482
H_2O	0.0998	59.414	5.926	59.837	5.972
O_2	0.0998	61.287	6.116	61.616	6.149
N_2	0.7505	57.436	43.106	57.750	43.321
			$\hat{s}_{prod}$ = 58.603		$\hat{s}_{prod}$ = 58.924

Interpolating,

$$\hat{s}_{\text{prod}} = 58.603 + \frac{2674 - 2600}{2700 - 2600} \times (58.924 - 58.603)$$
$$= 58.839 \text{ Btu/lbmole-}^\circ\text{R}$$

Substituting into Eq. (11·7),

$$\frac{\dot{\mathcal{P}}_s}{\dot{\mathfrak{N}}_{\text{prod}}} = 58.839 - 0.0499 \times 43.58 - 0.1995 \times 50.27 - 0.7505 \times 44.41$$
$$= 13.313 \text{ Btu/lbmole-}^\circ\text{R} \geq 0$$

Since a positive entropy-production rate is obtained, the process assumed does not violate the second law. Note that the reaction is not reversible (because it produces entropy).

We assumed that the products of combustion contain no CO, NO, or other compounds and that the reaction was "complete." The second-law structure provides a means for determining the equilibrium composition of a reacting mixture, and we now turn to this important application of thermodynamics.

11·5 GENERAL CONDITIONS FOR CHEMICAL EQUILIBRIUM OF A MIXTURE

An extremely important aspect of the theory of chemical reactions is the determination of the equilibrium composition of a mixture of chemically reactive constituents. In this section we derive some general conditions for chemical equilibrium from basic thermodynamic considerations. These conditions will be expressed in terms of thermodynamic properties of the mixture; however, there is some difficulty in ascribing properties such as temperature and pressure in the absence of equilibrium. A similar problem arose in Chap. Ten when we discussed equilibrium between phases of a mixture. There we assumed that each phase was separately in a thermodynamic equilibrium state, though the combined system of phases was not. The same approach is adopted here. To discuss the properties of a mixture not in chemical equilibrium, that is, not having the composition of the equilibrium mixture, we imagine shutting off the reaction, and evaluate the properties of the mixture as if it were a mixture of nonreacting gases in a thermodynamic equilibrium state. By this procedure we shall be able to establish the conditions of chemical equilibrium, and thereby the composition in the true equilibrium state.

Restricting our considerations to a mixture of simple compressible substances, we apply the first and second laws of thermodynamics to the mixture, which we assume to be at temperature T and pressure P. Defining $đW$ and $đQ$ to be energy additions to the mixture, the energy balance gives

$$dU = đQ + đW$$

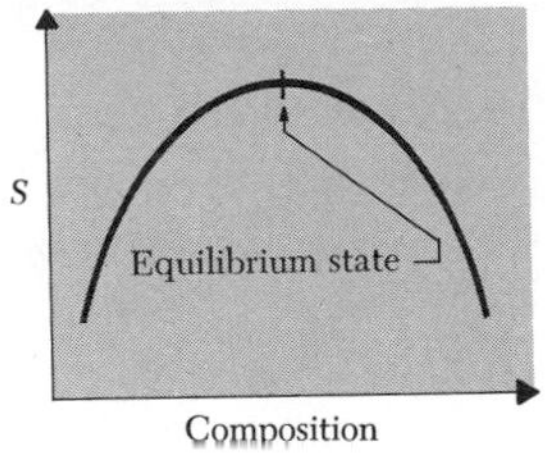

FIG. 11·2 *Equilibrium at constant volume and energy*

and the second law gives

$$đ\mathcal{P}_s = dS - \frac{đQ}{T} \geq 0$$

Since the pressure is uniform,

$$đW = -P\,dV$$

Combining the above three equations, we obtain

$$T\,đ\mathcal{P}_s = T\,dS - dU - P\,dV \geq 0 \tag{11·8}$$

Equation (11·8) tells us that any reaction which takes place must be such as to produce entropy. In particular, a reaction taking place in an insulated constant-volume vessel, where $dU = 0$ and $dV = 0$, must be such that

$$\blacktriangleright \quad dS \geq 0 \tag{11·9}$$

If we want to determine the equilibrium composition of a mixture reacting under these conditions, we need only determine the mixture entropy as a function of composition; the equilibrium composition for an isolated reaction is then the one which maximizes the entropy (Fig. 11·2).

We are more often interested in finding equilibrium compositions under other conditions. The condition for equilibrium in a reaction taking place at constant volume and temperature can be expressed in terms of the *Helmholtz function*,

$$\blacktriangleright \quad A \equiv U - TS \tag{11·10}$$

The differential of the Helmholtz function is

$$dA = dU - T\,dS - S\,dT$$

Upon combination with Eq. (11·8) we obtain

$$\blacktriangleright \quad dA + S\,dT + P\,dV \leq 0 \tag{11·11}$$

Hence, a reaction occurring at constant temperature and volume must be such as to decrease the Helmholtz function. The equilibrium composition of a mixture reacting in an isothermal constant-volume vessel is therefore the one having

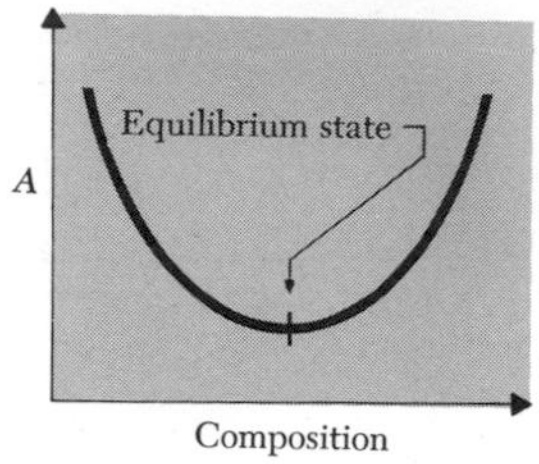

FIG. 11·3 *Equilibrium at constant volume and temperature*

the least value of the Helmholtz function for that volume and temperature (Fig. 11·3).

The most interesting situation is the reaction at constant pressure and temperature. To find the conditions for equilibrium under these conditions we need to bring in a function whose differential will involve the terms $T\,dS - dU - P\,dV$ in such a way as to cancel them out of Eq. (11·8) and replace them by differentials of pressure and temperature (which are then zero). The *Gibbs function* fills this need,

$$\blacktriangleright \qquad G \equiv U + PV - TS \tag{11·12}$$

Differentiating,

$$dG = dU + P\,dV + V\,dP - T\,dS - S\,dT$$

Combining with Eq. (11·8), we find

$$\blacktriangleright \qquad dG - V\,dP + S\,dT \leq 0 \tag{11·13}$$

Therefore, any reaction proceeding at constant temperature and pressure will be such that the Gibbs function of the mixture will continually decrease, until it reaches its minimum value at the final, equlibrium composition (Fig. 11·4).

The Gibbs function is instrumental in allowing us to determine the equilibrium composition of any reactive mixture of known pressure and temperature, regardless of whether or not these were kept constant during all of the reaction. Since the electrochemical potential relates the change in the Gibbs function of a mixture (considered as nonreacting) to changes in the amounts of its constituents [see Eq. (10·37)], it too is very important in chemical thermodynamics.

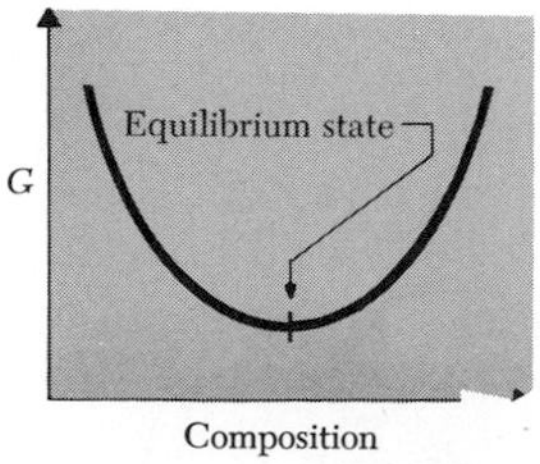

FIG. 11·4 *Equilibrium at constant pressure and temperature*

11·6 DEGREES OF REACTION FREEDOM: THE SIMPLE REACTIVE MIXTURE

Any reaction that takes place in a reactive mixture will be limited by the fact that atoms are conserved (that is, by the chemical equation). For example, consider the mixture CH_4, O_2, H_2O, CO, and CO_2. If no material is added to the mixture, any change in the composition must result from chemical reaction. Denoting a change in mole number by $d\mathfrak{N}$, the constraining conditions are,† for conservation of C,

$$d\mathfrak{N}_{CH_4} + d\mathfrak{N}_{CO} + d\mathfrak{N}_{CO_2} = 0 \tag{11·14a}$$

for conservation of O,

$$2d\mathfrak{N}_{O_2} + d\mathfrak{N}_{H_2O} + d\mathfrak{N}_{CO} + 2d\mathfrak{N}_{CO_2} = 0 \tag{11·14b}$$

and for conservation of H,

$$4d\mathfrak{N}_{CH_4} + 2d\mathfrak{N}_{H_2O} = 0 \tag{11·14c}$$

We have three constraints and five constituents. Thus only two *degrees of reaction freedom* exist for the mixture. For instance, we could consider CH_4 and CO as the two independent components; then, from Eqs. (11·14), we find

$$d\mathfrak{N}_{H_2O} = -2d\mathfrak{N}_{CH_4} \tag{11·15a}$$
$$d\mathfrak{N}_{CO_2} = -d\mathfrak{N}_{CH_4} - d\mathfrak{N}_{CO} \tag{11·15b}$$
$$d\mathfrak{N}_{O_2} = \tfrac{1}{2}d\mathfrak{N}_{CO} + 2d\mathfrak{N}_{CH_4} \tag{11·15c}$$

It is evident that the number of degrees of reaction freedom of a mixture is equal to the number of possible compounds minus the number of kinds of atoms represented. We shall call a mixture having one degree of reaction freedom a *simple reactive mixture*. For example, the mixture CH_4, O_2, H_2O, and CO_2 is a simple reactive mixture.

11·7 EQUATIONS OF REACTION EQUILIBRIUM

Consider a simple reactive mixture having a chemical equation of the form

▶ $$\nu_1 C_1 + \nu_2 C_2 \leftrightarrows \nu_3 C_3 + \nu_4 C_4 \tag{11·16}$$

where $C_1, \ldots, C_4$ denote the chemical constituents, and $\nu_1, \ldots, \nu_4$ are the stoichiometric coefficients. From Eq. (10·36) it follows that the difference in the Gibbs function of the mixture (considered as nonreacting) between any two states having the same temperature and pressure, but infinitesimally different

† As in calculus, $d\mathfrak{N}$ always denotes an infinitesimal *increase* in $\mathfrak{N}$. Each mole of CH_4 contains the same number of carbon atoms as one mole of CO, and twice as many hydrogen atoms as one mole of H_2O.

compositions, is

$$dG_{T,P} = \hat{\mu}_1 \, d\mathfrak{N}_1 + \hat{\mu}_2 \, d\mathfrak{N}_2 + \hat{\mu}_3 \, d\mathfrak{N}_3 + \hat{\mu}_4 \, d\mathfrak{N}_4 \tag{11·17}$$

However, in our reacting mixture the changes in mole numbers are related through the chemical equation, and

$$d\mathfrak{N}_2 = \frac{\nu_2}{\nu_1} d\mathfrak{N}_1 \tag{11·18a}$$

$$d\mathfrak{N}_3 = -\frac{\nu_3}{\nu_1} d\mathfrak{N}_1 \tag{11·18b}$$

$$d\mathfrak{N}_4 = -\frac{\nu_4}{\nu_1} d\mathfrak{N}_1 \tag{11·18c}$$

From Eqs. (11·17) and (11·18), we see that for any reaction at constant temperature and pressure, since G must decrease,

▶ $$(\hat{\mu}_1\nu_1 + \hat{\mu}_2\nu_2 - \hat{\mu}_3\nu_3 - \hat{\mu}_4\nu_4) \, d\mathfrak{N}_1 \leq 0$$

It then follows that

If

$$\hat{\mu}_1\nu_1 + \hat{\mu}_2\nu_2 > \hat{\mu}_3\nu_3 + \hat{\mu}_4\nu_4$$

then $d\mathfrak{N}_1 < 0$ *and the reaction proceeds to the right, and if*

$$\hat{\mu}_1\nu_1 + \hat{\mu}_2\nu_2 < \hat{\mu}_3\nu_3 + \hat{\mu}_4\nu_4$$

then $d\mathfrak{N}_1 > 0$ *and the reaction proceeds to the left.*

The condition of chemical equilibrium for a simple reactive mixture is therefore

▶ $$\hat{\mu}_1\nu_1 + \hat{\mu}_2\nu_2 = \hat{\mu}_3\nu_3 + \hat{\mu}_4\nu_4 \tag{11·19}$$

This is called the *equation of reaction equilibrium;* it is a relation among the intensive properties of the products and reactants. We see that in order to determine the composition of a mixture after chemical equilibrium has been attained we must know the electrochemical potentials as functions of temperature, pressure, and the mole fractions.

The conditions for equilibrium of more complex mixtures are obtained in a similar manner. For example, for the first mixture considered in the previous section, CH_4, O_2, H_2O, CO, and CO_2, the change in the Gibbs function for any infinitesimal reaction at constant temperature and pressure would be

$$dG_{T,P} = \hat{\mu}_{CH_4} \, d\mathfrak{N}_{CH_4} + \hat{\mu}_{O_2} \, d\mathfrak{N}_{O_2} + \hat{\mu}_{H_2O} \, d\mathfrak{N}_{H_2O} + \hat{\mu}_{CO} \, d\mathfrak{N}_{CO} + \hat{\mu}_{CO_2} \, d\mathfrak{N}_{CO_2}$$

Using the constraining conditions, Eqs. (11·15), we find

$$dG_{T,P} = (\hat{\mu}_{CH_4} + 2\hat{\mu}_{O_2} - 2\hat{\mu}_{H_2O} - \hat{\mu}_{CO_2}) \, d\mathfrak{N}_{CH_4} + (\tfrac{1}{2}\hat{\mu}_{O_2} + \hat{\mu}_{CO} - \hat{\mu}_{CO_2}) \, d\mathfrak{N}_{CO}$$

At equilibrium the Gibbs function must be a minimum with respect to each and every independent variation of the mixture composition. In other words, dG must be zero for any $d\mathfrak{N}_{CH_4}$ and any $d\mathfrak{N}_{CO}$. This requires the *two* equations of reaction equilibrium,

$$\hat{\mu}_{CH_4} + 2\hat{\mu}_{O_2} = 2\hat{\mu}_{H_2O} + \hat{\mu}_{CO_2} \tag{11·20a}$$
$$\hat{\mu}_{CO_2} = \tfrac{1}{2}\hat{\mu}_{O_2} + \hat{\mu}_{CO} \tag{11·20b}$$

These equations can be directly associated with the two chemical equations

$$CH_4 + 2O_2 \rightleftarrows 2H_2O + CO_2 \tag{11·21a}$$
$$CO_2 \rightleftarrows \tfrac{1}{2}O_2 + CO \tag{11·21b}$$

In general, one equation of reaction equilibrium will be obtained for each degree of reaction freedom. The coefficients of the electrochemical potentials for each equation of reaction equilibrium will be identical with the coefficients of the constituent in the associated simple chemical equation. It should be mentioned that the job of determining what constituents to put in the mixture list is not a simple one and generally requires considerable experience.

11·8 REACTIONS IN PERFECT-GAS MIXTURES

The equation of reaction equilibrium provides the means for determining equilibrium composition of reacting perfect-gas mixtures. In Chap. Ten we found that the electrochemical potential of one constituent of a perfect-gas mixture is given by

$$\hat{\mu}_i = \hat{g}_i(T, P) + \mathfrak{R}T \ln \chi_i \tag{11·22}$$

Since the equation of reaction equilibrium will involve the Gibbs functions of the constituents, it is convenient to define the Gibbs-function change for a complete unit reaction ΔG_r

$$\Delta G_r \equiv \sum_{\text{prod}} \nu_i \hat{g}_i - \sum_{\text{react}} \nu_i \hat{g}_i$$

For the special reaction of Eq. (11·19),

$$\Delta G_r = \nu_3\hat{g}_3(T, P) + \nu_4\hat{g}_4(T, P) - \nu_1\hat{g}_1(T, P) - \nu_2\hat{g}_2(T, P) \tag{11·23}$$

Combining Eqs. (11·19), (11·22), and (11·23), we have

$$\Delta G_r + \mathfrak{R}T \ln \frac{\chi_3^{\nu_3}\chi_4^{\nu_4}}{\chi_1^{\nu_1}\chi_2^{\nu_2}} = 0 \tag{11·24}$$

If ΔG_r is known, this equation plus equations indicating the relative abundances of the elements in the mixture may be solved simultaneously to obtain the constituent mole fractions in the equilibrium mixture.

The value of ΔG_r will depend on both temperature and pressure. However, the pressure effect is easily separated. Denoting P_0 as an arbitrarily chosen reference pressure, it follows from Eq. (8·38) and the definition of the Gibbs function that

$$\hat{g}(T, P) = \hat{g}(T, P_0) + \mathcal{R}T \ln \frac{P}{P_0} \tag{11·25}$$

Hence

$$\Delta G_r(T, P) = \Delta G_r(T, P_0) + \mathcal{R}T \ln \left(\frac{P}{P_0}\right)^{\nu_3+\nu_4-\nu_1-\nu_2}$$

Note that $\Delta G_r(T, P_0)$ is a function only of T for a selected reference pressure. Equation (11·24) then may be written as

$$\left(\frac{\chi_3^{\nu_3}\chi_4^{\nu_4}}{\chi_1^{\nu_1}\chi_2^{\nu_2}}\right)\left(\frac{P}{P_0}\right)^{\nu_3+\nu_4-\nu_1-\nu_2} = \exp\left[\frac{-\Delta G_r(T, P_0)}{\mathcal{R}T}\right]$$

Since the right-hand side is a function only of temperature, the left-hand side is independent of pressure. We define the *equilibrium constant* for the reaction by

$$\blacktriangleright \quad K(T) \equiv \left(\frac{\chi_3^{\nu_3}\chi_4^{\nu_4}}{\chi_1^{\nu_1}\chi_2^{\nu_2}}\right)\left(\frac{P}{P_0}\right)^{\nu_3+\nu_4-\nu_1-\nu_2} \tag{11·26}$$

Note that the equilibrium constant is a dimensionless property of the equilibrium mixture and is a function only of the mixture temperature.†

The term ΔG_r is sometimes called the *free-energy change* for the reaction. The reference pressure P_0 is normally taken as 1 atm; values of ΔG_r (298°K, 1 atm) are tabulated in handbooks under the name "standard free-energy change" for the reaction. Note that

$$\blacktriangleright \quad K(T) = \exp\left[\frac{-\Delta G_r(T, P_0)}{\mathcal{R}T}\right] \tag{11·27}$$

The equilibrium constant can be calculated if ΔG_r is known. Values of K for several reactions are given in Table B·14. Equation (11·26) is often called the *law of mass action;* it is not a law in the sense of the first and second laws of thermodynamics, but is merely a definition of the equilibrium constant.

The equilibrium composition of a given simple reactive mixture of perfect gases can be determined from the equilibrium constant. Perfect-gas mixtures with more degrees of reaction freedom require one additional equilibrium constant for each additional degree of freedom.

† It does, however, depend on the choice of P_0. In other texts $K(T)$ is normally defined as

$$\frac{\chi_3^{\nu_3}\chi_4^{\nu_4}}{\chi_1^{\nu_1}\chi_2^{\nu_2}} P^{\nu_3+\nu_4-\nu_1-\nu_2}$$

which gives it the dimensions of pressure to the $\nu_3 + \nu_4 - \nu_1 - \nu_2$ power. Since tabulations in the literature always employ P in atmospheres, the numerical values of these equilibrium constants will agree with Eq. (11·26) for $P_0 = 1$ atm.

As an example, let us determine the equilibrium composition of a mixture of CO, CO_2, and O_2 at 3000°K and 10 psia. We suppose that the mixture contains one carbon atom for every five oxygen atoms. The chemical equation is

$$CO_2 \rightleftarrows CO + \tfrac{1}{2}O_2$$

so the equilibrium constant is

$$K(T) = \frac{\chi_{CO}\chi_{O_2}^{1/2}}{\chi_{CO_2}}\left(\frac{P}{P_0}\right)^{1+1/2-1}$$

From Table B·14 the equilibrium constant for this mixture at 3000°K is seen to be such that

$$\log_{10} K = -0.469 \qquad K = 0.340$$

Then Eq. (11·26) becomes

$$\frac{\chi_{CO}\chi_{O_2}^{1/2}}{\chi_{CO_2}} = 0.340 \times \left(\frac{10}{14.7}\right)^{-1/2} = 0.412 \tag{11·28a}$$

The sum of the mole fractions must be unity,

$$\chi_{CO} + \chi_{O_2} + \chi_{CO_2} = 1 \tag{11·28b}$$

A third condition is given by the fact that one carbon atom is present for every five oxygen atoms,

$$\frac{\chi_{CO_2} + \chi_{CO}}{2\chi_{CO_2} + \chi_{CO} + 2\chi_{O_2}} = \frac{1}{5} \tag{11·28c}$$

Equations (11·28) form a set of three simultaneous equations for the three unknown mole fractions. Their solution must be obtained by some numerical scheme; we find

$$\chi_{CO} = 0.128$$
$$\chi_{O_2} = 0.625$$
$$\chi_{CO_2} = 0.247$$

This gives the equilibrium composition of a mixture of CO, CO_2, and O_2 at 3000°K and 10 psia.

The equilibrium composition of a perfect-gas mixture with more than one degree of reaction freedom requires simultaneous solution of a larger set of algebraic equations, with additional equations coming from the additional reaction equations and their associated equilibrium constants. We shall have more to say about the practical aspects of such calculations later in this chapter.

Two other quantities appearing in the literature on chemical thermodynamics are the enthalpy and entropy changes for a complete unit reaction,

▶ $$\Delta H_r \equiv \nu_3\hat{h}_3 + \nu_4\hat{h}_4 - \nu_1\hat{h}_1 - \nu_2\hat{h}_2 \tag{11·29}$$

▶ $$\Delta S_r = \nu_3\hat{s}_3 + \nu_4\hat{s}_4 - \nu_1\hat{s}_1 - \nu_2\hat{s}_2 \tag{11·30}$$

For a mixture of perfect gases ΔH_r will depend only on temperature, since the enthalpies are functions only of temperature. However, ΔS_r will depend on both temperature and pressure.

The dependence of the equilibrium constant on temperature can be related to the enthalpy change for a complete unit reaction. Differentiating Eq. (11·27),

$$\frac{dK}{dT} = \frac{1}{\mathcal{R}T^2}\left[\Delta G_r(T, P_0) - T\frac{d\Delta G_r(T, P_0)}{dT}\right]K$$

The fourth differential equation of state derived in Chap. Eight was

$$dg = -s\,dT + v\,dP$$

Applying this to the changes for a complete unit reaction at fixed pressure, we find

$$\frac{d\Delta G_r(T, P_0)}{dT} = -\Delta S_r$$

From the equations above and the definition of the specific Gibbs function, it also follows that

$$\Delta G_r = \Delta H_r - T\,\Delta S_r$$

Hence the derivative of the equilibrium constant may be expressed as

$$\frac{1}{K}\frac{dK}{dT} = \frac{\Delta H_r(T)}{\mathcal{R}T^2}$$

or

▶ $$\frac{d(\ln K)}{dT} = \frac{\Delta H_r(T)}{\mathcal{R}T^2} \qquad (11\cdot 31)$$

This is called the *van't Hoff equation* and it is very important in chemical thermodynamics. It permits determination of the enthalpy change for a complete unit reaction solely from equilibrium-composition data.

In the literature on fuel combustion $\Delta H_r(298°K)$ is called the "heating value" of the fuel. The term "higher heating value" is used when the H_2O in the products is in liquid form; the "lower heating value" pertains to products containing gaseous H_2O. The latter is more commonly used, since the vapor form normally exists at reaction temperatures.

The standardized enthalpy and absolute entropy, together with the equilibrium constant, provide a sound theoretical basis for computation of states of reacting mixtures and energy analyses of control volumes in which reactions occur. Usually it is necessary to resort to digital-computer calculations, and rather elaborate computer programs for combustion analysis have been developed by groups engaged in serious combustion calculations. Hand calculations for a large class of hydrocarbon reactions are now possible with the aid of charts and tables.† Some of these charts employ slightly different datum states and methods, but the fundamental ideas are the same as we have presented here.

11·9 APPLICATION TO THE FUEL CELL

Consider a fuel cell burning hydrogen and oxygen, as shown in Fig. 11·5. The maximum electrical energy output per mole of water formed and the maximum cell voltage can be determined with the theory developed in this chapter.

We assume steady flow, steady state, and negligible kinetic- and potential-energy changes for the fluids, and consider only the electrostatic potential energy of the electrons. The cell temperature and fluid temperatures are assumed to be equal. An energy balance, made over an infinitesimal time period, then gives

$$(\hat{h}\,đ\mathfrak{N})_{H_2O} - (\hat{h}\,đ\mathfrak{N})_{H_2} - (\hat{h}\,đ\mathfrak{N})_{O_2} + đQ + \mathsf{e}(\mathcal{E}_b - \mathcal{E}_a)\,đN_e = 0$$

where e denotes the charge on an electron, and $đN_e$ is the number of electrons passing through the control volume. Applying the second law, we obtain

$$đ\mathcal{P}_s = (\hat{s}\,đ\mathfrak{N})_{H_2O} - (\hat{s}\,đ\mathfrak{N})_{H_2} - (\hat{s}\,đ\mathfrak{N})_{O_2} + \frac{đQ}{T} \geq 0$$

The equality will hold if the processes within the cell are reversible. Otherwise the inequality must be used. Combining the first- and second-law equations,

† Many tables use F for the Gibbs function. See for example the *JANAF Interim Tables of Thermochemical Data*, vols. 1–4, Dow Chemical Company, Midland, Mich., 1960.

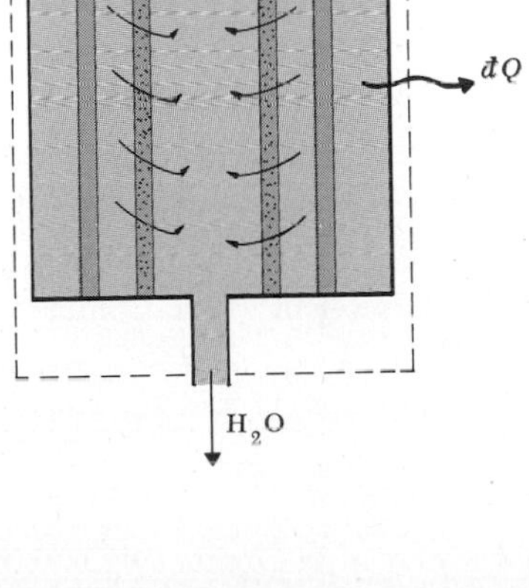

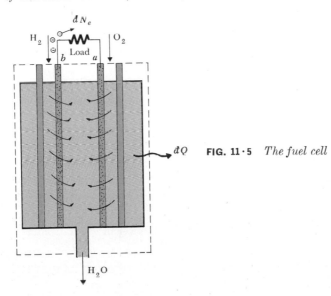

FIG. 11·5 *The fuel cell*

we obtain

$$\mathsf{e}(\mathcal{E}_b - \mathcal{E}_a)\, đN_e \leq -\, [(\mathcal{G}\, đ\mathfrak{N})_{H_2O} - (\mathcal{G}\, đ\mathfrak{N})_{H_2} - (\mathcal{G}\, đ\mathfrak{N})_{O_2}] \tag{11·32}$$

The chemical equation is

$$H_2 + \tfrac{1}{2}O_2 \rightleftarrows H_2O$$

Since stoichiometric reaction is assumed, Eq. (11·32) may be written as

$$đE_{\text{elect}} = (\mathcal{E}_b - \mathcal{E}_a)\mathsf{e}\, đN_e \leq -\Delta G_r\, đ\mathfrak{N}_{H_2O} \tag{11·33}$$

Here $đE_{\text{elect}}$ represents the useful electrical energy output. The value of ΔG_r for this reaction is equivalent to −238,000 joules/mole of H_2O. Hence the maximum possible electrical energy output of such a cell is 238,000 joules for each mole of water produced.

The maximum cell voltage can be obtained by considering the reactions at the electrodes. At the anode

$$H_2 + 2OH^- \rightarrow 2H_2O + 2e^-$$

and at the cathode

$$\tfrac{1}{2}O_2 + H_2O + 2e^- \rightarrow 2OH^-$$

The net amount of water production associated with the transfer of two electrons through the load is one molecule. The number of electrons passed for each mole of water formation is then $2N_0$, where N_0 is Avogadro's number. Dividing Eq. (11·33) by $-2\mathsf{e}N_0$ (a positive quantity), it becomes

$$\mathcal{E}_a - \mathcal{E}_b \leq -\frac{\Delta G_r}{2N_0\mathsf{e}} = \frac{-238{,}000}{2 \times 6.023 \times 10^{23} \times (-1.602 \times 10^{-19})}$$

$$\mathcal{E}_a - \mathcal{E}_b \leq 1.23 \text{ volts}$$

The efficiency of the fuel cell is defined as the actual energy output per mole of water formation to the maximum possible output calculated above. Like the isentropic efficiency of a compressor, it compares the actual output to the output of an idealized device and is not an energy-conversion efficiency.

SELECTED READING

Lee, J., and F. Sears, *Thermodynamics*, 2d ed., chap. 14, Addison-Wesley Publishing Co., Inc., Reading, Mass., 1962.

Van Wylen, G., and R. Sonntag, *Fundamentals of Classical Thermodynamics*, chap. 13, John Wiley & Sons, Inc., New York, 1965.

Wark, K., *Thermodynamics*, chaps. 14 and 15, McGraw-Hill Book Company, New York, 1966.

Zemansky, M. W., *Heat and Thermodynamics*, 4th ed., chaps. 17 and 18, McGraw-Hill Book Company, New York, 1957.

QUESTIONS

11·1 What are reactants, products, and chemical equations?
11·2 What is a stoichiometric mixture?
11·3 Why is it essential that the enthalpies and entropies of all substances be tied to a common base when chemical reactions are considered?
11·4 Is the energy of a substance ever really zero? Is its entropy?
11·5 What basic principles are employed in a calculation of the temperature following combustion in an adiabatic steady-flow device?
11·6 What is the condition for equilibrium in a mixture of reacting substances held at constant temperature and pressure?
11·7 How is the chemical potential related to the Gibbs function of a mixture (considered as nonreactive)?
11·8 What is meant by degree of reaction freedom?
11·9 What is a simple reactive mixture?
11·10 What is the enthalpy of formation?
11·11 What is the standard free energy of formation?
11·12 What is the enthalpy of reaction?
11·13 To what kind of reactive mixture does the equilibrium constant pertain?
11·14 How can you tell what will happen when some substances are put together in a constant-pressure constant-temperature chamber?
11·15 How would you go about calculating the composition of air, considered as a mixture of O_2, O, N_2, N, and NO, at 3000°K?
11·16 Partial pressures can be measured by simple volumetric means. How, then, can the enthalpy of reaction be determined without any energy measurements?
11·17 How many equilibrium constants would be needed for the determination of the equilibrium composition of a mixture of CO_2, CO, O_2, O, H_2O, OH, N_2, NO, and NO_2?
11·18 Can thermodynamics be used to determine the output voltage of a battery?

PROBLEMS

11·1 Compute the standardized enthalpy and entropy of a mixture of 50 percent CO_2 and 50 percent H_2O (by mass) at 2 atm pressure and 100°F.

11·2 Determine, from the *Handbook of Chemistry and Physics*, the standardized enthalpy of ozone and atomic oxygen at 18°C and 2 atm.

11·3 Propane (C_3H_8) and oxygen in stoichiometric proportions react in a steady-flow water-cooled burner. The reactants both enter at 90°F and 2 atm and emerge at 850°F. The products flow rate is 250 lbm/hr. What is the rate of energy transfer as heat to the cooling water? Assume that the products contain only CO_2 and H_2O.

11·4 Acetylene is burned in a constant-pressure water-cooled burner at 30 psia. Twice the stoichiometric amount of air is provided, and the reactants enter at 40°F. The products emerge at 200°F, and the total flow rate is 10 lbm/min. Water enters the cooling jacket at 60°F and 40 psia and emerges at 1 atm and 180°F. What water flow rate must be provided? The products contain only CO_2, H_2O, O_2, and N_2.

11·5 Hydrogen is to be burned with oxygen to produce a 3000°F flame. Neglecting dissociation, determine the composition of the product gases and specify the ratios of the oxygen and hydrogen flow rates. $P = 1$ atm, and the burner is adiabatic.

11·6 Determine the adiabatic flame temperature for propane burning in air (*a*) stoichiometrically, (*b*) with twice the stoichiometric air, and (*c*) with four times the stoichiometric air. Assume complete combustion in each case.

11·7 Find the mole fractions of O present in equilibrium oxygen at 1000°K and at 5000°K ($P = 1$ atm).

11·8 Find the mole fractions of N present in equilibrium nitrogen at 1000°K and 5000°K ($P = 1$ atm).

11·9 Assuming that air is composed of O_2, O, N_2, N, and NO, and that only O_2 and N_2 are present in significant amounts at room temperatures in the ratio 3.76 moles of N_2 per mole of O_2, determine the composition of equilibrium air at 1000°K and 1 atm.

11·10 Using the data in Table B·13, calculate the equilibrium constant for the reaction $CO_2 \rightleftarrows CO + \frac{1}{2}O_2$ at 1000°K and compare your result with the value given in Table B·14.

11·11 Using the data in Table B·13, calculate the equilibrium constant for the dissociation of O_2 at 2500°K and compare your result with the value given in Table B·14 (see also Prob. 11·2).

11·12 Using the data in Table B·13, calculate the equilibrium constant for the gaseous reaction $CO_2 + H_2 \rightleftarrows CO + H_2O$ at 298°K. Derive an expression that would let you obtain this instead from Table B 14 in terms of the equilibrium constants for simpler reactions.

11·13 Using the data in the *Handbook of Chemistry and Physics* and the van't Hoff equation determine the value of the equilibrium constant for the reaction $C + 2H_2 \rightleftarrows CH_4$ at 500°C. Assume that ΔH_r does not vary appreciably over the low-temperature range.

11·14 Calculate and plot the percentage of ionization in cesium at 10^{-2} and 10^{-4} atm over the range of ionization (the electrons may be treated as a monatomic perfect gas with $\hat{M} = 5.48 \times 10^{-4}$ g/gmole).

11·15 Calculate and plot the percentage of ionization in sodium at 10^{-2} and 10^{-4} atm over the range of ionization (the electrons may be treated as a monatomic perfect gas with $\hat{M} = 5.48 \times 10^{-4}$ g/gmole).

11·16 Determine the number of free electrons and ions per cm³ in argon seeded with 1 percent cesium (by mass) at 1 atm, and 1000°K (the electrons may be treated as a monatomic perfect gas with $\hat{M} = 5.48 \times 10^{-4}$ g/gmole). Neglect argon ionization.

11·17 Determine the number of free electrons and ions per cm³ in argon seeded with sodium at 1 atm and 1000°K (the electrons may be treated as a monatomic perfect gas with $\hat{M} = 5.48 \times 10^{-4}$ g/gmole). Neglect argon ionization.

11·18 Work the previous two problems. Which seed seems most desirable to attain a plasma with high electrical conductivity?

11·19 Determine the maximum energy output per mole of CO_2 for a fuel cell operating on CO and O_2 at 298°K and 1 atm. Assume that the products contain only CO_2.

11·20 A commercial heater must provide 1000 ft³/min of hot gas at 400°F, 1 atm pressure. Design an appropriate system, specifying the fuel, flow rates, and so on.

11·21 The burner for a large power station must provide boiler heating at the rate of 3×10^8 Btu/hr. The maximum flame temperature is to be 1500°F, and the products can leave the boiler at no less than 1200°F. Design a burner system, specifying the fuel, flow rates, and so on.

11·22 The burner in a small engine must handle 10 lbm/sec of air, heating it to 1600°F. Any liquid hydrocarbon fuel may be used. Design a burner system, specifying the fuel requirements.

11·23 A particular plasma gas dynamics experiment requires a plasma at 800°K, 1 atm having 10^{14} free electrons per cm^3. Specify an inert carrier gas, an easily ionizable seed, and the mass fractions that would produce the desired plasma.

CHAPTER TWELVE

AN INTRODUCTION TO STATISTICAL THERMODYNAMICS

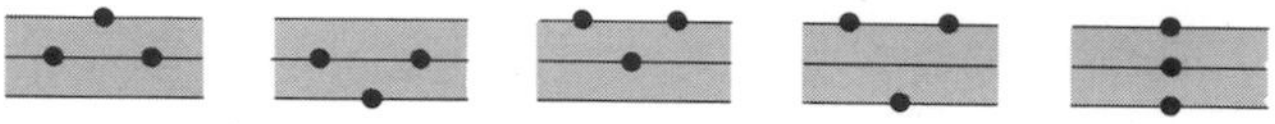

12·1 THE GENERAL APPROACH

The objective of statistical thermodynamics is the quantitative prediction of thermodynamic equations of state. Recalling the developments in Chap. Eight, we note that while thermodynamic theory provides certain very useful relations among the thermodynamic properties, it does not give us any means for direct quantitative evaluation of any properties. Statistical thermodynamics adds information about the microscopic structure of the substance; this information, together with the equations from thermodynamics relating the thermodynamic properties, allows one to predict values for all the thermodynamic properties in every thermodynamic state.

The entropy is the key thermodynamic function in statistical thermodynamics; all other thermodynamic properties can be calculated immediately if the entropy is known as a function of state. For example, if the function $s(u, v)$ is known for a simple compressible substance, then

$$T = \frac{1}{(\partial s/\partial u)_v} \qquad P = T\left(\frac{\partial s}{\partial v}\right)_u$$
$$h = u + Pv \qquad g = h - Ts \qquad c_P = \left(\frac{\partial h}{\partial T}\right)_P \tag{12·1}$$

The central aim in statistical thermodynamics is therefore the construction of a satisfactory equation for the entropy.

The entropy is calculated from its basic definition (Chap. Six),

$$\blacktriangleright \qquad S = -\mathsf{k} \sum_i p_i \ln p_i \tag{12·2}$$

where k is the Boltzmann constant and p_i is the *probability* that the system under study exists in its *i*th *allowed quantum state* at any particular time. The probability can be viewed as the fraction of a large number of macroscopically identical systems (an *ensemble* of systems) in which the *i*th quantum state would be found. The new input in statistical thermodynamics is the specification of the allowed quantum states; this information comes from quantum mechanics.

Since the aim is to predict the equilibrium properties, one seeks the distribution p_i that maximizes the entropy of some isolated system. A variety of different kinds of isolated systems are employed in these analyses. In a *microcanonical* analysis the isolated system is simply the system under study. Since the system is isolated, the allowed quantum states all have the same energy. The distribution that maximizes the entropy of a microcanonical system has equal probability of each allowed quantum state (Chap. Six). If there are Ω allowed quantum states, then $p_i = 1/\Omega$ and

$$S = \mathsf{k} \ln \Omega \tag{12·3}$$

The value of Ω depends upon the energy of the system and any external constraints which enter through their effects on the allowed quantum states as prescribed by quantum mechanics. An ensemble of isolated systems formed just from the system of interest is called a *microcanonical ensemble*, and the distribution $p_i = 1/\Omega$ which maximizes S is called the *microcanonical distribution.*

Often it is more convenient to consider some other type of isolated system. For example, one might form an isolated system from the system under study and a large *thermal energy reservoir* (Chap. Seven). The TER is considered to be sufficiently large that it can absorb all the energy of the system without appreciable change in temperature. Since its temperature T always remains constant, its entropy is [see Eq. (7·28)]

$$S_{\text{TER}} = \frac{U_{\text{TER}}}{T} \tag{12·4}$$

where U_{TER} is its energy. The entropy of the system of interest is again given by Eq. (12·2); the entropy of the combined isolated system is then

$$S_C = -\mathsf{k} \sum_i p_i \ln p_i + \frac{U_{\text{TER}}}{T} \tag{12·5}$$

and the p_i's which maximize S_C would yield the equilibrium distribution for the system of interest. Systems treated in this manner are called *canonical systems;* an ensemble of such systems is a *canonical ensemble;* and the distribution p_i within the system of interest which maximizes S_C is called the *canonical distribution.*

If the number of particles within the system of interest can vary, then it is convenient to form an isolated system consisting of the system under study, a thermal energy reservoir, and *constituent reservoirs* (Chap. Eleven). The CR's are presumed to be sufficiently large that they can absorb all of that constituent without appreciable change in their electrochemical potentials $\hat{\mu}_l$ and temperature T. The entropy of a CR is then [see Eq. (10·40)]

$$S_{\text{CR}l} = \frac{U_{\text{CR}} - \hat{\mu}_l \mathfrak{N}_l}{T} \tag{12·6}$$

where $\mathfrak{N}_l$ is the number of moles in the CR for constituent l. The entropy of the system of interest is again given by Eq. (12·2), and the entropy of the combined isolated system is then

$$S_C = -\mathsf{k} \sum_i p_i \ln p_i + \sum_l \frac{U_{\text{CR}l} - \hat{\mu}_l \mathfrak{N}_l}{T} + \frac{U_{\text{TER}}}{T} \tag{12·7}$$

Systems treated in this manner are called *grand canonical* systems; an ensemble of such systems is a *grand canonical ensemble;* and the distribution p_i within the system of interest that maximizes S_C is called the *grand canonical distribution.*

A statistical thermodynamic analysis begins with a decision about the kind of ensemble to be considered (microcanonical, canonical, grand canonical, . . .). One next finds the allowed quantum states for the system of interest using quantum-mechanical theory. This usually involves solution of the *Schrödinger equation,* a partial differential equation postulated for exactly this purpose. Physical insight and assumptions are usually involved in the solution of this equation, and it is here that the "microscopic modeling" takes place. Having found the allowed states, one then proceeds to calculate the entropy using the equilibrium distribution appropriate for the chosen ensemble. The thermodynamic equations of state are then developed by differentiation using thermodynamic equations [Eqs. (12·1)].

12·2 THE NUCLEAR SPIN SYSTEM

A relatively simple illustration is provided by the system of nuclear spins in a paramagnetic crystal. It is known that the relaxation time for the spin system is several orders of magnitude shorter than that for the lattice oscillations, and hence the spin system attains an equilibrium state well before any significant interaction with the lattice can occur. The spin system can consequently be considered as being isolated from the lattice system, and a microcanonical treatment used.

Let's consider a model in which each nucleus can exist in either a "spin-up" or "spin-down" state with respect to the applied magnetic field. Suppose the spin energies associated with these states are ε_+ and ε_-, respectively. These two energies would depend on the strength of the applied magnetic field, and a quantum-mechanical analysis would be necessary to find this dependence. We can carry the analysis quite far without such a calculation.

Suppose there are N nuclei, with n_+ and n_- in the spin-up and spin-down states, respectively. The total energy of the system is then

$$U = n_+\varepsilon_+ + n_-\varepsilon_-$$

Denoting $f = n_+/N$ and $\varepsilon_t = \varepsilon_+ - \varepsilon_-$, we can write

$$U = N(\varepsilon_t f + \varepsilon_-) \tag{12·8}$$

Note that the energy depends on the fraction in each state and on the strength of the applied magnetic field.

In a microcanonical analysis we treat an isolated system of fixed energy, which in this case fixes f. If $f = 1$ all the nuclei are in the spin-up state; there is but one allowed state for which this occurs. If $1 > f > 0$ there will be more than one allowed state. For example, if $f = 1/N$, then one nucleus is in the spin-up state and the rest are in the spin-down state. There are N allowed states of this kind. If $f = 2/N$, then two nuclei are in the up-state, the rest having spin down. Since there are N sites to choose for the first up-state, and $N - 1$ different ones for the second, there are $N(N - 1)$ different possible site combinations. However, the ordering of these two sites is unimportant, and hence the number of different site pairs at which the up-states might be found is only $N(N - 1)/2$. A general expression for the number of allowed quantum states is†

$$\Omega = \frac{N!}{n_+!n_-!} \tag{12·9}$$

The (equilibrium) entropy of the system is therefore

$$S = \mathsf{k} \ln \left[\frac{N!}{n_+!n_-!}\right] \tag{12·10}$$

If n_+ and n_- are both large, the factorials can be evaluated with the aid of *Stirling's approximation*,

$$\ln n! \approx n \ln n - n \qquad n \gg 1 \tag{12·11}$$

† The nuclei are considered to be identified by their position in the crystal lattice. A particular allowed quantum state is one in which specific nuclei have specific states. If there are n_+ in the up-state and n_- in the down-state, the total number of such system states is given in Eq. (12·9). To show this, imagine a string of N boxes representing the N states to be assigned, with the first n_+ boxes representing the up-states and the remaining n_- representing the down-states. Consider the possible assignments of N markers representing the nuclei, one to a box. There are N markers to choose for the first box; for each such choice there are $N - 1$ choices for the second box; for each first-second choice there are $N - 2$ possible third choices. There are therefore $N(N - 1)(N - 2) \cdots 1 = N!$ possible ways to assign the markers to the string of N boxes. Now, certain of these assignments will lead to the same nuclei being in the up- and down-states. If n_+ particular markers have been assigned to the up boxes, there are $n_+!$ different ways to arrange those markers within the n_+ boxes, and hence the count of $N!$ is too high by a factor of $n_+!$ Similarly, the count is also too high by a factor of $n_-!$ Hence, the proper count for the number of allowed quantum states is Eq. (12·9). For example, if there are five nuclei with two in the up-state and three in the down-state, there are $5!/(2!3!) = 10$ possible states. These are shown in Fig. 12·1.

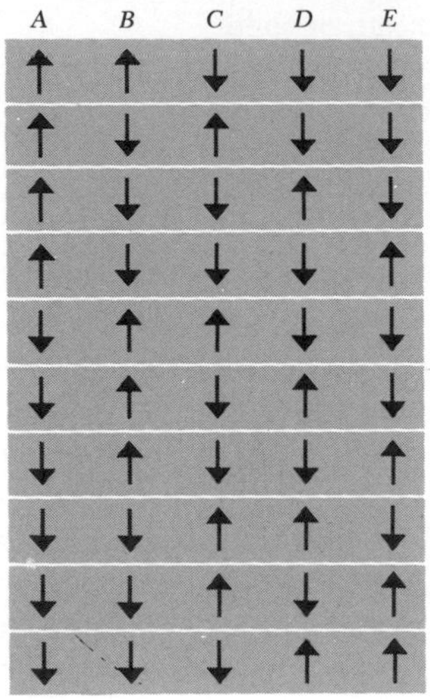

FIG. 12·1 *The 10 system quantum states for five particles with spin, $f = 2/5$*

Then,

$$\begin{aligned} S &= \mathsf{k}(N \ln N - N - n_+ \ln n_+ + n_+ - n_- \ln n_- + n_-) \\ &= \mathsf{k}N[-f \ln f - (1 - f) \ln (1 - f)] \end{aligned}$$

Noting that S depends explicitly only upon f, we use the thermodynamic definition of temperature [Eq. (7·24)], and have

$$\frac{1}{T} \equiv \left(\frac{\partial S}{\partial U}\right)_{\mathbf{M}} = \frac{dS}{df}\left(\frac{\partial f}{\partial U}\right)_{\mathbf{M}}$$

Carrying out the differentiations, holding ε_+ and ε_- constant, we have

$$\frac{1}{T} = \frac{\mathsf{k}}{\varepsilon_t} \ln \left(\frac{1 - f}{f}\right)$$

from which

$$f = \frac{1}{1 + \exp(\varepsilon_t/\mathsf{k}T)} \tag{12·12}$$

Now, if we learn ε_t as a function of the applied magnetic field from the quantum-mechanical calculation, we can calculate the fraction in each state at any temperature from Eq. (12·12).

Of particular interest in paramagnetic resonance is the *population difference* $n_- - n_+$, which can be expressed as

$$\frac{n_- - n_+}{N} = 1 - 2f = \tanh \frac{\varepsilon_t}{2\mathsf{k}T} \tag{12·13}$$

The variation of this function with temperature is shown in Fig. 12·2. We remark that in treating the spin system as an isolated system we permit it to

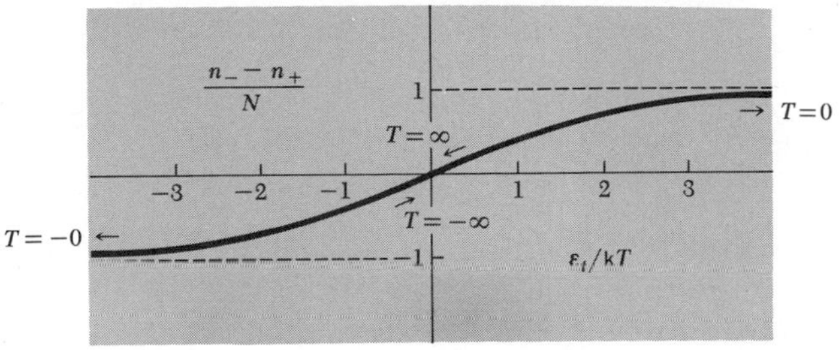

FIG. 12·2 *Population difference as a function of temperature for a spin system*

have a "temperature" of its own, different from that of the crystal lattice. This "spin temperature" can be negative as Fig. 12·2 shows. The operation of solid-state masers depends upon the momentary existence of a negative population difference,† which occur when the system is at a negative spin temperature. This can be accomplished by first allowing the spin system to equilibrate with the lattice at some positive temperature, and then suddenly reversing the magnetic field. The spin system then acquires a negative population difference, that is, a negative temperature.

12·3 A GENERAL THEORY FOR CANONICAL SYSTEMS

There are many problems for which the canonical approach to calculation of the distribution p_i is most appropriate. The gas in a rigid vessel cannot really be isolated from energy exchange with the vessel walls, and hence at any moment the energy of the gas will not necessarily equal its average value, that is, the value of interest in thermodynamics. But it is reasonable to treat the combined system consisting of the gas and the vessel as an isolated system, and this is the approach normally taken. The vessel becomes the thermal energy reservoir, and the system is then of the canonical type described in Sec. 12·1. We shall now develop a general formalism for canonical systems, and then illustrate this formalism by some examples. Each member of a canonical ensemble is imagined to consist of a replication of the system under study and a thermal energy reservoir at temperature T. The entropy of the combined system is given by Eq. (12·5). If we view the equilibrium p_i as an estimate of the fraction of time which the system of interest spends in its ith allowed quantum state, then the average energy is [see Eq. (6·3)]

$$U = \sum_i p_i \epsilon_i \tag{12·14}$$

where ϵ_i is the energy of quantum state i. Denoting the total energy of the combined system by U_C, we have

$$U_C = \sum_i p_i \epsilon_i + U_{\text{TER}}$$

† A. E. Siegman, *Microwave Solid-State Masers*, McGraw-Hill Book Company, New York, 1964.

Substituting into Eq. (12·5), we express the entropy of the combined system as

$$S_C = -\mathrm{k} \sum_i p_i \ln p_i - \sum_i \frac{p_i \epsilon_i}{T} + \frac{U_C}{T} \tag{12·15}$$

When the system of interest has come to thermal equilibrium with the TER, the entropy S_C will have reached its maximum value, and p_i will take the equilibrium distribution. Our objective, then, is to find the p_i which maximize S_C. Since the p_i must add up to unity, not all are freely variable. Let's imagine that $p_2, p_3, \ldots, p_n$ are freely variable, and adjust p_1 to maintain $\Sigma p_i = 1$. Consider then a change in S_C,

$$dS_C = \sum_{i=1}^{n} \frac{\partial S_C}{\partial p_i} dp_i = \sum_{i=2}^{n} \frac{\partial S_C}{\partial p_i} dp_i + \frac{\partial S_C}{\partial p_1} dp_1$$

But

$$\sum_{i=1}^{n} p_i = 1 \tag{12·16}$$

so

$$\sum_{i=1}^{n} dp_i = 0$$

Substituting for dp_1,

$$dS_C = \sum_{i=2}^{n} \left(\frac{\partial S_C}{\partial p_i} - \frac{\partial S_C}{\partial p_1} \right) dp_i$$

Since dS_C must vanish for any arbitrary $dp_2, dp_3, \ldots, dp_n$, we set

$$\frac{\partial S_C}{\partial p_i} - \frac{\partial S_C}{\partial p_1} = 0 \qquad i = 2, 3, \ldots, n \tag{12·17}$$

Now,

$$\frac{\partial S_C}{\partial p_i} = -\mathrm{k}\left(1 + \ln p_i + \frac{\epsilon_i}{\mathrm{k}T}\right)$$
$$\frac{\partial S_C}{\partial p_1} = -\mathrm{k}\left(1 + \ln p_1 + \frac{\epsilon_1}{\mathrm{k}T}\right) \tag{12·18}$$

We note that Eqs. (12·17) and (12·18) state that $1 + \ln p_i + \epsilon_i/\mathrm{k}T$ has the same value for all i. Hence the *canonical distribution* may be written as

$$\blacktriangleright \qquad p_i = \frac{1}{Z} \exp\left(\frac{-\epsilon_i}{\mathrm{k}T}\right) \tag{12·19}$$

The function Z is found by applying Eq. (12·16), which gives

$$\blacktriangleright \qquad Z = \sum_{i=1}^{n} \exp\left(\frac{-\epsilon_i}{\mathrm{k}T}\right) \tag{12·20}$$

Z is called the *partition function*, or *state sum*. Note that the summation is over the allowed quantum states i of the system of interest; Z is a function of the energies of the quantum states and of the system temperature.†

The entropy of the system of interest can now be expressed as

$$S = -\mathrm{k} \sum_i p_i \ln \left[\frac{1}{Z} \exp \left(\frac{-\epsilon_i}{\mathrm{k}T} \right) \right]$$

$$= +\mathrm{k} \sum_i p_i \cdot \ln Z + \sum_i \frac{p_i \epsilon_i}{T}$$

But, using Eq. (12·14) and Eq. (12·16),

$$\blacktriangleright \quad S = \mathrm{k} \ln Z + \frac{U}{T} \tag{12·21}$$

In order to calculate the partition function we must know the allowed quantum states for the system. These must be obtained from a quantum-mechanical analysis, and will depend on the extensive constraints imposed upon the system. For example, for a simple compressible substance the allowed quantum states and hence Z depend upon the volume in which the molecules must be found. Since S is extensive, $\ln Z$ must be extensive.

For a simple compressible substance, the pressure is found from its thermodynamic definition [Eq. (7·20)],

$$P \equiv T \left(\frac{\partial S}{\partial V} \right)_U = \mathrm{k}T \left(\frac{\partial \ln Z}{\partial V} \right)_U \tag{12·22}$$

Note that P is indeed intensive. We see that knowledge of the partition function permits quantitative evaluation of all of the thermodynamic properties, and this is why it is so important in statistical thermodynamics.

The partition function represents a sum over all of the allowed system quantum states. Since only the energies of these states are involved, it is often more convenient to calculate this sum by summing over the energies of the allowed states. If there are g_j system quantum states having energy ϵ_j, then we can replace the sum over states [Eq. (12·20)] by a *sum over energy levels*,

$$\blacktriangleright \quad Z = \sum_j g_j \exp \left(\frac{-\epsilon_j}{\mathrm{k}T} \right) \tag{12·23}$$

Note that the sum of Eq. (12·23) has fewer terms than that of Eq. (12·20). If $g_j > 1$, then the jth energy level is said to be *degenerate*, and g_j is the *amount of degeneracy*.

Evaluation of the partition function is often simplified if the system can be broken down into a number of independent subsystems. This is possible when

† Z should not be confused with the compressibility factor Pv/RT used in Chap. Eight.

the allowed quantum states of one subsystem are independent of the quantum states taken by the other subsystems, and when a "private" energy can be assigned to each subsystem. For example, the translational and vibrational quantum states of gas molecules can be treated as independent, and hence the translational and vibrational systems can be treated separately. Each will contribute to the total system energy and entropy. If the energies of two independent systems A and B are denoted by ϵ_{Ai} and $\epsilon_{Bi'}$, then the partition functions of these two systems are

$$Z_A = \sum_i \exp\left(\frac{-\epsilon_{Ai}}{\mathsf{k}T}\right)$$

$$Z_B = \sum_{i'} \exp\left(\frac{-\epsilon_{Bi'}}{\mathsf{k}T}\right)$$

The partition function Z for the combined system is the sum over all allowed quantum states of the combined system. If systems A and B are distinguishable from one another, each combined system state is formed by one of the allowed quantum states of A and one of B. Hence,

$$\begin{aligned} Z &= \sum_i \sum_{i'} \exp\left[\frac{-(\epsilon_{Ai} + \epsilon_{Bi'})}{\mathsf{k}T}\right] \\ &= \left[\sum_i \exp\left(\frac{-\epsilon_{Ai}}{\mathsf{k}T}\right)\right]\left[\sum_{i'} \exp\left(\frac{-\epsilon_{Bi'}}{\mathsf{k}T}\right)\right] \\ &= Z_A \cdot Z_B \end{aligned}$$

The partition function for a system composed of independent distinguishable subsystems is therefore the product of their individual partition functions. The entropy and energy of the combined system are therefore the sums of the entropies and energies of the independent distinguishable subsystems.

A few systems can be treated by considering each particle as an independent distinguishable subsystem. For example, Einstein proposed a model of solids in which each atom in the crystal lattice was presumed to oscillate with its own "private" energy and to be identified by its position in the crystal lattice. For such a system of independent distinguishable particles, the partition function for a single particle is

$$Z_p = \sum_{i'} \exp\left(\frac{-\varepsilon_{i'}}{\mathsf{k}T}\right) \tag{12·24}$$

where $\varepsilon_{i'}$ is the energy of a particle in its i'th quantum state. Then, if there are N particles, the partition function for the entire system of *distinguishable* particles is

$$Z = Z_p{}^N \tag{12·25}$$

The entropy of a system of N independent distinguishable particles is then

$$S = \mathsf{k}N \ln Z_p + \frac{U}{T} \tag{12·26}$$

When the particles are indistinguishable, it is not possible to write the system partition function Z in terms of the particle partition function Z_p, except for a very special case. Suppose there is at most one particle in each particle quantum state; we call this a *sparsely populated system.* For a given set of particle quantum state populations (0 or 1), there are $N!$ permutations of the particles over the particle state assignments; each permutation makes a separate quantum state if the particles are distinguishable, but the permutations correspond to the same quantum state if the particles are indistinguishable. Hence for every term in the state sum for indistinguishable particles there will be $N!$ identical terms in the state sum for distinguishable particles. We therefore conclude that, for a canonical system of N independent *indistinguishable* particles in which no more than one particle occupies each particle quantum state,

$$Z = \frac{Z_p{}^N}{N!} \tag{12·27}$$

This simplification of Z is particularly important in the statistical analysis of an ideal gas. The entropy of a *sparsely populated system* of N independent *indistinguishable* particles is then, from Eq. (12·21),

$$S = \mathsf{k}N \ln Z_p - \mathsf{k} \ln N! + \frac{U}{T}$$

For large N Stirling's approximation, Eq. (12·11), is valid, and

$$S = \mathsf{k}N \left(\ln \frac{Z_p}{N} + 1 \right) + \frac{U}{T} \tag{12·28}$$

The calculation of the system energy is often facilitated by knowledge of the partition function. Noting from Eq. (12·20) that

$$\left(\frac{\partial Z}{\partial T}\right)_{\epsilon_i} = \frac{1}{\mathsf{k}T^2} \sum_i \epsilon_i \exp\left(\frac{-\epsilon_i}{\mathsf{k}T}\right)$$

and recalling that

$$U = \sum p_i \epsilon_i = \frac{1}{Z} \sum_i \epsilon_i \exp\left(\frac{-\epsilon_i}{\mathsf{k}T}\right)$$

we see that U can be calculated from

$$U = \mathsf{k}T^2 \left(\frac{\partial \ln Z}{\partial T}\right)_{\epsilon_i} \tag{12·29}$$

For a system of N independent distinguishable particles, or for a sparsely populated system of N indistinguishable particles, the equivalent equation is

$$\blacktriangleright \quad U = N\mathrm{k}T^2 \left(\frac{\partial \ln Z_p}{\partial T}\right)_{\varepsilon_{i'}} \tag{12·30}$$

The subscripts in Eqs. (12·29) and (12·30) indicate that the quantum state energies are all held fixed in differentiating the partition function.

12·4 SIMPLE OSCILLATOR SYSTEMS

An oscillator is any system that can vibrate at certain frequencies and amplitudes permitted by quantum mechanics. A *simple oscillator* is one that vibrates at a single frequency, with a selection of amplitudes governed by quantum theory. For example, the vibrational states of diatomic gas molecules can be treated by considering the molecules to be simple oscillators. Simple models of orbiting electrons also take this approach. We assume that all oscillators within the system vibrate at the same frequency ν, but their individual energies will depend on the amplitudes of vibration. When an atom jumps from one quantum state to one of lesser energy, it will emit one or more photons of this frequency. Since the energy of a photon is $\mathrm{h}\nu$, we presume that the differences in energy between the various vibrational states must be an integer multiple of the energy of a single photon. The allowed quantum states of single oscillators are therefore presumed to be

$$\varepsilon_{i'} = i'\mathrm{h}\nu + \varepsilon_m \qquad i' = 0, 1, 2, 3, \ldots \tag{12·31}$$

where ε_m is the least energy that the oscillator can possess. This is the reasoning used by Einstein before the advent of quantum theory. A quantum-mechanical analysis, involving solution of the Schrödinger equation, also gives this result, with $\varepsilon_m = \frac{1}{2}\mathrm{h}\nu$.

We treat the oscillators as independent. The partition function of a single oscillator is then [Eq. (12·25)]

$$Z_p = \sum_{i'=0}^{\infty} \exp\left[\frac{-(i'\mathrm{h}\nu + \varepsilon_m)}{\mathrm{k}T}\right] \tag{12·32}$$

The sum has a very simple evaluation for this case. Carrying out the divisions, we observe that

$$\frac{1}{1 - \exp(-\mathrm{h}\nu/\mathrm{k}T)} = 1 + \exp\left(\frac{-\mathrm{h}\nu}{\mathrm{k}T}\right) + \exp\left(\frac{-2\mathrm{h}\nu}{\mathrm{k}T}\right) + \cdots$$
$$= \sum_{i=0}^{\infty} \exp\left(\frac{-i\mathrm{h}\nu}{\mathrm{k}T}\right)$$

so that

$$\blacktriangleright \quad Z_p = \frac{\exp(-\varepsilon_m/\mathrm{k}T)}{1 - \exp(-\mathrm{h}\nu/\mathrm{k}T)} \tag{12·33}$$

Applying Eq. (12·30), the energy of a system of N identical oscillators is found as

$$U = \frac{N\mathsf{h}\nu}{\exp(\mathsf{h}\nu/\mathsf{k}T) - 1} + \varepsilon_m N \qquad (12\cdot 34)$$

This holds both for systems of distinguishable oscillators and sparsely populated systems of indistinguishable oscillators. Note that if the characteristic frequency ν is constant, the energy of the oscillator system depends only upon temperature.

12·5 THE EINSTEIN SOLID

Einstein applied the theory of simple oscillator systems to a solid. In his model each atom is pictured as possessing three degrees of freedom for independent vibration, and hence a crystal containing N atoms is treated as a canonical system of $3N$ independent distinguishable simple oscillators. An equation for the energy of the solid is obtained immediately from Eq. (12·34) by replacing N by $3N$. Expressed on a per-atom basis,

$$\frac{U}{N} = \frac{3\mathsf{h}\nu}{\exp(\mathsf{h}\nu/\mathsf{k}T) - 1} + 3\varepsilon_m \qquad (12\cdot 35)$$

Note that the energy per atom is $3\varepsilon_m$ at $T = 0$; this corresponds to a state in which each atom is in its lowest possible energy. Since there is only one system quantum state with this feature, the entropy at $T = 0$ should vanish. The entropy is found from Eq. (12·26) as

$$\frac{S}{N} = -3\mathsf{k}\ln\left[1 - \exp\left(\frac{-\mathsf{h}\nu}{\mathsf{k}T}\right)\right] + \frac{3\mathsf{h}\nu/T}{\exp(\mathsf{h}\nu/\mathsf{k}T) - 1} \qquad (12\cdot 36)$$

Note that $S \to 0$ as $T \to 0$, in accordance with the third law of thermodynamics (Chap. Eleven).

The molal specific heat is obtained from its definition,

$$\hat{c}_v \equiv \left(\frac{\partial \hat{u}}{\partial T}\right)_{\hat{v}}$$

Now, $\hat{u} = \mathsf{N}_0 U/N$, where N_0 is the number of atoms per mole (Avogadro's number). Since $\mathsf{N}_0\mathsf{k} = \mathfrak{R}$, where $\mathfrak{R}$ is the universal gas constant, differentiation of the energy gives

$$\blacktriangleright \quad \hat{c}_v = 3\mathfrak{R}\left(\frac{\mathsf{h}\nu}{\mathsf{k}T}\right)^2 \frac{\exp(\mathsf{h}\nu/\mathsf{k}T)}{[\exp(\mathsf{h}\nu/\mathsf{k}T) - 1]^2} \qquad (12\cdot 37)$$

This equation was first derived by Einstein in 1907. At high temperatures

$$\exp\left(\frac{\mathsf{h}\nu}{\mathsf{k}T}\right) \approx 1 + (\mathsf{h}\nu/\mathsf{k}T) + \cdots$$

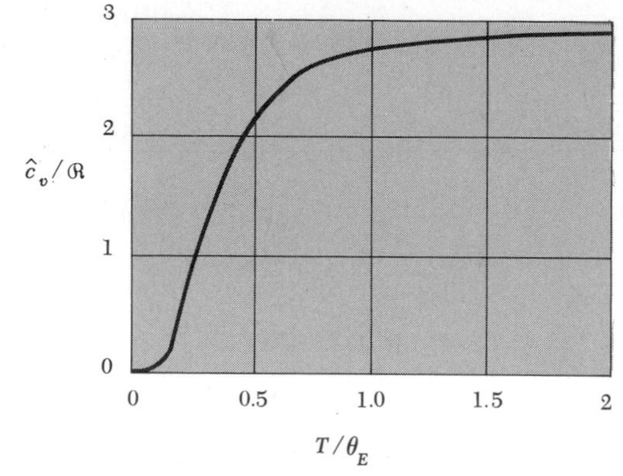

FIG. 12·3 *Specific heat of an Einstein solid*

so that the molal specific heat of a solid should approach a value of

$$\hat{c}_v = 3\mathcal{R} \tag{12·38}$$

as temperature is increased. This is indeed found to be a good approximation for many solids at moderate temperatures. Equation (12·37) indicates that $\hat{c}_v$ must approach zero as the temperature decreases, which is also in agreement with experiment. In fact, prequantum treatments failed to satisfactorily explain this decrease, and Einstein's result was one of the first great successes of quantum theory.

The appearance of the gas constant in the thermodynamic equation of state for a solid might seem puzzling. It results simply from the use of the Boltzmann constant in the definition of entropy.

By comparing the specific-heat prediction of the Einstein model with experimental results, a value for the characteristic frequency ν can be selected which gives the best agreement between theory and experiment. It is customary to represent this frequency by a *characteristic temperature* θ_E, defined as

$$\theta_E \equiv \frac{\mathsf{h}\nu}{\mathsf{k}}$$

The dimensionless parameter $\mathsf{h}\nu/\mathsf{k}T$ then becomes simply θ_E/T. The characteristic temperatures for soft substances are typically low (for silver, $\theta_E \approx$ 200°K), and higher values are obtained for harder materials ($\theta_E \approx$ 2000°K for diamond). The specific heat of an Einstein solid is shown in Fig. 12·3.

12·6 THE DEBYE MODEL OF A SOLID

The Einstein model is based on the postulated independence of the vibrational modes of the atoms. However, this is not very realistic, for the atoms are very tightly coupled. A better model would consider the vibrational modes of the crystal lattice as a whole, and a theory based on this model has been given by Debye. The total number of modes of vibration for a system of N masses is

3N; Debye approximated these frequencies by a continuous range of possible frequencies but terminated this range at an upper limit, denoted by $\nu_{\max}$. This limit emerges as an undetermined constant of the Debye theory and as represented by the characteristic *Debye temperature,*

$$\theta_D \equiv \frac{h\nu_{\max}}{k}$$

The specific heat emerges from Debye's theory in the form

$$\frac{\hat{c}_v}{\mathcal{R}} = f\left(\frac{\theta_D}{T}\right)$$

Figure 12·4 shows this functional relationship, and Table 12·1 gives the values of the Debye temperature for several solids.

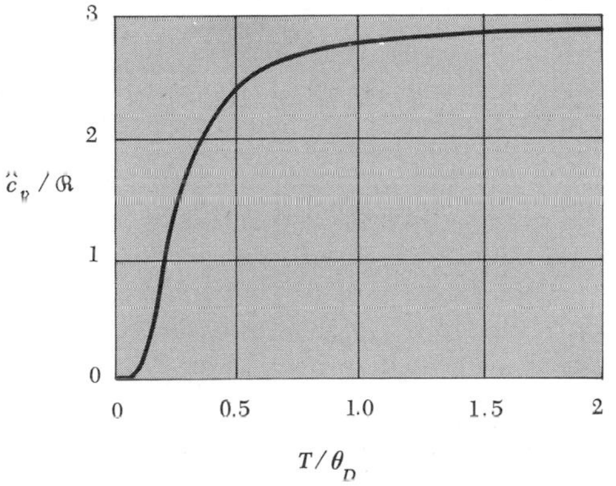

FIG. 12·4 *Specific heat of a Debye solid*

TABLE 12·1 DEBYE TEMPERATURES OF SELECTED SOLIDS

Substance		*Temperature range, °K*	θ_D, °K
Lead	Pb	14–573	88
Mercury	Hg	23–301	96
Sodium	Na	50–240	172
Silver	Ag	35–873	215
Copper	Cu	14–773	315
Aluminum	Al	19–773	398
Iron	Fe	32–95	453
Diamond	C	30–1169	1860

At temperatures much less than θ_D, the Debye specific heat may be approximated by

$$\frac{\hat{c}_v}{\mathcal{R}} = \frac{12}{5}\pi^4\left(\frac{T}{\theta_D}\right)^3 + \cdots$$

The Debye specific heat is seen to vanish as the cube of the temperature as absolute zero is approached, and this behavior has considerable experimental support.

12·7 THE MONATOMIC PERFECT GAS

In a gas that is not too dense the translational kinetic energy of the molecules is large compared to the energy associated with intermolecular forces, and the gas is usually treated as a canonical system of independent particles. For monatomic molecules at temperatures that are not too great the rotational, spin, and electronic contributions to the energy are either small or unchanged, and hence one need only consider the translational energy contributon.

We must first determine the allowed translational quantum states for a single particle. To do this properly requires solution of the Schrödinger equation and a fair amount of insight into quantum mechanics. Our approach here will be to provide an intuitive basis for a postulate about the form of the translational quantum-state equation using the *Heisenberg uncertainty principle.*

The Heisenberg uncertainty principle states that we can never measure both the momentum and position of a particle with arbitrary precision. Determination of position requires that light (or radiation of some chosen frequency) be emitted by or bounced off the particle in question, but this radiation carries momentum, and the interaction of this momentum with the particle alters its course in an unavoidable, uncorrectable way. It is true that we can use very low frequency radiation to keep the momentum changes small, but then the wavelength of the radiation is large, and we have difficulty in accurately discerning the position. We can measure position precisely only at the expense of accuracy in our knowledge of momentum. The limits of accuracy can be estimated very simply using the relations between the momentum and wavelength of radiation. One finds that the order of magnitude of the uncertainty in position Δx and the uncertainty in momentum in the x direction $\Delta \mathsf{p}_x$ are such that

$$\Delta x \, \Delta \mathsf{p}_x \approx \mathsf{h} \tag{12·39}$$

Here h is Planck's constant.

It is not particularly important that we know where a molecule is, as long as it is within the boundaries. Suppose we consider that the system has the shape of a square box of length L on each side. According to the uncertainty principle, if we require knowledge of the position of the molecule to the accuracy L, we can measure its momentum in any direction to the accuracy

$$\Delta \mathsf{p}_x \approx \frac{\mathsf{h}}{L}$$

This suggests that a useful model might be that the translational quantum states for a molecule are such that the difference in momentum between two

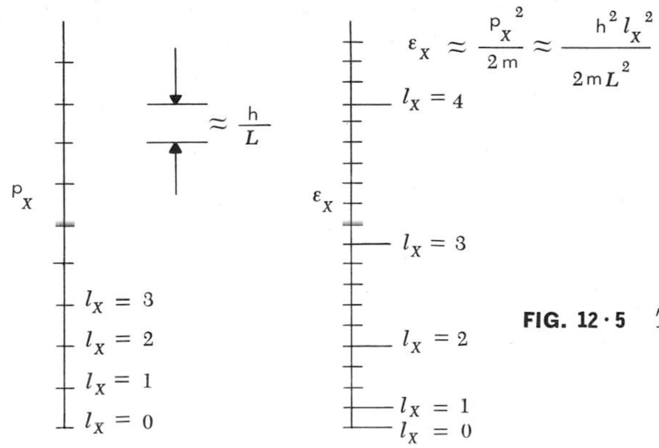

FIG. 12·5 *Translational quantum states*

successive states is of the order of h/L. The resulting momentum levels and energy levels for the motion in the x direction are shown schematically in Fig. 12·5. The integers l_x are translational *quantum numbers,* or integers identifying the quantum state. The momentum levels are equally spaced, which means that the energy associated with translational motion in the x direction should be proportional to the *square* of l_x. We therefore postulate that the energies of the allowed translational quantum states for each molecule of mass m are related to the quantum numbers l_x, l_y, and l_z (corresponding to motion in the x, y, and z directions) by an equation of the form

$$\varepsilon_{l_x,l_y,l_z} = \frac{C}{mV^{2/3}}(l_x^2 + l_y^2 + l_z^2) \tag{12·40}$$

Here the constant C is expected to be of the order of $h^2/2$, and V represents the system volume ($V = L^3$). Although we start out with this as a postulate, it is also the result obtained by solution of the Schrödinger equation, the only difference being that the constant C is obtained as $h^2/8$.

In a solid, molecules are distinguishable by their location in the lattice, but the mobility of gas molecules and the limits on following a molecule imposed by the uncertainty principle force us to consider gas molecules as indistinguishable. We shall assume, subject to a posteriori justification, that the particle quantum states are sparsely populated, which permits us to use the approximation Eq. (12·27) for the system partition function.

Each particle quantum state is specified by the three numbers l_x, l_y, and l_z. The totality of all particle quantum states can be represented by the infinite set of points in an eighth-sector of *quantum-number space* (Fig. 12·6).

The partition function for a particle can now be written as the sum over all possible particle quantum states,

$$Z_p = \sum_{l_x=0}^{\infty}\sum_{l_y=0}^{\infty}\sum_{l_z=0}^{\infty} \exp\left(\frac{-C}{mV^{2/3}kT}\right)(l_x^2 + l_y^2 + l_z^2)$$

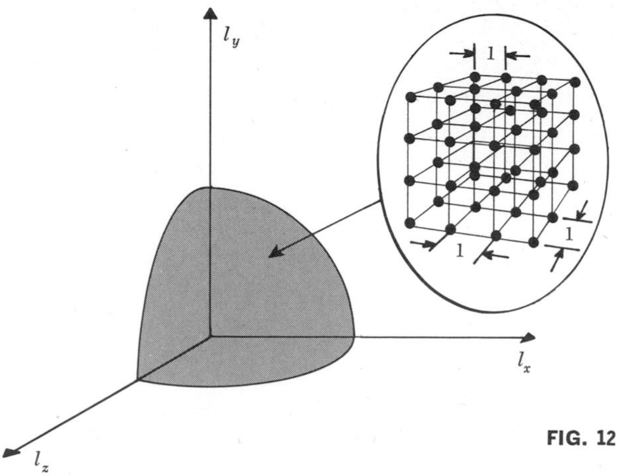

FIG. 12·6 *Quantum-number space*

Since all three sums are identical, we put

$$Z_p = \left(\sum_{l=0}^{\infty} e^{-\lambda l^2}\right)^3$$

$$\lambda = \frac{C}{\mathrm{m}V^{2/3}\mathrm{k}T}$$

As can be seen from inspection of Fig. 12·7, the sum can be thought of as an area. Since the energy levels are very close together, the height of adjacent bars will differ only slightly. We can therefore approximate the sum by an integral,

$$\sum_{l=0}^{\infty} e^{-\lambda l^2} \approx \int_0^{\infty} e^{-\lambda x^2}\, dx$$

This difficult integral can fortunately be evaluated in closed form, and it appears

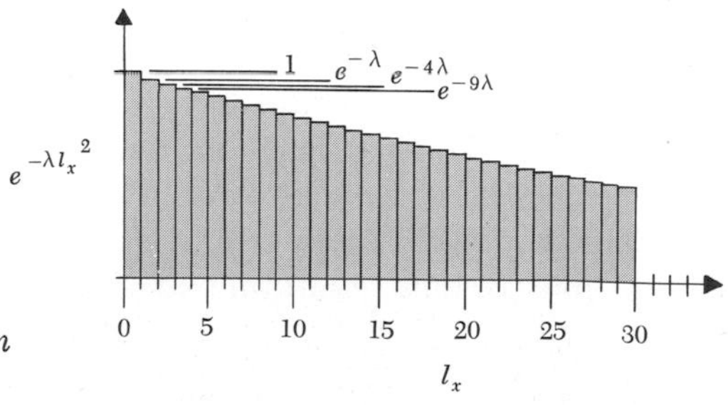

FIG. 12·7 *Approximating the sum by an integral*

in most integral tables. We find

$$Z_p = \left[\frac{1}{2}\left(\frac{\pi}{\lambda}\right)^{1/2}\right]^3 = \left[\frac{1}{2}\left(\frac{\pi m k T}{C}\right)^{1/2}\right]^3 V \qquad (12\cdot41)$$

We can now justify the assumption of sparse population of the particle quantum states. The probability distribution for particle quantum states is found from Eq. (12·10) as

$$p_{i'} = \frac{1}{Z_p}\exp\left(\frac{-\varepsilon_{i'}}{kT}\right)$$

The probability $p_{i'}$ can be viewed as an estimate of the fraction of particles in quantum state i'. Hence the number of particles in a quantum state having energy $\varepsilon_{i'}$ is

$$n_{i'} = \frac{N}{Z_p}\exp\left(\frac{-\varepsilon_{i'}}{kT}\right) = \frac{N}{V}\left[2\left(\frac{C}{\pi m k T}\right)^{1/2}\right]^3 \exp\left(\frac{-\varepsilon_{i'}}{kT}\right) \qquad (12\cdot42)$$

For helium atoms ($m = 6.7 \times 10^{-27}$ kg) at 300°K, the *number density* N/V is of the order of $10^{25}/\text{m}^3$ at room pressures. Taking $C = h^2/8$, the coefficient of the exponential above is

$$10^{25}\left[2\left(\frac{6.6^2 \times 10^{-68}}{8\pi \times 6.7 \times 10^{-27} \times 1.4 \times 10^{-23} \times 300}\right)^{1/2}\right]^3 \approx 10^{-6}$$

The exponential itself is never larger than unity, and hence there is of the order of one particle per million particle quantum states! The sparse population idealization would certainly seem appropriate.

We next use Eq. (12·30) to find the energy. From Eq. (12·41),

$$\left(\frac{\partial \ln Z_p}{\partial T}\right)_{\varepsilon_{i'}} = \frac{3}{2T}$$

and hence

$$\blacktriangleright \qquad U = \tfrac{3}{2}NkT \qquad (12\cdot43)$$

Note that the internal energy depends on the temperature only.

The entropy is then given by Eq. (12·28) as

$$\blacktriangleright \qquad S = Nk\left(\ln\frac{Z_p}{N} + \frac{5}{2}\right) \qquad (12\cdot44)$$

The pressure is obtained from Eq. (12·22). Noting that constant U implies constant T, we write

$$P = NkT\left(\frac{\partial \ln Z_p}{\partial V}\right)_T = \frac{NkT}{V} \qquad (12\cdot45)$$

Now, the number of molecules corresponding to a mass M is related to Avogadro's number N_0 (the number of molecules in a mole of the substance) and to the molal mass $\hat{M}$ (amount of mass per mole) by

$$N = \frac{\mathrm{N}_0 M}{\hat{M}} = \frac{\mathrm{N}_0 \rho V}{\hat{M}}$$

Furthermore, the Boltzmann constant can be defined in terms of the universal gas constant $\mathcal{R}$ and Avogadro's number by

$$\mathsf{k} = \frac{\mathcal{R}}{\mathrm{N}_0}$$

Equation (12·45) may therefore be written in the form

$$\blacktriangleright \qquad Pv = \frac{\mathcal{R}}{\hat{M}} T$$

which is the defining equation for the perfect gas used in previous chapters. Note that we derived the equation of state from more fundamental microscopic bases.

Recalling the empirical definition of temperature introduced in Chap. Three, we see that the thermodynamic temperature T in Eq. (12·45) and the empirical temperature are indeed identical, as we have indicated elsewhere. It is clear from this example that the use of the Boltzmann constant in the defining equation for entropy permits this exact correspondence between the thermodynamic and empirical temperature scales.

The molal internal energy of the gas may be expressed as

$$\hat{u} = \frac{U}{N} \mathrm{N}_0 = \frac{3}{2} \mathcal{R} T \tag{12·46}$$

The molal specific heat at constant volume is therefore

$$\blacktriangleright \qquad \hat{c}_v = \left(\frac{\partial \hat{u}}{\partial T}\right)_{\hat{v}} = \frac{3}{2} \mathcal{R} \tag{12·47}$$

The molal enthalpy is

$$\hat{h} = \hat{u} + P\hat{v} = \frac{5}{2} \mathcal{R} T$$

The molal specific heat at constant pressure is therefore

$$\blacktriangleright \qquad \hat{c}_P = \left(\frac{\partial \hat{h}}{\partial T}\right)_P = \frac{5}{2} \mathcal{R} \tag{12·48}$$

and has the same value for every monatomic gas. The ratio of specific heats is seen to be

$$k = \frac{\hat{c}_P}{\hat{c}_v} = \frac{5}{3} = 1.6667 \qquad (12\cdot49)$$

It should be remembered that these results pertain to a rather idealized monatomic gas and are simple in form only because the models employed are unusually simple. Note that the specific heats predicted by the rather sophisticated statistical analysis are identical with those obtained from very simple kinetic arguments in Chap. Eight.

12·8 EXTENSIONS FOR POLYATOMIC GASES

Quantum-statistical treatments of polyatomic gases are not much more involved in principle than the foregoing monatomic-gas analysis but are considerably more difficult in detail. We shall indicate the general approach and present some of the more important results of such calculations.

The most important difference between atoms and molecules is in the variety of energy modes available to polyatomic molecules. In addition to translational energy, a polyatomic molecule may possess energy because of rotation about its center of mass and vibration of the atoms under the influence of the molecular binding forces. Although other forms of energy are occasionally important, these modes are the primary ones at moderate temperatures. The rotational and vibrational energies are "internal" to the molecule, and consequently are independent of the translational energy. Vibration influences the rotational moment of inertia only slightly, and thus a good approximation is that the rotational and vibrational energies are completely independent. If the molecules are far apart, so that the intermolecular energy of the system is negligible, they may be treated as being totally independent. The partition function for a single particle then becomes the focal point of the theory. It is defined as

$$\blacktriangleright \quad Z_p = \sum_{i'} \exp\left[-\frac{(\varepsilon_{\text{tr}} + \varepsilon_{\text{rot}} + \varepsilon_{\text{vib}})_{i'}}{kT}\right]$$

Here ε_{tr}, ε_{rot}, and ε_{vib} denote the translational, rotational, and vibrational contributions to the energy of a molecule in quantum state i', and the summation is to be carried out over all quantum states available to a molecule. Every possible vibrational quantum state must be counted with every possible combination of rotational and translational quantum states. The partition function may therefore be written as

$$Z_p = \sum_{j'} \left(\exp\left[-\frac{(\varepsilon_{\text{tr}})_{j'}}{kT}\right] \sum_{k'} \left\{ \exp\left[-\frac{(\varepsilon_{\text{rot}})_{k'}}{kT}\right] \sum_{l'} \exp\left[-\frac{(\varepsilon_{\text{vib}})_{l'}}{kT}\right]\right\}\right)$$

However, since the sums are independent, this becomes

$$Z_p = Z_{tr} Z_{rot} Z_{vib} \tag{12·50}$$

where the translational, rotational, and vibrational partition functions are

$$Z_{tr} = \sum_{j'} \exp\left[-\frac{(\varepsilon_{tr})_{j'}}{kT}\right]$$

$$Z_{rot} = \sum_{k'} \exp\left[-\frac{(\varepsilon_{rot})_{k'}}{kT}\right]$$

$$Z_{vib} = \sum_{l'} \exp\left[-\frac{(\varepsilon_{vib})_{l'}}{kT}\right]$$

Now, we again consider that the particles are independent, indistinguishable, and sparsely populate their quantum states. Equation (12·30) allows the internal energy to be expressed as

$$\blacktriangleright \quad U = NkT^2\left[\left(\frac{\partial \ln Z_{tr}}{\partial T}\right)_V + \left(\frac{\partial \ln Z_{rot}}{\partial T}\right)_V + \left(\frac{\partial \ln Z_{vib}}{\partial T}\right)_V\right] \tag{12·51}$$
$$= U_{tr} + U_{rot} + U_{vib}$$

Note that the total system energy is the sum of the three independent contributions. The translational contribution to the internal energy is again given by Eq. (12·43). Equation (12·28) then gives the entropy,

$$\blacktriangleright \quad S = k\left(N \ln \frac{Z_{tr}}{N} + \frac{5}{2}\right) + kN \ln Z_{rot} + kN \ln Z_{vib} \tag{12·52}$$
$$= S_{tr} + S_{rot} + S_{vib}$$

We can therefore think of each of the three independent energy modes as contributing to the system entropy. The specific heats are likewise expressible in terms of the contributions of the various energy modes,

$$\blacktriangleright \quad \hat{c}_v = (\hat{c}_v)_{tr} + (\hat{c}_v)_{rot} + (\hat{c}_v)_{vib} \tag{12·53}$$

For gases at room temperatures the most important contributions to the specific heat are made by the translational and rotational modes, but the vibrational contribution becomes very important at elevated temperatures. This explains why the specific heats of polyatomic gases increase with increasing temperature (see Figs. 12·10, B·17).

We have already evaluated the translational partition function and determined the translational contribution to $\hat{c}_v$ as $\frac{3}{2}\mathcal{R}$. The evaluation of the rotation partition function for even the simplest diatomic molecule is mathematically quite involved. The result may be expressed in terms of quantum indices and the dimensionless grouping $h^2/(8\pi^2 IkT)$, where I is the moment of inertia of the diatomic molecule. It is customary to define a *characteristic tem-*

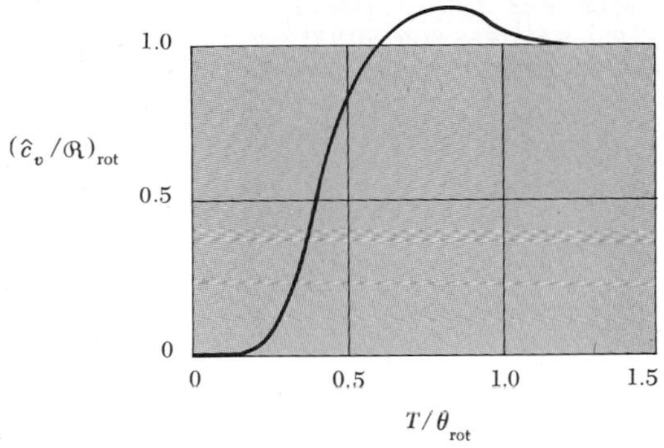

FIG. 12·8 *Rotational contribution to the specific heat of a diatomic gas*

perature, θ_{rot}, by setting the group above equal to θ_{rot}/T. For temperatures much greater than the characteristic temperature the rotational partition function becomes simply†

$$Z_{rot} = \frac{T}{\theta_{rot}} \qquad T \gg \theta_{rot}$$

The rotational contribution to the energy of a diatomic gas at temperatures well above the characteristic temperature is then

$$U_{rot} = N\mathrm{k}T \qquad T \gg \theta_{rot}$$

which corresponds to a contribution to $\hat{c}_v$

$$(\hat{c}_v)_{rot} = \mathcal{R} \qquad T \gg \theta_{rot}$$

The rotational contribution to $\hat{c}_v$ is indicated in Fig. 12·8. Characteristic temperatures for several gases are given in Table 12·2. From inspection of this table we see that the assumption that $T \gg \theta_{rot}$ is valid except at very low temperatures. Then, if we neglect the vibrational contribution, the specific heat of a diatomic gas at temperatures which are not too low is

▶ $$\hat{c}_v = (\hat{c}_v)_{tr} + (\hat{c}_v)_{rot} = \tfrac{3}{2}\mathcal{R} + \mathcal{R} = \tfrac{5}{2}\mathcal{R} \qquad (12\cdot 54)$$

Since $\hat{c}_P - \hat{c}_v = \mathcal{R}$ for any perfect gas, for a diatomic gas

▶ $$\hat{c}_P = \tfrac{7}{2}\mathcal{R} \qquad (12\cdot 55)$$

and the ratio of specific heats is

▶ $$k = \frac{\hat{c}_P}{\hat{c}_v} = \frac{7}{5} = 1.4 \qquad (12\cdot 56)$$

† For molecules with two different atoms. For molecules with two identical indistinguishable atoms this partition function must be divided by 2. Figure 12·8 applies when the atoms are distinguishable. The behavior for indistinguishable atoms is similar, with $\hat{c}_v \to \mathcal{R}$ as $T/\theta_{rot} \to \infty$.

TABLE 12·2 CHARACTERISTIC TEMPERATURES FOR ROTATION OF DIATOMIC MOLECULES

Gas	θ_{rot}, °K
H_2	85.5
HCl	15.3
N_2	2.86
CO	2.77
NO	2.47
O_2	2.09
Cl_2	0.347
K_2	0.081

TABLE 12·3 CHARACTERISTIC TEMPERATURES FOR VIBRATION OF DIATOMIC MOLECULES

Gas	θ_{vib}, °K
H_2	6140
HCl	4300
N_2	3340
CO	3120
NO	2740
O_2	2260
Cl_2	810
K_2	140

This prediction is in excellent agreement with experiments for many diatomic gases at temperatures which are neither too low nor too high.

At higher temperatures the vibrational mode becomes increasingly important. The partition function for an oscillator with one natural frequency of vibration ν [Eq. (12·33)] may be applied directly to a diatomic molecule. Thus

$$Z_{vib} = \frac{\exp(-\varepsilon_m/kT)}{1 - \exp(-h\nu/kT)}$$

We define a *characteristic temperature* for vibration as

$$\theta_{vib} \equiv h\nu/k$$

Performing the required differentiation, the vibrational contribution to the specific heat of a diatomic gas is found as [compare Eq. (12·37)]

$$(\hat{c}_v)_{vib} = \mathcal{R}\left(\frac{\theta_{vib}}{T}\right)^2 \frac{e^{\theta_{vib}/T}}{[e^{\theta_{vib}/T} - 1]^2} \tag{12·57}$$

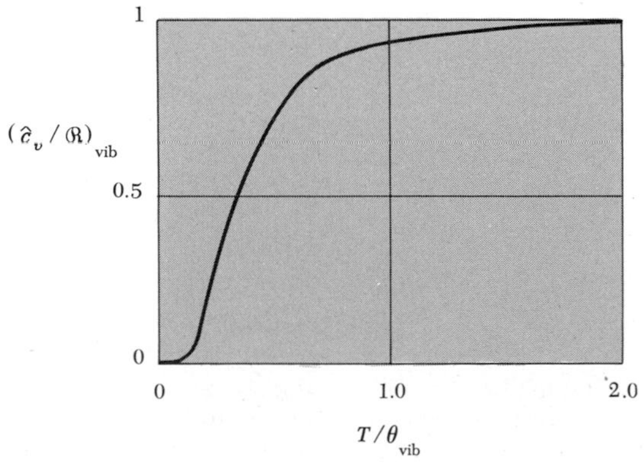

FIG. 12·9 *Vibrational contribution to the specific heat of a diatomic gas*

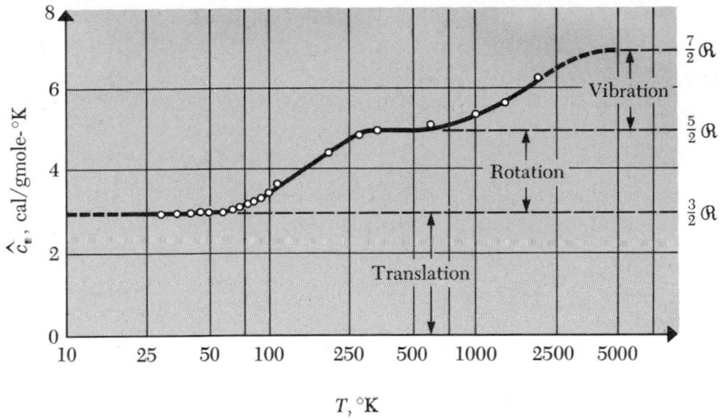

FIG. 12·10 *Specific heat of ordinary hydrogen.*

This contribution is shown in Fig. 12·9; the vibrational frequency may be determined from spectrographic measurements, and typical values for the characteristic temperature are given in Table 12·3. Note that the vibrational contribution to $\hat{c}_v$ approaches $\mathcal{R}$ at very high temperatures. Thus, at temperatures much greater than characteristic temperatures for both rotation and vibration, the specific heats of a diatomic gas will approach

$$\hat{c}_v \approx \tfrac{5}{2}\mathcal{R} + \mathcal{R} = \tfrac{7}{2}\mathcal{R}$$
$$\hat{c}_P \approx \tfrac{9}{2}\mathcal{R}$$
$$k \approx \tfrac{9}{7} = 1.285$$

Note that as more modes become excited at increased temperatures the specific heats both increase, but their ratio decreases.

Spectrographic data play an important role in determining the vibrational contribution to the specific heats. The spectrograph shows lines at frequencies corresponding to the vibrational frequencies of the molecule, and the skilled spectroscopist can determine these frequencies with great precision. This is particularly important for high-temperature gases, where measurement of specific heats by direct temperature and energy measurements is often impractical.

Figure 12·10 shows the predicted and measured $\hat{c}_v$ for normal hydrogen. Note the order in which the modes are excited as T increases.

12·9 GRAND CANONICAL SYSTEMS

Free electrons in a metal and photons in an enclosure are examples of systems in which the number of particles is not fixed. The statistical thermodynamic treatment of such systems must include possible variations in the number of particles within the system, and hence the *grand canonical* approach is used. We imagine that the system under study interacts with a thermal energy reservoir and component reservoirs, and that the combined system is isolated. The allowed quantum states for the system under study then include states with any system energy and with any number of particles. It is in this latter scope that the allowed quantum states for a grand canonical system differ from those of a canonical system. We shall now outline the formalism of this approach, and mention the results of some applications.

The entropy of the combined system is given by Eq. (12·7). The total energy in all the reservoirs is simply $U_C - U$, where U is the internal energy of the system under study. We again interpret U as an average [Eq. (12·14)], and hence the total energy in the reservoirs may be expressed as

$$U_C - \sum_i p_i \epsilon_i$$

For simplicity we restrict ourselves to a system of only one type of particle. Since the number of particles in the combined isolated system is fixed, the number of particles within the component reservoir is $N_C - N$, where N_C is the total number of particles in the combined system and N is the number within the system under study. N should be viewed as an average, and hence we put

$$N = \sum_i p_i n_i \tag{12·58}$$

where n_i is the number of particles within the system of interest when it is in its ith quantum state. Making the substitutions above in Eq. (12·7), the entropy of the combined isolated system can be expressed in terms of the distribution p_i as

$$S = -\mathsf{k} \sum_i p_i \ln p_i + \frac{\mu^*}{T} \sum_i p_i n_i - \frac{1}{T} \sum p_i \epsilon_i - \frac{\mu^*}{T} N_C + \frac{U_C}{T}$$

where μ^* is the *electrochemical potential per particle*. We again seek the equilibrium distribution p_i which maximizes the entropy of the combined isolated system. The constraint Eq. (12·16) must again be applied to ensure that the total probability is unity. The maximization process was illustrated in Sec. 12·3; the result for a grand canonical system composed of one kind of particle is

$$p_i = \frac{1}{\mathcal{Z}} \exp\left(\frac{-\epsilon_i}{\mathsf{k}T} + \frac{\mu^* n_i}{\mathsf{k}T}\right) \tag{12·59}$$

The denominator $\mathcal{Z}$, which is independent of the quantum state, is the *grand partition function*, or the *grand state-sum*. Applying Eq. (12·16), one finds

$$\mathcal{Z} = \sum_i \exp\left(\frac{-\epsilon_i}{\mathsf{k}T} + \frac{\mu^* n_i}{\mathsf{k}T}\right) \tag{12·60}$$

The grand partition function plays the same role in the theory of grand canonical systems as the partition function does in analysis of canonical systems. Once it has been evaluated, the other thermodynamic properties can be found immediately. In particular, it is not very difficult to show that the average energy of the system is

$$U = \mathrm{k}T^2 \left(\frac{\partial \ln \mathcal{Z}}{\partial T}\right)_{\epsilon_i, n_i, \mu^*/\mathrm{k}T} \tag{12·61}$$

and the average number of particles in the system is

$$N = \mathrm{k}T \left(\frac{\partial \ln \mathcal{Z}}{\partial \mu^*}\right)_{\epsilon_i, n_i, T} \tag{12·62}$$

Often the energy of the system can be represented as the sum of the "private" energies of the individual particles, in which case evaluation of the grand partition function is considerably simplified. Two kinds of grand canonical systems of this type are important. A *Bose-Einstein* system (BE) is one in which the particles are indistinguishable from one another and any number of particles can assume any of the quantum states allowed for individual particles. Photons are an example of a BE system. A *Fermi-Dirac* system (FD) is one in which the particles are indistinguishable and no two particles can exist in the same quantum state. This restriction is the *Pauli exclusion principle,* which quantum theory indicates applies to a particular class of particles, including electrons. The grand partition functions for BE and FD systems can be cast into very neat forms, as we shall now demonstrate.

Let

$$\beta = \frac{1}{\mathrm{k}T} \qquad \alpha = \frac{\mu^*}{\mathrm{k}T}$$

and let $\varepsilon_{i'}$ denote the energy of a particle in its i'th quantum state. Then consider the following expansions:

$$\frac{1}{1 - e^{-\beta\varepsilon_1+\alpha}} = 1 + e^{-\beta\varepsilon_1+\alpha} + e^{-2\beta\varepsilon_1+2\alpha} + \cdots$$

$$\frac{1}{1 - e^{-\beta\varepsilon_2+\alpha}} = 1 + e^{-\beta\varepsilon_2+\alpha} + e^{-2\beta\varepsilon_2+2\alpha} + \cdots$$

Now, the product of these expansions is

$$\frac{1}{(1 - e^{-\beta\varepsilon_2+\alpha})(1 - e^{-\beta\varepsilon_2+\alpha})} = 1 + [e^{-\beta\varepsilon_1+\alpha} + e^{-\beta\varepsilon_2+\alpha}]$$
$$+ [e^{-2\beta\varepsilon_1+2\alpha} + e^{-\beta\varepsilon_1-\beta\varepsilon_2+2\alpha} + e^{-2\beta\varepsilon_2+2\alpha}]$$
$$+ [e^{-3\beta\varepsilon_1+3\alpha} + e^{-2\beta\varepsilon_1-\beta\varepsilon_2+3\alpha} + e^{-\beta\varepsilon_1-2\beta\varepsilon_2+3\alpha} + e^{-3\varepsilon_2+3\alpha}] + \cdots$$

The first term (1) represents a system quantum state with no particles. The second group of terms represents the two system quantum states with one particle in each of the first two particle quantum states. The third group represents all possible system quantum states involving two particles distributed over the first two particle quantum states. The fourth group of terms represents all system quantum state arrangements involving three particles in the first two particle quantum states. We see that the product represents the terms in the grand state-sum involving any number of particles distributed over the first two particle quantum states. It is easy to see that the continued product†

$$\prod_{i'} (1 - e^{-\beta \varepsilon_{i'} + \alpha})^{-1}$$

would give a term accounting for any number of particles distributed in any way over all the possible particle quantum states. This is precisely the grand partition function for a BE system, so

$$\mathcal{Z}_{\mathrm{BE}} = \prod_{i'} \left\{1 - \exp\left[\frac{-(\varepsilon_{i'} - \mu^*)}{\mathrm{k}T}\right]\right\}^{-1} \tag{12·63}$$

By carrying out a few terms of the continued product, one can similarly show that the grand partition function for a FD system is

$$\mathcal{Z}_{\mathrm{FD}} = \prod_{i'} \left\{1 + \exp\left[\frac{-(\varepsilon_{i'} - \mu^*)}{\mathrm{k}T}\right]\right\} \tag{12·64}$$

The terms of this product account precisely for all system quantum states involving any number of particles distributed in any way which does not put more than one particle in each particle quantum state i'.

Since the logarithm of a product is the sum of the logarithm of individual terms,

$$\ln \mathcal{Z}_{\mathrm{BE}} = -\sum_{i'} \ln \left\{1 - \exp\left[\frac{-(\varepsilon_{i'} - \mu^*)}{\mathrm{k}T}\right]\right\} \tag{12·65}$$

$$\ln \mathcal{Z}_{\mathrm{FD}} = +\sum_{i'} \ln \left\{1 + \exp\left[\frac{-(\varepsilon_{i'} - \mu^*)}{\mathrm{k}T}\right]\right\} \tag{12·66}$$

Applying Eq. (12·62), one finds that the average number of particles in a BE system is

$$N_{\mathrm{BE}} = \sum_{i'} \frac{1}{\exp\left[(\varepsilon_{i'} - \mu^*)/\mathrm{k}T\right] - 1} \tag{12·67}$$

Since the total number of particles is the sum of the number of particles in each particle quantum state, we can interpret each term in the sum in Eq. (12·67) as the average number of particles in particle quantum state i',

$$N_{i'\mathrm{BE}} = \frac{1}{\exp\left[(\varepsilon_{i'} - \mu^*)/\mathrm{k}T\right] - 1} \tag{12·68}$$

† The symbol Π represents a continued product, analogous to the continued sum represented by Σ.

This is called the *Bose-Einstein distribution.* The corresponding results for FD systems are

$$N_{\mathrm{FD}} = \sum_{i'} \frac{1}{\exp\,[(\varepsilon_i - \mu^*)/kT] + 1} \tag{12·69}$$

$$N_{i'\mathrm{FD}} = \frac{1}{\exp\,[(\varepsilon_i - \mu^*)/kT] + 1} \tag{12·70}$$

This is called the *Fermi-Dirac distribution.*

Figure 12·11 shows the quantum-state populations for three different temperatures for BE and FD systems. Of particular interest is the fact that in FD systems at very low temperatures, particle quantum states having energies greater than the "Fermi level" μ^* are virtually unpopulated, while every quantum state with energy less than μ^* is almost always populated. At $T = 0$ the Pauli exclusion principle requires that more than one state be populated in an FD system. In contrast, all of the particles in a BE system at $T = 0$ will be in the quantum state of lowest energy (the "ground" state).

For small values of $(\varepsilon_{i'} - \mu^*)/kT$ the average particle quantum state population for a BE system becomes very small, and hence the BE distribution [Eq. (12·68)] approaches the FD distribution [Eq. (12·70)]. Both can then be approximated by

$$N_{i'} \approx \exp\left[\frac{-(\varepsilon_{i'} - \mu^*)}{kT}\right] \tag{12·71}$$

which is sometimes referred to as the *Maxwell-Boltzmann* (MB) *distribution.* Note that an exponential distribution of similar form was found for the case of a canonical system of a fixed number of independent indistinguishable particles with sparse quantum-state population [Eq. (12·42)].

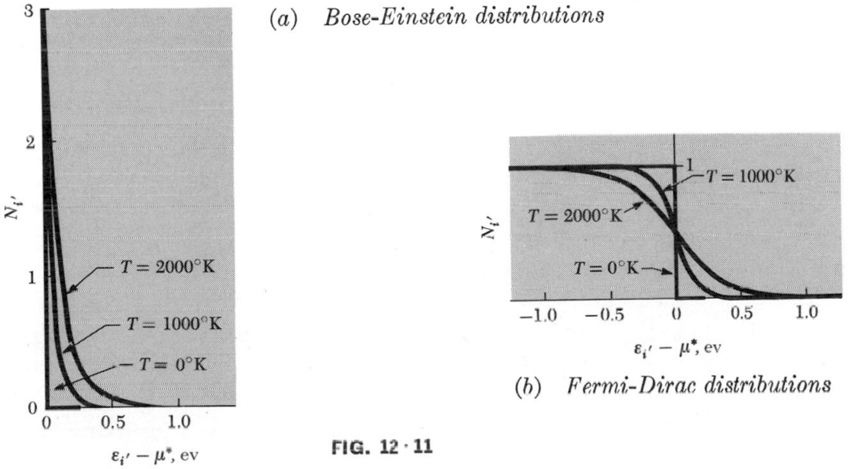

(*a*) *Bose-Einstein distributions*

(*b*) *Fermi-Dirac distributions*

FIG. 12·11

12·10 THE DISTRIBUTION OF FREE ELECTRONS IN METALS

A simplified model of the free electrons within a metal treats the electrons as a dilute gas obeying the Pauli exclusion principle. The allowed quantum states for electron translational motion within a volume of metal are assumed to be the same as for a monatomic molecule [Eq. (12·40)]. In addition, each electron is allowed to take one of two spin states. The FD model is used, and hence the number of electrons in any particular quantum state is given by Eq. (12·70).

One would especially like to know μ^*, for all the electrons have energy less than μ^* at $T = 0$ and most have energies less than μ^* at normal temperatures. If we can determine the total number of free electrons, we can calculate μ^* quite simply.

The allowed quantum states can be represented by points in "quantum-number space" (Fig. 12·6). Those points lying inside an eighth-sphere of radius l correspond to all the translational quantum states with energy less than [see Eq. (12·40)]

$$\varepsilon_{\max} = \frac{\mathsf{h}^2 l^2}{8\mathsf{m} V^{2/3}} \tag{12·72}$$

The number of points within this eighth-sphere is approximately its volume, or $\pi l^3/6$. Since there are two allowed spin states for each translational quantum state, the total number of electron quantum states with translational energies less than $\varepsilon_{\max}$ is $\pi l^3/3$. If there are N free electrons, each occupying one of these quantum states, the maximum quantum index which is filled is

$$l = \left(\frac{3N}{\pi}\right)^{1/3}$$

The energy corresponding to this l is μ^*. Hence

$$\mu^* = \frac{\mathsf{h}^2}{8\mathsf{m}} \left(\frac{3N}{\pi V}\right)^{2/3} \tag{12·73}$$

An assumption about the number of free electrons per atom and knowledge of the atomic density would allow one to calculate immediately the *Fermi level* μ^*.

We remark that at $T = 0$ only two electrons can be at rest (one with each allowed spin) because of the Pauli exclusion principle. The other free electrons must be in motion, and hence the often-heard notion that $T = 0$ is a state where all motion ceases is not correct.

Equation (12·70) gives the number of electrons in each quantum state. Of more interest is the number of electrons at each energy level. At absolute zero there are two electrons at each of the translational quantum states in the eighth-sphere of Fig. 12·6. The number of translational quantum states lying between l and $l + dl$ in quantum-number space is approximately the

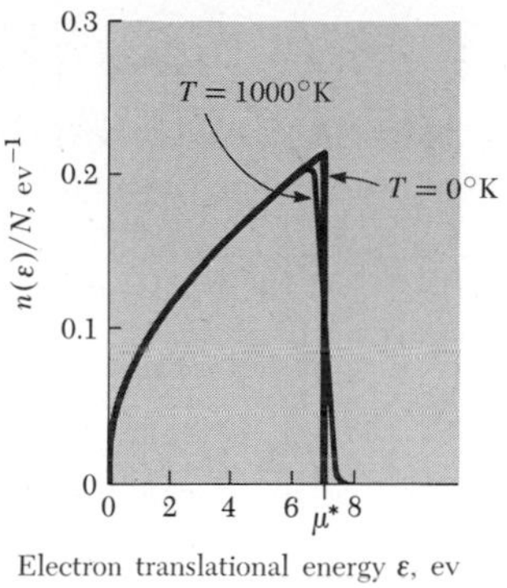

FIG. 12·12 *Distribution of electrons in copper*

volume contained between an eighth-sphere of radius l and another of radius $l + dl$, or $\frac{1}{2}\pi l^2\, dl$. Corresponding to the band dl is a band of energies $d\varepsilon$. The number of electrons in this band is defined as $n(\varepsilon)\, d\varepsilon$. At $T = 0$ there are two electrons in each translational quantum state, and hence

$$n(\varepsilon)\, d\varepsilon = \pi l^2\, dl = \pi l^2 \frac{dl}{d\varepsilon}\, d\varepsilon$$

From Eq. (12·40),

$$\frac{dl}{d\varepsilon} = \frac{4\mathrm{m} V^{2/3}}{\mathrm{h}^2 l}$$

So

$$n(\varepsilon) = \frac{4\pi \mathrm{m}}{\mathrm{h}^2} V^{2/3} l$$

Substituting for l from Eq. (12·40),

$$n(\varepsilon) = \frac{4\sqrt{8}\,\pi \mathrm{m}^{3/2}}{\mathrm{h}^3} \varepsilon^{1/2} V \qquad \text{at } T = 0 \tag{12·74}$$

Figure 12·12 shows the distribution of electrons in copper calculated here at 0°K and the corresponding distribution at a higher T calculated from the FD distribution. Note that there is very little difference between these two distributions, and consequently the 0°K distribution can be used at room temperatures for some purposes.

SELECTED READING

Knuth, E., *Statistical Thermodynamics*, chaps. 2, 3, 6, and 9, McGraw-Hill Book Company, New York, 1966.

Lay, J., *Thermodynamics*, sec. 13.16, Charles E. Merrill Books, Inc., Columbus, Ohio, 1963.

Lee, J., F. Sears, and D. Turcotte, *Statistical Thermodynamics*, chap. 12, Addison-Wesley Publishing Co., Inc., Reading, Mass., 1963.

Sonntag, R., and G. J. Van Wylen, *Fundamentals of Statistical Thermodynamics*, chaps. 6 and 7, John Wiley & Sons, Inc., New York, 1966.

Tribus, M., *Thermostatics and Thermodynamics*, secs. 12.9, 15.20, and 15.21, D. Van Nostrand Co., Inc., Princeton, N.J., 1961.

Zemansky, M., and H. Van Ness, *Basic Engineering Thermodynamics*, chap. 15, McGraw-Hill Book Company, New York, 1966.

QUESTIONS

12·1 What is an ensemble? What is a quantum state? What is the meaning of p_i?

12·2 Why is the entropy so important in statistical thermodynamics?

12·3 What is a microcanonical system? How does it differ from a canonical system? From a grand canonical system?

12·4 What is the difference between the system quantum states and the particle quantum states? Can you think of a case where particle quantum states cannot be defined?

12·5 Is the partition function extensive?

12·6 What is a vibrational frequency?

12·7 What is k and how is it related to $\mathcal{R}$?

12·8 What is a system of independent particles?

12·9 What does molecular vibration do to c_P for gases?

12·10 What is the Bose-Einstein distribution? How does it differ from the Fermi-Dirac distribution?

12·11 Why are there some electrons still moving in a metal at 0°K?

12·12 What is the maximum translational energy of an electron in a metal at 0°K?

PROBLEMS

12·1 Consider a solid cubic array of molecules of two types, A and B. If there are n_A molecules of A and n_B of B, what is the entropy associated with their position? Assume each site may take either type of molecule with equal probability.

12·2 Suppose in the lattice of Prob. 12·1 the molecules of A must be surrounded by molecules of B, and, neglecting edge effects, there are equal numbers of molecules of A and B. What is the positional entropy?

12·3 Derive an expression for the partition function for an oscillator with two independent degrees of oscillation, and two independent frequencies ν_1 and ν_2, assuming that the allowed quantum states for each mode are given by Eq. (12·31). This represents a simple model of the vibrational states of a triatomic molecule with a central atom connected to two outboard atoms. Determine the vibrational contribution to $\hat{c}_P$ and $\hat{c}_v$ for an ideal gas composed of such molecules.

12·4 Extend the Einstein model by assuming that the atoms can vibrate in three independent different directions and that ε_m and ν are the same for the three modes. Express $\hat{c}_v$ in terms of three characteristic temperatures. How would these parameters be evaluated?

12·5 Derive an expression for $\hat{c}_P$ in terms of the partition function Z.

12·6 Derive an expression for $\hat{g}$ in terms of the partition function Z.

12·7 Derive an expression for the molal enthalpy $\hat{h}$ in terms of the partition function Z.

12·8 Calculate the vibrational, rotational, and translational contributions to $\hat{c}_v$ for HCl at 30°K, 100°K, 1000°K, and 3000°K.

12·9 Calculate the vibrational, rotational, and translational contributions to $\hat{c}_P$ for CO at 30°K, 100°K, 300°K, 1000°K, and 3000°K.

12·10 Spectroscopic measurements of the vibrational characteristic temperature of Br_2 indicate a value of 465°K. The rotational characteristic temperature is 0.12°K. Calculate $\hat{c}_P$ at 200°K and at 700°K for this diatomic gas.

12·11 Using the tabulated characteristic temperatures for rotation and vibration, calculate the specific heat of CO over the range 0–1000°K, and calculate the enthalpy, relative to its value at 0°K, over this range, and compare with data given in Table B·13.

12·12 Do Prob. 12·11 for HCl.

12·13 Do Prob. 12·11 for NO.

12·14 Verify that the thermodynamic definition of the electrochemical potential is satisfied by the grand canonical model.

12·15 Derive an expression for the pressure in terms of the grand partition function $\mathcal{Z}$.

12·16 Find an expression similar to Eq. (12·63) for the grand partition function in a system consisting of two different kinds of independent boseons.

12·17 Find an expression similar to Eq. (12·64) for the grand partition function in a system consisting of two independent kinds of fermions.

12·18 Assuming that there is one free electron per atom in the crystal lattice, calculate the Fermi level (ev) of tungsten.

12·19 Do Prob. 12·18 for silver.

12·20 Using the 0°K Fermi distribution, calculate the number of free electrons per cm^3 in tungsten at 500°K. Make the assumption of Prob. 12·18.

12·21 Do Prob. 12·20 for silver.

12·22 Consider an electron in a metal with kinetic energy ε. If the electric field immediately outside the metal has uniform strength **E**, what must be the value of ε in order for the electron to escape from the metal? How is this energy related to the Fermi level? Under what conditions can there be electron emissions from a metal at 0°K?

CHAPTER THIRTEEN

SOME ASPECTS OF MOLECULAR KINETICS

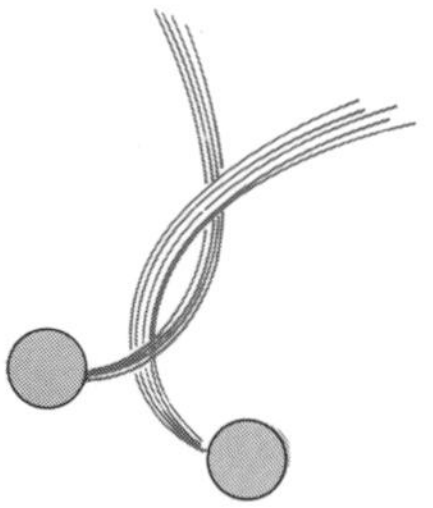

13·1 THE DISTRIBUTION OF TRANSLATIONAL VELOCITIES IN A GAS

A byproduct of the statistical thermodynamic analysis of ideal monatomic gas is an equation for the number of molecules in each of the allowed translational quantum states [Eq. (12·42)]. Since the translational mode is assumed to be independent of the other energy modes for polyatomic gases, the same distribution over the translational quantum states applies to any ideal gas. A great deal can be learned about the kinetics of molecular motion from the translational velocity distribution. We shall first develop this distribution, and then use it to examine certain aspects of intermolecular collisions and collisions with the container wall.

The closeness of the translational velocity levels allows us to represent the discrete velocity distribution by a continuous *velocity-distribution function.* We define $f(\mathsf{V})\,d\mathsf{V}$ as the fraction of the molecules having speeds between V and $\mathsf{V} + d\mathsf{V}$. Our present aim is to determine this function.

The allowed translational quantum states are prescribed by Eq. (12·40). Each state can be represented by one point in the eighth-sector of *quantum-number space* shown in Fig. 12·6. All molecules for which $l^2 = l_x^2 + l_y^2 + l_z^2$ has a given value will be moving at the same speed, though they will be heading in all different directions. We would like to calculate the number moving at each speed, regardless of their direction. Now, from Eq. (12·42) we see that there are the same number of particles in each of the particle quantum states having the same value of l. The number of such states is therefore important. Consider now a band of states in quantum-number space lying between two infinitesimally separated eighth-spheres of radius l and $l + dl$, respectively. Considering l to be much larger than unity, the number of quantum states in this band is equal to the volume of the band, or

$$\tfrac{1}{2}\pi l^2\, dl$$

Now, the average number of molecules in each of these quantum states is $n_{i'}(l)$; from Eq. (12·42),

$$n_{i'}(l) = \frac{N}{Z_p} \exp\left[-\frac{\varepsilon_{i'}(l)}{\mathrm{k}T}\right]$$

The energy of any molecule in one of these quantum states is

$$\varepsilon_{i'}(l) = \frac{Cl^2}{\mathrm{m}V^{2/3}} = \frac{1}{2g_c}\,\mathrm{m}\mathsf{V}^2$$

and so the quantum index l is related to the corresponding velocity by

$$l = \frac{\mathrm{m}\mathsf{V}}{(2g_cC)^{1/2}}\,V^{1/3}$$

The number of molecules having speeds within the range corresponding to dl is therefore

$$\begin{aligned} n_{i'}(l)\,\frac{1}{2}\,\pi l^2\,dl &= \frac{N}{Z_p}\exp\left(-\frac{\mathrm{m}\mathsf{V}^2}{2g_c\mathrm{k}T}\right)\frac{1}{2}\,\pi\,\frac{\mathrm{m}^2\mathsf{V}^2}{2g_cC}\,V^{2/3}\,\frac{\mathrm{m}V^{1/3}}{(2g_cC)^{1/2}}\,d\mathsf{V} \\ &= \frac{NV}{Z_p}\,\frac{\pi}{2}\left(\frac{\mathrm{m}^2}{2g_cC}\right)^{3/2}\mathsf{V}^2\exp\left(-\frac{\mathrm{m}\mathsf{V}^2}{2g_c\mathrm{k}T}\right)d\mathsf{V} \end{aligned}$$

but this is just $Nf(\mathsf{V})\,d\mathsf{V}$. Then, using the expression for Z_p given by Eq. (12·41), we find

$$\blacktriangleright \quad f(\mathsf{V})\,d\mathsf{V} = \left(\frac{2}{\pi}\right)^{1/2}\left(\frac{\mathrm{m}}{g_c\mathrm{k}T}\right)^{3/2}\mathsf{V}^2\exp\left(-\frac{\mathrm{m}\mathsf{V}^2}{2g_c\mathrm{k}T}\right)d\mathsf{V} \qquad (13\cdot 1)$$

This velocity-distribution function is called the *Maxwell-Boltzmann distribution,* after two men who obtained it independently (not in the manner which we used). The Maxwell-Boltzmann distribution is shown in Fig. 13·1.

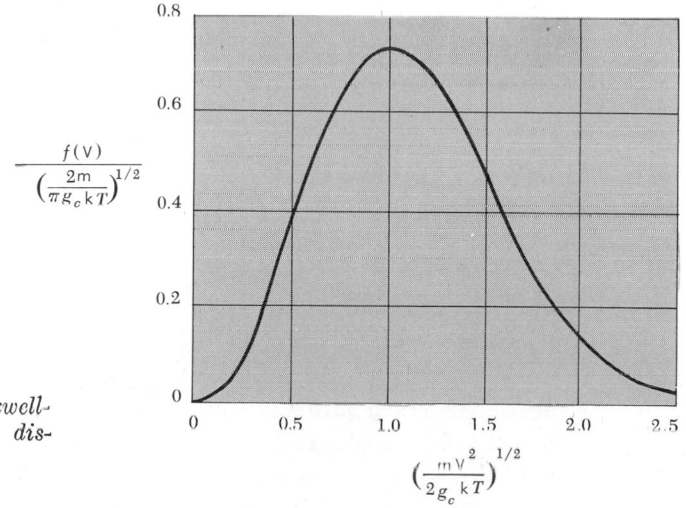

FIG. 13·1 *The Maxwell-Boltzmann velocity distribution*

The *mean speed* of the molecules V_m is defined as

$$V_m \equiv \int_0^\infty V f(V)\, dV \tag{13·2}$$

Employing the Maxwell-Boltzmann distribution, we obtain

$$V_m = \left(\frac{2}{\pi}\right)^{1/2} \left(\frac{m}{g_c kT}\right)^{3/2} \left(\frac{1}{2}\frac{m}{g_c kT}\right)^{-4/2} \int_0^\infty x^3 e^{-x^2}\, dx$$

The integral has the value ½. The mean speed is then

$$V_m = \left(\frac{8}{\pi}\frac{g_c kT}{m}\right)^{1/2} \tag{13·3}$$

The *root-mean-square speed* V_{rms} is defined as that velocity characteristic of the average translational energy per molecule; then

$$V_{rms}^2 \equiv \int_0^\infty V^2 f(V)\, dV \tag{13·4}$$

From Eq. (12·43) it follows that

$$\frac{U_{tr}}{N} = \frac{1}{2}\frac{mV_{rms}^2}{g_c} = \frac{3}{2}kT$$

which leads to

$$V_{rms} = \left(\frac{3g_c kT}{m}\right)^{1/2} \tag{13·5}$$

TABLE 13·1 INTEGRALS FOR THE MAXWELL-BOLTZMANN DISTRIBUTION

x	$\int_0^x x^2 e^{-x^2}\, dx$	$\int_0^x x^3 e^{-x^2}\, dx$	$\int_0^x x^4 e^{-x^2}\, dx$
0	0	0	0
0.2	0.0016	0.0004	0.0001
0.4	0.0194	0.0058	0.0018
0.6	0.0583	0.0256	0.0121
0.8	0.1179	0.0676	0.0419
1.0	0.1895	0.1321	0.1003
1.2	0.2612	0.2110	0.1871
1.4	0.3234	0.2915	0.2918
1.6	0.3708	0.3624	0.3979
1.8	0.4030	0.4170	0.4903
2.0	0.4227	0.4542	0.5608
2.2	0.4336	0.4769	0.6083
2.4	0.4390	0.4893	0.6367
2.6	0.4410	0.4943	0.6490
∞	$\sqrt{\pi}/4$	½	$3\sqrt{\pi}/8$

In helium at room temperature (293°K) the root-mean-square speed is

$$V_{rms} = \left(\frac{3 \times 1 \times 1.380 \times 10^{-23}\ \text{kg-m}^2/\text{sec}^2\text{-°K} \times 293\text{°K}}{6.7 \times 10^{-27}\ \text{kg}}\right)^{1/2} = 1340\ \text{m/sec}$$

It is indeed a rather awesome observation that we are continually being struck by molecules of oxygen, nitrogen, and other elements moving at speeds of the order of 1000 m/sec!

A tabulation of integrals pertinent to the Maxwell-Boltzmann distribution is given in Table 13·1.

13·2 COLLISIONS WITH THE WALL

To examine the nature of the particle-wall interactions we first relate the normal force per unit of area acting on the boundaries of our gas to the thermodynamic pressure. This analysis will be similar to the kinetic analysis in Chap. Eight, but somewhat more rigorous. Consider the interaction of a single molecule with the "wall" (Fig. 13·2). For our kinetic model we assume that

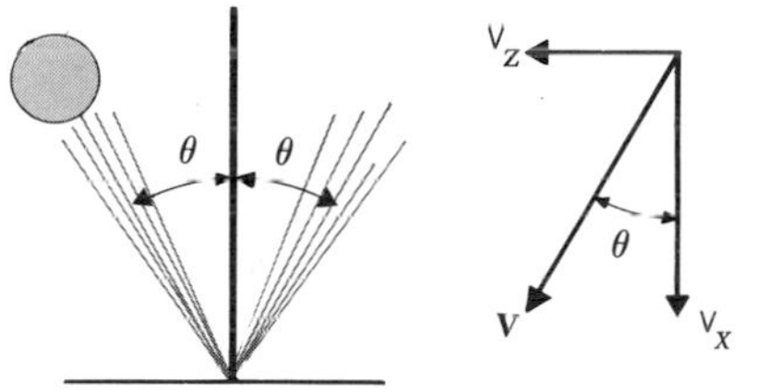

FIG. 13·2 *A wall interaction*

the collision is perfectly elastic, so that the molecule is reflected at an angle equal to its angle of incidence. This is an extremely oversimplified picture of what actually occurs, but the results of an analysis based on this model display the essential features we seek. In turning the molecule, the wall must exert a force. From integration of Newton's second law the normal component of the impulse delivered by the particle is found to be

$$\int F_n\, dt = \frac{2mV \cos\theta}{g_c} \qquad (13\cdot6)$$

The integration is to be carried out over the very short period of interaction.

We must add the contributions of every molecule that strikes the wall. Consider an elemental wall area dA, as shown in Fig. 13·3. Within the prismoidal box of height $V_x\, dt$ many molecules are flying about in all directions. If we consider only those molecules moving with velocity V, we see that every one of these contained within the box will strike the wall in time dt, provided that no interactions with other molecules occur in this time. Let us assume that dt can be made small enough that collisions between molecules within the little box can be ignored. The number of molecules (having this velocity)

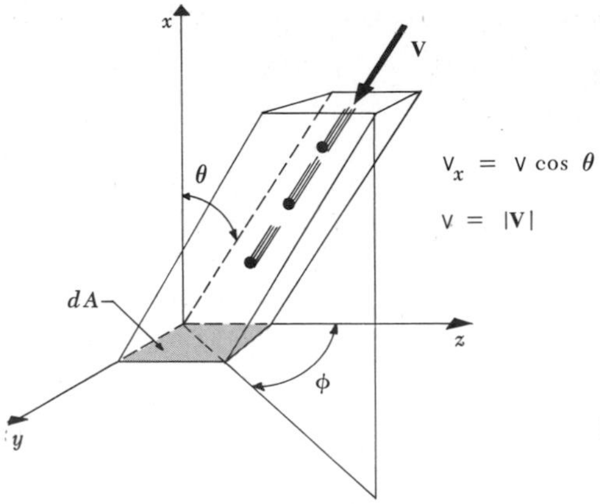

FIG. 13·3 *Computing the impact rate*

that strike the wall in time dt is then the volume of the box times the number of particles per unit of volume that have this velocity. The volume of the box is

$$V = dA \cos\theta \, \mathsf{V} \, dt$$

To determine the number of molecules per unit of volume having this velocity we consider Fig. 13·4. Any molecule having velocity components V_x, V_y, and V_z, with $\mathsf{V}^2 = \mathsf{V}_x^2 + \mathsf{V}_y^2 + \mathsf{V}_z^2$, can be represented by some point on a sphere in velocity space. We assume that there is no preferential direction within the gas, so that the points on the sphere in velocity space are equally distributed over the sphere. The fraction of all molecules moving with absolute speed V that have directions such that θ lies in the increment $d\theta$ and ϕ lies in the increment $d\phi$ is therefore simply the ratio of the little area on the sphere subtended by $d\theta$ and $d\phi$ to the total area of the sphere,

$$\frac{\mathsf{V}^2 \sin\theta \, d\theta \, d\phi}{4\pi \mathsf{V}^2} = \frac{1}{4\pi} \sin\theta \, d\theta \, d\phi$$

We further assume that the fraction of molecules that have speed between V and V + dV is given by the velocity distribution function $f(\mathsf{V})\, d\mathsf{V}$. The total

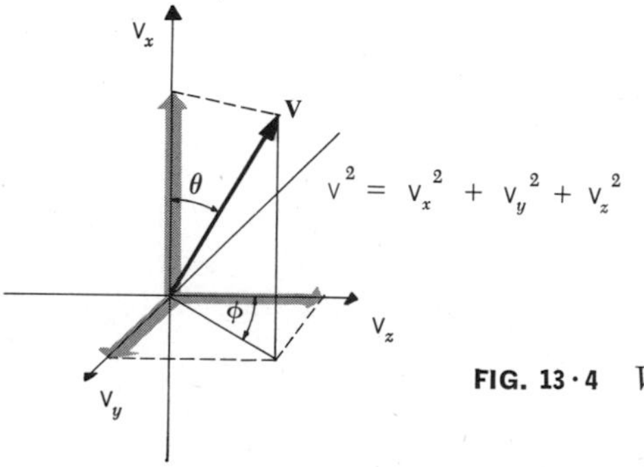

FIG. 13·4 *Velocity space*

number of molecules moving with speed between V and $\mathsf{V} + d\mathsf{V}$ in directions such that θ lies in the increment $d\theta$ and ϕ lies in the increment $d\phi$ which strike the wall in time dt is therefore

$$\frac{N}{V}\, dA \cos\theta\, \mathsf{V}\, dt\, \frac{1}{4\pi} \sin\theta\, d\theta\, d\phi\, f(\mathsf{V})\, d\mathsf{V}$$

Here N/V represents the number density, the number of molecules per unit of volume. To compute the number of molecules that strike the wall in a given time, we must sum up (integrate) over all possible values for V, θ, and ϕ. The average rate at which molecules strike the wall, per unit of area, is therefore

$$J_N = \int_{\phi=0}^{2\pi} \int_{\theta=0}^{\pi/2} \int_{\mathsf{V}=0}^{\infty} \frac{N}{4\pi V} \sin\theta \cos\theta\, \mathsf{V} f(\mathsf{V})\, d\mathsf{V}\, d\theta\, d\phi$$

Performing the θ and ϕ integrations, we may express the integral in terms of the mean speed as

$$J_N = \frac{N}{4V} \mathsf{V}_m$$

For the Maxwell-Boltzmann distribution we find

$$J_N = \frac{N}{4V}\left(\frac{8}{\pi}\frac{g_c \mathsf{k} T}{\mathsf{m}}\right)^{1/2}$$

Using the perfect-gas equation of state, we may replace N/V by $P/\mathsf{k}T$ and obtain

$$▶ \qquad J_N = \frac{P}{(2\pi \mathsf{m} \mathsf{k} T/g_c)^{1/2}} \qquad (13\cdot 7)$$

For example, in helium at 1 atm pressure [1.01×10^5 (kg-m/sec^2)/m^2] and 293°K the rate at which molecules strike the surface is

$$J_N = \frac{1.01 \times 10^5 \text{ kg-m/sec}^2\text{-m}^2}{(2\pi \times 6.7 \times 10^{-27} \text{ kg} \times 1.38 \times 10^{-23} \text{ kg-m}^2/\text{sec}^2\text{-°K} \times 293\text{°K})^{1/2}}$$
$$= 7.8 \times 10^{27}/\text{sec-m}^2$$

We next compute the average normal force per unit of area that these molecules exert on the wall. Using Eq. (13·6), we obtain

$$P = \frac{\mathsf{F}_n}{A}$$
$$= \frac{1}{\tau}\int_{t=0}^{\tau} \iiint \frac{2\mathsf{m}\mathsf{V}}{g_c} \cos\theta\, \frac{N}{V} \cos\theta\, \mathsf{V}\, \frac{1}{4\pi} \sin\theta\, d\theta\, d\phi\, f(\mathsf{V})\, d\mathsf{V}\, dt$$
$$= \int_{\phi=0}^{2\pi} \int_{\theta=0}^{\pi/2} \int_{\mathsf{V}=0}^{\infty} \frac{\mathsf{m}}{2g_c} \frac{1}{\pi} \frac{N}{V} \sin\theta \cos^2\theta\, \mathsf{V}^2 f(\mathsf{V})\, d\mathsf{V}\, d\theta\, d\phi$$

After performing the spatial integrations we may express the pressure in terms of the root-mean-square speed as

$$P = \frac{\mathsf{m}}{3g_c} \frac{N}{V} \mathsf{V}^2_{\mathrm{rms}} \tag{13·8}$$

which is identical with the result we obtained by our simple analysis in Chap. Eight.

13·3 COLLISIONS BETWEEN MOLECULES

Let us now examine the nature of collisions between molecules. We use the word "collision" rather loosely, for it is doubtful that a real collision, in the billiard-ball sense, ever occurs. The molecules in a perfect gas are sufficiently separated that any particle-particle interaction is small. Only when the particles come very close to one another will their interactions be important. We might picture a "collision" as occurring in the manner of Fig. 13·5.

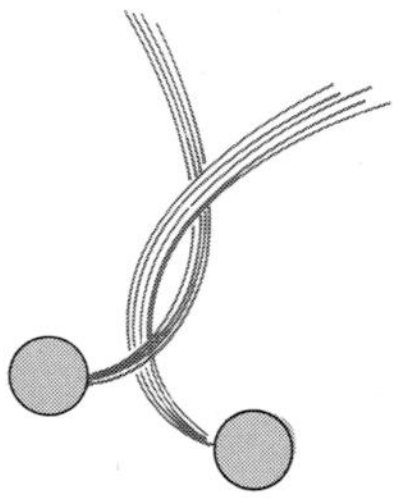

FIG. 13·5 *A typical collision*

The forces acting between colliding molecules are extremely complicated. At long range two molecules tend to be attracted by mutual gravitation, and the force follows the inverse-distance-square behavior. At shorter range the electrostatic forces between electrons of the two molecules come into play, and the force becomes highly repulsive. It is not possible to measure these forces directly. However, by assuming certain forms for the force-distance relationship we can calculate various properties and adjust the assumed force behavior to find the best agreement between experimental and theoretical values. A commonly employed force-distance relationship is the *Lennard-Jones model*, shown in Fig. 13·6. A simpler model treats the molecules as hard spheres, which interact only upon direct contact. This simpler model is quite useful in obtaining a microscopic picture of molecular interactions.

An important parameter is the *collision cross section*. Suppose we are sitting on one molecule, watching another coming toward us. Imagine passing a plane through our molecule perpendicular to the (relative) velocity of the approaching one, as shown in Fig. 13·7. If the approaching molecule should pass within a certain area surrounding us, the intermolecular forces will be large enough that we say a "collision" has occurred. This area is defined as the "collision cross section"; for hard spheres of diameter D and d the collision

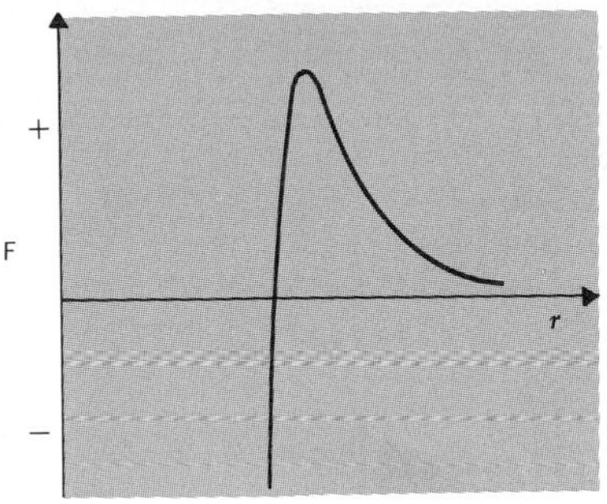

FIG. 13·6 *Force between molecules in the Lennard-Jones model*

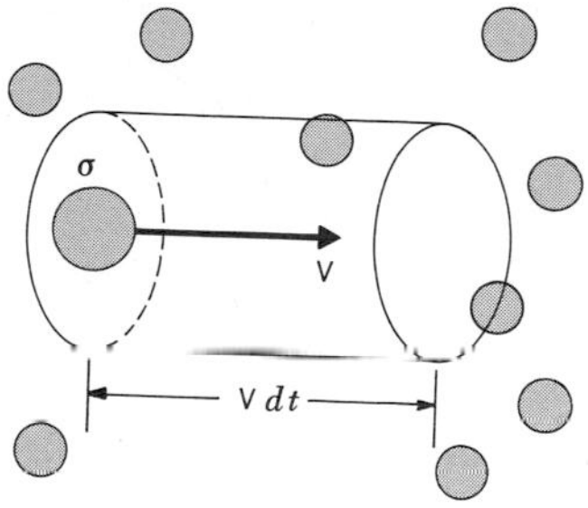

FIG. 13·7 *The collision cross section for hard spheres*

cross section† is $\pi(D + d)^2/4$. The collision cross section frequently appears in kinetic analyses, and such quantities as viscosity, thermal conductivity, and diffusion coefficients can be theoretically expressed in terms of the cross section (for a specific molecular model). Independent measurements of these quantities then allow us to back-calculate and deduce values for the effective collision cross section, and this is one means by which the "diameter" of atoms can be inferred. We shall denote the collision cross section of a molecule pair by σ.

Consider now a particle moving with velocity V through a field of stationary particles. (This might be thought of as a limiting case of a very high energy particle passing through a gas having a comparatively low mean velocity.) The number of particles per unit of volume is again N/V. The average rate at which the traveling particle will intercept the motionless particles, that is, the *collision frequency*, is (Fig. 13·8)

$$\blacktriangleright \quad f_c = \frac{\sigma \mathsf{V} N}{V} \qquad (13\cdot 9)$$

Therefore the average time between collisions τ_m will be determined by

$$f_c \tau_m = 1$$

$$\tau_m = \frac{1}{\sigma \mathsf{V} \cdot (N/V)}$$

† Only for hard spheres is σ independent of relative velocity.

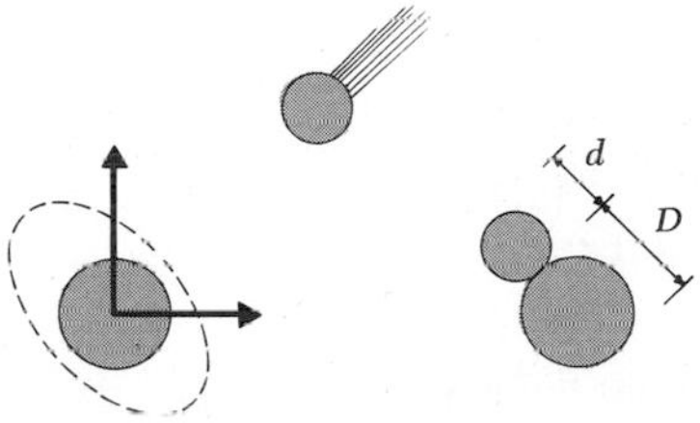

FIG. 13·8 *A moving particle*

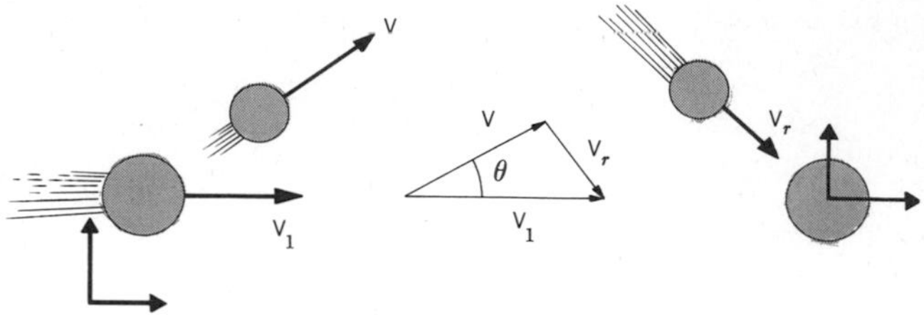

FIG. 13·9 *Collisions between moving particles*

We might think of this time as the "mean free time." The average distance traveled between collisions,

$$\blacktriangleright \qquad \Lambda = \mathsf{V}\tau_m = \frac{1}{\sigma \cdot (N/V)} \tag{13·10}$$

is termed the *mean free path* of the traveling particle.

Let us now consider a particle moving with speed V_1 through moving gas molecules, for which the velocity-distribution function $f(\mathsf{V})\, d\mathsf{V}$ is known. The mean free time and mean free path for this particle will differ from the simple expressions we have just obtained. To make the revised calculation we imagine climbing aboard the traveling particle and watching all the other moving molecules (Fig. 13·9). We first consider all particles moving with velocity between V and $\mathsf{V} + d\mathsf{V}$, having directional angles such that θ lies in the increment $d\theta$ and ϕ lies in the increment $d\phi$. These will appear to be moving toward (or away from) us at the relative velocity V_r, where

$$\mathsf{V}_r^2 = \mathsf{V}_1^2 + \mathsf{V}^2 - 2\mathsf{V}_1\mathsf{V}\cos\theta$$

From our earlier reasoning it is apparent that the fraction of particles which we see moving in this manner is

$$f(\mathsf{V})\,\frac{\sin\theta}{4\pi}\,d\phi\,d\theta\,d\mathsf{V}$$

The rate at which our particle will "collide" with particles having this velocity is then

$$\sigma\mathsf{V}_r\frac{N}{V}f(\mathsf{V})\,\frac{\sin\theta}{4\pi}\,d\phi\,d\theta\,d\mathsf{V}$$

Now, to calculate the rate of collision with all molecules of the gas through which we are moving we must sum up (integrate) over all possible values of V, ϕ, and θ. The collision frequency f_c is therefore

$$f_c = \int_{\mathsf{V}=0}^{\infty}\int_{\theta=0}^{\pi}\int_{\phi=0}^{2\pi}\frac{\sigma N}{4\pi V}\,\mathsf{V}_r(\mathsf{V}_1,\,\mathsf{V},\,\theta)f(\mathsf{V})\sin\theta\,d\phi\,d\theta\,d\mathsf{V}$$

Integrating over ϕ, substituting for V_r, and assuming that σ is constant, we find

$$f_c = \frac{\sigma N}{2V} \int_{V=0}^{\infty} \int_{\theta=0}^{\pi} (V_1^2 + V^2 - 2V_1V \cos\theta)^{1/2} \sin\theta \, f(V) \, d\theta \, dV$$

We next perform the integration over θ,

$$\int_{\theta=0}^{\pi} (V_1^2 + V^2 - 2V_1V\cos\theta)^{1/2} \sin\theta \, d\theta = \frac{1}{3V_1V} (V_1^2 + V^2 - 2V_1V\cos\theta)^{3/2} \Big|_0^{\pi}$$

$$= \frac{1}{3V_1V} [(V_1^2 + V^2 + 2V_1V)^{3/2} - (V_1^2 + V^2 - 2V_1V)^{3/2}]$$

$$= \frac{1}{3V_1V} [(V_1 + V)^3 - |V_1 - V|^3]$$

The absolute-value sign is necessary in order that the second term always be subtracted. The collision frequency then becomes

$$f_c = \frac{\sigma N}{6V} \int_{V=0}^{\infty} \frac{1}{V_1V} [(V_1 + V)^3 - |V_1 - V|^3] f(V) \, dV \qquad (13 \cdot 11)$$

The remaining integration can be performed for the Maxwell-Boltzmann distribution, but the results are not sufficiently different from a simpler analysis to reward the effort. Instead, we shall handle here the case where every molecule of the target gas moves at the same speed V_m. The distribution function for such a gas is a delta function, having unity area, as shown in Fig. 13·10. The only contribution to the integral therefore comes when $V = V_m$, and the collision frequency is

$$f_c = \frac{\sigma(N/V)}{6} \frac{1}{V_1V_m} [(V_1 + V_m)^3 - |V_1 - V_m|^3]$$

Suppose now that the traveling particle is itself a molecule of the target gas, so that $V_1 = V_m$. The collision rate is then the average collision frequency

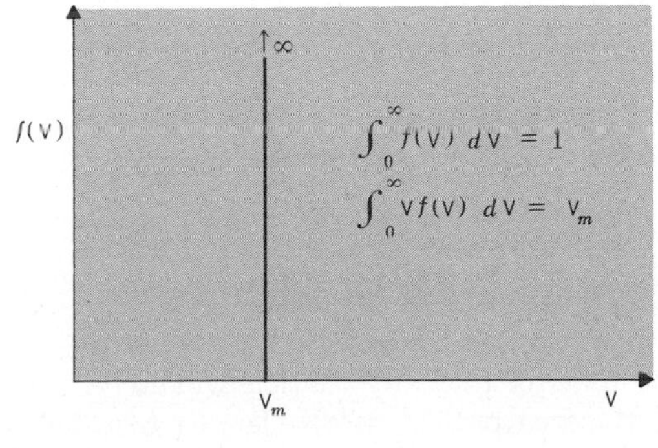

FIG. 13·10 *Distribution function for a uniform-speed gas*

between molecules in the gas, and is

$$f_c = \frac{4}{3} \sigma \mathsf{V}_m \frac{N}{V}$$

The mean free time of a particle in such a gas is therefore

$$\tau_m = \frac{1}{f_c} = \frac{3}{4\sigma \, \mathsf{V}_m \cdot (N/V)} \tag{13·12a}$$

and the mean free path is

$$\Lambda_m = \frac{3}{4\sigma \cdot (N/V)} \tag{13·12b}$$

Note that these expressions differ only slightly from those obtained when we ignored the motion of the target particles. It might be expected that the difference between these expressions and those obtained when the Maxwell-Boltzmann distribution is employed would be even smaller. This is quite the case, for the MB distribution yields

$$\tau_m = \frac{1}{\sqrt{2} \, \sigma \, \mathsf{V}_m \cdot (N/V)} \tag{13·13a}$$

$$\Lambda_m = \frac{1}{\sqrt{2} \, \sigma \cdot (N/V)} \tag{13·13b}$$

It must be remembered that the expressions previously obtained for τ_m and Λ_m represent averages. Some particles may be expected to collide after traveling a much shorter distance, and others may travel quite far before engaging in a collision. We can calculate very simply the probability that a particle will travel for time t without collision. Consider a collection of n_0 particles; suppose after time t that n of the original group have not yet had collisions. If the average collision frequency is $1/\tau_m$, then the number of particles of the group of n which will have collisions in the time interval dt will be $n \, dt/\tau_m$. This will further change the number in the group by

$$dn = -\frac{n \, dt}{\tau_m}$$

By integrating this equation from time zero to time t we obtain the number of particles from our original group that have not had collisions before time t. We then find

$$\frac{n}{n_0} = e^{-t/\tau_m}$$

We can interpret this ratio as the probability that any particle will go for time t with no collisions. We now define the free path Λ as the length traveled by

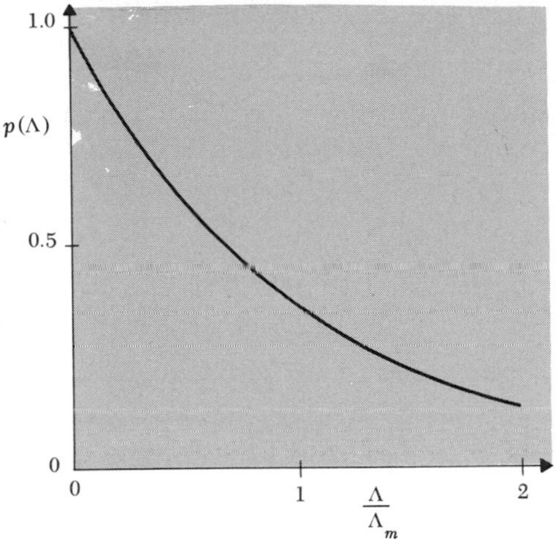

FIG. 13·11 *Distribution of free paths*

the particle before collision. The probability of a particle traveling a distance Λ is identical with the probability that it have the corresponding free time, and hence

$$p(\Lambda) = e^{-\Lambda/\Lambda_m} \tag{13·14}$$

This distribution of free paths is shown in Fig. 13·11.

In order to get some feeling for the numbers involved, let us calculate the mean collision frequency, free time, and free path for a helium atom in a sample of helium at 293°K and 1 atm pressure. The "diameter" of a helium atom is 2.6×10^{-8} cm, which corresponds to a collision cross section of about 2.1×10^{-19} m². The mass of a helium atom is 6.7×10^{-27} kg. Using the perfect-gas equation of state to calculate the number of particles per unit of volume, we find 2.6×10^{25} per m³ at 1 atm and 293°K. These values correspond to a mean collision frequency of 8.9×10^{9} per sec for a single particle or 2.3×10^{35} collisions per sec for the 2.6×10^{25} particles within the cubic meter. The mean free time is then approximately 1.1×10^{-10} sec, and the mean free path is 1.39×10^{-7} m. It is interesting to compare the mean free path with the average molecular spacing. For a particle density of 2.6×10^{25} per m³, the average spacing will be 3×10^{-9} m, two orders of magnitude shorter than the mean free path for a traveling helium atom. These distances are indeed small compared to macroscopic systems. However, in very rarified gases, as exist at high altitudes, gas molecules are few and far between, and mean free paths of the order of several feet are not uncommon.

13·4 EXPERIMENTAL VERIFICATION OF THE MAXWELL-BOLTZMANN VELOCITY DISTRIBUTION

The Maxwell-Boltzmann velocity distribution has been verified experimentally in many different ways, both direct and indirect. An example of an

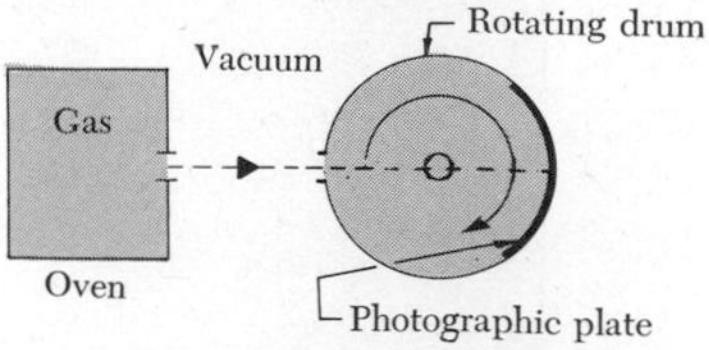

FIG. 13·12 *Verification of the Maxwell-Boltzmann distribution*

apparatus employed in direct verification is shown in Fig. 13·12. A narrow slit in an oven allows a beam of molecules to escape, which then impinges on a rapidly rotating drum. In the drum is another slit, so that molecules are periodically admitted to the inside of the drum. The inner walls of the drum are lined with a sensitive plate which captures all impinging molecules. This device is operated at very low density, so that only small corrections are necessary to take into account collisions between molecules which take place before they are collected on the inside of the drum. By measuring the amount of deposition as a function of angle along the inside of the drum, a direct check of the distribution function can be made.

An indirect verification can be made taking advantage of the fact that a beam of molecules moving toward an observer will show a Doppler shift in emitted radiation, and this shift can be seen in the spectroscope. Since not all molecules move at the same speed, the Doppler shift will depend on the speed of individual molecules, and the velocity distribution can be calculated from the measured spread and intensity of the spectral lines. Another indirect means is to maintain a miniature balance at very low temperature, so that any molecule striking the balance is "condensed." The rate of weight gain can be measured and compared with that predicted from the assumed Maxwell-Boltzmann distribution.

In all instances the Maxwell-Boltzmann distribution has been substantiated in cases where it is applicable, that is, for gases in equilibrium at low densities.

SELECTED READING

Lee, J., F. Sears, and D. Turcotte, *Statistical Thermodynamics,* chap. 2, Addison-Wesley Publishing Co., Inc., Reading, Mass., 1963.

Sonntag, R., and G. J. Van Wylen, *Fundamentals of Statistical Thermodynamics,* sec. 3.6, John Wiley & Sons, Inc., New York, 1966.

Tribus, M., *Thermostatics and Thermodynamics,* secs. 4.8–4.10, D. Van Nostrand Co., Inc., Princeton, N.J., 1961.

Wark, K., *Thermodynamics,* sec. 10.11, McGraw-Hill Book Company, New York, 1966.

QUESTIONS

13·1 What is a quantum index?

13·2 Are the translational energy levels degenerate?

13·3 Are the translational quantum states for a gas very heavily populated?
13·4 Why are the kinetics of molecular motion of interest?
13·5 Did we employ MB statistics in determining Maxwell-Boltzmann distribution?
13·6 Why do we use the Boltzmann constant in defining the entropy?
13·7 What is the difference between velocity and speed?
13·8 What is a velocity-distribution function?
13·9 Why is f (V) independent of θ?
13·10 What is the difference between V_m and V_{rms}?
13·11 What is velocity space? What is quantum-number space?
13·12 What is a mean free path? How could you use the free path as a gauge of the validity of the continuum idealization in a particular case?
13·13 What is a collision cross section?

PROBLEMS

13·1 Derive an expression for the rate of energy flow across a hypothetical plane within a gas. Consider only the molecules that cross from one side.
13·2 Derive an expression relating normal force per unit of area to the mean square velocity for a wall which always rebounds the particles normal to the wall, irrespective of their angle of incidence.
13·3 For a gas having a Maxwellian distribution show that the distribution function for one component of velocity, $f_\perp(V_\perp)$, has the form

$$\left(\frac{m}{2\pi g_c kT}\right)^{1/2} \exp\left(-\frac{mV_x^2}{2g_c kT}\right)$$

13·4 Derive an expression for the fraction of molecules that are moving at speeds less than V_m.
13·5 Calculate the mean free path in 80°F argon at 1 atm, 0.001 atm, and 0.000001 atm. What is the smallest sized projectile whose flight through argon at these pressures could reasonably be handled by continuum fluid mechanics?
13·6 Consider a 2-ft³ box of oxygen initially at 1 atm pressure and 100°C. The walls are coated with a "getter" which captures 1/1,000,000 of the impinging atoms. How long will it be before the pressure is down to ½ atm? Assume that the temperature is constant.
13·7 Consider a cubic box 1 ft on a side containing argon at 25°C and 1 atm. The outside of the box is evacuated. Estimate the maximum permissible pinhole size if the leakage rate is to be limited to 1 percent per day.
13·8 Determine the percentage of particles in helium at 80°C at 2 atm that are moving at speeds less than 1000 m/sec.
13·9 What is the probability that a proton having an energy of 10^6 ev can pass through a 1-mm layer of helium at 1 atm, 25°C, without a collision?
13·10 What must be the thickness of the helium layer in Prob. 13·9 to obtain a 50 percent probability that the proton will pass through the helium without collision?
13·11 At what pressure will there be a 50 percent probability that a 10^6-ev proton can pass through 1 cm³ of argon at 25°C without a collision? What is the argon number density (atoms/cm³) at this pressure and temperature?

13·12 Derive an expression for the frequency of collisions (per cm^3) between two molecules of different species in a gas mixture containing equal numbers of each species. Assume the species are independent particles in the sense of Chap. Twelve. Make any reasonable approximations along the lines of those used in Chap. Thirteen.

13·13 A simple model of condensation views the gas molecules as ideal, with a Maxwell-Boltzmann distribution. A nucleus of liquid forms, and as molecules strike this nucleus they are captured, thereby enlarging the drop. Derive a differential equation describing the growth of the drop diameter, assuming that its growth does not affect the availability of molecules from the gas. Does this seem like a reasonable model of the condensing process?

CHAPTER FOURTEEN

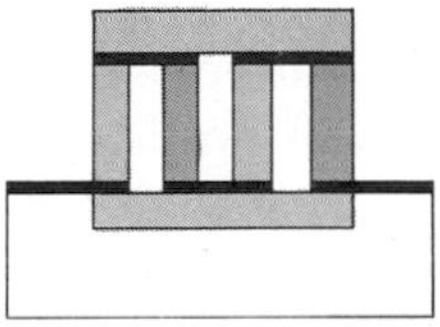

AN INTRODUCTION TO IRREVERSIBLE THERMODYNAMICS

14.1 IRREVERSIBLE PROCESSES

Heat flow through a bar, electron flow through a resistance, and spontaneous combustion of hydrazine are processes that have one thing in common: they are all irreversible. Our inquiries into thermodynamic theory have told us nothing about the rates at which energy and mass transfers occur; these rates are certainly determined by the microscopic nature of the matter involved, and consequently it might seem that the macroscopic methods of thermodynamics would be of little use in constructing a theory for process rates. This is by and large true, and we can learn a great deal more about electrical conduction phenomena from statistical mechanics than from broader macroscopic reasoning. Nevertheless, significant advances are being made in the understanding of irreversible processes through the use of the macroscopic methodology of thermodynamics, and this chapter provides an introduction to these ideas.

Irreversible processes might be grouped into two classes. In chemically reacting systems the irreversibility arises primarily because of departures from thermodynamic equilibrium that are essentially uniform throughout the volume in question. In contrast, the irreversibility in a flow process arises because of spatial variations in the intensive properties of substances. Both classes are of interest, but we shall confine our attention here to phenomena of nonreacting irreversible flow.

Where spatial variations in properties occur, we must be careful in defining the properties of matter. Certainly the extensive properties (energy, mass, volume, and entropy) have meaning in macroscopic systems that are not in thermodynamic states, but a bar that is hot at one end and cold at the other has no "temperature." However, temperature at a point in matter can be defined by the limiting operation of taking successively smaller and smaller volumes of matter around that point, isolating them, and determining their temperatures after they have reached equilibrium states. We can define the local pressure, electrochemical potential, and so on, in the same manner. This allows us to speak of the spatial distributions of the usual intensive thermodynamic properties, even in nonequilibrium situations.

We know from experience that electrical currents are set up by imposing a voltage difference across a wire and that heat flows are produced by imposed temperature differences. We might expect that these effects are completely independent; however, it is observed experimentally that an imposed voltage difference can give rise to a heat flow, and conversely that an imposed temperature difference can cause the flow of electrons. These phenomena are examples of *coupled irreversible flows;* they may be thought of as arising because the free-electron population in a conductor depends on temperature. A number of important devices operate because of these and other coupled irreversible effects, and they are of growing importance in engineering.

The objectives of irreversible thermodynamics are twofold. First, we seek to learn the kinds of flows that occur in coupled irreversible processes. Second, we should like to obtain expressions relating the rates of the flows of some driving forces. It might be expected that this would require the introduction of certain *rate coefficients* (such as electrical conductivity) and that a thermodynamic approach would provide some relations among these coefficients; this is indeed the case. In this chapter we shall set up a general framework for treatment of coupled irreversible flows and examine some cases of special interest.

14·2 ONE-DIMENSIONAL IRREVERSIBLE FLOWS: THE FLUX POSTULATE

Let us consider a length of material connecting two large systems, as shown in Fig. 14·1. Matter and energy may flow through the conductor, and we wish to learn how the rates of these flows are related to the properties of the bounding systems A and B.

Suppose a steady-state condition has been reached, and the flows of matter and energy have been established. They might be altered by changing the state of A or B. Intuition and experience tell us that changing the temperature, pressure, or voltage of either would certainly alter the flows, but it is unreasonable to expect any changes to result merely from adding more material to

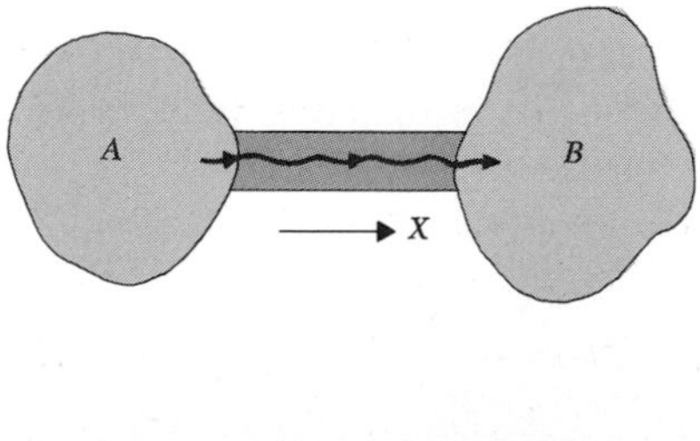

FIG. 14·1 *One-dimensional irreversible flows*

A or B, keeping their temperatures, pressures, and so on, fixed. We know from thermodynamics that A and B will be in equilibrium with one another when their temperatures, pressures, and electrochemical potentials are equal; it appears that the *intensive* states of A and B are all that should matter as far as the flows through the conductor are concerned.

The intensive state of a system such as A or B can be specified in a number of ways. If there are n species present in a single phase we can give values for the temperature, pressure, and mole fractions; however, only $n - 1$ of the mole fractions are independently variable, since their sum must always be unity. Consequently the intensive state of the system is completely fixed by specification of the set

$$T, P, \chi_2, \ldots, \chi_n$$

Alternatively, we may replace the mole fractions by the electrochemical potentials and fix the intensive state by specifying the set

$$T, P, \mu_2, \ldots, \mu_n$$

A third set of intensive parameters whose specification determines the intensive state is

$$\frac{1}{T}, \frac{P}{T}, -\frac{\mu_2}{T}, \ldots, -\frac{\mu_n}{T}$$

Alternatively, we may replace P by μ_1 and use the set

$$\blacktriangleright \quad \frac{1}{T}, -\frac{\mu_1}{T}, \ldots, -\frac{\mu_n}{T}$$

to fix the intensive state. These quantities are coefficients appearing in the Gibbs equation of the conductor and the entropy-production equation and are especially important, as we shall see. We shall call the last set the *natural intensive properties* of the system and introduce the following notation for their compact representation:

$$\phi_0 \equiv \frac{1}{T} \tag{14·1a}$$

$$\phi_i \equiv -\frac{\mu_i}{T} \qquad i \geq 1 \tag{14·1b}$$

It is interesting to note that there are $n + 1$ intensive properties in each of these sets. Furthermore, there are also $n + 1$ conserved quantities that may flow through the conductor (n species plus energy), and the natural intensive properties have a one-to-one association with the flows. Our intuition has told us that the $n + 1$ rates of steady flow are determined uniquely by the nature of the conductor and the values of the $n + 1$ intensive properties of A and B.

It is convenient to work with rates of flow per unit of cross-sectional area, or *fluxes*. We expect that the steady-state energy flux J_E is a function of the natural intensive properties of A and B, which we can represent implicitly as

$$J_E = J_E(\phi_{0A}, \phi_{1A}, \ldots, \phi_{nA}; \phi_{0B}, \phi_{1B}, \ldots, \phi_{nB})$$

However, we know that all flows will vanish when the natural intensive properties of A and B are equal. Hence energy flux is expected to be strongly dependent on the *differences* in the intensive properties and only weakly dependent on their absolute values. With this in mind we express the functional relationship above in an alternate form,

$$J_E = J_E(\Delta\phi_0, \Delta\phi_1, \ldots, \Delta\phi_n; \phi_{0A}, \phi_{1A}, \ldots, \phi_{nA})$$

where $\Delta\phi_i = \phi_{iA} - \phi_{iB}$. Similar functional relationships are expected for the several mass fluxes.

The treatment is further generalized if we work in terms of the property differences per unit of length of conductor. The natural intensive properties are such that the flows tend to take place from regions of low ϕ to regions of higher ϕ. It is therefore convenient to define a set of *driving forces* X_i as the *gradients* of the natural intensive properties,

$$\blacktriangleright \qquad X_i \equiv \frac{d\phi_i}{dx} \tag{14·2}$$

Our discussions suggest that the steady fluxes of energy and matter should depend on the local values of the driving forces and on the local intensive state of the matter within the conductor. Furthermore, no flows are expected when the driving forces are all zero. We formalize this in the flux postulate.

The fluxes of energy and matter in a one-dimensional irreversible flow are uniquely determined by the nature of the conducting medium, its local intensive state, and the local gradients in the natural intensive properties. The fluxes all vanish when these gradients are all zero.

Expressed mathematically, the flux postulate states that for a given conducting medium

$$\blacktriangleright \qquad J_i = J_i(X_0, X_1, \ldots, X_n; \text{and local intensive state}) \tag{14·3a}$$

$$J_i(0, 0, \ldots, 0; \text{and local intensive state}) = 0 \tag{14·3b}$$

For example, consider a pōrous conductor through which a single species flows under the influence of pressure and temperature gradients. We have

$$X_0 = \frac{d(1/T)}{dx}$$

$$X_1 = \frac{d(-\mu/T)}{dx}$$

Then, according to the flux postulate, the energy and mass fluxes may be expressed implicitly as

$$J_E = J_E\left(\frac{d(1/T)}{dx}, \frac{d(-\mu/T)}{dx}\right) \tag{14·4a}$$

$$J_M = J_M\left(\frac{d(1/T)}{dx}, \frac{d(-\mu/T)}{dx}\right) \tag{14·4b}$$

The flux postulate is the starting point in the theory of coupled irreversible flows and is the analog of the state postulate of thermodynamics.

14·3 ENTROPY PRODUCTION AND HEAT FLUX

Because of our choice of the natural intensive properties in defining the driving forces, the rate of entropy production per unit of volume may be expressed very concisely in terms of these forces and the energy and mass fluxes. We know from the second law that the entropy production must be positive, and this condition will provide some important information about the relationship between the fluxes and forces.

Imagine placing an elemental length of the conductor between two "reservoirs" $R1$ and $R2$, as shown in Fig. 14·2. We imagine transferring the constituents to and from either reservoir from pure phases through semipermeable membranes, so that these transfers of mass are all reversible. In addition, energy will be transferred as heat to or from the reservoirs; we assume that

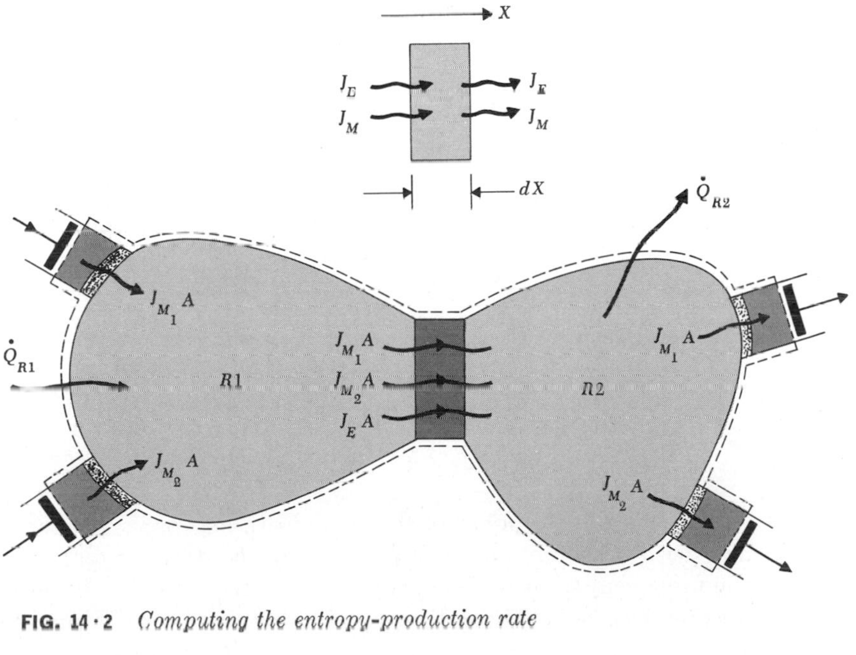

FIG. 14·2 *Computing the entropy-production rate*

these processes can also be made reversible. The flows of energy and mass to and from $R1$ and $R2$ will be adjusted so as to keep the states of $R1$, and $R2$, and the elemental piece of the conductor constant in time. Since the external transfers are all assumed to be reversible, all the irreversibility occurs in the conductor. By placing it in this hypothetical environment we can calculate the rate of entropy production due to this irreversibility.

Denoting the conductor flow area by A, we apply the second law to the control mass indicated by the dotted line in Fig. 14·2 and find

$$\dot{\mathcal{P}}_S = \left(\frac{\dot{Q}}{T}\right)_{R2} - \left(\frac{\dot{Q}}{T}\right)_{R1} + \sum_{i=1}^{n} J_{M_i}A[(s_i)_{R2} - (s_i)_{R1}] \geq 0$$

Here $(s_i)_{R1}$ and $(s_i)_{R2}$ denote the entropies of the ith constituent in the pure phases in equilibrium with $R1$ and $R2$. Energy balances on $R1$ and $R2$ give

$$J_E A = \sum_{i=1}^{n} J_{M_i}A(h_i)_{R1} + \dot{Q}_{R1} \tag{14·5a}$$

$$J_E A = \sum_{i=1}^{n} J_{M_i}A(h_i)_{R2} + \dot{Q}_{R2} \tag{14·5b}$$

Combining with the second-law equation, we obtain

$$\dot{\mathcal{P}}_S = J_E A\left(\frac{1}{T_{R2}} - \frac{1}{T_{R1}}\right) + \sum_{i=1}^{n} J_{M_i}A\left[\left(s_i - \frac{h_i}{T}\right)_{R2} - \left(s_i - \frac{h_i}{T}\right)_{R1}\right] \geq 0$$

Using Eq. (10·41), we may write this as

$$\frac{\dot{\mathcal{P}}_S}{A} = \left(\frac{1}{T_{R2}} - \frac{1}{T_{R1}}\right)J_E + \sum_{i=1}^{n}\left[\left(-\frac{\mu_i}{T}\right)_{R2} - \left(-\frac{\mu_i}{T}\right)_{R1}\right]J_{M_i}A \geq 0$$

To find the entropy production per unit of volume, σ, we divide by the length of the conductor and let this length become infinitesimal. This gives

$$\sigma = \frac{d(1/T)}{dx}J_E + \sum_{i=1}^{n}\frac{d(-\mu_i/T)}{dx}J_{M_i} \geq 0$$

We now introduce the shorthand notation

$$J_0 = J_E$$
$$J_i = J_{M_i} \qquad i \geq 1$$

Because there are the same number of fluxes and driving forces, we can associate one force with each flux and group them into conjugate pairs. We say that X_0 is the force conjugate to the energy flux J_0, X_1 is the force conjugate to mass flux J_1, and so forth. The entropy production per unit of volume then becomes

$$\sigma = \sum_{i=0}^{n} J_i X_i \geq 0 \tag{14·6}$$

In some cases it is convenient to work with the *heat flux*, defined as the portion of energy flux which cannot be identified with energy convection due to particle transfer. Referring to Eqs. (14·5) and neglecting kinetic and potential energies of the constituents, we see that the local heat flux is

$$q = J_E - \sum_{i=1}^{n} h_i J_{M_i} \tag{14·7}$$

The enthalpies h_i are evaluated for pure phases which would be in equilibrium through a rigid semipermeable membrane with the conductor at the point in question. Since heat is not a conserved quantity, we shall use the symbol q (rather than J_Q) for the local heat flux.

With this definition of heat flux, the entropy production per unit of volume may be expressed as

$$\sigma = \frac{d}{dx}\left(\frac{q}{T}\right) + \sum_{i=1}^{n} J_{M_i} \frac{d\mathcal{G}_i}{dx} \geq 0 \tag{14·8}$$

14·4 THE PHENOMENOLOGICAL EQUATIONS: ONSAGER COEFFICIENTS

Phenomenological equations describe the manner in which the fluxes depend on the gradients of the intensive properties. Ohm's law, which relates the flux of electrons in a conductor to the potential gradient, is an especially simple phenomenological equation. Any of the sets of intensive properties mentioned previously may be used in the phenomenological equations. While the natural intensive properties are not the most convenient set for practical use, their appearance in Eq. (14·6) suggests that it is to our advantage to use their gradients in first formulating the phenomenological equations, and subsequently transform to more convenient forms.

We know that the fluxes all vanish when the forces are all zero. A Taylor-series expansion of Eq. (14·3*a*) will therefore start out with linear terms in the forces, and we obtain

$$J_i = \sum_{j=0}^{n} \left(\frac{\partial J_i}{\partial X_j}\right)_0 X_j + \cdots \tag{14·9}$$

where the subscript 0 denotes that the derivative must be evaluated for all $X_i = 0$, and it is understood that the local intensive properties ϕ_i and all of the intensive property gradients except X_j are held constant during the differentiation. If the gradients are all sufficiently small, the higher order terms in this expansion may be neglected, and the phenomenological equations are then linear in the driving forces. Henceforth we make this approximation, and introduce the notation

$$L_{ij} \equiv \left(\frac{\partial J_i}{\partial X_j}\right)_0 \tag{14·10}$$

The phenomenological equations then become

$$\blacktriangleright \quad J_i = \sum_{j=0}^{n} L_{ij}X_j \qquad i = 1, 2, \ldots, n \tag{14·11}$$

The coefficients L_{ij} are called the *Onsager phenomenological coefficients.* They are independent of the local gradients but do depend on the local intensive state. Equations (14·11) are called the *linear phenomenological equations.*†

Some restrictions on the signs of the Onsager coefficients are provided by the requirement that the entropy-production rate be positive. Combining Eqs. (14·11) and (14·6), we have

$$\blacktriangleright \quad \sigma = \sum_{i=0}^{n}\sum_{j=0}^{n} L_{ij}X_iX_j \geq 0 \tag{14·12}$$

Setting all but one of the gradients to zero, it follows that for each and every i

$$\blacktriangleright \quad L_{ii} \geq 0$$

In many important situations only two flows are involved. Then

$$\sigma = L_{00}X_0^2 + (L_{01} + L_{10})X_0X_1 + L_{11}X_1^2 \geq 0 \tag{14·13}$$

In order that this be true for all possible values of X_1 and X_2, it is necessary that‡

$$\blacktriangleright \quad L_{00} \geq 0 \tag{14·14a}$$

$$\blacktriangleright \quad L_{11} \geq 0 \tag{14·14b}$$

$$\blacktriangleright \quad L_{00}L_{11} - \left(\frac{L_{01} + L_{10}}{2}\right)^2 \geq 0 \tag{14·14c}$$

The coefficients L_{ii} are called the *primary coefficients,* for they relate the flux of a quantity to the gradient of its conjugate driving force. The coefficients L_{ij}, for $i \neq j$, are called the *coupling coefficients.* They relate the induced fluxes to the gradients of the other forces. The entropy-production statement requires that every primary coefficient be positive. A condition on the coupling coefficients similar to Eq. (14·14c) can be obtained for systems with more than two possible flows.

† It is important to remember that linearity here refers to the powers of the *gradients,* and not to the powers to which T, μ, etc. appear in the phenomenological equations.

‡ To show Eq. (14·14c), make a change of variables

$$X_1' = X_1 + \frac{(L_{01} + L_{10})}{2L_{11}} X_0$$

14·5 THE ONSAGER RECIPROCITY POSTULATE

We mentioned earlier that the choice of the gradients of the natural intensive properties as the driving forces offered certain advantages. Examining Eqs. (14·12) and (14·13), we see that the entropy production has a very symmetric form in terms of the Onsager coefficients and the driving forces. The two coefficients L_{ij} and L_{ji} have the same dimensions and appear in exactly the same way in the entropy-production expression. We might suspect that a relationship between L_{ij} and L_{ji} exists, and this is indeed the case. At the present time no purely macroscopic development of this relationship is known, but the results of a microscopic theory suggest that the Onsager coefficients satisfy a reciprocity relation, with

$$L_{ij} = L_{ji} \tag{14·15}$$

The theory also predicts that this relationship must be modified if a magnetic field is present. We shall omit discussion of this case.

The theoretical basis for this *Onsager reciprocity relation* involves several idealizations and is little more than a plausibility argument. However, what measurements are available seem to confirm the truth of the reciprocity relation. Hopefully a more satisfying basis will be developed with continuing research in the area of irreversible thermodynamics, for we now accept the Onsager reciprocity as a basic postulate, as we did with the laws of thermodynamics, and use it in building our theory.

It is important to remember that the reciprocity postulate applies only when the fluxes of energy and matter are expressed in terms of the gradients of the natural intensive properties, and does not necessarily apply to arbitrarily chosen forces and flows.

14·6 APPLICATIONS TO THERMOELECTRIC PHENOMENA

As an illustration of the use of the analysis of coupled irreversible processes, let us consider thermoelectric phenomena. These are of importance in thermocouple instrumentation as well as in a variety of novel energy-conversion devices.

We consider a one-dimensional solid conductor along which energy and electrons may flow. Neglecting randomly oriented energy compared to the electrostatic potential for electrons, the electrochemical potential per unit of mass of electrons is $\mu = \mathsf{e}\mathcal{E}/\mathsf{m}$, where m is the mass of a single electron, e is the charge of an electron, and $\mathcal{E}$ is the local electrostatic potential. Following

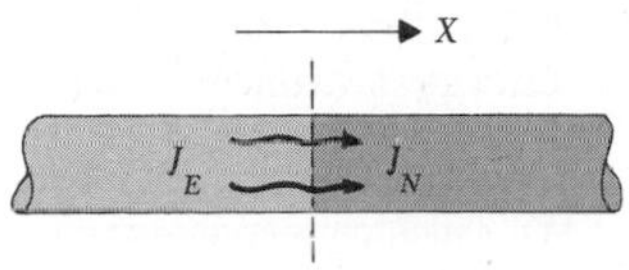

FIG. 14·3 *A one-dimensional electrical and thermal conductor*

the prescription for determining the rate equations for linear coupled irreversible flows, we write the phenomenological equations as

$$J_E = L_{00}\frac{d(1/T)}{dx} + L_{01}\frac{d[-\mathrm{e}\mathcal{E}/(\mathrm{m}T)]}{dx} \tag{14·16a}$$

$$J_M = L_{10}\frac{d(1/T)}{dx} + L_{11}\frac{d[-\mathrm{e}\mathcal{E}/(\mathrm{m}T)]}{dx} \tag{14·16b}$$

Applying the reciprocity postulate,

$$L_{01} = L_{10} \tag{14·16c}$$

It is more convenient to work with the electron-number flux $J_N = J_M/\mathrm{m}$. We put

$$\mathsf{L}_{00} = L_{00} \qquad \mathsf{L}_{10} = L_{10}/\mathrm{m}$$
$$\mathsf{L}_{01} = L_{01}/\mathrm{m} \qquad \mathsf{L}_{11} = L_{11}/\mathrm{m}^2$$

and the equations above reduce to

$$J_E = \mathsf{L}_{00}\frac{d(1/T)}{dx} + \mathsf{L}_{01}\frac{d(-\mathrm{e}\mathcal{E}/T)}{dx} \tag{14·17a}$$

$$J_N = \mathsf{L}_{10}\frac{d(1/T)}{dx} + \mathsf{L}_{11}\frac{d(-\mathrm{e}\mathcal{E}/T)}{dx} \tag{14·17b}$$

$$\mathsf{L}_{01} = \mathsf{L}_{10} \tag{14·17c}$$

The coefficients L_{ij} are expected to be functions of the local intensive state, that is, of temperature and electrostatic potential.†

It is instructive to expand the derivatives and express the fluxes in terms of the temperature and electrostatic potential gradients. We find

$$J_E = \left(-\frac{\mathsf{L}_{00}}{T^2} + \frac{\mathrm{e}\mathcal{E}}{T^2}\mathsf{L}_{01}\right)\frac{dT}{dx} - \frac{\mathrm{e}\mathsf{L}_{01}}{T}\frac{d\mathcal{E}}{dx} \tag{14·18a}$$

$$J_N = \left(-\frac{\mathsf{L}_{01}}{T^2} + \frac{\mathrm{e}\mathcal{E}}{T^2}\mathsf{L}_{11}\right)\frac{dT}{dx} - \frac{\mathrm{e}\mathsf{L}_{11}}{T}\frac{d\mathcal{E}}{dx} \tag{14·18b}$$

Note that the coefficients of the derivatives contain $\mathcal{E}$. The datum for $\mathcal{E}$ is arbitrary; however, the electron flux must not depend on the arbitrary choice of the point at which $\mathcal{E} = 0$. The coefficients L_{01} and L_{11} must depend on $\mathcal{E}$ in such a way that $\mathcal{E}$ drops out of the coefficients of Eq. (14·18b). This requires that they be expressible as

$$\mathsf{L}_{11} = \mathfrak{L}_{11}(T)$$
$$\mathsf{L}_{01} = \mathrm{e}\mathcal{E}\mathfrak{L}_{11}(T) + \mathfrak{L}_{01}(T)$$

The energy flux will depend on the choice of the $\mathcal{E}$ datum point, since part of the energy transfer is due to convected electron energy. However, the heat flux must be independent of the datum, and consequently q becomes more

† We consider a constant-pressure conductor.

useful than J_E. The heat flux is the excess of the energy flux over the electrical energy flux, or†

$$q = J_E - \mathsf{e}\mathcal{E}J_N$$

Substituting from Eqs. (14·18),

$$q = \frac{1}{T^2}[-\mathsf{L}_{00} + 2\mathsf{e}\mathcal{E}\mathsf{L}_{01} - (\mathsf{e}\mathcal{E})^2\mathsf{L}_{11}]\frac{dT}{dx} - \frac{\mathsf{e}}{T}(\mathsf{L}_{01} - \mathsf{e}\mathcal{E}\mathsf{L}_{11})\frac{d\mathcal{E}}{dx} \tag{14·19}$$

Requiring that q be independent of the datum value of $\mathcal{E}$, we see that L_{00} must be of the form‡

$$\mathsf{L}_{00} = \mathfrak{L}_{00}(T) + 2\mathsf{e}\mathcal{E}\mathsf{L}_{01} - (\mathsf{e}\mathcal{E})^2\mathsf{L}_{11}$$

or

$$\mathsf{L}_{00} = (\mathsf{e}\mathcal{E})^2\mathfrak{L}_{11}(T) + 2\mathsf{e}\mathcal{E}\mathfrak{L}_{01}(T) + \mathfrak{L}_{00}(T)$$

The rate equations for q and J_N may therefore be written as

$$q = -\frac{\mathfrak{L}_{00}}{T^2}\frac{dT}{dx} - \frac{\mathsf{e}\mathfrak{L}_{01}}{T}\frac{d\mathcal{E}}{dx} \tag{14·20a}$$

$$J_N = -\frac{\mathfrak{L}_{01}}{T^2}\frac{dT}{dx} - \frac{\mathsf{e}\mathfrak{L}_{11}}{T}\frac{d\mathcal{E}}{dx} \tag{14·20b}$$

The $\mathfrak{L}_{ij}$'s are functions only of temperature.§ Note that J_N represents the flow of a conserved quantity, while q does not.

We can relate the $\mathfrak{L}_{ij}$'s to more familiar transport properties of the substance. The *electrical conductivity* κ_e is defined by

$$\blacktriangleright \qquad \mathsf{e}J_N = -\kappa_e\frac{d\mathcal{E}}{dx} \quad \text{for} \quad \frac{dT}{dx} = 0 \tag{14·21}$$

Note that the term $\mathsf{e}J_N$ is the charge flow per unit of area of the conductor. Setting the temperature gradient equal to zero in Eq. (14·20b), we find

$$\mathsf{e}J_N = -\frac{\mathfrak{L}_{11}}{T}\mathsf{e}^2\frac{d\mathcal{E}}{dx}$$

and by comparison with Eq. (14·21) obtain

$$\kappa_e = \frac{\mathsf{e}^2\mathfrak{L}_{11}}{T} \tag{14·22}$$

The *thermal conductivity* κ_t is defined by

$$\blacktriangleright \qquad J_E = q = -\kappa_t\frac{dT}{dx} \qquad J_N = 0 \tag{14·23}$$

† We consider only the electrostatic potential energy of the electrons to be important.
‡ Note that the coefficients $\mathfrak{L}_{ij}$ are *independent* of $\mathcal{E}$.
§ In a constant-pressure system.

Setting $J_N = 0$ in Eq. (14·20b), solving for the gradient of $\mathcal{E}$ in terms of the temperature gradient, and substituting in Eq. (14·20a), we find

$$q = -\frac{\mathfrak{L}_{00}\mathfrak{L}_{11} - \mathfrak{L}_{01}^2}{\mathfrak{L}_{11}T^2}\frac{dT}{dx}$$

Then comparison with Eq. (14·23) yields

$$\kappa_t = \frac{\mathfrak{L}_{00}\mathfrak{L}_{11} - \mathfrak{L}_{01}^2}{\mathfrak{L}_{11}T^2} \tag{14·24}$$

You may verify that the restrictions placed on the Onsager coefficients by Eq. (14·14) demand that both the electrical and thermal conductivities be positive.

The rate equations indicate that a voltage gradient may be expected to arise along a wire through which energy flows (as heat), even though the current is zero. This is known as the *Seebeck effect* and was one of the first known phenomena of coupled irreversible flows. Setting $J_N = 0$, Eq. (14·20b) may be written as

$$\blacktriangleright \quad \left(\frac{d\mathcal{E}}{dT}\right)_{J_N=0} = -\frac{\mathfrak{L}_{01}}{\mathrm{e}T\mathfrak{L}_{11}} = -\epsilon \tag{14·25}$$

The property $\epsilon(T)$ is termed the *absolute thermoelectric power* of the conductor. It relates the potential gradient along the wire to the temperature gradient and the local intensive state and is a function only of temperature.

The rate equations for q and $\mathrm{e}J_N$ may be expressed in terms of the electrical and thermal conductivities, the absolute thermoelectric power, and the gradients of temperature and electrostatic potential. We obtain

$$q = -(\kappa_t + \epsilon^2\kappa_e T)\frac{dT}{dx} - \epsilon\kappa_e T\frac{d\mathcal{E}}{dx} \tag{14·26a}$$

$$\mathrm{e}J_N = -\epsilon\kappa_e\frac{dT}{dx} - \kappa_e\frac{d\mathcal{E}}{dx} \tag{14·26b}$$

Another convenient and informative relation is obtained by expressing the heat flux in terms of the temperature gradient and current flux. Eliminating the potential gradient from the above two equations, we find

$$q = -\kappa_t\frac{dT}{dx} + \epsilon T(\mathrm{e}J_N) \tag{14·27}$$

If the current $\mathrm{e}J_N$ is zero, we obtain *Fourier's law*,

$$q = -\kappa_t\frac{dT}{dx} \qquad \text{for} \qquad \mathrm{e}J_N = 0 \tag{14·28}$$

Note that a heat flux can exist in a conductor in which current is flowing even if $dT/dx = 0$.

The ratio q/T is the *entropy flux with heat,*

$$\frac{q}{T} = \frac{-\kappa_t}{T}\frac{dT}{dx} + \mathrm{e}J_N\epsilon \tag{14·29}$$

Note that entropy flux with heat is produced by a temperature gradient as well as by current flow.

The energy flux may also be expressed in terms of the temperature gradient and current flow. Since $J_E = q + \mathcal{E}\mathrm{e}J_N$, Eq. (14·27) leads to

$$J_E = -\kappa_t \frac{dT}{dx} + (\epsilon T + \mathcal{E})\mathrm{e}J_N \tag{14·30}$$

Consider now a thermally insulated conductor, hot at one end and cool at the other, through which no electric current flows. A certain steady-state temperature distribution will be set up within the conductor. Since the current flow is zero, the energy flux is just q and is constant along the conductor. The temperature distribution is determined by the applied temperature difference and the thermal conductivity through Eq. (14·30), and will be such that

$$\kappa_t \frac{dT}{dx} = \text{constant} \tag{14·31}$$

If a current is then passed through the conductor, the thermal insulation must be removed and the conductor must be cooled in order to maintain the initial temperature distribution. The required cooling is of interest and can be computed with the aid of an energy balance on an elemental length of the conductor (Fig. 14·4). Defining q_c as the required rate of heat transfer per unit of length of the wire, per unit of area of cross section, we obtain

$$q_c\,dx = J_E(x) - \left[J_E(x) + \frac{dJ_E}{dx}\,dx\right]$$

or

$$q_c = -\frac{dJ_E}{dx} \tag{14·32}$$

Differentiating Eq. (14·30) and substituting in Eq. (14·32), q_c becomes

$$q_c = \frac{d}{dx}\left(\kappa_t \frac{dT}{dx}\right) - \mathrm{e}J_N \frac{d(\epsilon T)}{dx} - \mathrm{e}J_N \frac{d\mathcal{E}}{dx}$$

Since the temperature distribution is to be unchanged when the current flows, the first term on the right is zero by Eq. (14·31). The potential gradient $d\mathcal{E}/dx$ may be evaluated from Eq. (14·26*b*); then q_c reduces to

$$q_c = -\mathrm{e}J_N\left(\epsilon \frac{dT}{dx} + T\frac{d\epsilon}{dx}\right) + \frac{\mathrm{e}J_N}{\kappa_e}\left(\epsilon\kappa_e \frac{dT}{dx} + \mathrm{e}J_N\right)$$

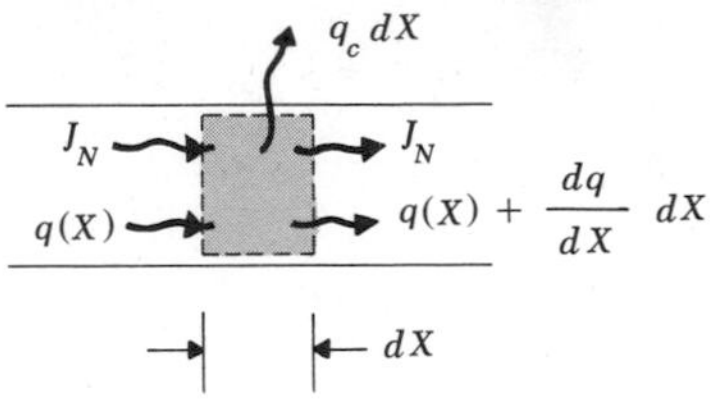

FIG. 14·4 *An externally cooled conductor*

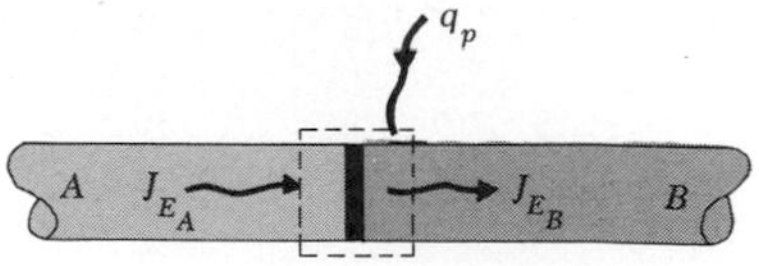

FIG. 14·5 *A junction of two isothermal conductors*

which further simplifies to

$$q_c = -\left(eJ_N T \frac{d\epsilon}{dT}\right)\frac{dT}{dx} + \frac{(eJ_N)^2}{\kappa_e} \tag{14·33}$$

The second term on the right is called the *Joule heat* and represents the cooling required to keep an isothermal conductor from increasing in temperature. The first term is called the *Thomson heat* and represents the additional cooling required because the current is flowing through a temperature gradient. The *Thomson coefficient* $\tau(T)$ is defined as

$$\blacktriangleright \qquad \tau \equiv T\frac{d\epsilon}{dT} \tag{14·34}$$

In terms of the Thomson coefficient,

$$q_c = -\tau e J_N \frac{dT}{dx} + \frac{(eJ_N)^2}{\kappa_e} \tag{14·35}$$

if $T(x)$ is the same as for $J_N = 0$.

Consider now a junction of two current-carrying conductors, as shown in Fig. 14·5. The temperature gradients are considered to be zero in either conductor. If the conductors are of dissimilar substances, the energy flow across the junction will be discontinuous, and energy will have to be transferred to or from the junction as heat. This phenomenon is known as the *Peltier effect.* Denoting the Peltier heat per unit of cross-sectional area of conductors by q_p, an energy balance on the junction yields

$$q_p = J_{E_B} - J_{E_A}$$

But because the current flow is continuous, Eq. (14·19) reduces this to

$$J_{E_A} - J_{E_B} = q_A - q_B \tag{14·36}$$

where q_A and q_B are the heat fluxes in the conductors. The heat flux and current flux in an isothermal conductor are related; setting the temperature gradient equal to zero in Eqs. (14·26) and dividing one by the other, we find

$$q = \epsilon T e J_N \qquad \text{for} \qquad \frac{dT}{dx} = 0 \tag{14·37}$$

Upon combination with the two previous equations, we obtain

▶ $$q_p = T \cdot (\epsilon_B - \epsilon_A) e J_N = \pi_{AB} e J_N \tag{14·38}$$

Here the *Peltier coefficient* $\pi_{AB}(T)$ is defined as the rate of energy transfer as heat to the junction per unit of charge flux,

▶ $$\pi_{AB} = T \cdot (\epsilon_B - \epsilon_A) \tag{14·39}$$

and is a function of the temperature† of the two materials forming the isothermal junction.

Equation (14·39), which relates the Peltier coefficient of the junction to the temperature and absolute thermoelectric powers of the two conductors, is termed the *second Kelvin relation*. Differentiating Eq. (14·39) and using Eq. (14·34), we obtain the *first Kelvin relation*,

▶ $$\frac{d\pi_{AB}}{dT} = (\epsilon_B - \epsilon_A) + (\tau_B - \tau_A) \tag{14·40}$$

The Kelvin relations are the principal contribution of the theory of irreversible thermodynamics in thermoelectric phenomena.

14·7 THE THERMOCOUPLE

Let us now consider the *thermocouple*, a device formed by three lengths of two dissimilar metallic conductors, as shown in Fig. 14·6. If the temperatures at a and b are identical, the voltage difference $\mathcal{E}_a - \mathcal{E}_b$ is a function only of the temperatures T_1 and T_2 and of the properties of the two materials A and B, provided that the current is zero. This makes the thermocouple useful as a

† We consider a constant-pressure system.

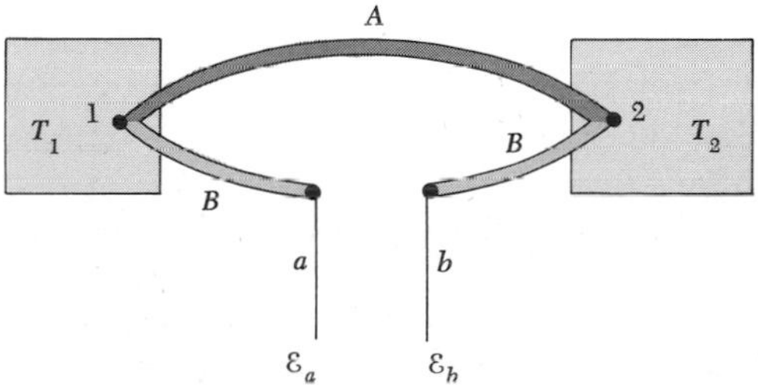

FIG. 14·6 *A simple thermocouple*

temperature-measuring device; of course, a bridge circuit or high-impedance voltmeter must be used to measure the voltage in order to make a measurement with negligible current flow. Integrating Eq. (14·25), we find

$$\mathcal{E}_a - \mathcal{E}_1 = -\int_{T_1}^{T_a} \epsilon_B(T)\, dT$$

$$\mathcal{E}_2 - \mathcal{E}_b = -\int_{T_b}^{T_2} \epsilon_B(T)\, dT$$

$$\mathcal{E}_1 - \mathcal{E}_2 = -\int_{T_1}^{T_2} \epsilon_A(T)\, dT$$

Adding and using the fact that $T_a = T_b$, we obtain

$$\mathcal{E}_a - \mathcal{E}_b = \int_{T_1}^{T_2} [\epsilon_A(T) - \epsilon_B(T)]\, dT \tag{14·41}$$

The integral is a function only of the materials and the two temperatures, irrespective of the length or diameter of the wires. Therefore, if T_1 is known, measurement of $\mathcal{E}_a - \mathcal{E}_b$ allows determination of T_2 if the absolute thermoelectric powers of the two materials are known. Thermocouple tables are simply experimentally determined values of the integral of Eq. (14·41) as a function of T_2 for a selected T_1, usually 0°C.

14·8 THE THERMOELECTRIC GENERATOR AND REFRIGERATOR

If a load resistor is placed across the output terminals of a thermocouple, current will flow, and the thermocouple becomes a power-producing device. Such *thermoelectric generators* have recently been developed to the point where they have certain advantages over more conventional power-producing systems. The thermoelectric generator is an inherently irreversible device, for it relies on the presence of a temperature gradient to develop the voltage (Seebeck effect). Consequently, it is limited to efficiencies considerably below those of conventional power-conversion equipment, which can, in the limit, be fully reversible. However, it is difficult to build efficient turbomachinery in small sizes, and so the thermoelectric generator becomes a system to be considered for continuous production of relatively small amounts of power. Moreover, its complete lack of moving parts provides the possibility of a high degree of reliability and lifetime not generally associated with conventional energy-conversion equipment. Thermoelectric generators in which the energy is supplied by a solar collector or a small nuclear reactor are being considered quite seriously for a variety of missions in space. Thermoelectric generators mounted on kerosene lamps are used in rural areas of the Soviet Union to power small radio receivers.

Practical thermoelectric devices employ semiconducting materials as the active elements. These are usually short (¼ to ½ in. long), mounted between a heated and a cooled insulating plate. Copper bus bars provide a series connection for the elements, as shown in Fig. 14·7.

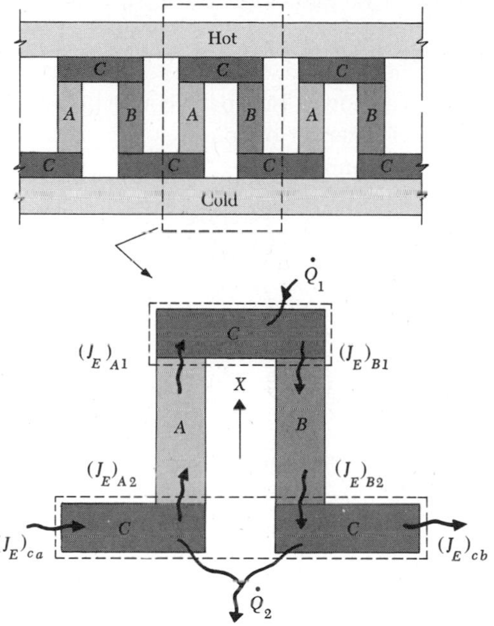

FIG. 14·7 *A thermoelectric generator*

We shall analyze a single element, making the following idealizations:

Steady flow steady state
Conductors A and B insulated along their sides and the flows through them one-dimensional
Negligible temperature and potential drop across the junctions (This neglects contact resistances, which in practice can be significant.)
Negligible temperature and voltage differences within any single copper bus bar

Energy balances on the upper and lower bus bars give†

$$\dot{Q}_1 = [(J_E)_{B1} - (J_E)_{A1}]A$$
$$\dot{Q}_2 = [(J_E)_{B2} - (J_E)_{A2}]A + [(J_E)_{Ca} - (J_E)_{Cb}]A_C$$

Here A and A_C denote the flow areas of the elements and lower bus bar, respectively. Using Eq. (14·30), taking proper account of the direction of flow in element B, and denoting the current flow $-eJ_NA$ by i,

$$\dot{Q}_1 = A\left[\left(\kappa_t \frac{dT}{dx}\right)_{B1} + \left(\kappa_t \frac{dT}{dx}\right)_{A1}\right] - i(\epsilon_{B1} - \epsilon_{A1})T_1 \qquad (14\cdot42a)$$

$$\dot{Q}_2 = A\left[\left(\kappa_t \frac{dT}{dx}\right)_{B2} + \left(\kappa_t \frac{dT}{dx}\right)_{A2}\right] - i(\epsilon_{B2} - \epsilon_{A2})T_2 \qquad (14\cdot42b)$$

† The subscripts $A1$, $A2$, $B1$, and $B2$ denote quantities evaluated in conductors A and B at 1 and 2.

An energy balance on the entire element gives

$$\dot{Q}_1 - \dot{Q}_2 = (J_E)_{Cb} - (J_E)_{Ca} = i(\mathcal{E}_a - \mathcal{E}_b)$$

Since the lower bus bars could be connected to a load, $(\mathcal{E}_a - \mathcal{E}_b)i$ represents the useful power output.

We denote

$$\dot{Q}_{L1} = +A\left[\left(\kappa_t \frac{dT}{dx}\right)_{A1} + \left(\kappa_t \frac{dT}{dx}\right)_{B1}\right] \tag{14·43a}$$

$$\dot{Q}_{L2} = +A\left[\left(\kappa_t \frac{dT}{dx}\right)_{A2} + \left(\kappa_t \frac{dT}{dx}\right)_{B2}\right] \tag{14·43b}$$

Then, from Eq. (14·39), the energy-conversion efficiency of the device is

$$\eta = \frac{(\mathcal{E}_a - \mathcal{E}_b)i}{\dot{Q}_1} = \frac{\dot{Q}_1 - \dot{Q}_2}{\dot{Q}_1} = 1 - \frac{-i\pi_{AB}(T_2) + \dot{Q}_{L2}}{-i\pi_{AB}(T_1) + \dot{Q}_{L1}} \tag{14·44}$$

Evaluation of the terms $\dot{Q}_{L1}$ and $\dot{Q}_{L2}$ would require determination of the temperature distribution $T(x)$ in each element. Since the energy flux along each element is constant, a differential equation describing the temperature distribution in an element may be obtained by differentiating Eq. (14·30) and setting the result to zero. Doing this, and then substituting for the potential gradient from Eq. (14·26b) and using Eq. (14·34), we obtain for element A

$$\frac{d}{dx}\left(\kappa_t \frac{dT}{dx}\right) = \tau \mathsf{e} J_N \frac{dT}{dx} - \frac{(\mathsf{e}J_N)^2}{\kappa_e} \tag{14·45}$$

The equation for element B is identical, except that J_N is replaced by $-J_N$.

Solution of Eq. (14·45) cannot be carried out unless the variations of the thermoelectric properties with temperature are known. For simplicity, let us assume that κ_e and κ_t are independent of temperature. Under this idealization the Thomson coefficient must be zero [Eq. (14·34)]. Then Eq. (14·45) reduces to

$$\frac{d^2T}{dx^2} = -\frac{(\mathsf{e}J_N)^2}{\kappa_e \kappa_t}$$

Integrating once,

$$\frac{dT}{dx} = -\frac{(\mathsf{e}J_N)^2}{\kappa_e \kappa_t} x + C_1$$

where C_1 is a constant of integration yet to be found. Integrating again,

$$T = -\frac{(\mathsf{e}J_N)^2}{\kappa_e \kappa_t}\frac{x^2}{2} + C_1 x + C_2$$

The two constants of integration can be evaluated from the conditions that

$$T = T_2 \qquad \text{at } x = 0$$
$$T = T_1 \qquad \text{at } x = L$$

and we find

$$T = -\frac{(eJ_N)^2}{\kappa_e\kappa_t}\frac{x^2}{2} + \left[\frac{T_1 - T_2}{L} + \frac{(eJ_N)^2}{2\kappa_e\kappa_t}L\right]x + T_2 \tag{14·46}$$

For simplicity, let us also assume that elements A and B have identical thermal and electrical conductivities. The expression above then holds for either element. Substituting this temperature distribution into Eqs. (14·43), we obtain

$$\dot{Q}_{L1} = 2A\kappa_t\left(\frac{T_1 - T_2}{L}\right) - \frac{(eJ_N)^2}{\kappa_e}AL$$
$$\dot{Q}_{L2} = 2A\kappa_t\left(\frac{T_1 - T_2}{L}\right) + \frac{(eJ_N)^2}{\kappa_e}AL$$

The term $L/(\kappa_e A)$ represents the *electrical resistance* R_e of a single element. Similarly, the term $L/(\kappa_t A)$ represents the *thermal resistance* R_t of an element. Thus

$$\dot{Q}_{L1} = \frac{2(T_1 - T_2)}{R_t} - i^2R_e$$
$$\dot{Q}_{L2} = \frac{2(T_1 - T_2)}{R_t} + i^2R_e$$

By substituting in Eq. (14·44), the efficiency is obtained as

$$\eta = 1 - \frac{-i\pi_{AB}(T_2) + \{[2(T_1 - T_2)/R_t] + i^2R_e\}}{-i\pi_{AB}(T_1) + \{[2(T_1 - T_2)/R_t] - i^2R_e\}} \tag{14·47}$$

Problem 14·4 centers on a quantitative study of the power output and efficiency for such an idealized thermoelectric generator.

Even though the thermoelectric generator is not a thermodynamically reversible device, by supplying sufficient electrical power to the device the direction of heat flows $\dot{Q}_1$ and $\dot{Q}_2$ can be reversed and the device operated as a thermoelectric refrigerator. This provides a nonmechanical means for cooling and may be useful in remote cooling of low-power electronic gear. The coefficients of performance of thermoelectric refrigerators are very low, for they are inherently irreversible devices. Problem 14·6 is a study of such a unit.

14·9 APPLICATION IN GASEOUS DIFFUSION

As a second example of the use of irreversible thermodynamics we consider the simultaneous diffusion of n species of gas molecules through a one-dimensional duct. We assume that the gas is perfect and that the duct is sufficiently large that the pressure is uniform within the duct. The pertinent fluxes to be considered are energy and mass of each species. The linear phenomenological equations are then

$$J_E = L_{00}\frac{d(1/T)}{dx} + \sum_{j=1}^{n} L_{0j}\frac{d(-\mu_j/T)}{dx} \tag{14·48a}$$

$$J_{M_i} = L_{i0}\frac{d(1/T)}{dx} + \sum_{j=1}^{n} L_{ij}\frac{d(-\mu_j/T)}{dx} \tag{14·48b}$$

In Chap. Ten we derived an expression for the electrochemical potential of a gas in a mixture of perfect gases. Expressing our result, Eq. (10·45), on a unit-of-mass (rather than a molal) basis,

$$\mu_j = g_j(T, P) + R_jT \ln \chi_j$$

Here $g_j(T, P)$ denotes the Gibbs function of the jth species evaluated at the mixture temperature and pressure. Therefore, in our constant-pressure duct,

$$\frac{d(\mu_i/T)}{dx} = \left[-\frac{g_j}{T^2} + \frac{1}{T}\left(\frac{\partial g_j}{\partial T}\right)_P\right]\frac{dT}{dx} + \frac{R_j}{\chi_j}\frac{d\chi_j}{dx}$$

The rate equations then become

$$J_E = \left\{-\frac{L_{00}}{T^2} - \sum_{j=1}^{n} L_{0j}\left[-\frac{g_j}{T^2} + \frac{1}{T}\left(\frac{\partial g_j}{\partial T}\right)_P\right]\right\}\frac{dT}{dx} - \sum_{j=1}^{n} L_{0j}\frac{R_j}{\chi_j}\frac{d\chi_j}{dx} \tag{14·49a}$$

$$J_{M_i} = \left\{-\frac{L_{i0}}{T^2} - \sum_{j=1}^{n} L_{ij}\left[-\frac{g_j}{T^2} + \frac{1}{T}\left(\frac{\partial g_j}{\partial T}\right)_P\right]\right\}\frac{dT}{dx} - \sum_{j=1}^{n} L_{ij}\frac{R_j}{\chi_j}\frac{d\chi_j}{dx} \tag{14·49b}$$

It is convenient to rewrite the mass-flux equations as

$$J_{M_i} = -D_{iT}\frac{dT}{dx} - \sum_{j=1}^{n} D_{ij}\frac{d\chi_j}{dx} \tag{14·50}$$

where

$$D_{ij} \equiv L_{ij}\frac{R_j}{\chi_j}$$

and the definition of D_{iT} is evident. The coefficient D_{iT} is called the *thermal-diffusion coefficient* for species i. The coefficient D_{ij} indicates the rate of mass flux of species i arising from a unit gradient in the mole fraction (or concentration) of species j. Because of the Onsager reciprocity,

$$L_{ij} = L_{ji}$$

and consequently

$$D_{ij} \frac{\chi_j}{R_j} = D_{ji} \frac{\chi_i}{R_i} \tag{14·51}$$

Since $L_{ii} > 0$ is required by the second law, it further follows that $D_{ii} > 0$.

We see that temperature gradients can lead to the flow of matter, and hence to nonuniformity of concentration. This provides a nonmechanical means for separation of gases, which has some importance in industrial applications. Areas in which the coupling between energy and mass transfer are very important include transpiration and ablative cooling of high-speed flight vehicles and very high-temperature power systems, such as magnetohydrodynamic power-converter channels.

14·10 SIMPLIFIED PHENOMENOLOGICAL EQUATIONS

In very many practical situations the coupled effects are of secondary importance, and a sufficiently accurate analysis may be obtained by considering only the primary effects. The simplified phenomenological equations were known well before the development of irreversible thermodynamics and will most likely be familiar.

If we consider a conductor at nearly constant temperature and are able to neglect the amount of electron flow induced by the temperature gradient, we have

$$▶ \quad eJ_N = -\kappa_e \frac{d\mathcal{E}}{dx} \tag{14·52}$$

which should be familiar as *Ohm's law*.

Neglecting the flows of matter produced by voltage and concentration gradients, we can approximate the heat flux through a conductor as

$$▶ \quad q = -\kappa_t \frac{dT}{dx} \tag{14·53}$$

This is *Fourier's law* of heat conduction.

If we can neglect diffusion of mass produced by voltage and temperature gradients and consider only the diffusion of species i due to a gradient in its concentration, we have

$$▶ \quad J_{M_i} = -D_{ii} \frac{d\chi_i}{dx} \tag{14·54}$$

which is *Fick's law* of diffusion.

Note that the second law has told us that the coefficients in these phenomenological equations are all positive. It may be safely said that the great majority of engineering is based on these simpler phenomenological laws, and the coupled effects have seldom been considered. However, the engineer is more and more frequently being faced with situations in which the coupled effects are important, and we must therefore be cognizant of their existence.

14·11 OTHER COUPLED IRREVERSIBLE PHENOMENA

There are many other kinds of coupled irreversible flows, and in recent years some have begun to be exploited in engineering systems. It is found that the imposition of a voltage difference across a tube gives rise to a pressure gradient, and we can conceive of nonmechanical pumps operating on this effect. Alternatively, by pumping the fluid through the tubes, electrical power could be removed. A recent study of electrokinetic energy conversion† showed that efficiencies of 0.4 percent could be obtained with water as the working fluid. Such poor performance is characteristic of inherently irreversible energy-conversion systems, and it is chiefly their lack of mechanical parts that has made them interesting from a practical standpoint.

A number of coupled phenomena are observed in thermomagnetic systems. If a temperature gradient is established in a conductor perpendicular to an applied magnetic field, an electric field will be developed in the third direction. This *Nernst effect* has been suggested as the basis for a solid-state direct-energy converter.‡ Highly effective magnetothermoelectric refrigerators have been built; these devices use magnetic fields to augment the Peltier and Seebeck effects.§

Some materials exhibit strong anisotropies in their internal structure, and as a result, the flow of heat in one direction can induce transverse variations in temperature. Mass diffusion through anisotropic media exhibits similar coupling.

By application of the methods used in our study of thermoelectricity, any of these coupled irreversible processes can be analyzed. The Onsager reciprocity provides important connections between the phenomenological coefficients, but the theory provides no means for evaluation of their magnitudes. Such was the case in the thermodynamics of equilibrium states; the Maxwell relations, and other equations derived from the first and second laws, related the specific heats, compressibilities, and so on, but did not predict their values. The microscopic analyses of Chaps. Twelve and Thirteen did, however, lead to theoretical values for specific classes of substances. The same sort of microscopic theory is required to supplement the thermodynamics of irreversible processes, that is, to provide quantitative predictions for the phenomenological coefficients. Using the laws of thermodynamics and experimentally determined equilibrium equa-

† J. F. Osterle, Electrokinetic Energy Conversion, *Trans. ASME*, vol. 31, series E, no. 2, p. 161, June, 1964.

‡ S. W. Angrist, A Nernst Effect Power Generator, *Trans. ASME*, vol. 85, series c, no. 1, p. 41, February, 1963.

§ R. Wolfe, Magnetothermoelectricity, *Scientific American*, June, 1964, p. 70.

tions of state, engineers have been able to build some amazing things, often with very little insight into the microscopic world. But today's technology is racing ahead faster than data for new situations can be accumulated, and the engineer of tomorrow will have to be able to make and properly interpret theoretical predictions of the properties of matter. We hope that this book has served as a useful start toward this end.

SELECTED READING

Callen, H., *Thermodynamics*, chaps. 16 and 17, John Wiley & Sons, Inc., New York, 1960.

Lee, J., F. Sears, and D. Turcotte, *Statistical Thermodynamics*, chap. 15, Addison-Wesley Publishing Co., Inc., Reading, Mass., 1963.

Roshenow, W., and H. Choi, *Heat, Mass, and Momentum Transfer*, chap. 19, Prentice-Hall, Inc., Englewood Cliffs, N.J., 1961.

Zemansky, M. W., *Heat and Thermodynamics*, 4th ed., sec. 10.14, McGraw-Hill Book Company, New York, 1957.

QUESTIONS

14·1 What is a coupled irreversible flow?
14·2 What is the flux postulate?
14·3 What are the Onsager coefficients?
14·4 Under what conditions is $L_{ij} = L_{ji}$?
14·5 What does thermodynamics tell us about the Onsager coefficients?
14·6 What is the Seebeck effect?
14·7 Is thermal conductivity a function of voltage?
14·8 Can the absolute thermoelectric power be either negative or positive?
14·9 Under what conditions is the cooling rate required to keep a current-carrying wire at constant temperature solely a function of the current flow, wire conductivity, and wire dimensions?
14·10 Is an emf developed across the junction of two dissimilar metals?
14·11 A good experimenter, when asked to help find the trouble with faulty thermocouple temperature measurements, remarked, "Let's check the leads first." Why was he more concerned about the leads than about the junctions themselves?
14·12 Why is a thermoelectric generator inherently an irreversible device?
14·13 Is it possible to cool a conductor by passing current through it?
14·14 Does the theory of irreversible thermodynamics allow prediction of the value of the thermal conductivity of a substance?

PROBLEMS

14·1 The absolute thermoelectric powers of the alloys chromel and alumel over the range 0–300°C are approximately $+23\ \mu v/C°$ and $-18\ \mu v/C°$, respectively. Estimate the voltage output of a chromel-alumel thermocouple when the "reference" junction is immersed in ice water at 1 atm pressure and the sensing junction is at 250°C. Sketch the thermocouple circuit, showing which wires to hook up to the positive and negative terminals of the high-impedance voltmeter or null potentiometer.

14·2 In good laboratory thermocouple practice the "reference" junction is placed in an ice-water bath at 0°C; when this is done for a high-purity copper-iron thermocouple, the Seebeck emf $\epsilon_c - \epsilon_i$ is found to be expressible in terms of the Celsius temperature t by

$$\mathcal{E}_A - \mathcal{E}_B = a_1 t + a_2 t^2 + a_3 t^3 \ \mu\text{v}$$

where

$$a_1 = -13.403$$
$$a_2 = +0.0137$$
$$a_3 = +0.00013$$

(*a*) What will be the reading (μv) of copper-iron thermocouple circuit when the reference junction is at 0°C and the measuring junction is 150°C? (*b*) Calculate the reading of such a circuit when the reference junction is at 100°C and the measuring junction is at 200°C. (*c*) Determine the Peltier coefficient and the difference in the Thomson coefficients of copper and iron at 100°C.

14·3 It is proposed that the temperature at a point on a hot copper wire might be measured by welding a small platinum wire to it at the point in question, welding another on the copper wire at some point where the temperature is known, and then reading the voltage across the two platinum leads in a cool place. How would you go about determining the unknown temperature, and what information would you need?

14·4 The semiconductor materials used in a thermoelectric generator would typically have the following properties:

	ϵ, *μv/C°*	$1/\kappa_e$, *ohm-cm*	κ_t, *watts/C°-cm*
p element	+230	1×10^{-3}	0.015
n element	−230	1×10^{-3}	0.015

These may be assumed to be independent of temperature. (*a*) Calculate the no-load voltage of a single generator element (one *pn* pair) when the hot junction is at 300°C and the cold junction is at 50°C, assuming that the length of each element is 1.0 cm and the cross-sectional area of each is 0.2 cm². (*b*) Calculate the efficiency and the electrical power output as functions of current. What load resistance should be used if the device is to operate at maximum power? Compare your efficiencies with Carnot-cycle performance.

14·5 Using the thermoelectric data of Prob. 14·4, design a thermoelectric generator that will deliver 1 watt of power at 4 volts when the hot junction is at 150°C and the cold junction is at 40°C. Such a generator might be used to turn a barbecue spit using energy supplied from the hot coals.

14·6 Using the thermoelectric data and element geometry of Prob. 14·4, determine the coefficient of performance of a thermoelectric refrigerator as a function of current where the hot junction is at 40°C and the cold junction is at −10°C.

What would be the fewest number of elements that would have to be used in series to produce 10,000 Btu/hr of cooling (typical of a household refrigerator), and what would be the electrical power requirement? (By way of comparison, typical household vapor-compression refrigerators use 1-hp motors.)

14·7 Using the thermoelectric data of Prob. 14·4, design a thermoelectric cooler that will remove 1 watt from electronic gear at 40°C and reject heat to an environment at 80°C.

14·8 Consider a one-dimensional conductor between two large reservoirs containing a single substance. Electrical effects are negligible. Set up the phenomenological equations and state the proper Onsager reciprocity. Show that the condition of no mass flow is of the form

$$\frac{dP/dx}{dT/dx} = \frac{-\mathfrak{L}_{01}}{\mathfrak{L}_{11}Tv}$$

where the coefficients $\mathfrak{L}$ are functions of only P and T. When liquid helium in a capillary tube is heated it can be made to flow rapidly, squirting as high as 1 ft in the air. Explain this "fountain effect" in terms of your theory.

14·9 Consider a mixture of two gases at constant pressure. The condition that their mole fractions add to unity provides an additional relation among the concentration gradients. Express the energy flux in terms of the temperature gradient and one of the mole-fraction gradients. Express the mass fluxes of components 1 and 2 in terms of the temperature gradient and their own mole-fraction gradients. Examine the special case where there is no net mass flow across a plane through the conductor; what else does this tell you?

14·10 From simple microscopic considerations develop a qualitative explanation showing how the coupling between flow of one constituent and flow of another might take place. It may be easier to think of one as having big molecules and the other as being much lighter. Do you think that the induced flows are in the same direction as the main flows? Can you explain thermal diffusion with your model?

APPENDIX A

UNIT SYSTEMS AND DIMENSIONAL EQUIVALENTS

The conceptual basis of unit systems was discussed in Chap. One. Table A·1 shows the dimensions of mechanical quantities in four commonly used unit systems. Note that the constant in Newton's second law, g_c, is arbitrarily taken as unity, except in the engineering system where its value of 32.17 ft-lbm/lbf-sec² is conceptually experimental. Three common electromagnetic unit systems are shown in Table A·2. Note that the differences are in the manner that charge is handled; some differences in the definitions are also involved. Table A·3 contains a selected list of dimensional equivalents, and Table A·4 gives values for several important physical constants.

Dimensional equivalents are most easily obtained by considering a given magnitude of the quantity in the two unit systems. Two examples of this procedure follow.

1 Find the equivalent of 1 newton of force in the engineering unit system. To determine this dimensional equivalent, consider a body having a mass of 1 kg being accelerated by a force at the rate of 1 m/sec². The force acting on the body is, in the mks system,

$$\mathsf{F} = ma = 1 \text{ kg-m/sec}^2$$

The mass of the body in the engineering system is (Table A·3) 2.2046 lbm. Its acceleration is

$$1 \text{ m} \times 3.280 \text{ (ft/m)/sec}^2 = 3.280 \text{ ft/sec}^2$$

In the engineering system the force is

$$\mathsf{F} = \frac{1}{g_c} ma = \frac{2.2046 \text{ lbm} \times 3.280 \text{ ft/sec}^2}{32.17 \text{ ft-lbm/lbf-sec}^2} = 0.2248 \text{ lbf}$$

Therefore,

$$1 \text{ newton} \equiv 1 \text{ kg-m/sec}^2 = 0.2248 \text{ lbf}$$

2 Determine the dimensional equivalents of the magnetic induction B and the magnetization M in the rationalized practical mksc and absolute magnetostatic cgs unit systems. This calculation is complicated by the difference in definition. We have

$$\mathsf{B} = \mathsf{H} + 4\pi\mathsf{M} \qquad \text{magnetostatic cgs system} \tag{A·1a}$$

$$\mathsf{B} = \mu_0(\mathsf{H} + \mathsf{M}) \qquad \text{mksc system} \tag{A·1b}$$

Consider two charges, each of 1 coul, separated by a distance of 1 m, moving in opposite directions perpendicular to the line between them at 1 m/sec.

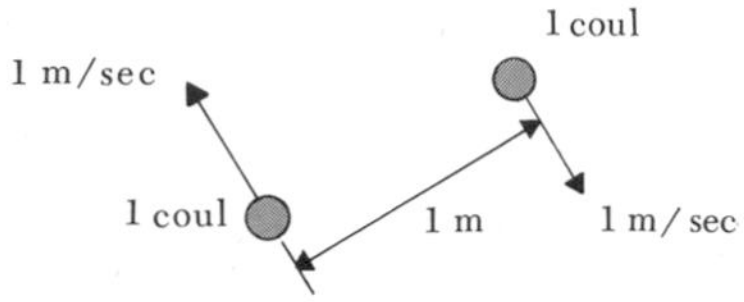

From the Biot-Savart law the force in the mksc system is

$$\mathsf{F} = \frac{1.256 \times 10^{-6}}{4\pi} \text{ kg-m/coul}^2 \times 1 \text{ coul}^2 \times 1 \text{ m}^2/\text{sec}^2 \times \frac{1 \text{ m}}{1 \text{ m}^3}$$

$$= \frac{1.256 \times 10^{-6}}{4\pi} \text{ kg-m/sec}^2 = 10^{-7} \text{ kg-m/sec}^2$$

In the absolute magnetostatic unit system the charge, distance, and speed have the magnitudes

$$\mathcal{Q} = 0.1 \text{ g}^{1/2}\text{-cm}^{1/2}$$
$$R = 100 \text{ cm}$$
$$\mathsf{V} = 100 \text{ cm/sec}$$

The force in the magnetostatic cgs system is therefore

$$\mathsf{F} = 0.1^2 \text{ g-cm} \times 100^2 \text{ cm}^2/\text{sec}^2 \, \frac{100 \text{ cm}}{100^3 \text{ cm}^3} = 0.01 \text{ g-cm/sec}^2$$

The magnetic induction B, in either system, is

$$\mathsf{B} = \frac{\mathsf{F}}{\mathsf{V}\mathcal{Q}} \tag{A·2}$$

In the rationalized practical mksc system

$$\mathsf{B} = \frac{10^{-7} \text{ kg-m/sec}^2}{1 \text{ coul} \times 1 \text{ m/sec}}$$
$$= 10^{-7} \text{ kg/coul-sec}$$

In the absolute magnetostatic cgs system

$$B = \frac{0.01 \text{ g-cm/sec}^2}{0.1 \text{ g}^{1/2}\text{-cm}^{1/2} \times 100 \text{ cm/sec}}$$
$$= 0.001 \text{ g}^{1/2}/\text{cm}^{1/2}\text{-sec}$$

In terms of the aliases

$$1 \text{ tesla} = 1 \text{ kg/coul-sec}$$
$$1 \text{ gauss} \equiv 1 \text{ g}^{1/2}/\text{cm}^{1/2}\text{-sec}$$

we have

$$10^{-7} \text{ tesla} = 0.001 \text{ gauss}$$

So for B

$$1 \text{ tesla} = 10^4 \text{ gauss}$$

We hasten to point out that the correspondence between tesla and gauss does not apply to H and M. To find the dimensional equivalents for H we consider a field with $B = 1$ tesla and $M = 0$. Then, in the rationalized practical mksc system,

$$H = \frac{B}{\mu_0}$$
$$= \frac{1 \text{ kg/coul-sec}}{1.256 \times 10^{-6} \text{ kg-m/coul}^2} = \frac{1}{1.256 \times 10^{-6}} \text{ coul/m-sec}$$

In the absolute magnetostatic cgs system $B = H = 10^4$ gauss. Equating the two values for H, we find

$$1 \text{ gauss of H} = \frac{1}{1.256 \times 10^{-2}} \text{ coul/m-sec}$$

To obtain the equivalents for M we imagine a field of 1 tesla with $H = 0$. Then, in the rationalized practical mksc unit system,

$$M = \frac{B}{\mu_0} = \frac{1}{1.256 \times 10^{-6}} \text{ coul/m-sec}$$

In the absolute magnetostatic cgs system

$$M = \frac{B}{4\pi} = \frac{10^4}{4\pi} \text{ gauss}$$

Equating the two magnetizations, we find

$$1 \text{ gauss of M} = 10^3 \text{ coul/m-sec}$$

The dimensional equivalence for B might be put in the form

$$1 \text{ gauss of B} = 10^{-4} \text{ kg/coul-sec}$$

This example illustrates the importance of keeping straight just what the dimensional equivalent is for. One gauss is not always equivalent to the same number of coul/m-sec; sometimes it is equivalent to a number of kg/coul-sec!

Converting units from one system to another is a confusing task which can be made simple by noting that multiplication of anything by unity leaves it unchanged. The number 1 can be written in many useful ways, two of which are

$$1 = \frac{12 \text{ in.}}{1 \text{ ft}}$$

$$1 = \frac{778.16 \text{ ft-lbf}}{1 \text{ Btu}}$$

Then, to express an energy density of 50 Btu/in.^{3} in terms of ft-lbf/ft^3,

$$\frac{E}{V} = 50 \text{ Btu/in.}^3 \times 778.16 \text{ ft-lbf/Btu} \times (12 \text{ in./ft})^3$$

$$= 6.72 \times 10^6 \text{ ft-lbf/ft}^3$$

You are encouraged to acquire the habit of always writing down units in a numerical problem. Dimensions provide an easy check on equations and are an essential part of the answer to any engineering problem.

TABLE A·1 MECHANICAL UNIT SYSTEMS

	Mks	*Cgs*	*Absolute engineering*	*Engineering*†
Primary quantities and their units				
Length	Meter, m	Centimeter, cm	Foot, ft	Foot, ft
Mass	Kilogram, kg	Gram, g	. . .	Pound mass, lbm
Time	Second, sec	Second, sec	Second, sec	Second, sec
Force	. . .	. . .	Pound force, lbf	Pound force, lbf
Newton's second law, $\mathsf{F} = \dfrac{m\,dV}{g_c\,dt}$	$g_c \equiv 1$ (selected)	$g_c \equiv 1$ (selected)	$g_c \equiv 1$ (selected)	$g_c = 32.17$ ft-lbm/lbf-sec^2 (experimental)
Secondary quantities and their units				
Force	kg-m/sec^2	g-cm/sec^2	. . .	. . .
Mass	. . .	. . .	lbf-sec^2/ft	. . .
Energy, $dW = \mathsf{F}\,dX$	kg-m^2/sec^2	g-cm^2/sec^2	ft-lbf	ft-lbf
Power, $\dot{W}$	kg-m^2/sec^3	g-cm^2/sec^3	ft-lbf/sec	ft-lbf/sec
Aliases				
Force	1 newton ≡ 1 kg-m/sec^2	1 dyne ≡ 1 g-cm/sec^2	. . .	. . .
Mass	. . .	. . .	1 slug ≡ 1 lbf-sec^2/ft	. . .
Energy	1 joule ≡ 1 kg-m^2/sec^2 = 1 newton-m	1 erg ≡ 1 g-cm^2/sec^2 = 1 dyne-cm	. . .	. . .
Power	1 watt ≡ 1 kg-m^2/sec^3 = 1 joule/sec	. . .	. . .	. . .

† A body having a weight of 1 lbf on the surface of the earth will have a mass of approximately 1 lbm.

TABLE A·2 ELECTROMAGNETIC UNIT SYSTEMS

	Mksc	*Absolute cgs electrostatic (esu)*	*Absolute cgs magnetostatic (emu)*
Primary quantities and their units			
Length	Meter, m	Centimeter, cm	Centimeter, cm
Mass	Kilogram, kg	Gram, g	Gram, g
Time	Second, sec	Second, sec	Second, sec
Charge	Coulomb, coul	. . .	. . .
Coulomb's law,	$k_C = \frac{1}{4\pi\epsilon_0}$	$k_C \equiv 1$ (selected)	$k_C = 0.8992 \times 10^{17}$ cm^2-sec^{-2} (experimental)
$\mathsf{F}_{12} = k_C \frac{Q_1 Q_2}{R_{12}^2}$	$\epsilon_0 = 8.854 \times 10^{-12}$ coul^2-sec^2-kg^{-1}-m^{-3} (experimental)		
Biot-Savart law, $\mathsf{F}_{12} = k_B \frac{Q_1 Q_2 \mathbf{V}_1 \times (\mathbf{V}_2 \times \mathbf{R})}{\|\mathbf{R}\|^3}$	$k_B = \frac{\mu_0}{4\pi}$ $\mu_0 = 1.256 \times 10^{-6}$ kg-m-coul^{-2} (experimental)	$k_B = 1.112 \times 10^{-17}$ sec^2-cm^{-2} (experimental)	$k_B \equiv 1$ (selected)
Secondary quantities and their units			
Charge	. . .	g$^{1/2}$-cm$^{3/2}$-sec^{-1}	g$^{1/2}$-cm$^{1/2}$
Current density, $J = \dot{Q}/A$	coul-m^{-2} sec^{-1}	g$^{1/2}$-cm$^{-1/2}$-sec^{-2}	g$^{1/2}$-cm$^{-3/2}$-sec^{-1}
Current, $I = \int \mathbf{J} \cdot d\mathbf{A}$	coul-sec^{-1}	g$^{1/2}$-cm$^{3/2}$-sec^{-2}	g$^{1/2}$-cm$^{1/2}$-sec^{-1}
Electric and magnetic fields, $\mathbf{F} = Q(\mathbf{E} + \mathbf{V} \times \mathbf{B})$			
Electric field strength $\mathbf{E}$	kg-m-coul^{-1}-sec^{-2}	g$^{1/2}$-cm$^{-1/2}$-sec^{-1}	g$^{1/2}$-cm$^{-1/2}$-sec^{-2}
Magnetic induction $\mathbf{B}$	kg-sec^{-1}-coul^{-1}	g$^{1/2}$-cm$^{-3/2}$	g$^{1/2}$-cm$^{-1/2}$-sec^{-1}

Electrical potential $\mathcal{E}$	kg-m^{2}-coul^{-1}-sec^{-2}	g$^{1/2}$-cm$^{1/2}$-sec^{-1}	g$^{1/2}$-cm$^{3/2}$-sec^{-2}
$d\mathcal{E} = \mathbf{E} \cdot d\mathbf{L}$			
Electric displacement, polarization:	$\mathbf{D} = \epsilon_0\mathbf{E} + \mathbf{P}$	$\mathbf{D} = \mathbf{E} + 4\pi\mathbf{P}$	
Displacement **D**	coul-m^{-2}	g$^{1/2}$-cm$^{-1/2}$-sec^{-1}	
Polarization **P**	coul-m^{-2}	g$^{1/2}$-cm$^{-1/2}$-sec^{-1}	
Magnetic field strength, magnetization:	$\mathbf{B} = \mu_0(\mathbf{H} + \mathbf{M})$		$\mathbf{B} = \mathbf{H} + 4\pi\mathbf{M}$
Magnetic field strength **H**	coul-m^{-1}-sec^{-1}		g$^{1/2}$-cm$^{-1/2}$-sec^{-1}
Magnetization **M**	coul-m^{-1}-sec^{-1}		g$^{1/2}$-cm$^{-1/2}$-sec^{-1}
Electric flux, $\Phi_E = \int \mathbf{E} \cdot d\mathbf{A}$	kg-m^{3}-coul^{-1}-sec^{-2}	g$^{1/2}$-cm$^{3/2}$-sec^{-1}	
Magnetic flux, $\Phi_B = \int \mathbf{B} \cdot d\mathbf{A}$	kg-m^{2}-coul^{-1}-sec^{-1}		g$^{1/2}$-cm$^{3/2}$-sec^{-1}
Electrical conductivity, J/E	coul^{2}-sec-kg^{-1}-m^{-3}	sec^{-1}	sec-cm^{-2}
Resistance, $R = \Delta\mathcal{E}/I$	kg-m^{2}-coul^{-2}-sec^{-1}	sec-cm^{-1}	cm-sec^{-1}
Capacitance, $C = I/(d\mathcal{E}/dt)$	coul^{2}-sec^{2}-kg^{-1}-m^{-2}	cm	sec^{2}-cm^{-1}
Inductance, $L = \Delta\mathcal{E}/(dI/dt)$	kg-m^{2}-coul^{-2}	sec^{2}-cm^{-1}	cm

Aliases			
Charge	. . .	1 statcoul ≡ 1 g$^{1/2}$-cm$^{3/2}$-sec^{-1}	1 abcoul ≡ 1 g$^{1/2}$-cm$^{1/2}$
Current	1 amp ≡ 1 coul-sec^{-1}	1 statamp ≡ 1 g$^{1/2}$-cm$^{3/2}$-sec^{-2}	1 abamp ≡ 1 g$^{1/2}$-cm$^{1/2}$-sec^{-1}
Magnetic induction	1 tesla ≡ 1 kg-sec^{-1}-coul^{-1}		1 gauss ≡ 1 g$^{1/2}$-cm$^{-1/2}$-sec^{-1}
Electric potential	1 volt ≡ 1 kg-m^{2}-coul^{-1}-sec^{-2}	1 statvolt ≡ 1 g$^{1/2}$-cm$^{1/2}$-sec^{-1}	1 abvolt ≡ 1 g$^{1/2}$-cm$^{3/2}$-sec^{-2}
Magnetic flux	1 weber ≡ 1 kg-m^{2}-coul^{-1}-sec^{-1}		
Resistance	1 ohm ≡ 1 kg-m^{2}-coul^{-2}-sec^{-1}	1 statohm ≡ 1 sec-cm^{-1}	1 abohm ≡ 1 cm-sec^{-1}
Capacitance	1 farad ≡ 1 coul^{2}-sec^{2}-kg^{-1}-m^{-2}	1 statfarad ≡ 1 cm	1 abfarad ≡ 1 sec^{2}-cm^{-1}
Inductance	1 henry ≡ 1 kg-m^{2}-coul^{-2}	1 stathenry ≡ 1 sec^{2}-cm^{-1}	1 abhenry ≡ 1 cm

TABLE A · 3 SELECTED DIMENSIONAL EQUIVALENTS

Length	1 m = 3.280 ft = 39.37 in.
	1 cm ≡ 10^{-2} m = 0.394 in. = 0.0328 ft
	1 mm ≡ 10^{-3} m
	1 micron (μ) ≡ 10^{-6} m
	1 angstrom (Å) ≡ 10^{-10} m
Time	1 hr ≡ 3600 sec = 60 min
	1 millisec ≡ 10^{-3} sec
	1 microsec (μsec) ≡ 10^{-6} sec
	1 nanosec (nsec) = 10^{-9} sec
Mass	1 kg ≡ 1000 g = 2.2046 lbm = 6.8521 × 10^{-2} slugs
	1 slug ≡ 1 lbf-sec²/ft = 32.174 lbm
Force	1 newton ≡ 1 kg-m/sec²
	1 dyne ≡ 1 g-cm/sec²
	1 lbf = 4.448 × 10^5 dynes = 4.448 newtons
Energy	1 joule ≡ 1 kg-m²/sec²
	1 Btu ≡ 778.16 ft-lbf = 1.055 × 10^{10} ergs = 252 cal
	1 cal ≡ 4.186 joules
	1 kcal ≡ 4186 joules = 1000 cal
	1 erg ≡ 1 g-cm²/sec²
	1 ev ≡ 1.602 × 10^{-19} joules
Power	1 watt ≡ 1 kg-m²/sec³ = 1 joule/sec
	1 hp ≡ 550 ft-lbf/sec
	1 hp = 2545 Btu/hr = 746 watts
	1 kw ≡ 1000 watts = 3413 Btu/hr
Pressure	1 atm ≡ 14.696 lbf/in.² = 760 torr
	1 mmHg = 0.01934 lbf/in.² ≡ 1 torr
	1 dyne/cm² = 145.04 × 10^{-7} lbf/in.²
	1 bar = 14.504 lbf/in.² ≡ 10^6 dynes/cm²
	1 micron (μ) ≡ 10^{-6} mHg = 10^{-3} mmHg
Volume	1 gal ≡ 0.13368 ft³
	1 liter ≡ 1000.028 cm³
Temperature	1 K° = 1 C° = 1.8 F° = 1.8 R°
	0°C corresponds to 32°F, 273.16°K, and 491.69°R
Magnetic quantities	1 gauss ≡ 1 $g^{1/2}/cm^{1/2}$-sec
	1 gauss = 10^3 coul/m-sec for M
	1 gauss = $(1/4\pi) \times 10^3$ coul/m-sec for H
	1 gauss = 10^{-4} tesla for B
	1 tesla ≡ 1 kg/coul-sec

TABLE A · 4 PHYSICAL CONSTANTS

Avogadro's number	$N_0 = 6.025 \times 10^{23}$/gmole
Boltzmann's constant	$k = 1.380 \times 10^{-23}$ joule/°K
Gas constant	$\mathcal{R} = 1545.33$ ft-lbf/lbmole-°R $= 8.317$ joule/gmole-°K $= 1.986$ Btu/lbmole-°R $= 1.986$ cal/gmole-°K
Planck's constant	$h = 6.625 \times 10^{-34}$ joule-sec
Coulomb constant	$1/4\pi\epsilon_0 = 8.987 \times 10^9$ kg-m^3/coul^2-sec^2
Biot-Savart constant	$\mu_0/4\pi = 1.0000 \times 10^{-7}$ kg-m/coul^2
Electronic charge	$e = -1.6021 \times 10^{-19}$ coul
Speed of light	$c = 2.998 \times 10^8$ m/sec
Newton constant	$g_c = 32.174$ ft-lbm/lbf-sec^2
Gravitational constant	$k_G = 6.67 \times 10^{-11}$ m^3/kg-sec^2

APPENDIX B

THERMODYNAMIC PROPERTIES OF SUBSTANCES

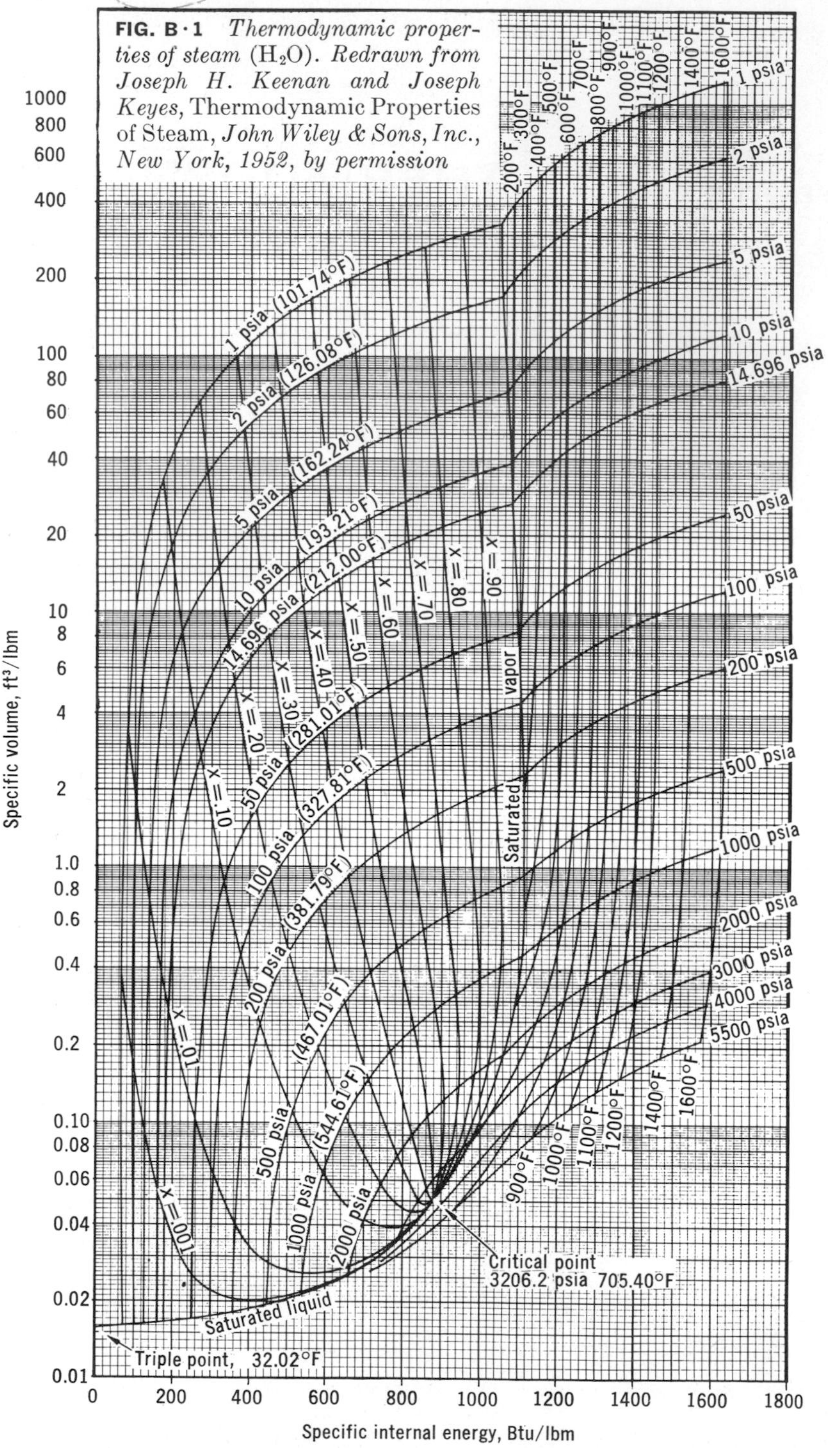

FIG. B·1 *Thermodynamic properties of steam* (H_2O). *Redrawn from Joseph H. Keenan and Joseph Keyes,* Thermodynamic Properties of Steam, *John Wiley & Sons, Inc., New York, 1952, by permission*

FIG. B·2 *Mollier diagram for steam* (H_2O). *From Joseph H. Keenan and Joseph Keyes,* Thermodynamic Properties of Steam, *John Wiley & Sons, Inc., New York, 1936, by permission*

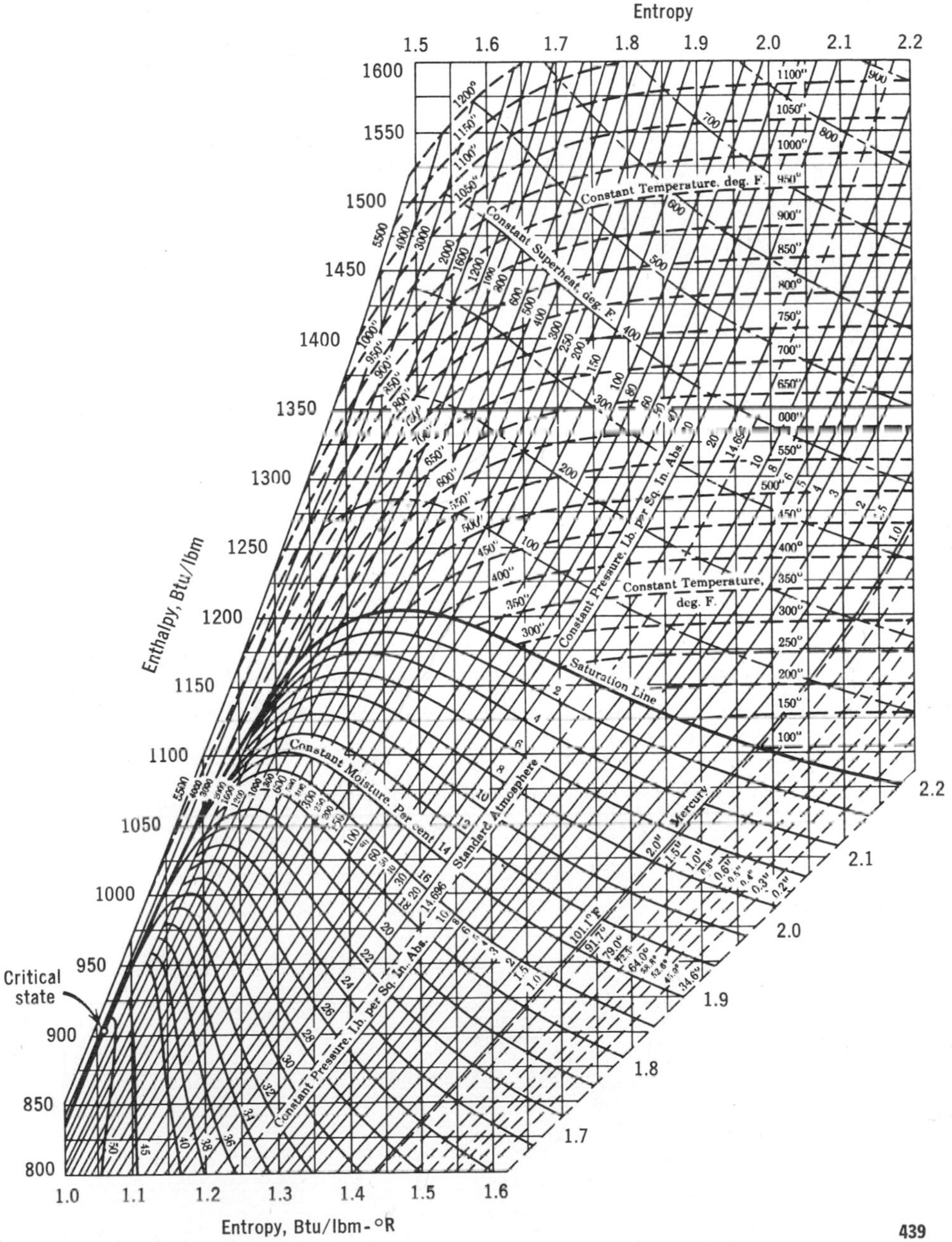

FIG. B·3 *Temperature-entropy diagram for steam* (H_2O). *From Joseph H. Keenan and Joseph Keyes,* Thermodynamic Properties of Steam, *John Wiley & Sons, Inc., New York, as adapted by Lay,* Thermodynamics, *Charles E. Merrill, Inc., Englewood Cliffs, N.J., 1963, by permission*

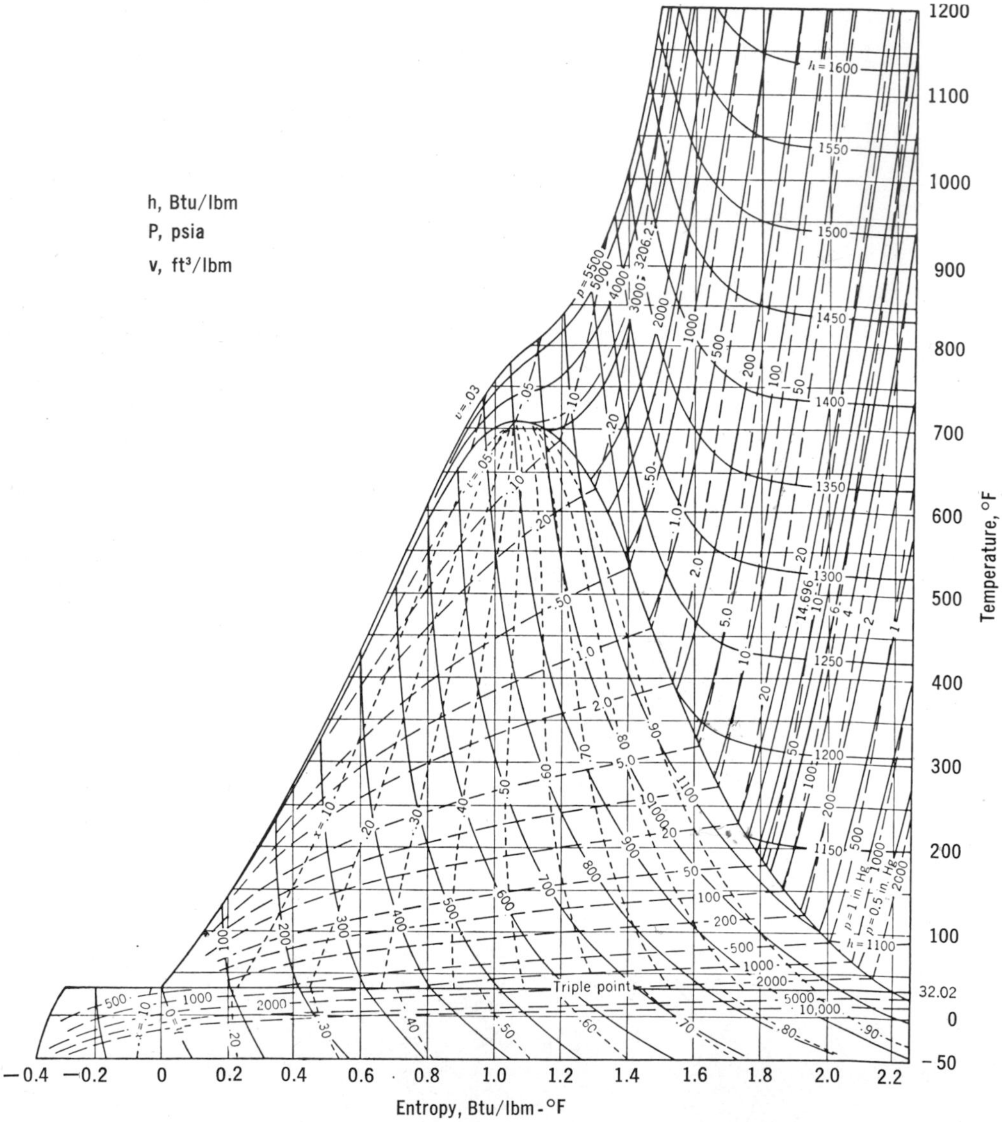

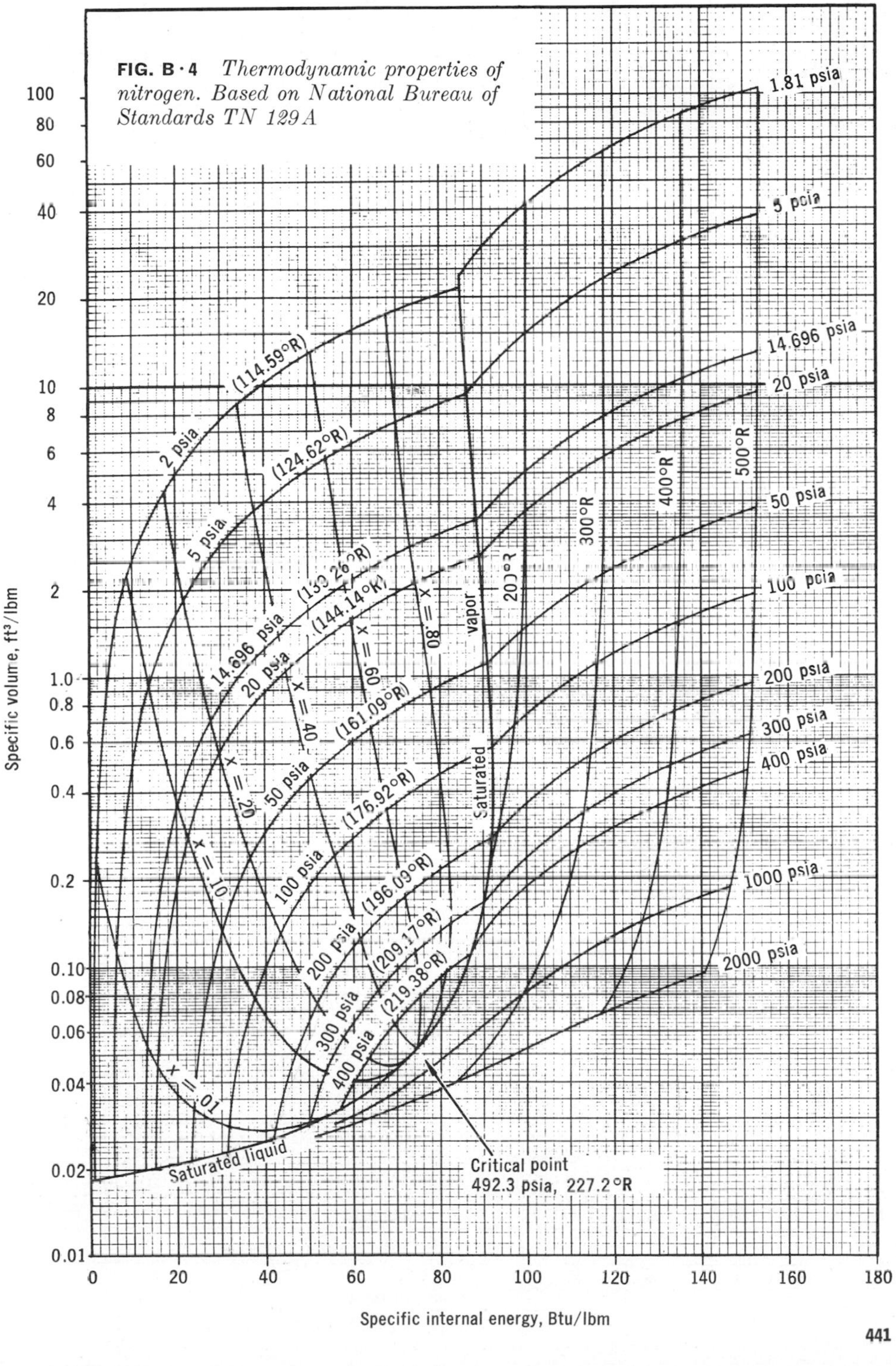

FIG. B·4 *Thermodynamic properties of nitrogen. Based on National Bureau of Standards TN 129A*

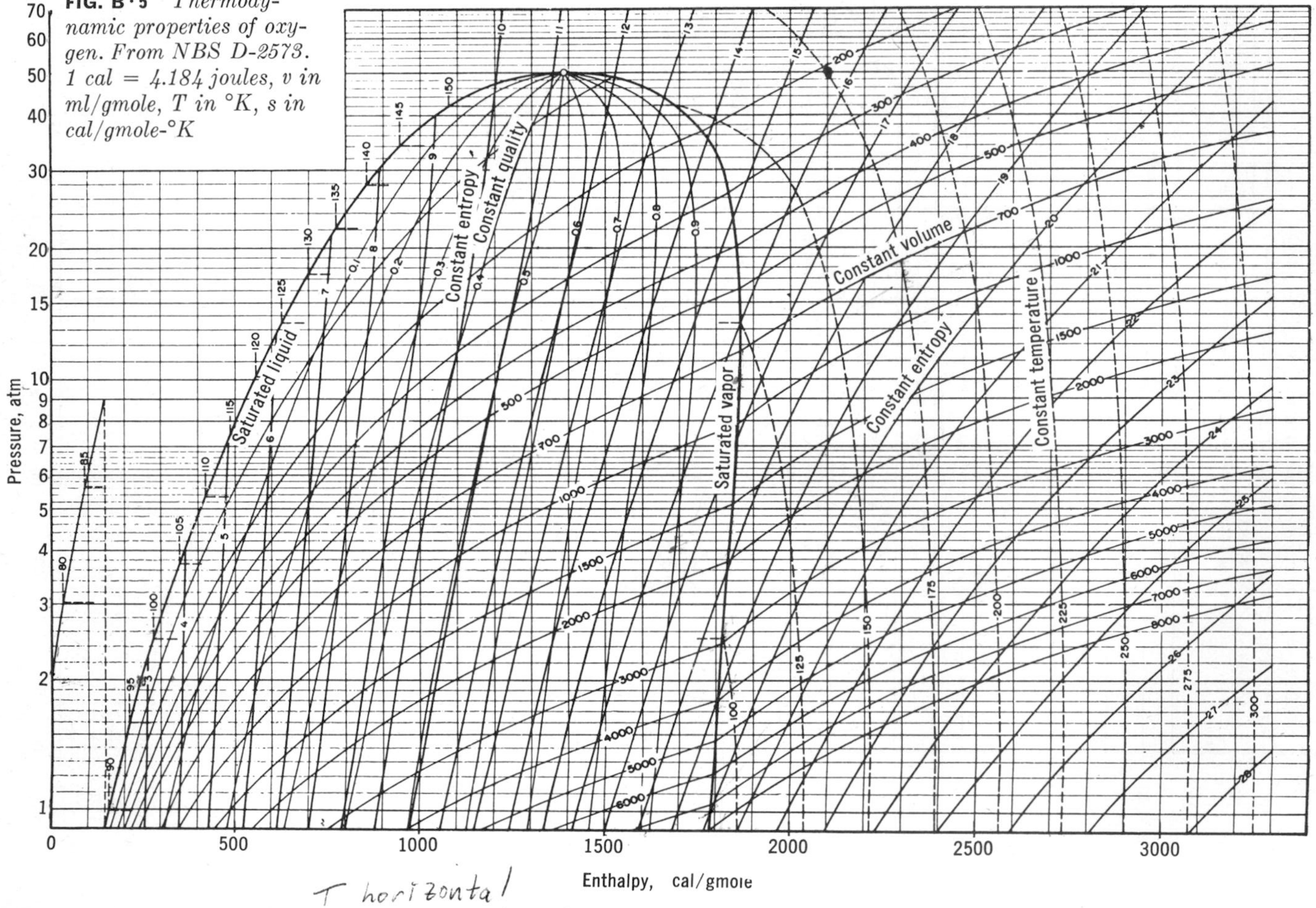

FIG. B·5 *Thermodynamic properties of oxygen. From NBS D-2573. 1 cal = 4.184 joules, v in ml/gmole, T in °K, s in cal/gmole-°K*

T horizontal under saturation curve

FIG. B·6 *Thermodynamic properties of carbon dioxide* (CO_2). *Diagram copy supplied by General Dynamics Corporation, Liquid Carbonic Division. T in °F, h in Btu/lbm, v in ft³/lbm, s in Btu/lbm-°F, at critical point P = 1066.3 psia, T = 87.8°F*

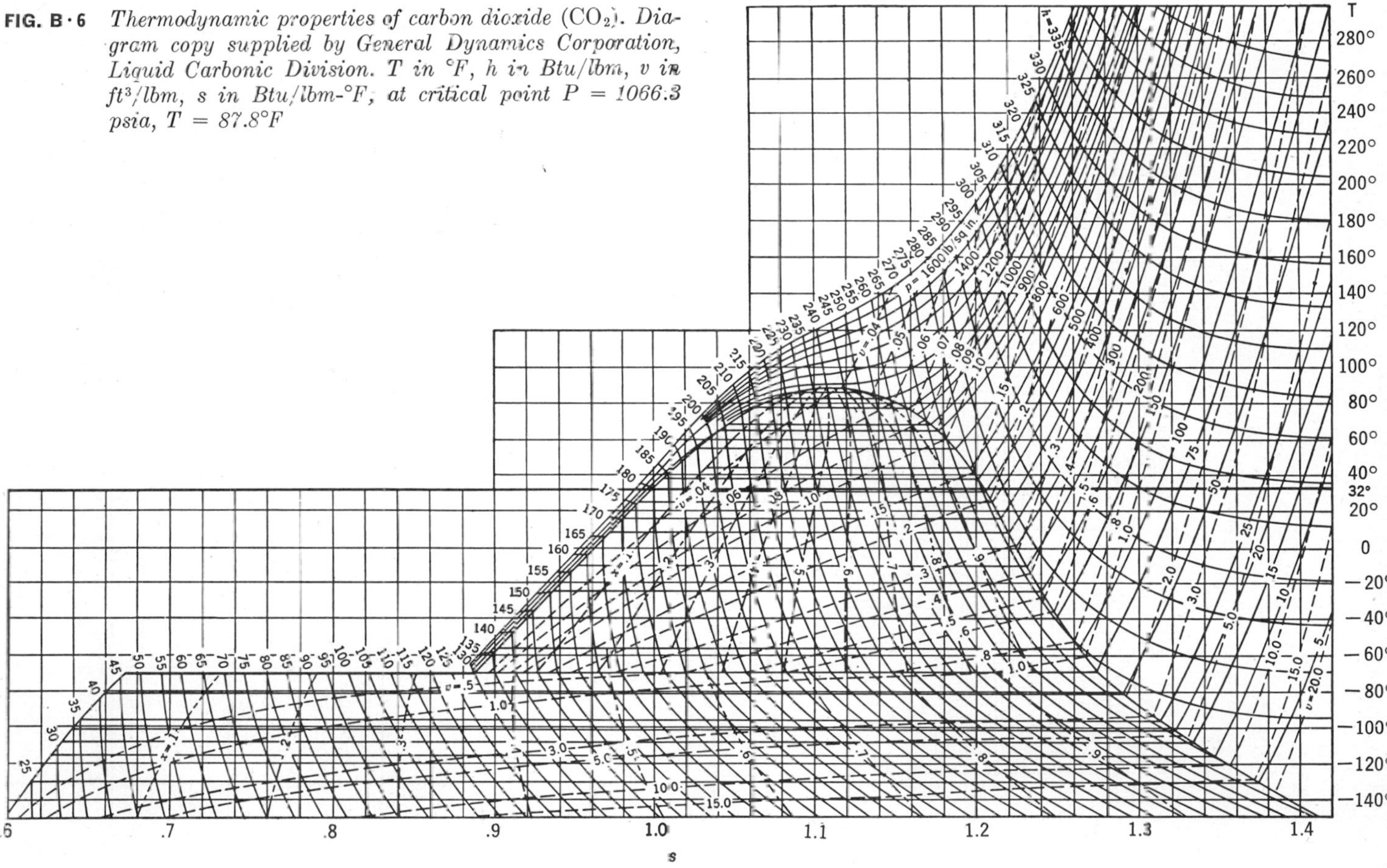

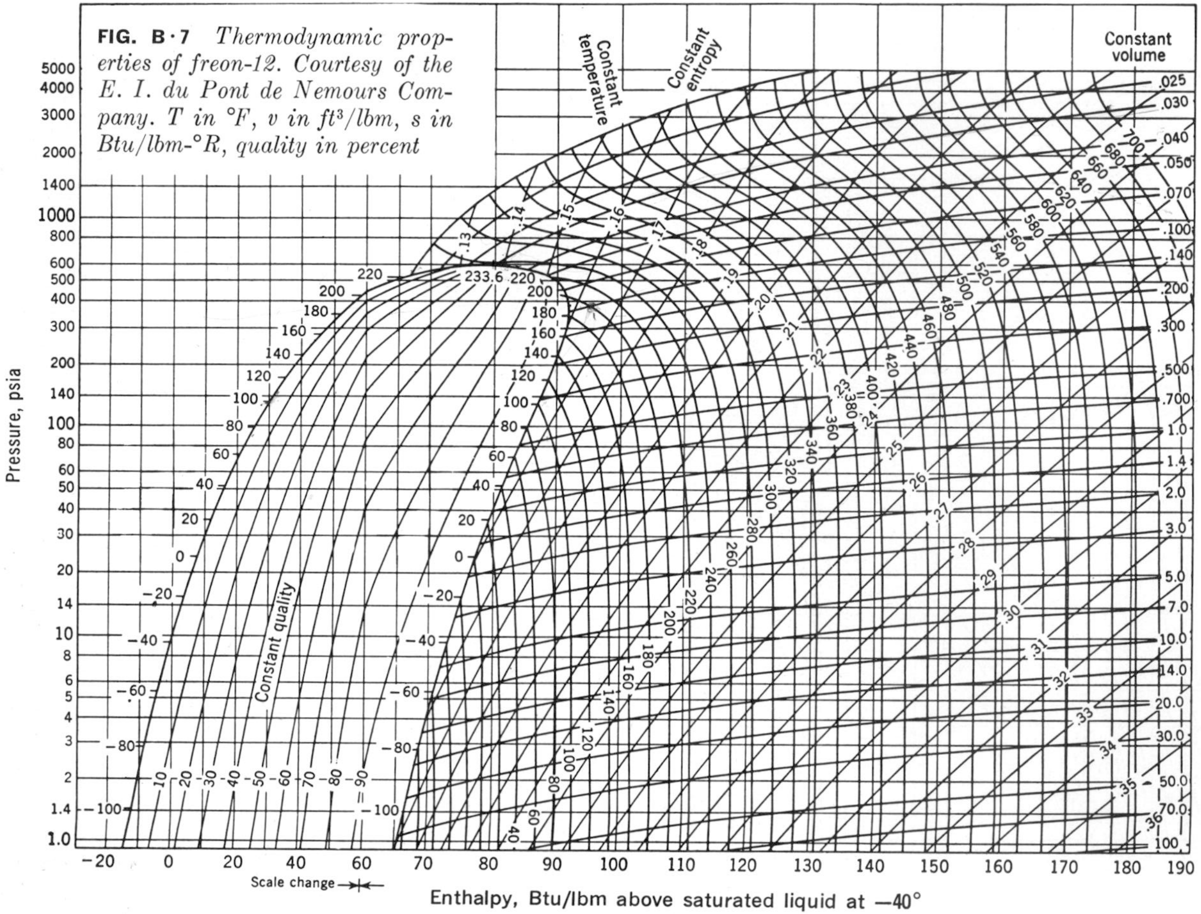

FIG. B·7 *Thermodynamic properties of freon-12. Courtesy of the E. I. du Pont de Nemours Company. T in °F, v in ft³/lbm, s in Btu/lbm-°R, quality in percent*

FIG. B·8 *Thermodynamic properties of air. From the National Bureau of Standards*

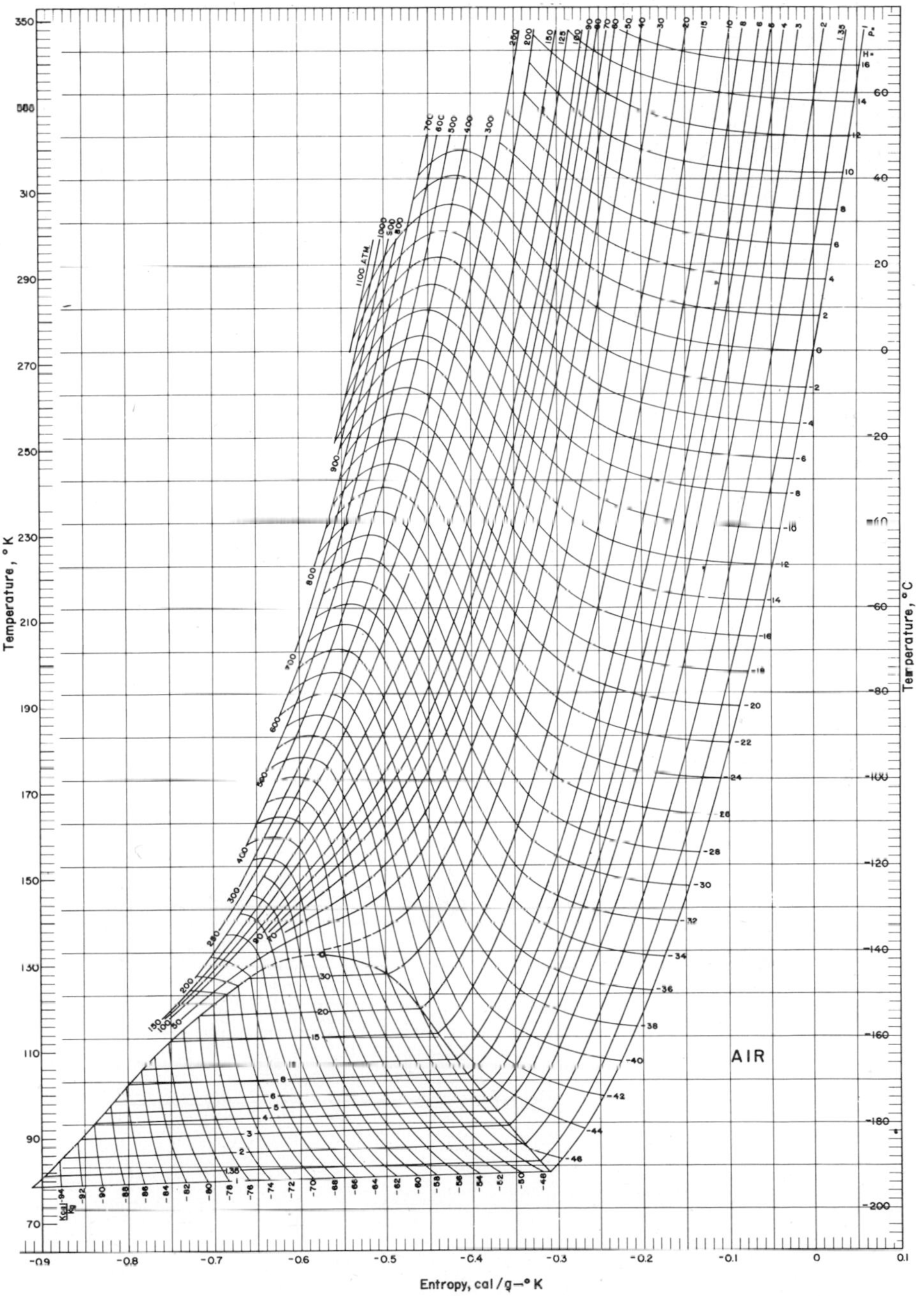

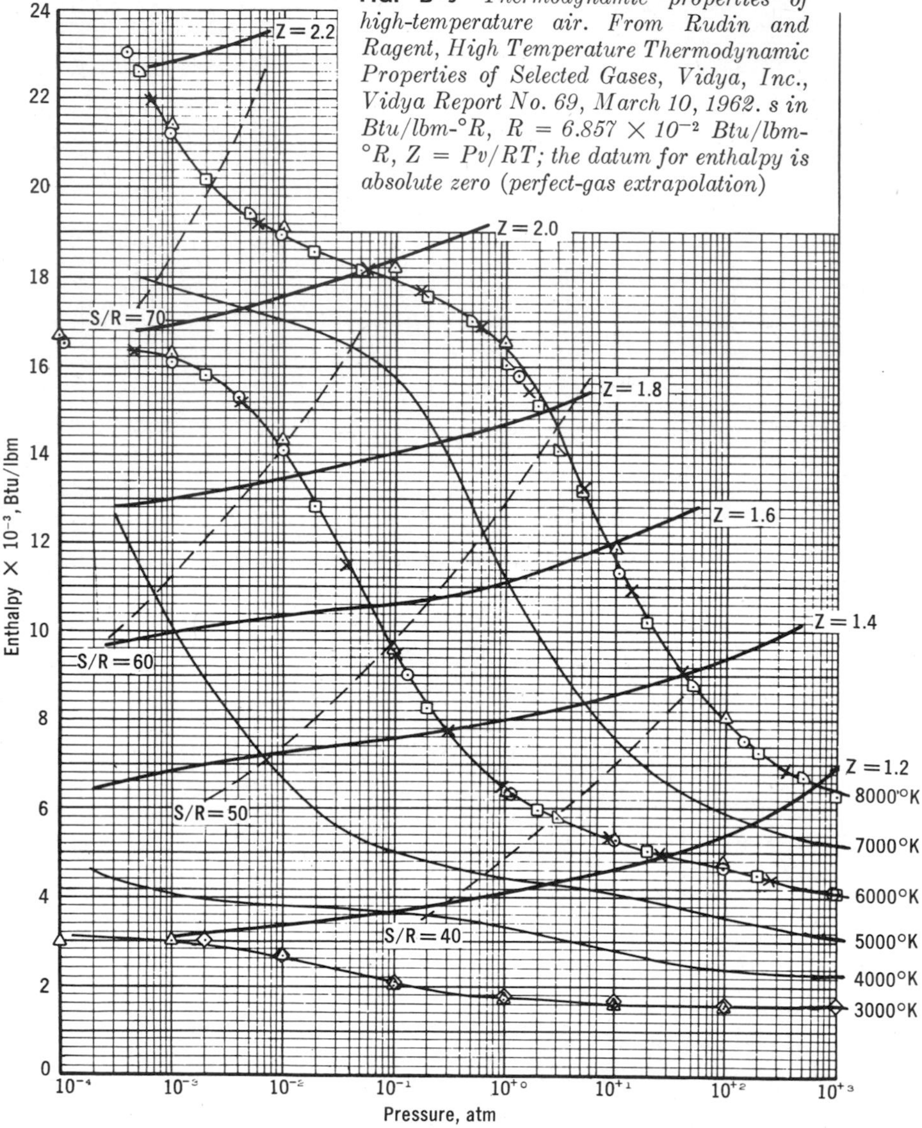

FIG. B·9 *Thermodynamic properties of high-temperature air. From Rudin and Ragent, High Temperature Thermodynamic Properties of Selected Gases, Vidya, Inc., Vidya Report No. 69, March 10, 1962. s in Btu/lbm-°R, $R = 6.857 \times 10^{-2}$ Btu/lbm-°R, $Z = Pv/RT$; the datum for enthalpy is absolute zero (perfect-gas extrapolation)*

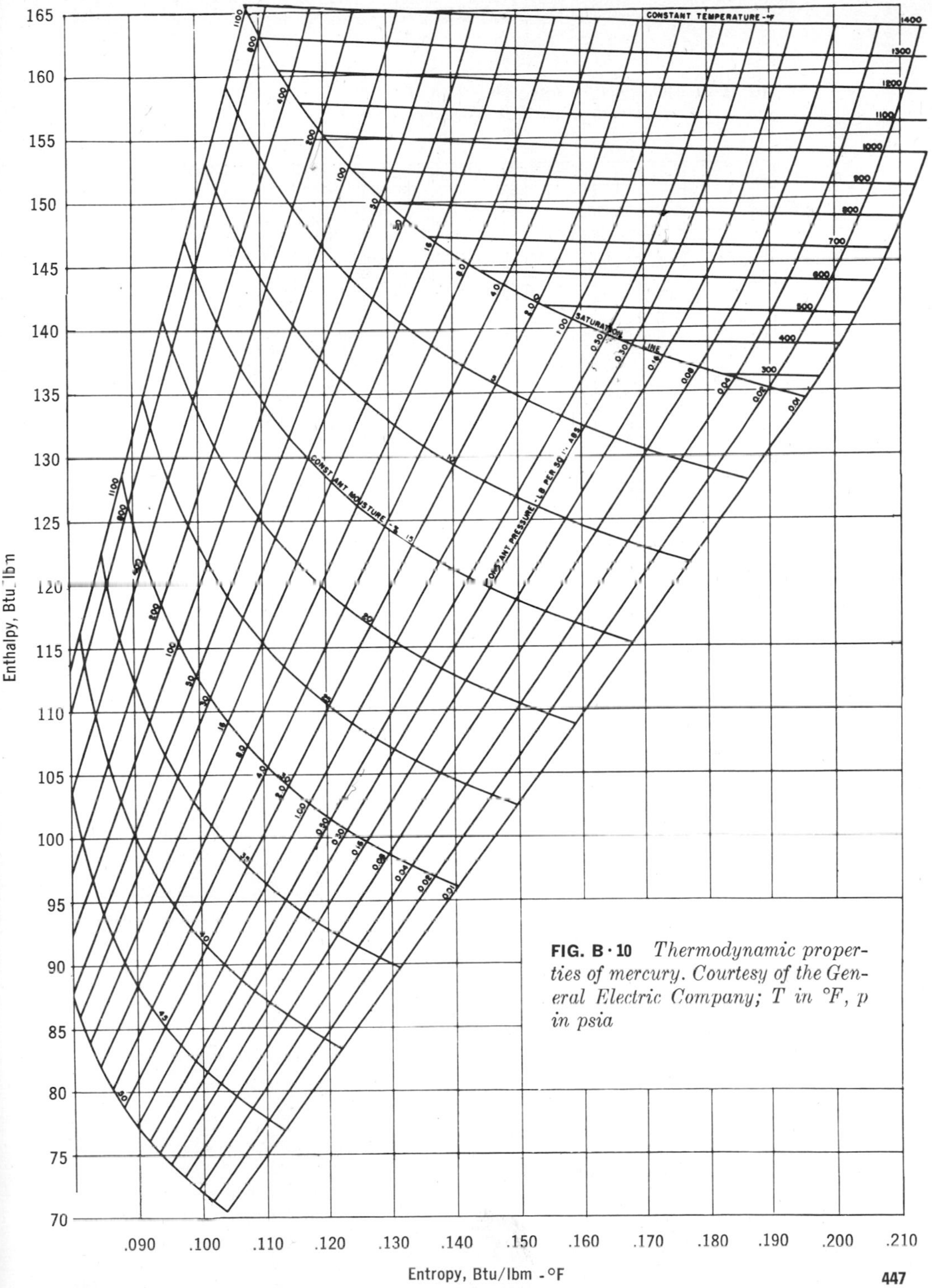

FIG. B · 10 *Thermodynamic properties of mercury. Courtesy of the General Electric Company; T in °F, p in psia*

FIG. B·11 *Thermodynamic properties of cesium. Redrawn from WADD Report 61-96*

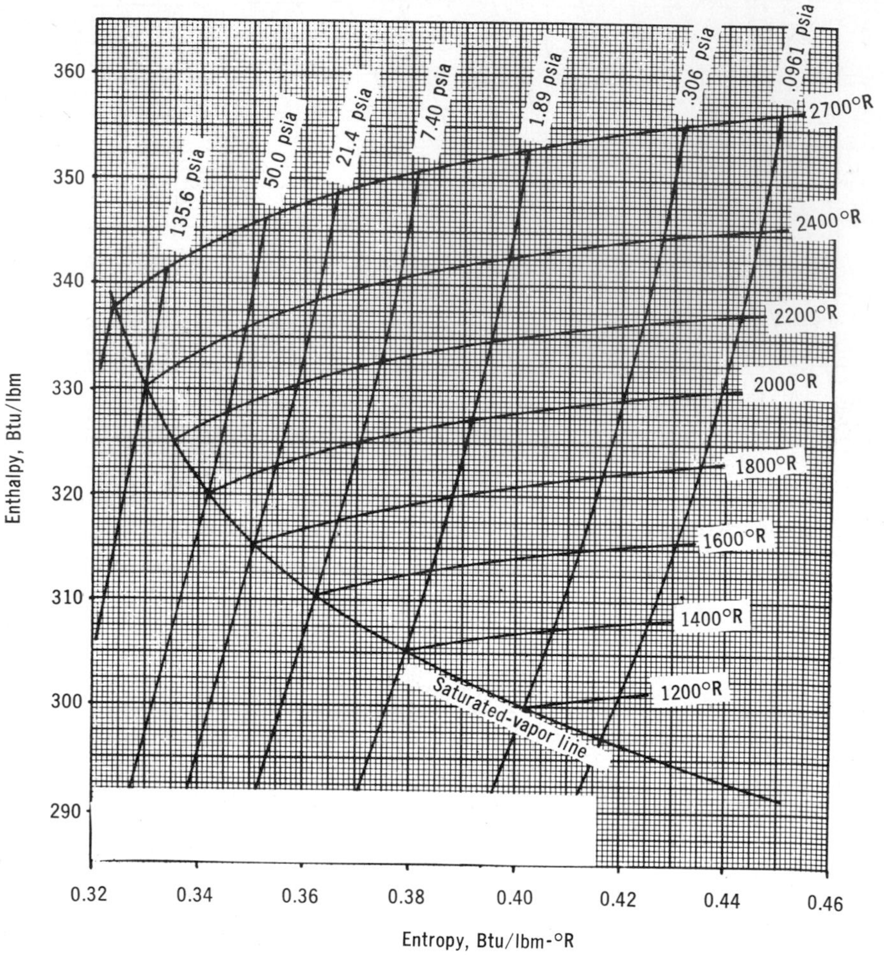

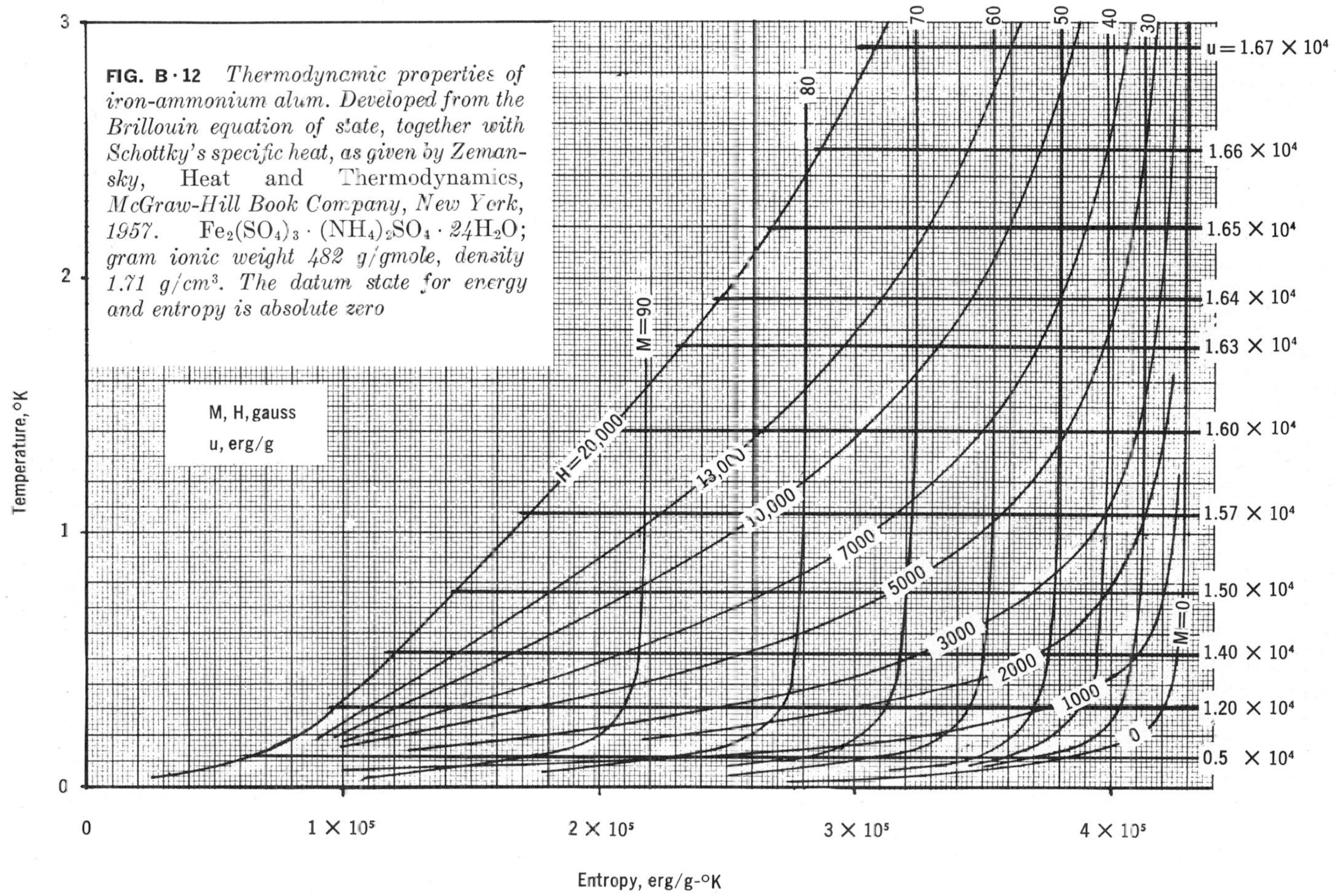

FIG. B·12 *Thermodynamic properties of iron-ammonium alum. Developed from the Brillouin equation of state, together with Schottky's specific heat, as given by Zemansky,* Heat and Thermodynamics, *McGraw-Hill Book Company, New York, 1957.* $Fe_2(SO_4)_3 \cdot (NH_4)_2SO_4 \cdot 24H_2O$; *gram ionic weight 482 g/gmole, density 1.71 g/cm*^{3}. *The datum state for energy and entropy is absolute zero*

FIG. B·13 *Psychrometric chart (for 1 atm pressure). Courtesy of the General Electric Company. Barometric pressure, 14.696 lbf/in.² (1 lbm = 7000 grains)*

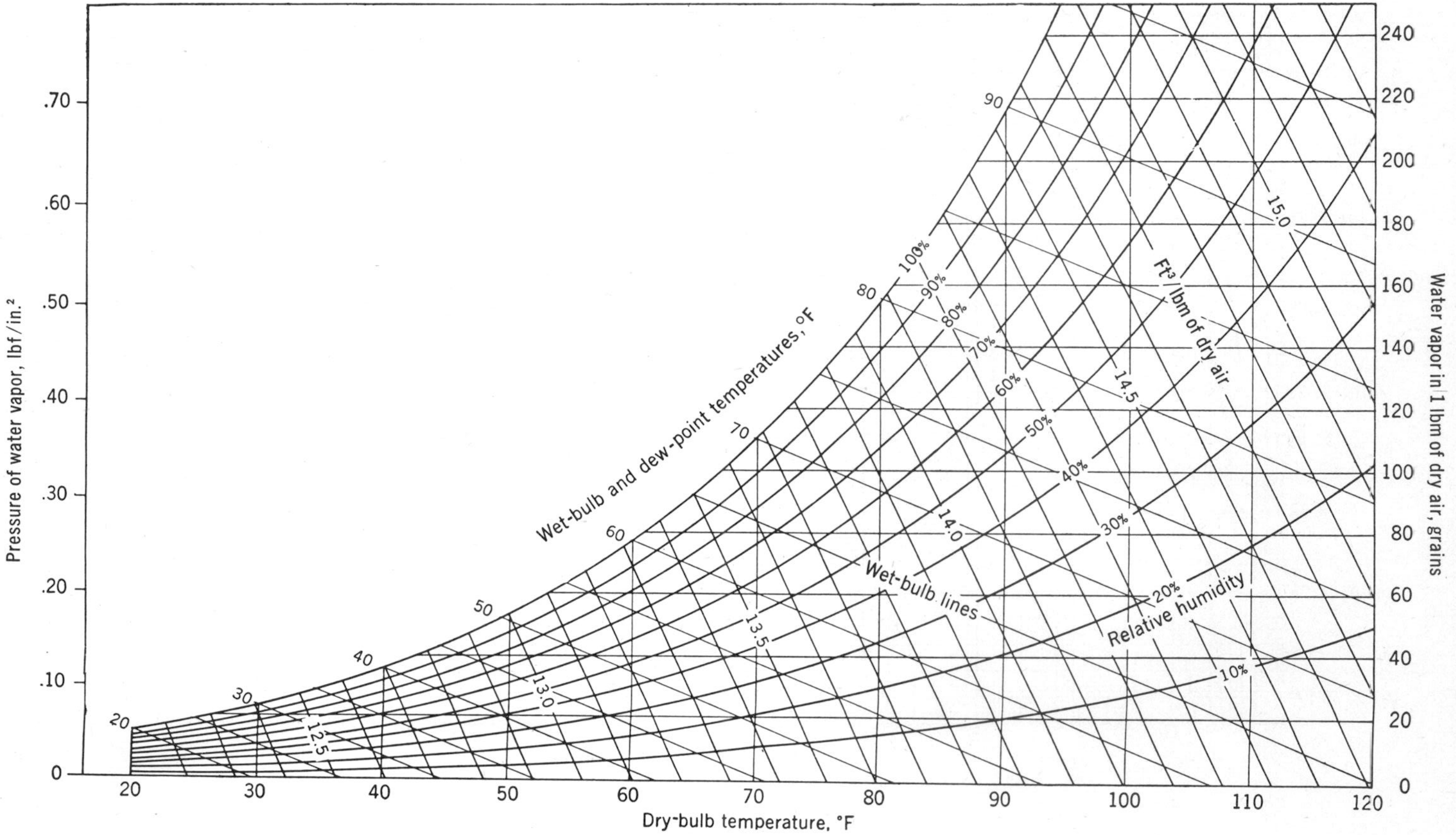

FIG. B·14a *Generalized compressibility chart—low-pressure range. Data from L. C. Nelson and E. F. Obert, Generalized Compressibility Charts,* Chem. En., *vol. [illegible]1, p. 203, 1954. Note:* $v/v_c \equiv P_c v/RT_c$

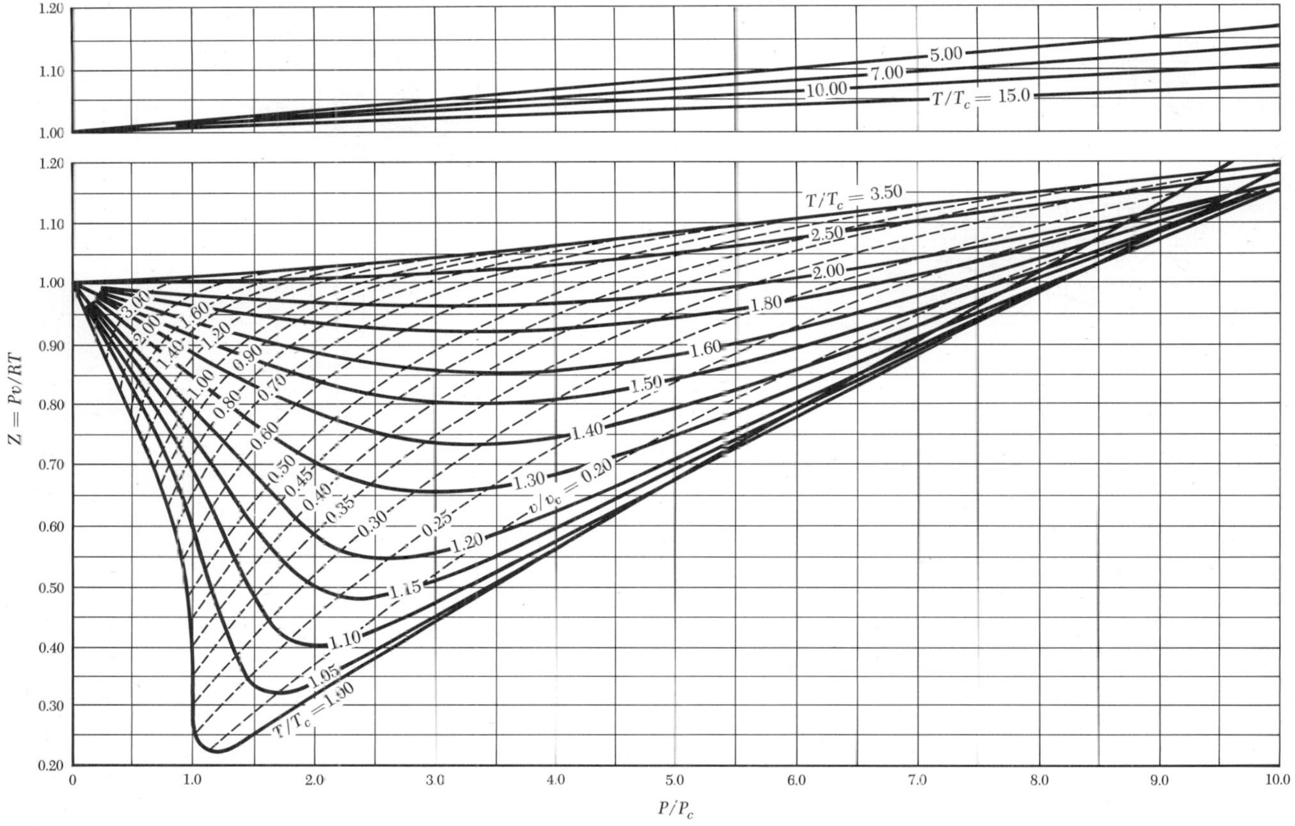

FIG. B·14b *Generalized compressibility chart—high-pressure range. Adapted from E. F. Obert,* Concepts of Thermodynamics, *McGraw-Hill Book Company, New York, 1960. Note:* $v/v_c \equiv P_c v/RT_c$

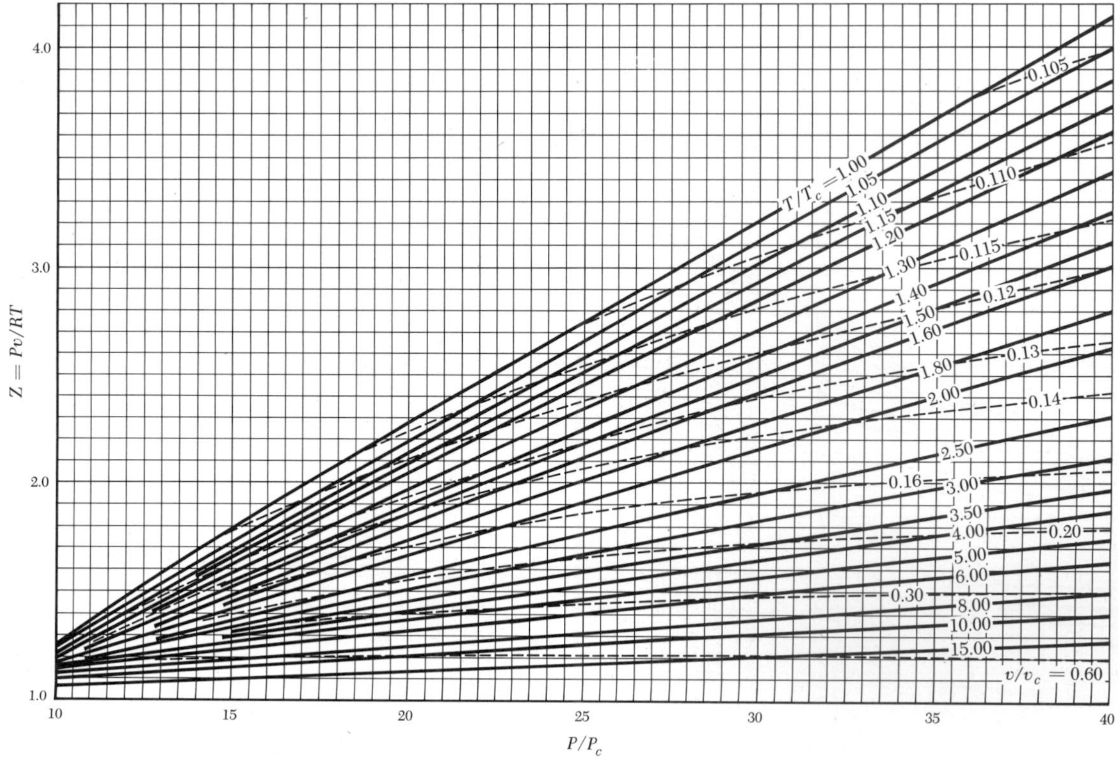

FIG. B·15 *Generalized enthalpy chart. Adapted from K. Wark,* Thermodynamics, *McGraw-Hill Book Company, New York, 1966*

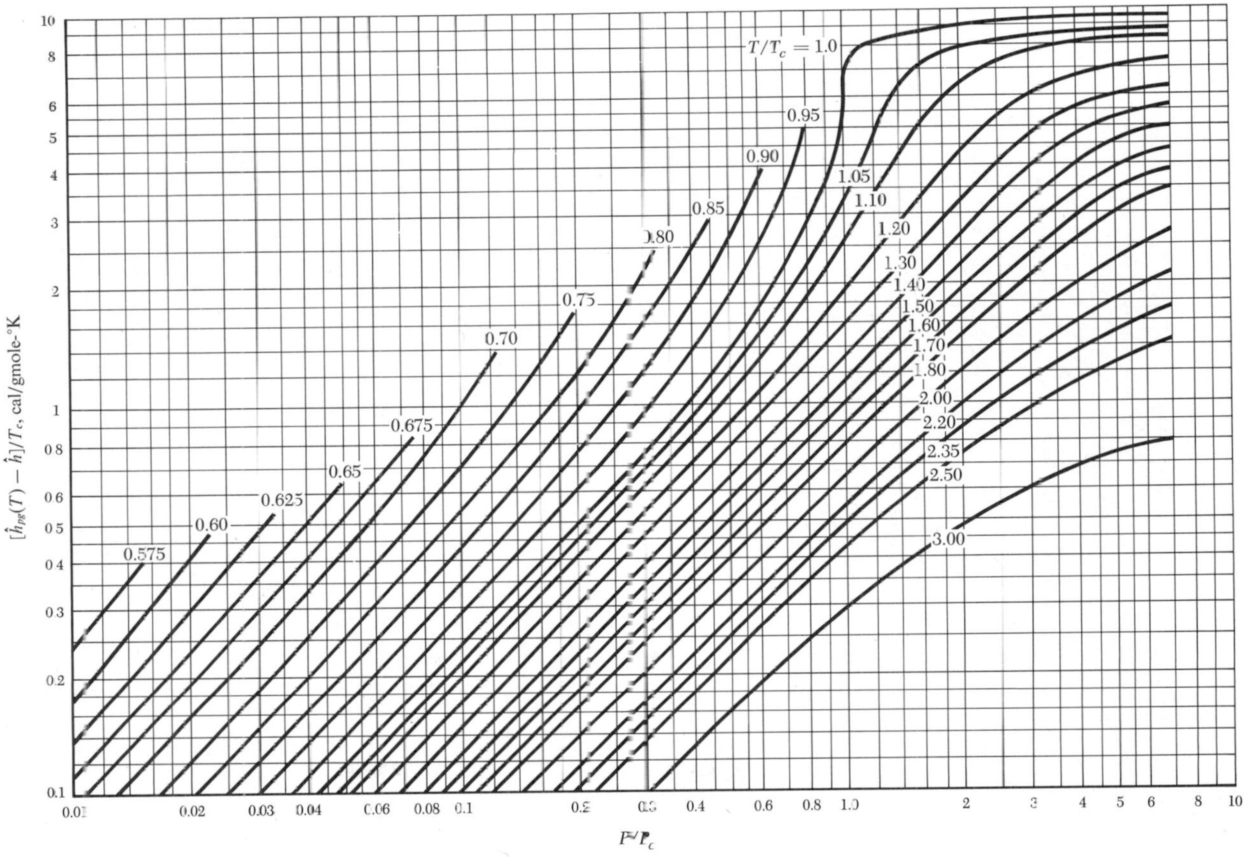

FIG. B·16 *Generalized entropy chart. Adapted from K. Wark,* Thermodynamics, *McGraw-Hill Book Company, New York, 1966*

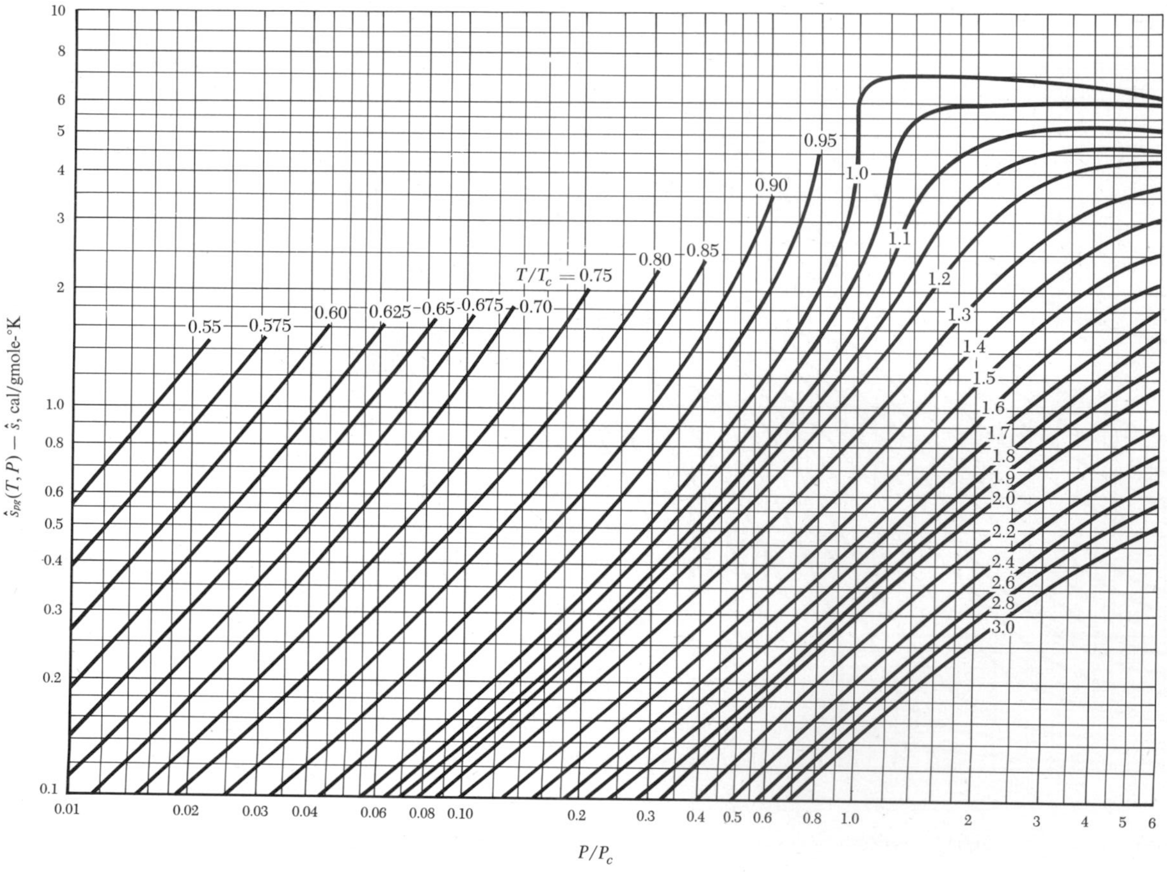

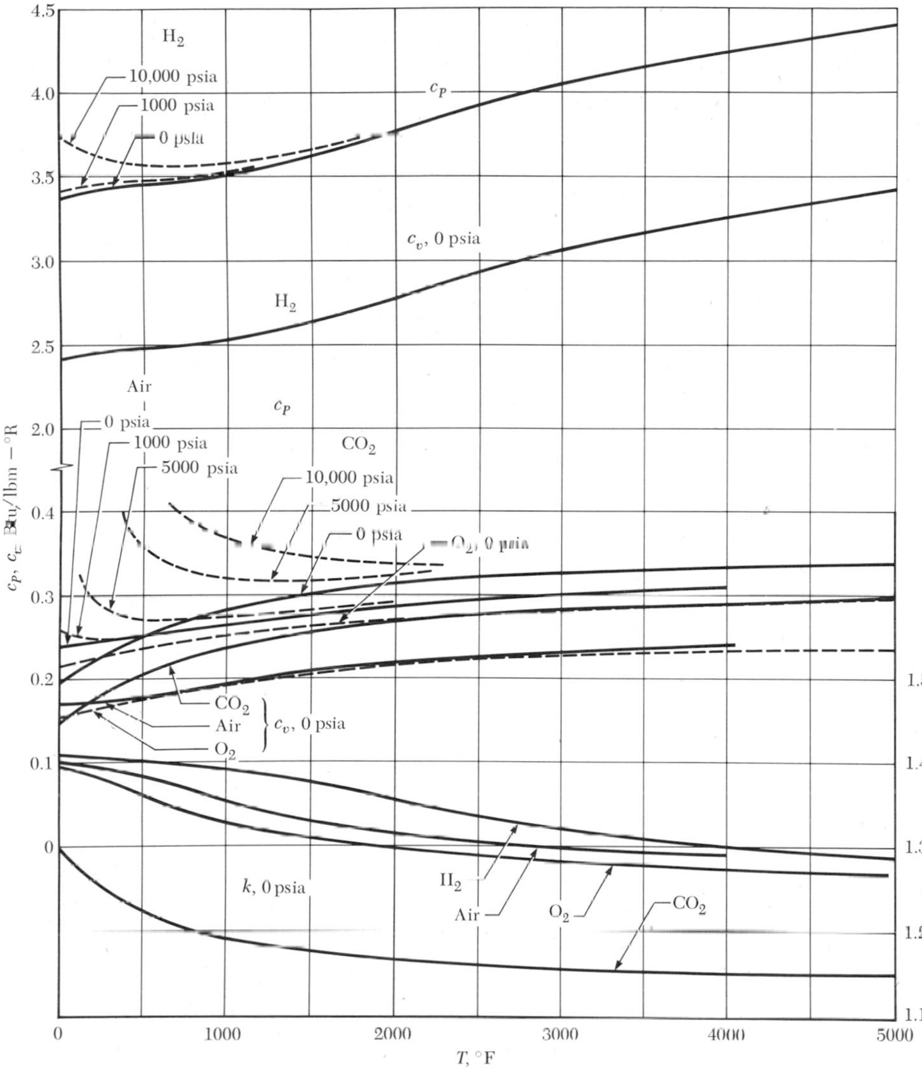

FIG. B·17 *Specific heats of selected gases. Data from National Bureau of Standards*

TABLE B·1A SATURATED H_2O: TEMPERATURE TABLE

Temp., °F	Abs. press., psia	Specific vol., ft³/lbm			Enthalpy, Btu/lbm			Entropy, Btu/lbm-°R		
		Sat. liq.	Evap.	Sat. vap.	Sat. liq.	Evap.	Sat. vap.	Sat. liq.	Evap.	Sat. vap.
T	P	v_f	v_{fg}	v_g	h_f	h_{fg}	h_g	s_f	s_{fg}	s_g
32	0.08854	0.01602	3306	3306	0.00	1075.8	1075.8	0.0000	2.1877	2.1877
35	0.09995	0.01602	2947	2947	3.02	1074.1	1077.1	0.0061	2.1709	2.1770
40	0.12170	0.01602	2444	2444	8.05	1071.3	1079.3	0.0162	2.1435	2.1597
45	0.14752	0.01602	2036.4	2036.4	13.06	1068.4	1081.5	0.0262	2.1167	2.1429
50	0.17811	0.01603	1703.2	1703.2	18.07	1065.6	1083.7	0.0361	2.0903	2.1264
60	0.2563	0.01604	1206.6	1206.7	28.06	1059.9	1088.0	0.0555	2.0393	2.0948
70	0.3631	0.01606	867.8	867.9	38.04	1054.3	1092.3	0.0745	1.9902	2.0647
80	0.5069	0.01608	633.1	633.1	48.02	1048.6	1096.6	0.0932	1.9428	2.0360
90	0.6982	0.01610	468.0	468.0	57.99	1042.9	1100.9	0.1115	1.8972	2.0087
100	0.9492	0.01613	350.3	350.4	67.97	1037.2	1105.2	0.1295	1.8531	1.9826
110	1.2748	0.01617	265.3	265.4	77.94	1031.6	1109.5	0.1471	1.8106	1.9577
120	1.6924	0.01620	203.25	203.27	87.92	1025.8	1113.7	0.1645	1.7694	1.9339
130	2.2225	0.01625	157.32	157.34	97.90	1020.0	1117.9	0.1816	1.7296	1.9112
140	2.8886	0.01629	122.99	123.01	107.89	1014.1	1122.0	0.1984	1.6910	1.8894
150	3.718	0.01634	97.06	97.07	117.89	1008.2	1126.1	0.2149	1.6537	1.8685
160	4.741	0.01639	77.27	77.29	127.89	1002.3	1130.2	0.2311	1.6174	1.8485
170	5.992	0.01645	62.04	62.06	137.90	996.3	1134.2	0.2472	1.5822	1.8293
180	7.510	0.01651	50.21	50.23	147.92	990.2	1138.1	0.2630	1.5480	1.8109
190	9.339	0.01657	40.94	40.96	157.95	984.1	1142.0	0.2785	1.5147	1.7932
200	11.526	0.01663	33.62	33.64	167.99	977.9	1145.9	0.2938	1.4824	1.7762

210	14.123	0.01670	27.80	27.82	178.05	971.6	1149.7	0.3090	1.4508	1.7598
212	14.696	0.01672	26.78	26.80	180.07	970.3	1150.4	0.3120	1.4446	1.7566
220	17.186	0.01677	23.13	23.15	188.13	965.2	1153.4	0.3239	1.4201	1.7440
230	20.780	0.01684	19.365	19.382	198.23	958.8	1157.0	0.3387	1.3901	1.7288
240	24.969	0.01692	16.306	16.323	208.34	952.2	1160.5	0.3531	1.3609	1.7140
250	29.825	0.01700	13.804	13.821	216.48	945.5	1164.0	0.3675	1.3323	1.6998
260	35.429	0.01709	11.746	11.763	228.64	938.7	1167.3	0.3817	1.3043	1.6860
270	41.858	0.01717	10.044	10.061	238.84	931.8	1170.6	0.3958	1.2769	1.6727
280	49.203	0.01726	8.628	8.645	249.06	924.7	1173.8	0.4096	1.2501	1.6597
290	57.556	0.01735	7.444	7.461	259.31	917.5	1176.8	0.4234	1.2238	1.6472
300	67.013	0.01745	6.449	6.466	269.59	910.1	1179.7	0.4369	1.1980	1.6350
310	77.68	0.01755	5.609	5.626	279.92	902.6	1182.5	0.4504	1.1727	1.6231
320	89.66	0.01765	4.896	4.914	290.28	894.9	1185.2	0.4637	1.1478	1.6115
330	103.06	0.01776	4.289	4.307	300.68	887.0	1187.7	0.4769	1.1233	1.6002
340	118.01	0.01787	3.770	3.788	311.13	879.0	1190.1	0.4900	1.0992	1.5891
350	134.63	0.01799	3.324	3.342	321.63	870.7	1192.3	0.5029	1.0754	1.5783
360	153.04	0.01811	2.939	2.957	332.18	862.2	1194.4	0.5158	1.0519	1.5677
370	173.37	0.01823	2.606	2.625	342.79	853.5	1196.3	0.5286	1.0287	1.5573
380	195.77	0.01836	2.317	2.335	353.45	844.6	1198.1	0.5413	1.0059	1.5471
390	220.37	0.01850	2.0651	2.0836	364.17	835.4	1199.6	0.5539	0.9832	1.5371
400	247.31	0.01864	1.8447	1.8633	374.97	826.0	1201.0	0.5664	0.9608	1.5272
410	276.75	0.01878	1.6512	1.6700	385.83	816.3	1202.1	0.5788	0.9386	1.5174
420	308.83	0.01894	1.4811	1.5000	396.77	806.3	1203.1	0.5912	0.9166	1.5078
430	343.72	0.01910	1.3308	1.3499	407.79	796.0	1203.8	0.6035	0.8947	1.4982
440	381.59	0.01926	1.1979	1.2171	418.90	785.4	1204.3	0.6158	0.8730	1.4887

TABLE B·1A SATURATED H_2O: TEMPERATURE TABLE (CONTINUED)

Temp., °F	*Abs. press., psia*	*Specific vol., ft³/lbm*			*Enthalpy, Btu/lbm*			*Entropy, Btu/lbm-°R*		
		Sat. liq.	*Evap.*	*Sat. vap.*	*Sat. liq.*	*Evap.*	*Sat. vap.*	*Sat. liq.*	*Evap.*	*Sat. vap.*
T	P	v_f	v_{fg}	v_g	h_f	h_{fg}	h_g	s_f	s_{fg}	s_g
450	422.6	0.0194	1.0799	1.0993	430.1	774.5	1204.6	0.6280	0.8513	1.4793
460	466.9	0.0196	0.9748	0.9944	441.4	763.2	1204.6	0.6402	0.8298	1.4700
470	514.7	0.0198	0.8811	0.9009	452.8	751.5	1204.3	0.6523	0.8083	1.4606
480	566.1	0.0200	0.7972	0.8172	464.4	739.4	1203.7	0.6645	0.7868	1.4513
490	621.4	0.0202	0.7221	0.7423	476.0	726.8	1202.8	0.6766	0.7653	1.4419
500	680.8	0.0204	0.6545	0.6749	487.8	713.9	1201.7	0.6887	0.7438	1.4325
520	812.4	0.0209	0.5385	0.5594	511.9	686.4	1198.2	0.7130	0.7006	1.4136
540	962.5	0.0215	0.4434	0.4649	536.6	656.6	1193.2	0.7374	0.6568	1.3942
560	1133.1	0.0221	0.3647	0.3868	562.2	624.2	1186.4	0.7621	0.6121	1.3742
580	1325.8	0.0228	0.2989	0.3217	588.9	588.4	1177.3	0.7872	0.5659	1.3532
600	1542.9	0.0236	0.2432	0.2668	617.0	548.5	1165.5	0.8131	0.5176	1.3307
620	1786.6	0.0247	0.1955	0.2201	646.7	503.6	1150.3	0.8398	0.4664	1.3062
640	2059.7	0.0260	0.1538	0.1798	678.6	452.0	1130.5	0.8679	0.4110	1.2789
660	2365.4	0.0278	0.1165	0.1442	714.2	390.2	1104.4	0.8987	0.3485	1.2472
680	2708.1	0.0305	0.0810	0.1115	757.3	309.9	1067.2	0.9351	0.2719	1.2071
700	3093.7	0.0369	0.0392	0.0761	823.3	172.1	995.4	0.9905	0.1484	1.1389
705.4	3206.2	0.0503	0	0.0503	902.7	0	902.7	1.0580	0	1.0580

Abridged from Joseph H. Keenan and Frederick G. Keyes, *Thermodynamic Properties of Steam,* John Wiley & Sons, Inc., New York, 1937. By permission of the authors.

TABLE B·1B SATURATED H_2O: PRESSURE TABLE

Abs. press., psia	Temp., °F	Specific vol., ft³/lbm		Enthalpy, Btu/lbm			Entropy, Btu/lbm-°R			Internal energy, Btu/lbm	
		Sat. liq.	Sat. vap.	Sat. liq.	Evap.	Sat. vap.	Sat. liq.	Evap.	Sat. vap.	Sat. liq.	Sat. vap.
P	T	v_f	v_g	h_f	h_{fg}	h	s_f	s_{fg}	s_g	u_f	u_g
1.0	101.74	0.01614	333.6	69.70	1036.3	1106.0	0.1326	1.8456	1.9782	69.70	1044.3
2.0	126.08	0.01623	173.73	93.99	1022.2	1116.2	0.1749	1.7451	1.9200	93.98	1051.9
3.0	141.48	0.01630	118.71	109.37	1013.2	1122.6	0.2008	1.6855	1.8863	109.36	1056.7
4.0	152.97	0.01636	90.63	120.86	1006.4	1127.3	0.2198	1.6427	1.8625	120.85	1060.2
5.0	162.24	0.01640	73.52	130.13	1001.0	[illegible]	0.2347	1.6094	1.8441	130.12	1063.1
6.0	170.06	0.01645	61.98	137.96	996.2	1134.2	0.2472	1.5820	1.8292	137.94	1065.4
7.0	176.85	0.01649	53.64	144.76	992.1	1136.9	0.2581	1.5586	1.8167	144.74	1067.4
8.0	182.86	0.01653	47.34	150.79	988.5	1139.3	0.2674	1.5383	1.8057	150.77	1069.2
9.0	188.28	0.01656	42.40	156.22	985.2	[illegible]	0.2759	1.5203	1.7962	156.19	1070.8
10	193.21	0.01659	38.42	161.17	982.1	1143.3	0.2835	1.5041	1.7876	161.14	1072.2
14.696	212.00	0.01672	26.80	180.07	970.3	1150.4	0.3120	1.4446	1.7566	180.02	1077.5
15	213.03	0.01672	26.29	181.11	969.7	1150.8	0.3135	1.4415	1.7549	181.06	1077.8
20	227.96	0.01683	20.089	196.16	960.1	1156.3	0.3356	1.3962	1.7319	196.10	1081.9
25	240.07	0.01692	16.303	208.42	952.1	1160.6	0.3533	1.3606	1.7139	208.34	1085.1
30	250.33	0.01701	13.746	218.82	945.3	1164.1	0.3680	1.3313	1.6993	218.73	1087.8
35	259.28	0.01708	11.898	227.91	939.2	1167.1	0.3807	1.3063	1.6870	227.80	1090.1
40	267.25	0.01715	10.498	236.03	933.7	1169.7	0.3919	1.2844	1.6763	235.90	1092.0
45	274.44	0.01721	9.401	243.36	928.6	1172.0	0.4019	1.2650	1.6669	243.22	1093.7
50	281.01	0.01727	8.515	250.09	924.0	1174.1	0.4110	1.2474	1.6585	249.93	1095.3
55	287.07	0.01732	7.787	256.30	919.6	1175.9	0.4193	1.2316	1.6509	256.12	1096.7
60	292.71	0.01738	7.175	262.09	915.5	1177.6	0.4270	1.2168	1.6438	261.90	1097.9
65	297.97	0.01743	6.655	267.50	911.6	1179.1	0.4342	1.2032	1.6374	267.29	1099.1

TABLE B·1B SATURATED H_2O: PRESSURE TABLE (CONTINUED)

Abs. press., psia	Temp., °F	Specific vol., ft³/lbm		Enthalpy, Btu/lbm			Entropy, Btu/lbm-°R			Internal energy, Btu/lbm	
		Sat. liq.	Sat. vap.	Sat. liq.	Evap.	Sat. vap.	Sat. liq.	Evap.	Sat. vap.	Sat. liq.	Sat. vap.
P	T	v_f	v_g	h_f	h_{fg}	h_g	s_f	s_{fg}	s_g	u_f	u_g
70	302.92	0.01748	6.206	272.61	907.9	1180.6	0.4409	1.1906	1.6315	272.38	1100.2
75	307.60	0.01753	5.816	277.43	904.5	1181.9	0.4472	1.1787	1.6259	277.19	1101.2
80	312.03	0.01757	5.472	282.02	901.1	1183.1	0.4531	1.1676	1.6207	281.76	1102.1
85	316.25	0.01761	5.168	286.39	897.8	1184.2	0.4587	1.1571	1.6158	286.11	1102.9
90	320.27	0.01766	4.896	290.56	894.7	1185.3	0.4641	1.1471	1.6112	290.27	1103.7
95	324.12	0.01770	4.652	294.56	891.7	1186.2	0.4692	1.1376	1.6068	294.25	1104.5
100	327.81	0.01774	4.432	298.40	888.8	1187.2	0.4740	1.1286	1.6026	298.08	1105.2
110	334.77	0.01782	4.049	305.66	883.2	1188.9	0.4832	1.1117	1.5948	305.30	1106.5
120	341.25	0.01789	3.728	312.44	877.9	1190.4	0.4916	1.0962	1.5878	312.05	1107.6
130	347.32	0.01796	3.455	318.81	872.9	1191.7	0.4995	1.0817	1.5812	318.38	1108.6
140	353.02	0.01802	3.220	324.82	868.2	1193.0	0.5069	1.0682	1.5751	324.35	1109.6
150	358.42	0.01809	3.015	330.51	863.6	1194.1	0.5138	1.0556	1.5694	330.01	1110.5
160	363.53	0.01815	2.834	335.93	859.2	1195.1	0.5204	1.0436	1.5640	335.39	1111.2
170	368.41	0.01822	2.675	341.09	854.9	1196.0	0.5266	1.0324	1.5590	340.52	1111.9
180	373.06	0.01827	2.532	346.03	850.8	1196.9	0.5325	1.0217	1.5542	345.42	1112.5
190	377.51	0.01833	2.404	350.79	846.8	1197.6	0.5381	1.0116	1.5497	350.15	1113.1
200	381.79	0.01839	2.288	355.36	843.0	1198.4	0.5435	1.0018	1.5453	354.68	1113.7
250	400.95	0.01865	1.8438	376.00	825.1	1201.1	0.5675	0.9588	1.5263	375.14	1115.8
300	417.33	0.01890	1.5433	393.84	809.0	1202.8	0.5879	0.9225	1.5104	392.79	1117.1
350	431.72	0.01913	1.3260	409.69	794.2	1203.9	0.6056	0.8910	1.4966	408.45	1118.0
400	444.59	0.0193	1.1613	424.0	780.5	1204.5	0.6214	0.8630	1.4844	422.6	1118.5
450	456.28	0.0195	1.0320	437.2	767.4	1204.6	0.6356	0.8378	1.4734	435.5	1118.7
500	467.01	0.0197	0.9278	449.4	755.0	1204.4	0.6487	0.8147	1.4634	447.6	1118.6

550	476.94	0.0199	0.8424	460.8	743.1	120[illegible].9	0.6608	0.7934	1.4542	458.8	1118.2
600	486.21	0.0201	0.7698	471.6	731.6	120[illegible].2	0.6720	0.7734	1.4454	469.4	1117.7
650	494.90	0.0203	0.7083	481.8	720.5	120[illegible].3	0.6826	0.7548	1.4374	479.4	1117.1
700	503.10	0.0205	0.6554	491.5	709.7	120[illegible].2	0.6925	0.7371	1.4296	488.8	1116.3
750	510.86	0.0207	0.6092	500.8	699.2	1200.0	0.7019	0.7204	1.4223	498.0	1115.4
800	518.23	0.0209	0.5687	509.7	688.9	119[illegible].6	0.7108	0.7045	1.4153	506.6	1114.4
850	525.26	0.0210	0.5327	518.3	678.8	119[illegible].1	0.7194	0.6891	1.4085	515.0	1113.3
900	531.98	0.0212	0.5006	526.6	668.8	119[illegible].4	0.7275	0.6744	1.4020	523.1	1112.1
950	538.43	0.0214	0.4717	534.6	659.1	119[illegible].7	0.7355	0.6602	1.3957	530.9	1110.8
1000	544.61	0.0216	0.4456	542.4	649.4	119[illegible].8	0.7430	0.6467	1.3897	538.4	1109.4
1100	556.31	0.0220	0.4001	557.4	630.4	118[illegible].8	0.7575	0.6205	1.3780	552.9	1106.4
1200	567.22	0.0223	0.3619	571.7	611.7	118[illegible].4	0.7711	0.5956	1.3667	566.7	1103.0
1300	577.46	0.0227	0.3293	585.4	593.2	1178.6	0.7840	0.5719	1.3559	580.0	1099.4
1400	587.10	0.0231	0.3012	598.7	574.7	117[illegible].4	0.7963	0.5491	1.3454	592.7	1095.4
1500	596.23	0.0235	0.2765	611.6	556.3	116[illegible].9	0.8082	0.5269	1.3351	605.1	1091.2
2000	635.82	0.0257	0.1878	671.7	463.4	1135.1	0.8619	0.4230	1.2849	662.2	1065.5
2500	668.13	0.0287	0.1307	730.6	360.5	109[illegible].1	0.9126	0.3197	1.2322	717.3	1030.6
3000	695.36	0.0346	0.0858	802.5	217.8	1020.3	0.9731	0.1885	1.1615	783.4	972.7
3206.2	705.40	0.0503	0.0503	902.7	0	90[illegible].7	1.0580	0	1.0580	872.9	872.9

Abridged from Joseph H. Keenan and Frederick G. Keyes, *Thermodynamic Properties of Steam*, John Wiley & Sons, Inc., New York, 1937. By permission of the authors.

TABLE B·2 PROPERTIES OF SUPERHEATED STEAM

Abs. press., psia (sat. temp.)		*Temperature, °F*												
		200	*300*	*400*	*500*	*600*	*700*	*800*	*900*	*1000*	*1100*	*1200*	*1400*	*1600*
	v, ft³/lbm	392.6	452.3	512.0	571.6	631.2	690.8	750.4	809.9	869.5	929.1	988.7	1107.8	1227.0
1	*h*, Btu/lbm	1150.4	1195.8	1241.7	1288.3	1335.7	1383.8	1432.8	1482.7	1533.5	1585.2	1637.7	1745.7	1857.5
(101.74)	*s*, Btu/lbm-°R	2.0512	2.1153	2.1720	2.2233	2.2702	2.3137	2.3542	2.3923	2.4283	2.4625	2.4952	2.5566	2.6137
	v, ft³/lbm	78.16	90.25	102.26	114.22	126.16	138.10	150.03	161.95	173.87	185.79	197.71	221.6	245.4
5	*h*, Btu/lbm	1148.8	1195.0	1241.2	1288.0	1335.3	1383.6	1432.7	1482.6	1533.4	1585.1	1637.7	1745.7	1857.4
(162.24)	*s*, Btu/lbm-°R	1.8718	1.9370	1.9942	2.0456	2.0927	2.1361	2.1767	2.2148	2.2509	2.2851	2.3178	2.3792	2.4363
	v, ft³/lbm	38.85	45.00	51.04	57.05	63.03	69.01	74.98	80.95	86.92	92.88	98.84	110.77	122.69
10	*h*, Btu/lbm	1146.6	1193.9	1240.6	1287.5	1335.1	1383.4	1432.5	1482.4	1533.2	1585.0	1637.6	1745.6	1857.3
(193.21)	*s*, Btu/lbm-°R	1.7927	1.8595	1.9172	1.9689	2.0160	2.0596	2.1002	2.1383	2.1744	2.2086	2.2413	2.3028	2.3598
	v, ft³/lbm	...	30.53	34.68	38.78	42.86	46.94	51.00	55.07	59.13	63.19	67.25	75.37	83.48
14.696	*h*, Btu/lbm	...	1192.8	1239.9	1287.1	1334.8	1383.2	1432.3	1482.3	1533.1	1584.8	1637.5	1745.5	1857.3
(212.00)	*s*, Btu/lbm-°R	...	1.8160	1.8743	1.9261	1.9734	2.0170	2.0576	2.0958	2.1319	2.1662	2.1989	2.2603	2.3174
	v, ft³/lbm	...	22.36	25.43	28.46	31.47	34.47	37.46	40.45	43.44	46.42	49.41	55.37	61.34
20	*h*, Btu/lbm	...	1191.6	1239.2	1286.6	1334.4	1382.9	1432.1	1482.1	1533.0	1584.7	1637.4	1745.4	1857.2
(227.96)	*s*, Btu/lbm-°R	...	1.7808	1.8396	1.8918	1.9392	1.9829	2.0235	2.0618	2.0978	2.1321	2.1648	2.2263	2.2834
	v, ft³/lbm	...	11.040	12.628	14.168	15.688	17.198	18.702	20.20	21.70	23.20	24.69	27.68	30.66
40	*h*, Btu/lbm	...	1186.8	1236.5	1284.8	1333.1	1381.9	1431.3	1481.4	1532.4	1584.3	1637.0	1745.1	1857.0
(267.25)	*s*, Btu/lbm-°R	...	1.6994	1.7608	1.8140	1.8619	1.9058	1.9467	1.9850	2.0212	2.0555	2.0883	2.1498	2.2069
	v, ft³/lbm	...	7.259	8.357	9.403	10.427	11.441	12.449	13.452	14.454	15.453	16.451	18.446	20.44
60	*h*, Btu/lbm	...	1181.6	1233.6	1283.0	1331.8	1380.9	1430.5	1480.8	1531.9	1583.8	1636.6	1744.8	1856.7
(292.71)	*s*, Btu/lbm-°R	...	1.6492	1.7135	1.7678	1.8162	1.8605	1.9015	1.9400	1.9762	2.0106	2.0434	2.1049	2.1621

	v, ft³/lbm	...	...	6.220	7.020	7.797	8.562	9.322	10.077	10.830	11.582	12.332	13.830	15.325
80	h, Btu/lbm	...	...	1230.7	1281.1	1330.5	1379.9	1429.7	1480.1	1531.3	1583.4	1633.2	1744.5	1856.5
(312.03)	s, Btu/lbm-°R	...	...	1.6791	1.7346	1.7836	1.8281	1.8694	1.9079	1.9442	1.9787	2.0115	2.0731	2.1303
	v, ft³/lbm	...	...	4.937	5.589	6.218	6.835	7.446	8.052	8.656	9.259	9.860	11.060	12.258
100	h, Btu/lbm	...	...	1227.6	1279.1	1329.1	1378.9	1428.9	1479.5	1530.8	1582.9	1635.7	1744.2	1856.2
(327.81)	s, Btu/lbm-°R	...	...	1.6518	1.7085	1.7581	1.8029	1.8443	1.8829	1.9193	1.9538	1.9867	2.0484	2.1056
	v, ft³/lbm	...	...	4.081	4.636	5.165	5.683	6.195	6.702	7.207	7.710	8.212	9.214	10.213
120	h, Btu/lbm	...	...	1224.4	1277.2	1327.7	1377.8	1428.1	1478.8	1530.2	1582.4	1635.3	1743.9	1856.0
(341.25)	s, Btu/lbm-°R	...	...	1.6287	1.6869	1.7370	1.7822	1.8237	1.8625	1.8990	1.9335	1.9664	2.0281	2.0854
	v, ft³/lbm	...	...	3.468	3.954	4.413	4.861	5.301	5.738	6.172	6.604	7.035	7.895	8.752
140	h, Btu/lbm	...	...	1221.5	1275.2	1326.4	1376.8	1427.3	1478.2	1529.7	1581.9	1634.9	1743.5	1855.7
(353.02)	s, Btu/lbm-°R	...	...	1.6087	1.6683	1.7190	1.7645	1.8063	1.8451	1.8817	1.9163	1.9493	2.0110	2.0683
	v, ft³/lbm	...	...	3.008	3.443	3.849	4.244	4.631	5.015	5.396	5.775	6.152	6.906	7.656
160	h, Btu/lbm	...	...	1217.6	1273.1	1325.0	1375.7	1426.4	1477.5	1529.1	1581.4	1634.5	1743.2	1855.5
(363.53)	s, Btu/lbm-°R	...	...	1.5908	1.6519	1.7033	1.7491	1.7911	1.8301	1.8667	1.9014	1.9344	1.9962	2.0535
	v, ft³/lbm	...	...	2.649	3.044	3.411	3.764	4.110	4.452	4.792	5.129	5.466	6.136	6.804
180	h, Btu/lbm	...	...	1214.0	1271.0	1323.5	1374.7	1425.6	1476.8	1528.6	1581.0	1634.1	1742.9	1855.2
(373.06)	s, Btu/lbm-°R	...	...	1.5745	1.6373	1.6894	1.7355	1.7776	1.8167	1.8534	1.8882	1.9212	1.9831	2.0404
	v, ft³/lbm	...	...	2.361	2.726	3.060	3.380	3.693	4.002	4.309	4.613	4.917	5.521	6.123
200	h, Btu/lbm	...	...	1210.3	1268.9	1322.1	1373.6	1424.8	1476.2	1528.0	1580.5	1633.7	1742.6	1855.0
(381.79)	s, Btu/lbm-°R	...	...	1.5594	1.6240	1.6767	1.7232	1.7655	1.8048	1.8415	1.8763	1.9094	1.9713	2.0287
	v, ft³/lbm	...	...	2.125	2.465	2.772	3.066	3.352	3.634	3.913	4.191	4.467	5.017	5.565
220	h, Btu/lbm	...	...	1206.5	1266.7	1320.7	1372.6	1424.0	1475.5	1527.5	1580.0	1633.3	1742.3	1854.7
(389.86)	s, Btu/lbm-°R	...	...	1.5453	1.6117	1.6652	1.7120	1.7545	1.7939	1.8308	1.8656	1.8987	1.9607	2.0181

Properties of superheated steam

TABLE B·1B ~~SATURATED H_2O: PRESSURE TABLE (CONTINUED)~~

Abs. press., psia (sat. temp.)		Temperature, °F												
		200	*300*	*400*	*500*	*600*	*700*	*800*	*900*	*1000*	*1100*	*1200*	*1400*	*1600*
	v, ft³/lbm	...	...	1.9276	2.247	2.533	2.804	3.068	3.327	3.584	3.839	4.093	4.597	5.100
240	h, Btu/lbm	...	...	1202.5	1264.5	1319.2	1371.5	1423.2	1474.8	1526.9	1579.6	1632.9	1742.0	1854.5
(397.37)	s, Btu/lbm-°R	...	...	1.5319	1.6003	1.6546	1.7017	1.7444	1.7839	1.8209	1.8558	1.8889	1.9510	2.0084
	v, ft³/lbm	...	...	...	2.063	2.330	2.582	2.827	3.067	3.305	3.541	3.776	4.242	4.707
260	h, Btu/lbm	...	...	...	1262.3	1317.7	1370.4	1422.3	1474.2	1526.3	1579.1	1632.5	1741.7	1854.2
(404.42)	s, Btu/lbm-°R	...	..	...	1.5897	1.6447	1.6922	1.7352	1.7748	1.8118	1.8467	1.8799	1.9420	1.9995
	v, ft³/lbm	...	...	...	1.9047	2.156	2.392	2.621	2.845	3.066	3.286	3.504	3.938	4.370
280	h, Btu/lbm	...	...	...	1260.0	1316.2	1369.4	1421.5	1473.5	1525.8	1578.6	1632.1	1741.4	1854.0
(411.05)	s, Btu/lbm-°R	...	...	...	1.5796	1.6354	1.6834	1.7265	1.7662	1.8033	1.8383	1.8716	1.9337	1.9912
	v, ft³/lbm	...	...	...	1.7675	2.005	2.227	2.442	2.652	2.859	3.065	3.269	3.674	4.078
300	h, Btu/lbm	...	...	...	1257.6	1314.7	1368.3	1420.6	1472.8	1525.2	1578.1	1631.7	1741.0	1853.7
(417.33)	s, Btu/lbm-°R	...	...	...	1.5701	1.6268	1.6751	1.7184	1.7582	1.7954	1.8305	1.8638	1.9260	1.9835
	v, ft³/lbm	...	...	...	1.4923	1.7036	1.8980	2.084	2.266	2.445	2.622	2.798	3.147	3.493
350	h, Btu/lbm	...	...	...	1251.5	1310.9	1365.5	1418.5	1471.1	1523.8	1577.0	1630.7	1740.3	1853.1
(431.72)	s, Btu/lbm-°R	...	..	...	1.5481	1.6070	1.6563	1.7002	1.7403	1.7777	1.8130	1.8463	1.9086	1.9663
	v, ft³/lbm	...	...	...	1.2851	1.4770	1.6508	1.8161	1.9767	2.134	2.290	2.445	2.751	3.055
400	h, Btu/lbm	...	...	...	1245.1	1306.9	1362.7	1416.4	1469.4	1522.4	1575.8	1629.6	1739.5	1852.5
(444.59)	s, Btu/lbm-°R	...	...	...	1.5281	1.5894	1.6398	1.6842	1.7247	1.7623	1.7977	1.8311	1.8936	1.9513

Abs. press., psia (sat. temp.)		Temperature, °F													
		500	550	600	620	640	660	680	700	800	900	1000	1200	1400	1600
	v, ft³/lbm	1.1231	1.2155	1.3005	1.3332	1.3652	1.3967	1.4278	1.4584	1.6074	1.7516	1.8929	2.170	2.443	2.714
450	h, Btu/lbm	1238.4	1272.0	1302.8	1314.6	1326.2	1337.5	1348.8	1359.9	1414.3	1467.7	1521.0	1628.6	1738.7	1851.9
(456.28)	s, Btu/lbm-°R	1.5095	1.5437	1.5735	1.5845	1.5951	1.6054	1.6153	1.6250	1.6699	1.7108	1.7486	1.8177	1.8803	1.9381
	v, ft³/lbm	0.9927	1.0800	1.1591	1.1893	1.2188	1.2478	1.2763	1.3044	1.4405	1.5715	1.6996	1.9504	2.197	2.442
500	h, Btu/lbm	1231.3	1266.8	1298.6	1310.7	1322.6	1334.2	1345.7	1357.0	1412.1	1466.0	1519.6	1627.6	1737.9	1851.3
(467.01)	s, Btu/lbm-°R	1.4919	1.5280	1.5588	1.5701	1.5810	1.5915	1.60[illegible]6	1.6115	1.6571	1.6982	1.7363	1.8056	1.8683	1.9262
	v, ft³/lbm	0.8852	0.9686	1.0431	1.0714	1.0989	1.1259	1.1523	1.1783	1.3038	1.4241	1.5414	1.7706	1.9957	2.219
550	h, Btu/lbm	1223.7	1261.2	1294.3	1306.8	1318.9	1330.8	1342.5	1354.0	1409.9	1464.3	1518.2	1626.6	1737.1	1850.6
(476.94)	s, Btu/lbm-R°	1.4751	1.5131	1.5451	1.5568	1.5680	1.5787	1.5890	1.5991	1.6452	1.6868	1.7250	1.7946	1.8575	1.9155
	v, ft³/lbm	0.7947	0.8753	0.9463	0.9729	0.9988	1.0241	1.0489	1.0732	1.1899	1.3013	1.4096	1.6208	1.8279	2.033
600	h, Btu/lbm	1215.7	1255.5	1289.9	1302.7	1315.2	1327.4	1339.3	1351.1	1407.7	1462.5	1516.7	1625.5	1736.3	1850.0
(486.21)	s, Btu/lbm-°R	1.4586	1.4990	1.5323	1.5443	1.5558	1.5667	1.5773	1.5875	1.6343	1.6762	1.7147	1.7846	1.8476	1.9056
	v, ft³/lbm	...	0.7277	0.7934	0.8177	0.8411	0.8639	0.8860	0.9077	1.0108	1.1082	1.2024	1.3853	1.5641	1.7405
700	h, Btu/lbm	...	1243.2	1280.6	1294.3	1307.5	1320.3	1332.8	1345.0	1403.2	1459.0	1513.9	1623.5	1734.8	1848.8
(503.10)	s, Btu/lbm-°R	...	1.4722	1.5084	1.5212	1.5333	1.5449	1.5559	1.5665	1.6147	1.6573	1.6963	1.7666	1.8299	1.8881
	v, ft³/lbm	...	0.6154	0.6779	0.7006	0.7223	0.7433	0.7635	0.7833	0.8763	0.9633	1.0470	1.2088	1.3662	1.5214
800	h, Btu/lbm	...	1229.8	1270.7	1285.4	1299.4	1312.9	1325.9	1338.6	1398.6	1455.4	1511.0	1621.4	1733.2	1847.5
(518.23)	s, Btu/lbm-°R	...	1.4467	1.4863	1.5000	1.5129	1.5250	1.5366	1.5476	1.5972	1.6407	1.6801	1.7510	1.8146	1.8729
	v, ft³/lbm	...	0.5264	0.5873	0.6089	0.6294	0.6491	0.6680	0.6863	0.7716	0.8506	0.9262	1.0714	1.2124	1.3509
900	h, Btu/lbm	...	1215.0	1260.1	1275.9	1290.9	1305.1	1318.8	1332.1	1393.9	1451.8	1508.1	1619.3	1731.6	1846.3
(531.98)	s, Btu/lbm-°R	...	1.4216	1.4653	1.4800	1.4938	1.5066	1.5187	1.5303	1.5814	1.6257	1.6656	1.7371	1.8009	1.8595

TABLE B·2 PROPERTIES OF SUPERHEATED STEAM (CONTINUED)

Abs. press., psia (sat. temp.)		*Temperature, °F*													
		500	*550*	*600*	*620*	*640*	*660*	*680*	*700*	*800*	*900*	*1000*	*1200*	*1400*	*1600*
	v, ft³/lbm	...	0.4533	0.5140	0.5350	0.5546	0.5733	0.5912	0.6084	0.6878	0.7604	0.8294	0.9615	1.0893	1.2146
1000	h, Btu/lbm	...	1198.3	1248.8	1265.9	1281.9	1297.0	1311.4	1325.3	1389.2	1448.2	1505.1	1617.3	1730.0	1845.0
(544.61)	s, Btu/lbm-°R	...	1.3961	1.4450	1.4610	1.4757	1.4893	1.5021	1.5141	1.5670	1.6121	1.6525	1.7245	1.7886	1.8474
	v, ft³/lbm	...	...	0.4532	0.4738	0.4929	0.5110	0.5281	0.5445	0.6191	0.6866	0.7503	0.8716	0.9885	1.1031
1100	h, Btu/lbm	...	...	1236.7	1255.3	1272.4	1288.5	1303.7	1318.3	1384.3	1444.5	1502.2	1615.2	1728.4	1843.8
(556.31)	s, Btu/lbm-°R	...	...	1.4251	1.4425	1.4583	1.4728	1.4862	1.4989	1.5535	1.5995	1.6405	1.7130	1.7775	1.8363
	v, ft³/lbm	...	...	0.4016	0.4222	0.4410	0.4586	0.4752	0.4909	0.5617	0.6250	0.6843	0.7967	0.9046	1.0101
1200	h, Btu/lbm	...	...	1223.5	1243.9	1262.4	1279.6	1295.7	1311.0	1379.3	1440.7	1499.2	1613.1	1726.9	1842.5
(567.22)	s, Btu/lbm-°R	...	...	1.4052	1.4243	1.4413	1.4568	1.4710	1.4843	1.5409	1.5879	1.6293	1.7025	1.7672	1.8263
	v, ft³/lbm	...	...	0.3174	0.3390	0.3580	0.3753	0.3912	0.4062	0.4714	0.5281	0.5805	0.6789	0.7727	0.8640
1400	h, Btu/lbm	...	...	1193.0	1218.4	1240.4	1260.3	1278.5	1295.5	1369.1	1433.1	1493.2	1608.9	1723.7	1840.0
(587.10)	s, Btu/lbm-°R	...	...	1.3639	1.3877	1.4079	1.4258	1.4419	1.4567	1.5177	1.5666	1.6093	1.6836	1.7489	1.8083
	v, ft³/lbm	...	...	...	0.2733	0.2936	0.3112	0.3271	0.3417	0.4034	0.4553	0.5027	0.5906	0.6738	0.7545
1600	h, Btu/lbm	...	...	...	1187.8	1215.2	1238.7	1259.6	1278.7	1358.4	1425.3	1487.0	1604.6	1720.5	1837.5
(604.90)	s, Btu/lbm-°R	...	...	...	1.3489	1.3741	1.3952	1.4137	1.4303	1.4964	1.5476	1.5914	1.6669	1.7328	1.7926
	v, ft³/lbm	...	...	...	...	0.2407	0.2597	0.2760	0.2907	0.3502	0.3986	0.4421	0.5218	0.5968	0.6693
1800	h, Btu/lbm	...	...	...	...	1185.1	1214.0	1238.5	1260.3	1347.2	1417.4	1480.8	1600.4	1717.3	1835.0
(621.03)	s, Btu/lbm-°R	...	...	...	...	1.3377	1.3638	1.3855	1.4044	1.4765	1.5301	1.5752	1.6520	1.7185	1.7786
	v, ft³/lbm	...	...	...	...	0.1936	0.2161	0.2337	0.2489	0.3074	0.3532	0.3935	0.4668	0.5352	0.6011
2000	h, Btu/lbm	...	...	...	...	1145.6	1184.9	1214.8	1240.0	1335.5	1409.2	1474.5	1596.1	1714.1	1832.5
(635.82)	s, Btu/lbm-°R	...	...	...	...	1.2945	1.3300	1.3564	1.3783	1.4576	1.5139	1.5603	1.6384	1.7055	1.7660

	v, ft³/lbm	...	...	...	...	...	...	0.1484	0.1686	0.2294	0.2710	0.3061	0.3678	0.4244	0.4784
2500	h, Btu/lbm	...	...	...	...	...	...	1152.3	1176.8	1303.6	1387.8	1458.4	1585.3	1706.1	1826.2
(668.13)	s, Btu/lbm-°R	...	...	...	...	...	...	1.2687	1.3073	1.4127	1.4772	1.5273	1.6088	1.6775	1.7389
	v, ft³/lbm	...	...	...	...	...	...	...	0.0984	0.1760	0.2159	0.2476	0.3018	0.3505	0.3966
3000	h, Btu/lbm	...	...	...	...	...	...	...	1060.7	1267.2	1365.0	1441.8	1574.3	1698.0	1819.9
(695.36)	s, Btu/lbm-°R	...	...	...	...	...	...	...	1.1966	1.3690	1.4439	1.4984	1.5837	1.6540	1.7163
	v, ft³/lbm	...	...	...	...	...	...	. .	...	0.1583	0.1981	0.2288	0.2806	0.3267	0.3703
3206.2	h, Btu/lbm	...	...	...	...	...	...	. .	...	1250.5	1355.2	1434.7	1569.8	1694.6	1817.2
(705.40)	s, Btu/lbm-°R	...	...	...	...	...	...	. .	...	1.3508	1.4309	1.4874	1.5742	1.6452	1.7080
	v, ft³/lbm	...	...	...	...	...	...	. .	0.0306	0.1364	0.1762	0.2058	0.2546	0.2977	0.3381
3500	h, Btu/lbm	...	...	...	...	...	...	. .	780.5	1224.9	1340.7	1424.5	1563.3	1689.8	1813.6
	s, Btu/lbm-°R	...	...	...	...	...	...	. .	0.9515	0.3241	1.4127	1.4723	1.5615	1.6336	1.6968
	v, ft³/lbm	...	...	...	...	...	...	...	0.0287	0.1052	0.1462	0.1743	0.2192	0.2581	0.2943
4000	h, Btu/lbm	...	...	...	...	...	...	...	763.8	1174.8	1314.4	1406.8	1552.1	1681.7	1807.2
	s, Btu/lbm-°R	...	...	...	...	...	...	...	0.9347	1.2757	1.3827	1.4482	1.5417	1.6154	1.6795
	v, ft³/lbm	...	...	...	...	...	...	...	0.0276	0.0798	0.1226	0.1500	0.1917	0.2273	0.2602
4500	h, Btu/lbm	...	...	...	...	...	...	...	753.5	1113.9	1286.5	1388.4	1540.8	1673.5	1800.9
	s, Btu/lbm-°R	...	...	...	...	...	...	...	0.9235	1.2204	1.3529	1.4253	1.5235	1.5990	1.6640
	v, ft³/lbm	...	...	...	...	...	...	...	0.0268	0.0593	0.1036	0.1303	0.1696	0.2027	0.2329
5000	h, Btu/lbm	...	...	...	...	...	...	...	746.4	1047.1	1256.5	1369.5	1529.5	1665.3	1794.5
	s, Btu/lbm-°R	...	...	...	...	...	...	..	0.9152	1.1622	1.3231	1.4034	1.5066	1.5839	1.6499
	v, ft³/lbm	...	...	...	...	...	...	..	0.0262	0.0463	0.0880	0.1143	0.1516	0.1825	0.2106
5500	h, Btu/lbm	...	...	...	...	...	...	..	741.3	985.0	1224.1	1349.3	1518.2	1657.0	1788.1
	s, Btu/lbm-°R	...	...	...	...	...	...	..	0.9090	1.1093	1.2930	1.3821	1.4908	1.5699	1.6369

Abridged from Joseph H. Keenan and Frederick G. Keyes, *Thermodynamic Properties of Steam*, John Wiley & Sons, Inc., New York, 1937. By permission of the authors.

TABLE B·3 THERMODYNAMIC PROPERTIES OF SATURATED MERCURY

P, psia	T, °F	Enthalpy, Btu/lbm			Entropy, Btu/lbm-°R			Volume, ft³/lbm	
		Sat. liq.	Evap.	Sat. vap.	Liquid	Evap.	Sat. vap.	Sat. liq.	Sat. vap.
0.010	233.57	6.668	127.732	134.400	0.01137	0.18428	0.19565	1.21×10^{-3}	3637
0.020	259.88	7.532	127.614	135.146	0.01259	0.17735	0.18994	1.21	1893
0.030	276.22	8.068	127.540	135.608	0.01332	0.17332	0.18664	1.21	1292
0.050	297.97	8.778	127.442	136.220	0.01427	0.16821	0.18248	1.21	799
0.100	329.73	9.814	127.300	137.114	0.01561	0.16126	0.17687	1.22	416
0.200	364.25	10.936	127.144	138.080	0.01699	0.15432	0.17131	1.22×10^{-3}	217.3
0.300	385.92	11.639	127.047	138.686	0.01783	0.15024	0.16807	1.22	148.6
0.400	401.98	12.159	126.975	139.134	0.01844	0.14736	0.16580	1.22	113.7
0.500	415.00	12.568	126.916	139.484	0.01892	0.14511	0.16403	1.22	92.18
0.600	425.82	12.929	126.868	139.797	0.01932	0.14328	0.16260	1.23	77.84
0.800	443.50	13.500	126.788	140.288	0.01994	0.14038	0.16032	1.23×10^{-3}	59.58
1.00	457.72	13.959	126.724	140.683	0.02045	0.13814	0.15859	1.24	48.42
2.00	504.93	15.476	126.512	141.988	0.02205	0.13116	0.15321	1.24	25.39
3.00	535.25	16.439	126.377	142.816	0.02302	0.12706	0.15008	1.24	17.50
5.00	575.7	17.741	126.193	143.934	0.02430	0.12188	0.14618	1.24	10.90
7.00	604.7	18.657	126.065	144.722	0.02516	0.11846	0.14362	1.25×10^{-3}	8.04
10.00	637.0	19.685	125.919	145.604	0.02610	0.11483	0.14093	1.25	5.81
20.00	706.0	21.864	125.609	147.473	0.02800	0.10779	0.13579	1.26	3.09
40.00	784.4	24.345	125.255	149.600	0.03004	0.10068	0.13072	1.27	1.648
60.00	835.7	25.940	125.024	150.964	0.03127	0.09652	0.12779	1.28	1.144

80	874.8	27.149	124.849	152.008	0.03218	0.09356	0.12574	1.29×10^{-3}	0.885
100	906.8	28.152	124.706	152.858	0.03290	0.09127	0.12417	1.29	0.725
150	969.4	30.000	124.424	154.791	0.03425	0.08707	0.12132	1.30	0.507
200	1017.2	31.560	124.209	155.769	0.03523	0.08411	0.11934	1.31	0.392
250	1057.2	32.784	124.029	156.813	0.03603	0.08178	0.11781	1.31	0.322
300	1091.2	33.824	123.876	157.700	0.03669	0.07989	0.11658	1.32×10^{-3}	0.276
400	1148.4	35.535	123.620	159.185	0.03775	0.07688	0.11463	1.32	0.215
450	1173.2	36.315	123.509	159.824	0.03820	0.07566	0.11386	1.32	0.194
500	1196.0	37.006	123.406	160.412	0.03861	0.07455	0.11316	1.33	0.177
600	1236.8	38.245	123.221	161.466	0.03932	0.07264	0.11196	1.34	0.151
700	1273.3	39.339	123.058	162.397	0.03993	0.07102	0.11095	1.34×10^{-3}	0.132
800	1306.1	40.324	122.910	163.234	0.04047	0.06961	0.11008	1.34	0.118
900	1336.2	41.226	122.775	164.001	0.04095	0.06837	0.10932	1.35	0.106
1000	1364.0	42.056	122.649	164.705	0.04139	0.06726	0.10865	1.35	0.098
1100	1390.0	42.828	122.533	165.361	0.04179	0.06625	0.10804	1.36	0.090

From Lucian A. Sheldon, *Thermodynamic Properties of Mercury Vapor*, General Electric Company. Liquid densities from WADC TR-59-598.

TABLE B·4 THERMODYNAMIC PROPERTIES OF SATURATED CESIUM

T, °R	P, psia	Equilibrium molal mass, lbm/lbmole	Enthalpy, Btu/lbm		Entropy, Btu/lbm-°R		Volume, ft³/lbm	
			h_f	h_g	s_f	s_g	v_f	v_g
700	3.41×10^{-5}	133.0	4.14×10^{1}	2.84×10^{2}	1.796×10^{-1}	5.262×10^{-1}	8.765×10^{-3}	1.654×10^{6}
800	5.24×10^{-4}	133.2	4.71×10^{1}	2.87×10^{2}	1.873×10^{-1}	4.878×10^{-1}	8.841×10^{-3}	1.231×10^{5}
900	4.38×10^{-3}	133.5	5.29×10^{1}	2.90×10^{2}	1.940×10^{-1}	4.585×10^{-1}	8.918×10^{-3}	1.653×10^{4}
1000	2.39×10^{-2}	133.9	5.86×10^{1}	2.94×10^{2}	2.000×10^{-1}	4.356×10^{-1}	8.994×10^{-3}	3.347×10^{3}
1100	9.61×10^{-2}	134.6	6.43×10^{1}	2.97×10^{2}	2.055×10^{-1}	4.172×10^{-1}	9.070×10^{-3}	9.128×10^{2}
1200	3.06×10^{-1}	135.3	7.00×10^{1}	3.00×10^{2}	2.105×10^{-1}	4.022×10^{-1}	9.147×10^{-3}	3.109×10^{2}
1300	8.15×10^{-1}	136.3	7.57×10^{1}	3.02×10^{2}	2.150×10^{-1}	3.897×10^{-1}	9.223×10^{-3}	1.255×10^{2}
1400	1.89×10^{0}	137.3	8.15×10^{1}	3.054×10^{2}	2.193×10^{-1}	3.793×10^{-1}	9.300×10^{-3}	5.791×10^{1}
1500	3.91×10^{0}	138.5	8.72×10^{1}	3.080×10^{2}	2.232×10^{-1}	3.704×10^{-1}	9.376×10^{-3}	2.971×10^{1}
1600	7.40×10^{0}	139.7	9.29×10^{1}	3.104×10^{2}	2.269×10^{-1}	3.629×10^{-1}	9.452×10^{-3}	1.661×10^{1}
1700	1.29×10^{1}	141.0	9.86×10^{1}	3.128×10^{2}	2.304×10^{-1}	3.564×10^{-1}	9.529×10^{-3}	9.970×10^{0}
1800	2.14×10^{1}	142.3	1.04×10^{2}	3.152×10^{2}	2.337×10^{-1}	3.508×10^{-1}	9.605×10^{-3}	6.346×10^{0}
1900	3.34×10^{1}	143.6	1.10×10^{2}	3.177×10^{2}	2.367×10^{-1}	3.460×10^{-1}	9.682×10^{-3}	4.245×10^{0}
2000	5.00×10^{1}	144.9	1.15×10^{2}	3.201×10^{2}	2.397×10^{-1}	3.418×10^{-1}	9.758×10^{-3}	2.961×10^{0}
2100	7.20×10^{1}	146.2	1.21×10^{2}	3.226×10^{2}	2.425×10^{-1}	3.382×10^{-1}	9.834×10^{-3}	2.141×10^{0}
2200	1.00×10^{2}	147.5	1.27×10^{2}	3.251×10^{2}	2.451×10^{-1}	3.351×10^{-1}	9.911×10^{-3}	1.597×10^{0}
2300	1.35×10^{2}	148.8	1.32×10^{2}	3.276×10^{2}	2.477×10^{-1}	3.323×10^{-1}	9.987×10^{-3}	1.224×10^{0}
2400	1.78×10^{2}	150.0	1.38×10^{2}	3.302×10^{2}	2.501×10^{-1}	3.299×10^{-1}	1.006×10^{-2}	9.604×10^{-1}
2500	2.30×10^{2}	151.1	1.44×10^{2}	3.328×10^{2}	2.524×10^{-1}	3.278×10^{-1}	1.014×10^{-2}	7.694×10^{-1}
2600	2.92×10^{2}	152.3	1.50×10^{2}	3.355×10^{2}	2.547×10^{-1}	3.260×10^{-1}	1.022×10^{-2}	6.277×10^{-1}
2700	3.63×10^{2}	153.4	1.55×10^{2}	3.382×10^{2}	2.568×10^{-1}	3.244×10^{-1}	1.029×10^{-2}	5.206×10^{-1}

W. D. Weatherford et al., *Properties of Inorganic Energy-conversion and Heat-transfer Fluids for Space Applications,* WADD Report 61-96, November, 1961.

TABLE B · 5 PROPERTIES OF SATURATED FREON-12

		Enthalpy, Btu/lbm		*Entropy, Btu/lbm-°F*		*Density, lbm/ft³*	
T, °F	*P, psia*	*Sat. liq.*	*Sat. vap.*	*Sat. liq.*	*Sat. vap.*	*Sat. liq.*	*Sat. vap.*
−40	9.32	0	73.50	0	0.17517	94.58	0.2557
−30	12.02	2.03	74.70	0.00471	0.17387	93.59	0.3238
−20	15.28	4.07	75.87	0.00940	0.17275	92.58	0.4042
−10	19.20	6.14	77.05	0.01403	0.17175	91.57	0.4993
0	23.87	8.25	78.21	0.01869	0.17091	90.52	0.6109
+10	29.35	10.39	79.36	0.02328	0.17015	89.45	0.7402
20	35.75	12.55	80.49	0.02783	0.16949	88.37	0.8921
30	43.16	14.76	81.61	0.03233	0.16887	87.24	1.065
40	51.68	17.00	82.71	0.03680	0.16833	86.10	1.263
50	61.39	19.27	83.78	0.04120	0.16785	84.94	1.485
60	72.41	21.57	84.82	0.04568	0.16741	83.78	1.740
70	84.82	23.90	85.82	0.05009	0.16701	82.60	2.028
80	98.76	26.28	86.80	0.05446	0.16662	81.39	2.353
90	114.3	28.70	87.74	0.05882	0.16624	80.11	2.721
100	131.6	31.16	88.62	0.06316	0.16584	78.80	3.135
110	150.7	33.65	89.43	0.06749	0.16542	77.46	3.610
120	171.8	36.16	90.15	0.07180	0.16495	76.02	4.167

Abridged from the *Handbook of Chemistry and Physics,* American Rubber Company.

TABLE B·6 NOMINAL THERMODYNAMIC PROPERTIES OF GASES AT LOW PRESSURES

Substance	$\hat{M}$, *lbm/lbmole, g/gmole*	c_P, *Btu/lbm-°R*	$\hat{c}_P$, *Btu/lbmole-°R*	c_v, *Btu/lbm-°R*	$\hat{c}_v$, *Btu/lbmole-°R*	R, *ft-lbf/lbm-°R*	R, *Btu/lbm-°R*	$k = c_P/c_v$
Argon, A	39.94	0.123	4.91	0.074	2.96	38.65	0.0496	1.67
Helium, He	4.003	1.25	5.00	0.75	3.000	386.3	0.4963	1.66
Hydrogen, H_2	2.016	3.42	6.89	2.43	4.90	767.0	0.9856	1.41
Nitrogen, N_2	28.02	0.248	6.95	0.177	4.96	55.13	0.0708	1.40
Oxygen, O_2	32.00	0.219	7.01	0.156	4.99	48.24	0.0620	1.40
Carbon monoxide, CO	28.01	0.249	6.97	0.178	4.98	55.13	0.0708	1.40
Air	28.97	0.240	6.95	0.171	4.95	53.34	0.0686	1.40
Water vapor, H_2O	18.016	0.446	8.07	0.336	6.03	85.58	0.1099	1.33
Methane, CH_4	16.04	0.532	8.53	0.403	6.46	96.4	0.1236	1.32
Carbon dioxide, CO_2	44.01	0.202	8.91	0.156	6.87	35.1	0.0451	1.30
Sulfur dioxide, SO_2	64.07	0.154	9.87	0.122	7.82	24.1	0.0310	1.26
Acetylene, C_2H_2	26.04	0.409	10.65	0.333	8.67	59.4	0.0761	1.23
Ethylene, C_2H_4	28.05	0.374	10.49	0.304	8.53	55.1	0.0707	1.23
Ethane, C_2H_6	30.07	0.422	12.69	0.357	10.73	51.3	0.0658	1.18
Propane, C_3H_8	44.09	0.404	17.81	0.360	15.87	35.0	0.0450	1.12
Isobutane, C_4H_{10}	58.12	0.420	24.41	0.387	22.49	26.6	0.0342	1.09

Based on a compilation by J. Lay, *Thermodynamics*, Charles E. Merrill Books, Inc., Columbus, Ohio, 1963.

TABLE B·7 PROPERTIES OF COPPER AT 1 ATM

T, °K	$\hat{v}$, $cm^3/gmole$	β, 1/°K	κ, $cm^2/dyne$	$\hat{c}_P$, cal/gmole-°K	$\hat{c}_v$, cal/gmole-°K	$k = \hat{c}_P/\hat{c}_v$
0	(7.0)†	(0)	$(0.710) \times 10^{-12}$	(0)	(0)	1.00
50	(7.002)	$(11.5) \times 10^{-6}$	(0.712)	1.38	1.38	1.00
100	(7.008)	31.5	0.721	3.88	3.86	1.00
150	(7.018)	41.0	0.733	5.01	4.95	1.01
200	(7.029)	45.6	0.748	5.41	5.32	1.02
250	7.043	48.0	0.762	5.65	5.52	1.02
300	7.062	49.2	0.776	5.87	5.71	1.03
500	7.115	54.2	0.837	6.25	5.95	1.05
800	7.256	60.7	0.922	6.70	6.14	1.09
1200	7.452	69.7	1.030	7.34	6.34	1.16

From M. Zemansky, *Thermodynamics*, McGraw-Hill Book Company, New York, 1957.
† Values in parentheses are extrapolated.

TABLE B·8 THERMODYNAMIC PROPERTIES AT THE CRITICAL POINT

Substance	T, °K	P, atm	$\hat{v}$, $cm^3/gmole$	$Z = Pv/RT$
Air	132.41	37.25	92.35	
Argon, A	150.72	47.99	75	0.291
Helium, He	5.19	2.26	58	0.308
Carbon monoxide, CO	132.91	34.529	93	0.294
Hydrogen, H_2	33.24	12.797	65	0.304
Nitrogen, N_2	126.2	33.54	90	0.291
Oxygen, O_2	154.78	50.14	74	0.292
Carbon dioxide, CO_2	304.20	72.90	94	0.275
Sulfur dioxide, SO_2	430.7	77.8	122	0.269
Water, H_2O	647.27	218.167	56	0.230
Acetylene, C_2H_2	309.5	61.6	113	0.274
Ethane, C_2H_6	305.48	48.20	148	0.285
Ethylene, C_2H_4	283.06	50.50	124	0.270
n-Butane, C_4H_{10}	425.17	37.47	255	0.274
Methane, CH_4	190.7	45.8	99	0.290
Propane, C_3H_8	370.01	42.1	200	0.277

Based on a compilation by J. Lay, *Thermodynamics*, Charles E. Merrill Books, Inc., Columbus, Ohio, 1963.

TABLE B·9 THERMODYNAMIC PROPERTIES OF AIR AT LOW PRESSURES

T, °R	T, °F	h, Btu/lbm	p_r	u, Btu/lbm	v_r	ϕ, Btu/lbm-°R	T, °R	T, °F	h, Btu/lbm	p_r	u, Btu/lbm	v_r	ϕ, Btu/lbm-°R
100	−360	23.7	0.00384	16.9	9640	0.1971	1100	640	266.0	17.41	190.6	23.4	0.7743
120	−340	28.5	0.00726	20.3	6120	0.2408	1120	660	271.0	18.60	194.2	22.3	0.7788
140	−320	33.3	0.01244	23.7	4170	0.2777	1140	680	276.1	19.86	197.9	21.3	0.7833
160	−300	38.1	0.01982	27.1	2990	0.3096	1160	700	281.1	21.2	201.6	20.29	0.7877
180	−280	42.9	0.0299	30.6	2230	0.3378	1180	720	286.2	22.6	205.3	19.38	0.7920
200	−260	47.7	0.0432	34.0	1715	0.3630	1200	740	291.3	24.0	209.0	18.51	0.7963
220	−240	52.5	0.0603	37.4	1352	0.3858	1220	760	296.4	25.2	212.8	17.70	0.8005
240	−220	57.2	0.0816	40.8	1089	0.4067	1240	780	301.5	27.1	216.5	16.93	0.8047
260	−200	62.0	0.1080	44.2	892	0.4258	1260	800	306.6	28.8	220.3	16.20	0.8088
280	−180	66.8	0.1399	47.6	742	0.4436	1280	820	311.8	30.6	224.0	15.52	0.8128
300	−160	71.6	0.1780	51.0	624	0.4601	1300	840	316.9	32.4	227.8	14.87	0.8168
320	−140	76.4	0.2229	54.5	532	0.4755	1320	860	322.1	34.3	231.6	14.25	0.8208
340	−120	81.2	0.2754	57.9	457	0.4900	1340	880	327.3	36.3	235.4	13.67	0.8246
360	−100	86.0	0.336	61.3	397	0.5037	1360	900	332.5	38.4	239.2	13.12	0.8265
380	−80	90.8	0.406	64.7	347	0.5166	1380	920	337.7	40.6	243.1	12.59	0.8323
400	−60	95.5	0.486	68.1	305	0.5289	1400	940	342.9	42.9	246.9	12.10	0.8360
420	−40	100.3	0.576	71.5	270	0.5406	1420	960	348.1	45.3	250.8	11.62	0.8398
440	−20	105.1	0.678	74.9	241	0.5517	1440	980	353.4	47.8	254.7	11.17	0.8434
460	0	109.9	0.791	78.4	215.3	0.5624	1460	1000	358.6	50.3	258.5	10.74	0.8470
480	+20	114.7	0.918	81.8	193.6	0.5726	1480	1020	363.9	53.0	262.4	10.34	0.8506
500	40	119.5	1.059	85.2	174.9	0.5823	1500	1040	369.2	55.9	266.3	9.95	0.8542
520	60	124.3	1.215	88.6	158.6	0.5917	1520	1060	374.5	58.8	270.3	9.58	0.8568
540	80	129.1	1.386	92.0	144.3	0.6008	1540	1080	379.8	61.8	274.2	9.23	0.8611

560	100	133.9	1.574	99.5	131.8	0.6095	1560	1100	385.1	65.0	278.1	8.89	0.8646
580	120	138.7	1.780	98.9	120.7	0.6179	1580	1120	390.4	68.3	282.1	8.57	0.8679
600	140	143.5	2.00	102.3	110.9	0.6261	1600	1140	395.7	71.7	286.1	8.26	0.8713
620	160	148.3	2.25	105.8	102.1	0.6340	1620	1160	401.1	75.3	290.0	7.97	0.8746
640	180	153.1	2.51	109.2	94.3	0.6416	1640	1180	406.4	79.0	294.0	6.69	0.8779
660	200	157.9	2.80	112.7	87.3	0.6490	1660	1200	411.8	82.8	298.0	7.42	0.8812
680	220	162.7	3.11	116.1	81.0	0.6562	1680	1220	417.2	86.8	302.0	7.17	0.8844
700	240	167.6	3.45	119.6	75.2	0.6632	1700	1240	422.6	91.0	306.1	6.92	0.8876
720	260	172.4	3.81	123.0	70.1	0.6700	1720	1260	428.0	95.2	310.1	6.69	0.8907
740	280	177.2	4.19	126.5	65.4	0.6766	1740	1280	433.4	99.7	314.1	6.46	0.8939
760	300	182.1	4.61	130.0	61.1	0.6831	1760	1300	438.8	104.3	318.2	6.25	0.8970
780	320	186.9	5.05	133.5	57.2	0.6894	1780	1320	444.3	109.1	322.2	6.04	0.9000
800	340	191.8	5.53	137.0	53.6	0.6956	1800	1340	449.7	114.0	326.3	5.85	0.9031
820	360	196.7	6.03	140.5	50.4	0.7016	1820	1360	455.2	119.2	330.4	5.66	0.9061
840	380	201.6	6.67	144.0	47.3	0.7075	1840	1380	460.6	124.5	334.5	5.48	0.9091
860	400	206.5	7.15	147.5	44.6	0.7132	1860	1400	466.1	130.0	338.6	5.30	0.9120
880	420	211.4	7.76	151.0	42.0	0.7189	1880	1420	471.6	135.6	342.7	5.13	0.9150
900	440	216.3	8.41	154.6	39.6	0.7244	1900	1440	477.1	141.5	346.8	4.97	0.9179
920	460	221.2	9.10	158.1	37.4	0.7298	1920	1460	482.6	147.6	351.0	4.82	0.9208
940	480	226.1	9.83	161.7	35.4	0.7351	1940	1480	488.1	153.9	355.1	4.67	0.9236
960	500	231.1	10.61	165.3	33.5	0.7403	1960	1500	493.6	160.4	359.3	4.53	0.9264
980	520	236.0	11.43	168.8	31.8	0.7454	1980	1520	499.1	167.1	363.4	4.39	0.9293
1000	540	241.0	12.30	172.4	30.1	0.7504	2000	1540	504.7	174.0	367.6	4.26	0.9320
1020	560	246.0	13.22	176.0	28.6	0.7554	2020	1560	510.3	181.2	371.8	4.13	0.9348
1040	580	251.0	14.18	179.7	27.2	0.7602	2040	1580	515.8	188.5	376.0	4.01	0.9376
1060	600	256.0	15.20	183.3	25.8	0.7650	2060	1600	521.4	196.2	380.2	3.89	0.9403
1080	620	261.0	16.28	186.9	24.6	0.7696	2080	1620	527.0	204.0	384.4	3.78	0.9430

TABLE B·9 THERMODYNAMIC PROPERTIES OF AIR AT LOW PRESSURES (CONTINUED)

T, °R	T, °F	h, Btu/lbm	p_r	u, Btu/lbm	v_r	ϕ, Btu/lbm-°R	T, °R	T, °F	h, Btu/lbm	p_r	u, Btu/lbm	v_r	ϕ, Btu/lbm-°R
2100	1640	532.6	212	388.6	3.67	0.9456	2900	2440	761.4	815	562.7	1.318	1.0379
2120	1660	538.2	220	392.8	3.56	0.9483	2920	2460	767.3	839	567.1	1.289	1.0399
2140	1680	543.7	229	397.0	3.46	0.9509	2940	2480	773.1	864	571.6	1.261	1.0419
2160	1700	549.4	238	401.3	3.36	0.9535	2960	2500	779.0	889	576.1	1.233	1.0439
2180	1720	555.0	247	405.5	3.27	0.9561	2980	2520	784.8	915	580.6	1.206	1.0458
2200	1740	560.6	257	409.8	3.18	0.9587	3000	2540	790.7	941	585.0	1.180	1.0478
2220	1760	566.2	266	414.0	3.09	0.9612	3020	2560	796.5	969	589.5	1.155	1.0497
2240	1780	571.9	276	418.3	3.00	0.9638	3040	2580	802.4	996	594.0	1.130	1.0517
2260	1800	577.5	287	422.6	2.92	0.9663	3060	2600	808.3	1025	598.5	1.106	1.0536
2280	1820	583.2	297	426.9	2.84	0.9688	3080	2620	814.2	1054	603.0	1.083	1.0555
2300	1840	588.8	308	431.2	2.76	0.9712	3100	2640	820.0	1083	607.5	1.060	1.0574
2320	1860	594.5	319	435.5	2.69	0.9737	3120	2660	825.9	1114	612.0	1.038	1.0593
2340	1880	600.2	331	439.8	2.62	0.9761	3140	2680	831.8	1145	616.6	1.016	1.0612
2360	1900	605.8	343	444.1	2.55	0.9785	3160	2700	837.7	1176	621.1	0.995	1.0630
2380	1920	611.5	355	448.4	2.48	0.9809	3180	2720	843.6	1209	625.6	0.975	1.0649
2400	1940	617.2	368	452.7	2.42	0.9833	3200	2740	849.5	1242	630.1	0.955	1.0668
2420	1960	622.9	380	457.0	2.36	0.9857	3220	2760	855.4	1276	634.6	0.935	1.0686
2440	1980	628.6	394	461.4	2.30	0.9880	3240	2780	861.3	1310	639.2	0.916	1.0704
2460	2000	634.3	407	465.7	2.24	0.9904	3260	2800	867.2	1345	643.7	0.898	1.0722
2480	2020	640.0	421	470.0	2.18	0.9927	3280	2820	873.1	1381	648.3	0.880	1.0740
2500	2040	645.8	436	474.4	2.12	0.9950	3300	2840	879.0	1418	652.8	0.862	1.0758
2520	2060	651.5	450	478.8	2.07	0.9972	3320	2860	884.9	1455	657.4	0.845	1.0776
2540	2080	657.2	466	483.1	2.02	0.9995	3340	2880	890.9	1494	661.9	0.828	1.0794

2560	2100	663.0	481	487.5	1.971	1.0018	3360	2900	896.8	1533	666.5	0.812	1.0812
2580	2120	668.7	497	491.9	1.922	1.0040	3380	2920	902.7	1573	671.0	0.796	1.0830
2600	2140	674.5	514	496.3	1.876	1.0062	3400	2940	908.7	1613	675.6	0.781	1.0847
2620	2160	680.2	530	500.6	1.830	1.0084	3420	2960	914.6	1655	680.2	0.766	1.0864
2640	2180	686.0	548	505.0	1.786	1.0106	3440	2980	920.6	1697	684.8	0.751	1.0882
2660	2200	691.8	565	509.4	1.743	1.0128	3460	3000	926.5	1740	689.3	0.736	1.0899
2680	2220	697.6	583	513.8	1.702	1.0150	3480	3020	932.4	1784	693.9	0.722	1.0916
2700	2240	703.4	602	518.3	1.662	1.0171	3500	3040	938.4	1829	698.5	0.709	1.0933
2720	2260	709.1	621	522.7	1.623	1.0193	3520	3060	944.4	1875	703.1	0.695	1.0950
2740	2280	714.9	640	527.1	1.585	1.0214	3540	3080	950.3	1922	707.6	0.682	1.0967
2760	2300	720.7	660	531.5	1.548	1.0235	3560	3100	956.3	1970	712.2	0.670	1.0984
2780	2320	726.5	681	536.0	1.512	1.0256	3580	3120	962.2	2018	716.8	0.637	1.1000
2800	2340	733.3	702	540.4	1.478	1.0277	3600	3140	968.2	2068	721.4	0.645	1.1017
2820	2360	738.2	724	544.8	1.444	1.0297	3620	3160	974.2	2118	726.0	0.633	1.1034
2840	2380	744.0	746	549.3	1.411	1.0318	3640	3180	980.2	2170	730.6	0.621	1.1050
2860	2400	749.8	768	553.7	1.379	1.0338	3660	3200	986.1	2222	735.3	0.610	1.1066
2880	2420	755.6	791	558.2	1.348	1.0359	3680	3220	992.1	2276	739.9	0.599	1.1083

Abridged from Joseph H. Keenan and Joseph Kaye, *Gas Tables*, John Wiley & Sons, Inc., New York, 1948. By permission of the authors.

TABLE B·10 SPECIFIC HEATS OF SELECTED LIQUIDS

Substance	*State*	c_P, *Btu/lbm-°R*	*Substance*	*State*	c_P, *Btu/lbm-°R*
Water	1 atm, 32°F	1.007	Glycerin	1 atm, 50°F	0.554
	1 atm, 77°F	0.998		1 atm, 120°F	0.617
	1 atm, 212°F	1.007			
			Bismuth	1 atm, 800°F	0.0345
Ammonia	sat., 0°F	1.08		1 atm, 1000°F	0.0369
	sat., 120°F	1.22		1 atm, 1400°F	0.0393
Freon-12	sat., −40°F	0.211	Mercury	1 atm, 50°F	0.033
	sat., 0°F	0.217		1 atm, 600°F	0.032
	sat., 120°F	0.244			
			Sodium	1 atm, 200°F	0.33
Benzene	1 atm, 60°F	0.43		1 atm, 1000°F	0.30
	1 atm, 150°F	0.46			
			n-Butane	1 atm, 32°F	0.550
Light oil	1 atm, 60°F	0.43			
	1 atm, 300°F	0.54	Propane	1 atm, 32°F	0.576

Based on values from *Handbook of Chemistry and Physics,* American Rubber Company.

TABLE B·11 SPECIFIC HEATS OF SELECTED SOLIDS

$P = 1$ atm

Substance	*T, °C*	c_P, *cal/g-°K*	*Substance*	*T, °C*	c_P, *cal/g-°K*
Ice	−200	0.168	Lead	−270	0.00001
	−140	0.262		−259	0.0073
	−60	0.392		−100	0.0283
	−11	0.468		0	0.0297
	−2.6	0.500		+100	0.0320
				300	0.0356
Aluminum	−250	0.0039			
	−200	0.076	Iron	20	0.107
	−100	0.167			
	0	0.208	Silver	20	0.0558
	+100	0.225	Sodium	20	0.295
	300	0.248			
	600	0.277	Tungsten	20	0.034
			Graphite	20	0.17
Platinum	−256	0.00123			
	−152	0.0261	Wood	20	0.42
	0	0.0316			
	+500	0.0349	Rubber	20	0.44
	1000	0.0381	Mica	20	0.21

Based on values from the *Handbook of Chemistry and Physics,* American Rubber Company.

TABLE B · 12 STANDARDIZED ENTHALPIES AND ABSOLUTE ENTROPIES OF SUBSTANCES IN EQUILIBRIUM STATES AT 77°F (25°C) AND 1 ATM

Substance	$\hat{h}°$, *Btu/lbmole*	$\hat{s}°$, *Btu/lbmole-°R*
Hydrogen, H_2	0	31.194
Carbon, C	0	1.360
Oxygen, O_2	0	48.986
Nitrogen, N_2	0	45.755
Water (liquid), H_2O	−122,976	16.72
Carbon dioxide, CO_2	−169,183	51.032
Carbon monoxide, CO	−47,517	47.272
Methane, CH_4	−32,179	44.47
Ethane, C_2H_6	−36,401	54.81
Propane, C_3H_8	−44,647	64.47
n-Butane, C_4H_{10}	−53,627	74.05
Acetylene, C_2H_2	97,495	47.966
Benzene, C_6H_6	35,653	64.30

Based on tabulations of the National Bureau of Standards.

TABLE B·13 STANDARDIZED ENTHALPIES AND ABSOLUTE ENTROPIES FOR GASES AT LOW PRESSURE

$\hat{s} = \hat{\phi}(T) - \mathcal{R} \ln (P/P_0)$; $P_0 = 1$ atm; $\hat{h}$ in Btu/lbmole; $\hat{s}$ in Btu/lbmole-°R

T, °R	Oxygen $\hat{h}$	Oxygen $\hat{\phi}$	Nitrogen $\hat{h}$	Nitrogen $\hat{\phi}$	Hydrogen $\hat{h}$	Hydrogen $\hat{\phi}$	Air† $\hat{h}$	Air† $\hat{\phi}$
537	0	48.986	0	45.755	0	31.194	0	46.336
600	443.2	49.762	438.4	46.514	435.3	31.959	438.3	47.107
700	1154.2	50.858	1135.4	47.588	1129.9	33.031	1136.2	48.183
800	1876.9	51.821	1834.9	48.522	1826.8	33.961	2041.5	49.121
900	2612.8	52.688	2538.6	49.352	2525.0	34.784	2547.0	49.955
1000	3362.4	53.477	3248.4	50.099	3224.2	35.520	3263.2	50.710
1100	4125.3	54.204	3965.5	50.783	4014.3	36.188	3987.7	51.400
1200	4900.7	54.879	4690.5	51.413	4625.5	36.798	4721.0	52.038
1300	5687.8	55.508	5424.4	52.001	5328.4	37.360	5463.7	52.633
1400	6485.3	56.099	6167.4	52.551	6033.5	37.883	6215.8	53.190
1500	7292.0	56.656	6919.4	53.071	6741.2	38.372	6976.8	53.715
1600	8107.4	57.182	7680.2	53.561	7452.2	38.830	7746.6	54.212
1700	8930.5	57.680	8449.4	54.028	8167.1	39.264	9103.8	54.683
1800	9760.7	58.155	9226.8	54.472	8886.5	39.675	9310.1	55.425
1900	10597.0	58.607	10012.1	54.896	9610.6	40.067	9234.2	55.561
2000	11438.9	59.039	10804.9	55.303	10339.8	40.441	10903.4	55.971
2100	12285.8	59.451	11604.5	55.694	11074.2	40.799	11701.0	56.365
2200	13137.5	59.848	12410.3	56.068	11814.1	41.143	12522.3	56.743
2300	13993.7	60.228	13221.7	56.429	12559.5	41.475	13340.1	57.106
2400	14854.1	60.594	14038.4	56.777	13310.3	41.794	14162.9	57.456
2500	15718.3	60.946	14860.0	57.112	14067.0	42.104	14998.9	57.794
2600	16586.3	61.287	15686.3	57.436	14829.4	42.403	15822.0	58.120
2700	17457.8	61.616	16516.9	57.750	15597.5	42.692	16658.0	58.436
2800	18332.7	61.934	17351.6	58.053	16371.5	42.973	17497.6	58.742
2900	19211.0	62.242	18190.0	58.348	17151.2	43.247	18341.2	59.037
3000	20092.6	62.540	19032.0	58.632	17936.6	43.514	19188.0	59.324
3100	20977.4	62.831	19877.3	58.910	18727.4	43.773	20038.3	59.603
3200	21865.4	63.113	20725.5	59.179	19523.8	44.026	20891.4	59.874
3300	22756.5	63.386	21576.5	59.442	20325.2	44.273	21747.2	60.137
3400	23650.8	63.654	22430.2	59.697	21131.6	44.513	22605.9	60.394
3500	24548.2	63.914	23286.4	59.944	21942.6	44.748	23467.4	60.643
3600	25448.8	64.168	24144.9	60.186	22758.2	44.978	24331.0	60.887
3700	26352.4	64.415	25005.6	60.422	23578.2	45.203	25197.2	61.124
3800	27259.0	64.657	25868.4	60.652	24402.5	45.423	26065.8	61.356
3900	28168.5	64.893	26733.3	60.877	25230.8	45.638	26936.3	61.582
4000	29081.0	65.123	27599.9	61.097	26063.2	45.849	27808.9	61.803
4100	29996.5	65.350	28468.5	61.310	26899.5	46.056	28683.8	62.019
4200	30914.8	65.571	29338.6	61.520	27739.5	46.257	29560.4	62.230
4300	31836.0	65.788	30210.4	61.726	28583.2	46.456	30438.8	62.437
4400	32759.9	66.000	31083.6	61.927	29430.6	46.651	31318.9	62.639
4500	33686.7	66.208	31958.3	62.123	30281.3	46.842	32200.7	62.837
4600	34616.3	66.413	32834.3	62.316	31135.4	47.030	33084.3	63.031
4700	35548.5	66.613	33711.6	62.504	32022.7	47.215	33969.6	63.223
4800	36483.5	66.809	34590.0	62.689	32853.1	47.396	34276.4	63.408
4900	37421.0	67.003	35469.6	62.870	33716.6	47.574	35744.1	63.591
5000	38361.2	67.193	36350.3	63.049	34583.0	47.749	36633.4	63.771

† 78.03% N_2, 20.99% O_2, 0.98% A.

TABLE B · 13 STANDARDIZED ENTHALPIES AND ABSOLUTE ENTROPIES FOR GASES AT LOW PRESSURE (CONTINUED)

Water vapor		*Carbon monoxide*		*Carbon dioxide*		*Monatomic gases*	
$\hat{h}$	$\hat{\phi}$	$\hat{h}$	$\hat{\phi}$	$\hat{h}$	$\hat{\phi}$	$\hat{h}$	$\hat{\phi}$
−103968.0	45.079	−47517.0	47.272	−169183.0	51.032	0	36.942
−103471.6	45.970	−47078.5	48.044	−168612.3	52.038	212.7	37.512
−102660.9	47.219	−46380.5	49.120	−167661.2	53.503	809.2	38.278
−101839.4	48.316	−45678.3	50.058	−166660.3	54.839	1305.7	38.941
−101005.4	49.298	−44970.1	50.892	−165615.6	56.070	1802.1	39.525
−100157.4	50.191	−44254.3	51.646	−164531.1	57.212	2298.6	40.048
−99294.3	51.013	−43529.7	52.337	−163410.6	58.281	2795.1	40.522
−98415.9	51.777	−42795.7	52.976	−162257.9	59.283	3291.5	40.954
−97521.8	52.494	−42051.9	53.571	−161076.3	60.229	3788.0	41.351
−96611.5	53.168	−41298.5	54.129	−159868.5	61.124	4284.5	41.719
−95684.9	53.808	−40535.4	54.655	−158636.5	61.974	4781.0	42.061
−94741.4	54.418	−39763.1	55.154	−157383.5	62.783	5277.4	42.382
−93780.9	54.999	−38982.2	55.628	−156111.8	63.555	5773.9	42.683
−92803.3	55.559	−38193.3	56.078	−154821.0	64.292	6270.4	42.967
−91808.8	56.097	−37396.7	56.509	−153514.7	64.999	6766.8	43.235
−90797.3	56.617	−36593.3	56.922	−152193.8	65.676	7263.3	43.400
−89709.4	57.119	−35783.2	57.317	−150859.8	66.327	7759.8	43.732
−88725.5	57.605	−34967.1	57.696	−149513.5	66.953	8256.2	43.963
−87665.7	58.077	−34145.5	58.062	−148156.2	67.557	8752.7	44.183
−86590.6	58.535	−33319.1	58.414	−146788.5	68.139	9249.2	44.395
−85500.9	58.980	−32487.7	58.754	−145411.3	68.702	9745.7	44.597
−84396.8	59.414	−31652.2	59.081	−144025.4	69.245	10242.1	44.792
−83279.1	59.837	−30812.5	59.398	−142631.3	69.771	10738.6	44.980
−82148.3	60.248	−29969.3	59.705	−141229.7	70.282	11235.1	45.160
−81005.1	60.650	−29122.7	60.002	−139821.0	70.776	11731.5	45.334
−79850.0	61.043	−28273.1	60.290	−138405.9	71.255	12228.0	45.503
−78683.5	61.426	−27420.5	60.569	−136984.6	71.722	12724.5	45.663
−77506.1	61.801	−26565.3	60.841	−135557.8	72.175	13220.9	45.823
−76318.1	62.167	−25707.5	61.105	−134125.8	72.616	13717.4	45.973
−75120.3	62.526	−24847.2	61.362	132688.9	73.045	14213.9	46.124
−73912.8	62.876	−23984.7	61.612	−131247.3	73.462	14710.5	46.266
−72696.2	63.221	−23119.9	61.855	−129801.5	73.870	15206.8	46.408
−71470.9	63.557	−22253.0	62.093	−128351.9	74.267	15703.3	46.542
−70237.4	63.887	−21384.2	62.325	−126898.4	74.655	16199.8	46.676
−68996.1	64.210	−20513.6	62.551	−125441.5	75.033	16696.3	46.803
−67747.2	64.528	−19641.3	62.772	−123981.1	75.404	17192.7	46.931
−66490.9	64.839	−18767.4	62.988	−122517.4	75.765	17689.2	47.052
−65227.9	65.144	−17892.1	63.198	−121050.5	76.119	18185.6	47.173
−63958.3	65.444	−17015.3	63.405	−119580.4	76.464	18682.1	47.289
−62682.4	65.738	−16137.3	63.607	−118107.4	76.803	19178.6	47.404
−61400.4	66.028	−15257.9	63.805	−116631.5	77.135	19675.0	47.515
−60112.7	66.312	−14377.2	63.998	−115152.8	77.460	20171.4	47.625
−58819.4	66.591	−13495.5	64.188	−113671.4	77.779	20668.0	47.731
−57520.8	66.866	−12612.6	64.374	−112187.6	78.091	21164.5	47.836
−56217.3	67.135	−11728.7	64.556	−110701.2	78.398	21661.0	47.938
−54908.9	67.401	−10843.8	64.735	−109212.5	78.698	22157.4	48.039

Derived from Joseph H. Keenan and Joseph Kaye, *Gas Tables,* John Wiley & Sons, Inc., 1948, using standardized enthalpies based on NBS Circulars 467 and 500.

TABLE B·14 LOGARITHMS TO THE BASE 10 OF THE EQUILIBRIUM CONSTANT K FOR THE REACTION

$$\nu_1 C_1 + \nu_2 C_2 \rightleftarrows \nu_3 C_3 + \nu_4 C_4 \qquad K(T) = \frac{\chi_3^{\nu_3}\chi_4^{\nu_4}}{\chi_1^{\nu_1}\chi_2^{\nu_2}}\left(\frac{P}{P_0}\right)^{\nu_3+\nu_4-\nu_1-\nu_2} \qquad P_0 = 1 \text{ atm}$$

T, °K	$H_2 \rightleftarrows 2H$	$O_2 \rightleftarrows 2O$	$H_2O \rightleftarrows H_2 + \frac{1}{2}O_2$	$H_2O \rightleftarrows OH + \frac{1}{2}H_2$	$CO_2 \rightleftarrows CO + \frac{1}{2}O_2$	$N_2 \rightleftarrows 2N$	$\frac{1}{2}O_2 + \frac{1}{2}N_2 \rightleftarrows NO$	$Na \rightleftarrows Na^+ + e^-$	$Cs \rightleftarrows Cs^+ + e^-$
298	−71.210	−80.620	−40.047	−46.593	−45.043	−119.434	−15.187	−32.3	−25.1
400	−51.742	−58.513	−29.241	−33.910	−32.41	−87.473	−11.156	−24.3	−17.5
600	−32.667	−36.859	−18.663	−21.470	−20.07	−56.206	−7.219	−14.6	−10.0
800	−23.074	−25.985	−13.288	−15.214	−13.90	−40.521	−5.250	−9.58	−6.15
1000	−17.288	−19.440	−10.060	−11.444	−10.199	−31.084	−4.068	−6.54	−3.79
1200	−13.410	−15.062	−7.896	−8.922	−7.742	−24.619	−3.279	−4.47	−2.18
1400	−10.627	−11.932	−6.334	−7.116	−5.992	−20.262	−2.717	−2.97	−1.010
1600	−8.530	−9.575	−5.175	−5.758	−4.684	−16.869	−2.294	−1.819	−0.108
1800	−6.893	−7.740	−4.263	−4.700	−3.672	−14.225	−1.966	−0.913	+0.609
2000	−5.579	−6.269	−3.531	−3.852	−2.863	−12.016	−1.703	−0.175	+1.194
2200	−4.500	−5.064	−2.931	−3.158	−2.206	−10.370	−1.488	+0.438	+1.682
2400	−3.598	−4.055	−2.429	−2.578	−1.662	−8.992	−1.309	+0.956	+2.098
2600	−2.833	−3.206	−2.003	−2.087	−1.203	−7.694	−1.157	+1.404	+2.46
2800	−2.176	−2.475	−1.638	−1.670	−0.807	−6.640	−1.028	+1.792	+2.77
3000	−1.604	−1.840	−1.322	−1.302	−0.469	−5.726	−0.915	+2.13	+3.05
3200	−1.104	−1.285	−1.046	−0.983	−0.175	−4.925	−0.817	+2.44	+3.29
3500	−0.458	−0.571	−0.693	−0.557	+0.201	−3.893	−0.692	+2.84	+3.62
4000	+0.406	+0.382	−0.221	−0.035	+0.699	−2.514	−0.526	+3.38	+4.07
4500	+1.078	+1.125	+0.153	+0.392	+1.081	−1.437	−0.345	+3.82	+4.43
5000	+1.619	+1.719	+0.450	+0.799	+1.387	−0.570	−0.298	+4.18	+4.73

Based on information provided by the National Bureau of Standards; ionization of Cs and Na from Saha equation.

TABLE B·15 THE NATURAL ELEMENTS

Substance	*Symbol*	*Atomic number*	$\hat{M}$†	*Substance*	*Symbol*	*Atomic number*	$\hat{M}$
Aluminum	Al	13	26.97	Molybdenum	Mo	42	95.95
Antimony	Sb	51	121.76	Neodymium	Nd	60	144.27
Argon	A	18	39.944	Neon	Ne	10	20.183
Arsenic	As	33	74.91	Nickel	Ni	28	58.69
Barium	Ba	56	137.36	Nitrogen	N	7	14.008
Beryllium	Be	4	9.02	Osmium	Os	76	190.2
Bismuth	Bi	83	209.00	Oxygen	O	8	16.0000
Boron	B	5	10.82	Palladium	Pd	46	106.7
Bromine	Br	35	79.916	Phosphorus	P	15	30.98
Cadmium	Cd	48	112.41	Platinum	Pt	78	195.23
Calcium	Ca	20	40.08	Potassium	K	19	39.096
Carbon	C	6	12.010	Praseodymium	Pr	59	140.92
Cerium	Ce	58	140.13	Proctactinium	Pa	91	231
Cesium	Cs	55	132.91	Radium	Ra	88	226.05
Chlorine	Cl	17	35.457	Radon	Rn	86	222
Chromium	Cr	24	52.01	Rhenium	Re	75	186.31
Cobalt	Co	27	58.94	Rhodium	Rh	45	102.91
Columbium	Cb	41	92.91	Rubidium	Rb	37	85.48
Copper	Cu	29	63.54	Ruthenium	Ru	44	101.7
Dysprosium	Dy	66	162.46	Samarium	Sm	62	150.43
Erbium	Er	68	167.2	Scandium	Sc	21	45.10
Europium	Eu	63	152.0	Selenium	Se	34	78.96
Fluorine	F	9	19.00	Silicon	Si	14	28.06
Gadolinium	Gd	64	156.9	Silver	Ag	47	107.880
Gallium	Ga	31	69.72	Sodium	Na	11	22.997
Germanium	Ge	32	72.60	Strontium	Sr	38	87.63
Gold	Au	79	197.2	Sulfur	S	16	32.066
Hafnium	Hf	72	178.6	Tantalum	Ta	73	180.88
Helium	He	2	4.003	Tellurium	Te	52	127.61
Holmium	Ho	67	164.94	Terbium	Tb	65	159.2
Hydrogen	H	1	1.0080	Thallium	Tl	81	204.39
Indium	In	49	114.76	Thorium	Th	90	232.12
Iodine	I	53	126.92	Thulium	Tm	69	169.4
Iridium	Ir	77	193.1	Tin	Sn	50	118.70
Iron	Fe	26	55.85	Titanium	Ti	22	47.90
Krypton	Kr	36	83.7	Tungsten	W	74	183.92
Lanthanum	La	57	138.92	Uranium	U	92	238.07
Lead	Pb	82	207.21	Vanadium	V	23	50.95
Lithium	Li	3	6.940	Xenon	Xe	54	131.3
Lutecium	Lu	71	174.99	Ytterbium	Yb	70	173.04
Magnesium	Mg	12	24.32	Yttrium	Y	39	88.92
Manganese	Mn	25	54.93	Zinc	Zn	30	65.38
Mercury	Hg	80	200.61	Zirconium	Zr	40	91.22

Based on a tabulation published by the *Journal of the American Chemical Society.*
† $\hat{M}$ in g/gmole, kg/kg-mole, or lbm/lbmole.

NOMENCLATURE

A	Area
	Helmholtz function, $U - TS$ (11)†
	Constant in the distribution functions (12, 13)
a	Acceleration
a	Helmholtz function per unit of mass, $u - Ts$ (11)
$\hat{a}$	Helmholtz function per mole, $\hat{u} - T\hat{s}$
B, $\mathbf{B}$	Magnetic induction
C	Constant, defined where used
C	Curie constant of a substance
CM	Control mass
CV	Control volume
cop	Coefficient of performance
c	Speed of light
c_P	Specific heat at constant pressure
$\hat{c}_P$	Molal specific heat at constant pressure
c_v	Specific heat at constant volume
$\hat{c}_v$	Molal specific heat at constant volume
c	$c = c_P = c_v$ for an incompressible substance
c_{H}	Specific heat in a constant applied magnetic field
c_{M}	Specific heat at constant magnetization
D, $\mathbf{D}$	Electric displacement
D_{ij}	Diffusion coefficient
$\mathcal{E}$	Electrostatic potential
e	Charge of an electron
E	Energy
e	Energy per unit of mass
E, $\mathbf{E}$	Electric field strength
F, $\mathbf{F}$	Force
$f(x)$	Function of x
f	Fraction
f_c	Collision frequency

† Numbers in parentheses indicate chapters.

g_c	Constant in Newton's law, $\mathsf{F} = (1/g_c)Ma$
g_g	Local acceleration of gravity
g	Gibbs function per unit of mass, $h - Ts$
$\hat{g}$	Gibbs function per mole, $\hat{h} - T\hat{s}$
G	Gibbs function, $U + PV - TS$
ΔG_r	Gibbs-function change for a complete unit reaction
G, $\mathbf{G}$	Gravitational field strength
g	Magnetic Gibbs function per unit of mass, $h - Ts$
h	Enthalpy per unit of mass, $u + Pv$
$\hat{h}$	Enthalpy per mole, $u + Pv$
h	Magnetic enthalpy, $u - \mu_0 v\mathbf{H} \cdot \mathbf{M}$
h	Planck's constant
H, $\mathbf{H}$	Magnetic field strength
Δh_f°	Enthalpy of formation of a mole of compound from its elements at the standard reference state
ΔH_r	Enthalpy change for a complete unit reaction
i	Electric current
I	Moment of inertia
J_i	Flux of a conserved quantity
J_E	Energy flux
J_N	Particle-number flux
J_M	Mass flux
k	Ratio of specific heats, c_P/c_v
k	Boltzmann constant
k_N	Constant in Newton's law, $k_N = 1/g_c$
k_C	Constant in Coulomb's law, $k_C = 1/(4\pi\epsilon_0)$
k_B	Constant in Biot-Savart's law, $k_B = \mu_0/(4\pi)$
k_G	Constant in the gravitational law
K	Equilibrium constant for ideal-gas reactions
KE	Kinetic energy
$\mathcal{K}$	An amount of entropy transfer with heat
$\dot{\mathcal{K}}$	Rate of entropy transfer with heat
L	Length
L_{ij}	Onsager phenomenological coefficients
$\mathfrak{L}_{ij}$	Phenomenological coefficients which are independent of arbitrary datum choices
L_{ij}	Modified phenomenological coefficients
l	Quantum-state index
M	Mass
m	Molecular weight (dimensionless)
$\hat{M}$	Molal mass
m	Mass of a particle
$\dot{M}$	Mass flow rate
M, $\mathbf{M}$	Magnetic dipole moment per unit of volume

n, N	Number of particles
$\mathfrak{N}$	Number of moles
N_0	Avogadro's number
PE	Potential energy
P	Pressure
P, $\mathbf{P}$	Electric-dipole moment per unit of volume
$\mathcal{P}_E$, $\mathcal{P}_S$	Amounts of energy and entropy production
$\dot{\mathcal{P}}_E$, $\dot{\mathcal{P}}_S$	Rates of energy and entropy production
p	Probability
p	Momentum of a particle
p_r	Reduced pressure
P^*	Pressure ratio
	Pressure in a pure phase (10)
Q	An amount of energy transfer as heat
$\dot{Q}$	Rate of energy transfer as heat
$\mathcal{Q}$	Charge
q	Heat flux (14)
R	Gas constant for a particular gas, $R = \mathcal{R}/\hat{M}$
$\mathcal{R}$	Universal gas constant
r	Radius
S	Entropy
s	Entropy per unit of mass
$\hat{s}$	Entropy per mole
$\hat{s}^\circ$	Absolute entropy of a substance, per mole, at the standard reference state
ΔS_r	Entropy change for a complete unit reaction
T	Absolute temperature
T^*	Temperature ratio
t	Time
U	Internal energy
u	Internal energy per unit of volume
u	Internal energy per unit of mass
$\hat{u}$	Internal energy per mole
V	Volume
V	Velocity
V_m	Mean velocity
v	Volume per unit of mass
$\hat{v}$	Volume per mole
W	An amount of energy transfer as work
$\dot{W}$	Rate of energy transfer as work
x	Quality of a two-phase mixture
X	Directional coordinate
x_i	Generalized intensified property (specific volume, magnetization, etc.)

X_i	Gradient of a natural intensified property (14)
z	Number of quantum states in a quantum-state group
Z	Partition function
	Compressibility, $Z = Pv/RT$ (8)
$\mathcal{Z}$	Grand partition function
x, y, z	Coordinates
α	Isentropic compressibility
β	Isobaric compressibility
	Lagrange multiplier (6, 12, 13)
ϵ_i	Energy of a system in quantum state i
ε	Energy of a particle
	Absolute thermoelectric power (14)
ϵ_0	Permittivity of a vacuum
ϕ	Function of temperature for an ideal gas
	Relative humidity (10)
	Scalar potential (1)
ϕ_i	Natural intensive property (14)
γ	Specific humidity
κ	Isothermal compressibility
κ_e	Electrical conductivity
κ_t	Thermal conductivity
λ	Wavelength
Λ	Free path
Λ_m	Mean free path
μ	Electrochemical potential per unit of mass
$\hat{\mu}$	Electrochemical potential per mole
μ_0	Permeability of a vacuum
Ω	Number of quantum states
ω	Angular frequency
Ψ	Volume fraction
Φ	Mass fraction
η	Cycle energy-conversion efficiency
η_s	Isentropic efficiency
σ	Collision cross section (13)
	Entropy production per unit of volume (14)
	Interfacial tension (2)
θ	Angle
θ_E	Characteristic temperature for an Einstein solid
θ_D	Characteristic temperature for a Debye solid
θ_{rot}, θ_{vib}	Characteristic temperature for rotation and vibration
ν	Frequency
ν_i	Stoichiometric coefficients in a chemical equation

τ	Torque
	Thomson coefficient (14)
	Free time (13)
τ_m	Mean free time
ρ	Density
π_{AB}	Peltier coefficient
χ	Mole fraction

Special notations

d	An infinitesimal increase in a property of matter
$đ$	An infinitesimal amount of transfer by some mechanism
Δ	A finite increase in a property of matter
	$\Delta \equiv$ final $-$ initial
$(\partial y/\partial x)_z$	The partial derivative of y with respect to x, obtained from the function $y(x,z)$
$f(x)$, $f(x,y)$	Functional relations
$f \cdot (x)$	f times x, used to avoid misreading as the function $f(x)$
x	The time-average value of a quantity of x
$\tilde{x}$	The instantaneous value of a fluctuating quantity; the tilde is to emphasize the fluctuations
$\mathbf{B}$	The vector $\mathbf{B}$
B	The magnitude of vector $\mathbf{B}$
$\hat{u}$	A molal quantity
$\equiv$	Identity symbol, used when the equation defines the quantity on the left
$\sum_i x_i$	The sum $x_1 + x_2 + \cdots + x_n$
$\prod_i x_i$	The product $x_1 x_2 x_3 \cdots x_n$
$\dot{W}$, $\dot{Q}$, $\dot{M}$	Rates of transfer or flow; *not* to be interpreted as time derivatives

Frequently used subscripts

W_{12}, Q_{12}	Amounts of energy transfer as work and heat corresponding to a change from state 1 to state 2
W_1, Q_1	Amounts of energy transfer as work and heat for process 1; *not* to be interpreted as the "work and heat at state 1"
h_f, h_g, h_s	Saturated-liquid, saturated-vapor, and saturated-solid states
h_{fg}, s_{fg}	$h_g - h_f$, $s_g - s_f$, etc.
h_{crit}	The critical state
χ_i, L_{ij}	"Dummy indices" which could take on any of the possible integer values
S_{BE}, S_{MB}, S_{FD}	Bose-Einstein, Maxwell-Boltzmann, Fermi-Dirac statistical models

ANSWERS TO SELECTED PROBLEMS

1·5 $k_G M/r^2$
1·12 1 kg = 6.67×10^{-11} m^3/sec^2; 1 coul = 0.774 m^3/sec^2
2·11 150 ft-lbf; 15,150 ft-lbf; 30,150 ft-lbf
2·12 28,800 ft-lbf; 19,950 ft-lbf; 43,200 ft-lbf; 67,200 ft-lbf
2·18 72.5 Btu input
3·4 43.5 Btu/lbm
3·7 11.67 Btu/lbm
3·9 50.7 Btu/lbm
4·1 0.173 ft^3/lbm; 73.4 Btu/lbm; 0.0045; 0.9955
4·14 0.292 Btu/lbm-°R
4·21 408°F
4·24 $c_v \approx 4$ Btu/lbm-°R; $c_P = \infty$
4·27 M/C; C/T; C/M; $-C\mathsf{H}/\mathsf{M}^2$
5·2 $h_{fg} = 78$ Btu/lbm
5·5 81 Btu
5·9 19 Btu
5·13 1–2: $Q_{in} = c_P(T_2 - T_1)$; $W_{out} = R(T_2 - T_1)$
2–3: $Q_{out} = c_v(T_2 - T_3)$; $W = 0$
3–1: $Q_{out} = W_{in} = RT_1 \ln (P_1/P_3)$
$(W_{out} - W_{in})/Q_{in} = 0.0884$
5·20 2740 Btu/min
5·23 3.7 hp; 2.9 hp
5·31 960°F
5·37 385°F; 0.184
5·46 294,000 lbm/hr; 284×10^6 Btu/hr
6·2 $1/N$ if molecules are indistinguishable from one another.
$1/2^N$ if they are distinguishable from one another.
6·10 $1/6$; $1/6$; $10/36$;
H: 1, $5/6$, $26/36$, . . . , $1/2$
T: 0, $1/6$, $10/36$, . . . , $1/2$
S: 0, 0.455, 0.591, . . . , 0.692
6·15 $e^{10^{25.8}}$; $10^{(0.432 \times 10^{25.8} - 22.2)}$
6·19 $S_2 - S_1 = (0.41 - 0.37)$ Btu/°R > 0

7·4 $(\partial T/\partial u)_{\mathbf{M}} > 0$
7·17 797 Btu/hr-°R
7·20 1740 kw
7·22 0.06°K
7·27 0.1
8·8 0.60 Btu/lbm-°R; 0.93 Btu/lbm-°R; 0.30 Btu/lbm-°R
8·10 −0.5°C
8·17 $u_2 - u_1 = a(T_2 - T_1) + (b/2)(T_2^2 - T_1^2)$
$s_2 - s_1 = a \ln (T_2/T_1) + b(T_2 - T_1)$
8·22 $u_2 - u_1 = c_{\mathsf{P}}(T_2 - T_1)$
$s_2 - s_1 = c_{\mathsf{P}} \ln (T_2/T_1) - (vA/2)(\mathsf{P}_2^2 - \mathsf{P}_1^2)$
9·1 0.73
9·4 3120 fps
9·6 0.21
9·9 0.27; 1.13×10^4 lbm/hr; 12.8×10^6 Btu/hr
9·18 1.64; 0.65
9·19 0.614
9·29 67 lbf/lbm-sec; 1030 lbf/lbm-sec; 3×10^5 lbf/lbm-sec
10·4 $\chi_{\mathrm{He}} = 0.343$; $\chi_{\mathrm{O_2}} = 0.657$; $\hat{M} = 22.4$ lbm/lbmole; $c_P = 0.282$ Btu/lbm-°R
10·5 65°F; 0.013 lbm H_2O/lbm dry air; 0.43
10·11 0.44
10·16 $\chi_{\mathrm{CO_2}} = \chi_{\mathrm{He}} = 0.5$
11·3 1.12×10^6 Btu/hr
11·7 1.9×10^{-10}; 0.98
11·12 $\log_{10} K = -4.98$
11·16 $4.7 \times 10^{15}/\mathrm{cm}^3$
12·1 $S = \mathsf{k} \ln \left\{\frac{[(n_A + n_B)!]^2}{n_A! n_B!}\right\}$
12·5 $\mathfrak{M}\hat{c}_v = \mathsf{k}T^2 \left(\frac{\partial^2 \ln Z}{\partial T^2}\right)_{\epsilon_i} + 2\mathsf{k}T \left(\frac{\partial \ln Z}{\partial T}\right)_{\epsilon_i}$
12·10 $-P = \left(\frac{\partial U}{\partial V}\right)_{S,\mathfrak{N}} = -\mathsf{k}T \left(\frac{\partial \ln Z}{\partial T}\right)_{T,n_i}$
13·5 10^{-5} cm; 10^{-2} cm; 10 cm
13·7 0.2×10^{-8} cm^2
13·8 0.3
14·1 10.25 mv
14·4 0.11 volt; peak 0.33 watt at 5 amp, 0.64 volt; peak efficiency 0.12

INDEX